N.R. Grant
Plantagenet House
Turnham Green
Dussindale
Thorpe St. Andrew
Norwich

April 2000

MEDICINE for the Soul

W
E

MEDICINE for the Soul

The Life, Death and Resurrection of an English Medieval Hospital

St Giles's, Norwich, *c.* 1249–1550

CAROLE RAWCLIFFE

SUTTON PUBLISHING

First published in 1999 by
Sutton Publishing Limited · Phoenix Mill
Thrupp · Stroud · Gloucestershire · GL5 2BU

British Library Cataloguing in Publication Data
A catalogue record for this book is available from the British Library

ISBN 0 7509 2009 2

Half-title: Boss from St Giles's Hospital showing the Resurrection.

Frontispiece: Archdean John Derlyngton's bell tower constructed at the Great Hospital at the end of the fourteenth century. (Photograph Richard Tilbrook)

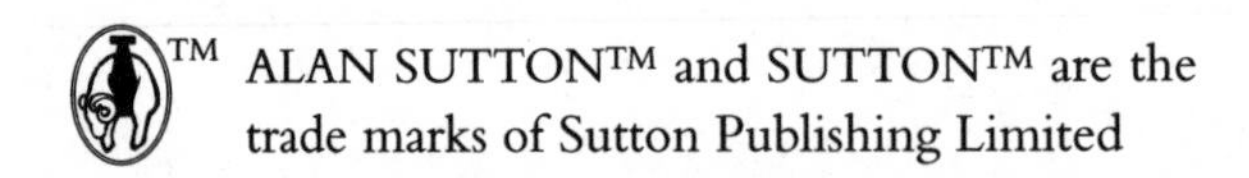

Typeset in 10.5/13pt Bembo Mono.
Typesetting and origination by
Sutton Publishing Limited.
Printed in Great Britain by
MPG, Bodmin, Cornwall.

For Hassell Smith and Richard Wilson

CONTENTS

ILLUSTRATIONS & MAPS

COLOUR PLATES BETWEEN PP. 110 AND 111

BLACK AND WHITE PLATES BETWEEN PP. 206 AND 207

MAPS

ACKNOWLEDGEMENTS

It seems a lifetime rather than a decade since Professor Barrie Dobson telephoned me unexpectedly in London to ask if I might be interested in writing the history of a hospital in Norwich. What initially had the makings of a modest research project compatible with my work as editor of the medieval section of *The History of Parliament* soon took on a life of its own. A tour of the institution in question (seen at its very best on a sunny day in spring rather than the depths of the East Anglian winter) and a rapid inspection of what was clearly the largest medieval hospital archive in England convinced me that it would have to be all or nothing. With generous help from the Wellcome Trust, and the encouragement of Dr David Allen, then Co-ordinator of its History of Medicine Programme, I was able to move to the University of East Anglia in 1992 and concentrate from then onwards upon the writing and teaching of medical history, which had already become of absorbing interest to me. My gratitude to the Trust and to Professor Dobson, who have together proved so supportive throughout my time in Norwich, may be imagined. The assistance of the staff of the Wellcome Institute Library, the Warburg Institute, the British Library Department of Manuscripts and the Institute of Historical Research, in London, and of the Library of the University of East Anglia is gratefully acknowledged. Having spent a considerable part of the last seven years in the Norfolk Record Office, I have good reason to value the friendly and efficient service offered by the archivists and administrative staff, despite the dislocation caused by the Norwich Library fire of 1994 and the ensuing move to new premises. Ms Rachel Farmer, Mr Paul Rutledge (now retired), Mrs Frieda Wilkins-Jones and their colleagues have answered countless enquiries, searched for missing documents and gone out of their way to facilitate the task of working on a large and only partially listed collection of manuscripts.

Writing the history of a medieval hospital is an interdisciplinary activity, which offers boundless opportunities to broaden one's own horizons. In the case of St Giles's hospital this has been literally true, and I owe a great debt to the staff, students and friends of the Centre of East Anglian Studies, now part of the School of History, UEA, who have introduced – and converted – a Yorkshirewoman raised on the foothills of Ilkley Moor to the attractions of a very different landscape. Dr John Blatchly, Mr Paul Fincham, Dr Judith Middleton-Stewart and Mr Norman Scarfe have combined hospitality with missionary zeal of the most persuasive kind. I have greatly benefited from the expert advice of Professor Bruce Campbell and Dr Susanna Wade-Martins with regard to agricultural practices on the hospital's estates, some of which lay in Broadland. It has been a particular pleasure to explore what is now one of the country's main tourist attractions out of season with Dr Martin George, formerly of the Nature Conservancy Council, who has patiently answered a barrage of questions about the changing environment.

Having long maintained an amateur interest in medieval music, I particularly enjoyed investigating this aspect of the hospital's history with expert guidance from Dr Roger Beeson, Dr Roger Bowers and Mr David Chadd. Answers to architectural problems (as well as some challenging questions) have come from Dr Paul Crossley, Dr Jonathan Finch, Mr Tim Pestell and Dr Jeremy Taylor. Discussions with Professor Roberta Gilchrist have invariably proved stimulating, and I must thank her for opening my eyes to the value of material culture in this type of study. Mr Bryan Ayers and Ms Jane Bown of the Norfolk Archaeology Unit and the palaeopathologist, Dr Ann Stirland, have been generous with their help. It is a privilege to be given constant access to the fine medieval buildings of the Great Hospital (as St Giles's became known after the Dissolution), and I would particularly like to thank the Master, Mr G.R. Kenney, and his wife for making this possible in the most obliging and hospitable fashion. The present residents, who are justifiably proud of their long heritage, have also taken a keen interest in this project. I, in turn, have learned a great deal from them. What the founder would have made of the construction of a bowling alley in the medieval infirmary is a moot point, but there can be little doubt that the continuity of his cherished enterprise would have given Bishop Walter Suffield nothing but satisfaction. The Great Hospital is now managed by a panel of Trustees, who have generously provided funding for the colour plates in this volume. They, too, have been most supportive: I am especially indebted to Mrs Doreen Green, Mrs Ann Knight, Mr John Thornton and their respective spouses for welcoming me so warmly to Norwich.

It is impossible here to thank all the people who have supplied references, information and suggestions over such a long period. Dr John Henderson's enthusiasm for the history of hospitals is infectious, and I have derived an enormous amount from our conversations. Dr Caroline Barron, Dr Clive Burgess, Professor Martha Carlin, Mr Paul Cattermole, Dr Christine Clark, Ms Samantha Crossman-Jelliff, Lt Col. Eric Gruber von Arni, Dr E.S. Leedham-Green, Dr Philippa Maddern, Professor Colin Richmond, Professor Joel T. Rosenthal, Mrs Elizabeth Rutledge, Mr Tony Simms, Dr Anthony Smith, Professor P.M. Stell, Mr Owen Thomson, Professor F.O. Touati, Professor Anthony Tuck, the late Dr Roger Virgoe and Mr Michael Youngs have helped in many ways. The problem of editing and collating two extremely long and verbose foundation charters was alleviated by Miss M.M. Condon and Dr Robert Ball, who gave sterling assistance as my deadline loomed. Mr Phillip Judge drew the maps with his customary expertise and Miss Chizuko Wesley typed part of the bibliography. Mr Richard Tilbrook has kindly photographed some of the hospital buildings for me. Having little natural affinity with computers, I recognise a special debt to Ms Elaine Phillips, who transformed some very rough manuscript tables into the finished product in Chapter III. Both she and Ms Claire Noble, my research students, have made a substantial contribution to this book, prompting me to look at evidence in new ways, and providing a constant stream of ideas. Many of the themes developed here began as lectures and seminars in the Medical History courses which Dr Steven Cherry and I have taught together at UEA. I am grateful to him and our students for their lively interest and involvement.

Collaboration with Mr Peter Clifford and the staff of Sutton Publishing, with whom I have maintained such a long and fruitful association, remains a pleasure. Ms Jane Crompton and my copy editor, Ms Sarah Moore, have attacked an alarmingly long manuscript with consummate professionalism, seeing it quickly and painlessly through the press. Generous as always, my former colleague, Dr Linda Clark, cast her keen editorial eye over earlier drafts. She, Miss Elizabeth Danbury, Ms Rochelle Haussman, Miss Joan Henderson and Mr A.D.K. Hawkyard have provided the moral support which really counts in an *annus horribilis* such as 1994, marked, in true medieval fashion, by illness as well as fire. My parents, too, have proved a tower of strength, as has Mr Peter Martin, the very personification of calm reassurance. In their different ways, he and the irrepressible Captain Zarco (another devotee of the East Anglian countryside) have invested as much in this project as the author.

It remains for me to thank my present colleagues, the secretarial staff and Faculty of the School of History at UEA, and in particular of the School's new Wellcome Unit for the History of Medicine. In these days of research assessment exercises and galloping bureaucracy, it is easy to forget why one actually became an academic. Fortunately, the School still boasts a number of scholars who have not yet succumbed to progress. Professor Christopher Harper-Bill, whose erudition is exceeded only by his kindness, has read and commented on the first part of this book, making freely available his encyclopaedic knowledge of the medieval episcopate. I owe Dr Andy Wood a similar debt for suggestions and advice about the sixteenth century, provided with his customary enthusiasm and insight. Whatever errors remain are entirely my own. This book is dedicated to two former Directors of the Centre of East Anglian Studies, who in their official capacity helped to set up 'The Great Hospital Project' and provided the necessary institutional support for its completion. But it is their friendship and encouragement, offered unstintingly over the last seven years, which deserves real thanks and due acknowledgement.

Carole Rawcliffe
University of East Anglia, January 1999

ABBREVIATIONS

BCL	Bachelor of Civil Law
BCnL	Bachelor of Canon Law
BL	British Library Department of Manuscripts
BRUC	A.B. Emden, *A Biographical Register of the University of Cambridge* (Cambridge, 1963)
BRUO	A.B. Emden, *A Biographical Register of the University of Oxford to 1500* (3 vols, 1957–9)
CCR	*Calendar of Close Rolls*
CIMisc.	*Calendar of Inquisitions Miscellaneous*
CPL	*Calendar of Papal Letters*
CPR	*Calendar of Patent Rolls*
DCL	Doctor of Civil Law
DCN	Dean and Chapter of Norwich
DCnL	Doctor of Canon Law
EconHR	*Economic History Review*
EETS	Early English Text Society
EHR	*English Historical Review*
GH	Great Hospital (St Giles's)
HMC	*Reports of the Royal Commission on Historical Manuscripts*
LPFD	*Calendar of Letters and Papers, Foreign and Domestic, Henry VIII*
NCC	Norwich Consistory Court
NCR	Norwich City Records (Norfolk Record Office)
NPD	Norwich Private Deeds (Norwich City Records, Cases 3–4)
NRO	Norfolk Record Office
NRS	Norfolk Record Society
PCC	Probate Court of Canterbury
Phi	Phillipps Manuscripts (Norfolk Record Office)
PRO	Public Record Office
PSIA(H)	*Proceedings of the Suffolk Institute of Archaeology and Natural History (and History)*
reg.	register
RS	Rolls Series
TRHS	*Transactions of the Royal Historical Society*
UEA	University of East Anglia
VCH	*Victoria County History*

INTRODUCTION

Writing the history of premodern hospitals, an endeavour which crosses many interdisciplinary boundaries and illuminates wide areas of our past, should need no apologia. Yet the authors of such works, and especially of studies which, unfashionably, concentrate upon single institutions, still feel obliged to justify the time and effort expended. The exercise sometimes seems to be of limited interest to a narrow coterie of specialists. It can appear even more recondite where the great majority of medieval foundations is concerned, since any claim to 'medical relevance' is demonstrably out of the question, at least so far as this loaded phrase is generally understood in the West today.[1] Ideas about health and healing, and thus about the role of the hospital, have undergone a dramatic transformation since Walter Suffield, bishop of Norwich, sought to cure his soul and the souls of the sick poor by founding St Giles's in the mid-thirteenth century. Yet an awareness of development and change, of the wider historical perspective, has sometimes proved elusive. 'Of the writing of hospital histories there is no end', J.R. Guy complained as recently as 1985, bemoaning the fact that this 'growth industry' was rarely matched by a corresponding improvement in scholarship or sharpening of insight.[2] The future now looks brighter. If, in the past, hospital historians have often fallen victim to the 'tunnel vision' and obsessive preoccupation with bald chronological detail which have so exasperated reviewers, the balance is gradually being redressed.[3] The last few years have witnessed the publication of a number of important monographs and articles on Italian, French and Spanish institutions which contextualise and enrich our understanding by setting hospitals (literally as well as figuratively) in the wider landscape.[4] They have, moreover, fostered a greater appreciation of the discipline in other areas. The study of premodern hospitals not only adds a new dimension to religious and ecclesiastical history, but – at its best – is also valuable for the light it sheds upon a range of cultural, urban, social and economic issues.

Institutional care of the sick, in the widest spiritual as well as physical sense, is a broad theme with wide resonances. Although almost all English medieval hospitals and a significant proportion of continental institutions offered little or nothing in the way of professional medical or surgical facilities, they none the less provide a fascinating insight into changing reactions to poverty and disease. F.O. Touati's magisterial study of leprosy and *leprosaria* in the province of Sens, for example, traces with subtlety and precision the various influences which saw the gradual transformation of the leper from a figure touched by God to a social outcast, consigned (like many of the paupers we shall meet in the following pages) to life on the margins.[5] Notwithstanding the criticisms noted above, histories of specific institutions, such as that produced in 1997 to mark the 750th anniversary of the London hospital of St Mary Bethlehem, can likewise broaden our view of changing medical, social and religious responses to the human predicament.[6] They show, too, how afflictions such as madness, leprosy or the pox present a mirror to society, reflecting its own shifting concerns and anxieties.

As will become apparent in the course of this book, the history of medieval English hospitals is a rich but as yet only partially mined seam, with considerable potential for further exploitation. Although a significant number of local and antiquarian studies appeared in the first half of the twentieth century, so little interest was shown in the broader picture that for almost ninety years Rotha M. Clay's introductory survey, *The Mediaeval Hospitals of England* (London, 1909), remained the standard – indeed only – general work of reference. Wide-ranging in the institutions covered, and imaginative in its use of source material, it none the less lacked a scholarly apparatus and could thus frustrate rather than help the specialist reader. Nor did it provide much in the way of historical background. What was, even so, to prove a durable *vade mecum* was finally enlarged and updated in 1995 by Nicholas Orme and Margaret Webster, whose study of *The English Hospital 1070–1570* (Yale University Press), develops the theme of institutional diversity, viewed from an essentially regional perspective. The juxtaposition of papers on continental and English hospitals in an influential collection of essays edited by Lindsay Granshaw and Roy Porter had, meanwhile, suggested interesting similarities and striking contrasts, while testifying to the vigour of research then in progress.[7]

As Orme and Webster so clearly demonstrate, it is impossible to generalise, and thus all the more important to undertake detailed case studies wherever possible. The destruction and despoliation of hospital buildings at the Dissolution of the Monasteries, the often pejorative findings of earlier inquiries and visitation reports, and the widespread loss of archival evidence have combined to produce a gloomy picture of decline and decay, if not of overt corruption. In many cases this is clearly justified. Yet we cannot ignore some equally striking evidence of sustained artistic patronage, high standards of musicianship and liturgical display, ambitious building programmes and achievements in the field of education, which are clear indicators of changing priorities and functions. They also speak volumes about the political connections established by specific institutions and their staff, a topic which has hitherto been as neglected as that of the contribution made by such establishments to the religious life of the urban elite. Any discussion of art in hospitals will invariably focus upon such lavishly endowed houses as Santa Maria Nuova in Florence, Santa Maria della Scala in Siena, the Hôtel Dieu in Beaune and the hospital of St John in Bruges. Neither St Giles's, Norwich, nor any other English house could boast a Roger van der Weyden or a Domenico di Bartolo, but several were richly decorated and possessed substantial collections of books, vestments and plate. Although it owned nothing to rival the Ursula shrine executed by Hans Memling for the sisters of St John's, the London hospital of St Anthony also housed relics of the martyr and her virgins, two 'heads garnished with silver' being displayed among the notable collection to be found there at the close of the fifteenth century.[8]

The reserves of plate and other ecclesiastical furnishings owned by another London house, St Mary Spital in Bishopsgate, were even more impressive, and explain why Henry VIII's commissioners were so anxious to acquire the larger and wealthier urban foundations.[9] Our knowledge of this important hospital, and of the extent to which its architectural development was driven by the growing demand for spiritual services on the part of wealthy patrons, derives largely from a series of excavations undertaken between 1976 and 1989.[10] It is, indeed, through the work of archaeologists that some of the most exciting and significant recent advances have been made in the study of English hospitals, and the artificial barriers between investigation in the field and in the archives have at last begun to disappear. Collaboration between historians and archaeologists helps to fill the great *lacunae* following the loss of so much documentary and architectural evidence at the Dissolution. It can also provide the kind of information about the layout, function and redevelopment of precincts rarely described in the records, however full. The work of Roberta Gilchrist has proved especially stimulating in this regard. She has alerted historians to the importance of topography and material culture in the study of hospitals of all types, from the meanest *leprosarium* to the richest monastic community.[11]

The transformation of hospitals into liturgical centres for the commemoration of the Christian departed and the attendant marginalisation of the vagrant poor has been admirably described by Miri Rubin, whose work on medieval Cambridge and its environs performs the additional service of setting a specifically regional study firmly in a European context.[12] It is important to remember that the men and women who endowed and supported the hospitals of medieval Norwich and of other English cities shared charitable ideals and concerns about the hereafter current throughout Christendom. Their fear of vagrancy and contempt for the 'workshy' likewise transcended national boundaries.[13] This book begins with the history of one bishop who was almost canonised, and ends with that of a second who narrowly escaped being burnt at the stake. The aims and assumptions of the two men, one catholic, the other protestant, were very different, but neither of them envisaged the role of hospitals or poor relief in narrow, provincial terms. St Giles's hospital, like so many scattered across Europe, was founded in the shadow of the fourth Lateran council; it was the creation of a reforming, cosmopolitan bishop who had studied in Paris and boasted many connections in Rome; its purpose, as expressed in two lengthy foundation charters, was to further the work of the Church Militant and Universal, which it did with considerable panache and authority for the next three centuries.

A tendency in recent writing on urban history (termed the 'community school' by a not uncritical Christopher Dyer) is to stress the sense of unity and mutual cooperation fostered by late medieval civic elites, and, by extension, their collective altruism towards less fortunate members of society.[14] Numerous examples of individual philanthropy, and of a sustained commitment to public welfare have, for instance, been documented by Patricia Cullum (Yorkshire) and A.D. Brown (the diocese of Salisbury), although their evidence still points to a strict selectivity directed at the deserving, respectable and shamefaced poor.[15] Specifically local factors may well have been crucial in determining levels of provision. Badly affected by the crises of 1315–22, seriously depopulated by successive outbreaks of plague and subject to repeated eruptions of disorder during the late fourteenth and early fifteenth centuries, the 'community' of Norwich was far from homogenous. No almshouses of any note or durability were endowed in the city, although Bishop Despenser, famous for his brutal suppression of the 1381 East Anglian uprising and his hatred of heresy, did help to rebuild St Giles's hospital at about this time.[16] Compassion for the unemployed artisan or homeless pauper is unlikely to have ranked as high on his scale of priorities as the need to promote religious orthodoxy in an appropriate setting. That St Giles's was an institution run by and for an influential elite, drawn from the pillars of the lay and ecclesiastical establishment, is amply attested by the surviving records. The insurgents who burnt it in 1549 had long memories; they knew well enough, like other rebels before them, that hospitals could be repressive as well as generous.

This brings us back to our apologia. Notwithstanding its role in urban politics, does a relatively modest hospital such as St Giles's really merit such a lengthy and detailed history? To survive on the same site for 750 years, functioning successively and without interruption as a hospital, almshouse and retirement home, is alone an achievement which deserves commemoration. Few medieval English hospitals can claim as much, and no other now possesses anything to rival its combination of documentary and architectural sources, supported, in addition, by an outstanding range of civic records and one of the finest monastic archives in the country.[17] For the first three centuries of its history, however, St Giles's was fairly typical of its kind: although it never possessed the wealth or status of the great Augustinian hospitals of London and York, it occupied a distinguished place among the scores of charitable institutions founded in the provincial centres of late twelfth- and thirteenth-century England, and of hundreds of similar establishments then being endowed across Europe.[18] Unlike most of them, however, it still stands as a manifestation of 'the actual, as distinct from the historiographical, stuff of the charitable past'.[19] Indeed, because of the widespread destruction of hospital buildings and records during the 1530s and 1540s, the Great Hospital (as St Giles's is known today) now appears unique. A substantial part of the medieval fabric, including the late fourteenth-century chancel, nave (which has functioned continuously from 1270 as St Helen's parish church), infirmary and bell-tower, together with the fifteenth-century cloisters, refectory and master's lodgings, has outlasted centuries of change. Some of these buildings were subject to drastic internal alterations after the Dissolution, and the precinct as a whole has been extensively developed since, but it requires little imagination to envisage the site as it might have appeared in the late Middle Ages. This is partly due to the fact that much of the surrounding area (riparian meadows, medieval bridge and tower, cathedral precinct, episcopal palace and Carnary Chapel) conveys a strong sense of past topography, but also because so much additional evidence can be found in the hospital's own archive.

Now housed in the Norfolk Record Office, this comprises a cartulary, hundreds of medieval deeds and documents of title, a substantial body of miscellaneous legal records and an even more impressive collection of fourteenth, fifteenth and early-sixteenth century accounts. Although the coverage is patchy for certain periods, most notably the years just before the Dissolution, when vital records undoubtedly found their way into the hands of the aldermen who took charge of St Giles's in 1547, the breadth of financial and administrative evidence – both at a central and local level – is remarkable.[20] There is good reason to suppose that the Norwich antiquary, John Kirkpatrick, who served as treasurer of the Great Hospital, planned to write its history, but his early death in 1728 terminated the project. 'Better far he had contented himself with amassing less and turning what he had got to account', his posthumous editor observed: a warning any historian following in his footsteps quickly takes to heart.[21] When Francis Blomefield came to describe the hospital in the Norwich volume of his *Topographical History of Norfolk*, he confined his attention to the most accessible medieval charters and left the bulk of the archive alone.[22] It has not been systematically explored since. We are, however, fortunate that so many of the accounts kept by the receiver-general, the steward and the collector of rents in Norwich have survived in relatively good condition, since they constitute our principal source of evidence for daily life in the precinct from the early fourteenth century onwards. No English hospital will ever yield the type of evidence about patients and their care available for institutions such as Santa Maria Nuova in Florence, or the Hôtel Dieu, Paris, but it has none the less proved possible to devote the best part of a chapter to this topic. Such an exercise is facilitated by the availability of over 1,800 wills left by citizens of Norwich between 1370 and 1532.[23] Testamentary evidence is, of course, grist to the prosopographer's mill: an abundance of biographical detail, collected for each of the hospital's twenty-seven medieval masters, enables us to reconstruct the complex networks of power and patronage thanks to which St Giles's survived successive financial crises and, indeed, weathered the treacherous waters of the Dissolution.

The sharply contrasting world of patron and pauper beyond the hospital walls emerges with remarkable clarity, not least from the evidence of excavations undertaken in areas occupied by the medieval proletariat. Besides its fine archaeological heritage, Norwich also boasts an outstanding collection of medieval and early modern civic records, ranging from enrolled and private deeds to guild accounts, from court rolls and administrative memoranda to corporation minute books. It is thus possible to examine in unusual detail the relations between St Giles's hospital and the rulers of Norwich, while investigating at a more personal level the contacts between individual masters and members of the civic hierarchy. The key to success in later medieval England lay, as we shall see, in the skilful deployment of 'good lordship', and the masters were accomplished players in both the temporal and spiritual spheres. They were, moreover, as their archive reveals, efficient and conscientious administrators – a fact which will surprise historians whose image of the medieval hospital is one of indifference, incompetence and malversation. Nor were the deserving poor who found relief at its gates and in its beds (albeit in declining numbers) subject to neglect or abuse. Worth between £100 and £120 a year during the early fifteenth century, the hospital's net income and, indeed, the masters' lifestyle, ranked on a par with that enjoyed by leading members of the English gentry, although its responsibilities were considerably more onerous.[24] Like other English landowners, lay and ecclesiastical, St Giles's had to fight hard to remain solvent, employing a number of carefully calculated strategies to buy itself out of recession. Paramount among these was the sale of spiritual services, which not only supplied a growing demand for posthumous commemoration on the part of the ruling elite, but had the added attraction of generating – and sustaining – investment. An inevitable consequence of these developments was a transition from the open ward infirmary (which gave free access to the hospital church) to the more selective *domus pauperum*, where a small band of almsmen was given separate lodgings. The number of priests and choristers meanwhile grew to provide the necessary ritual. If we are to fully to understand and successfully interpret the changing role of the medieval hospital, then the unending search for economic stability must rank high on the list of topics for investigation.

A combination of powerful friends, strict managerial accountability and a limited, but viable, programme of poor relief ensured the hospital's continuity during the difficult years of the English Reformation, when the rejection of the doctrine of purgatory deprived many similar institutions of their *raison d'être*. Unusually detailed evidence concerning its acquisition by the rulers of Norwich in 1547, and its integration into a comprehensive scheme for public education and welfare is to be found among the city records. We can trace the hesitant steps in this direction essayed by the corporation long before the celebrated Census of the Poor was taken in 1570.[25] That crucial divide, which in England so often separates historians of medieval and early modern charity, and which tends, inevitably, to stress disruption and change rather than continuity and development can thus be bridged. The history of charitable effort in late sixteenth-century Norwich has been studied in depth by Margaret Pelling and John Pound, whose work provides an invaluable background to the last two chapters of this book.[26] It is hoped that the new material presented here about the role of hospitals in the city's strategy for coping with manifold social, economic and epidemiological problems will contribute further to the rapidly growing literature on the subject of early modern urban responses to the poor.[27] The story of one modest institution, left in obscurity for the best part of four centuries, has still many lessons to teach us.

CHAPTER I

MEDICINE FOR THE SOUL

Ac olde and hore, that helples ben and nedy,
And wymmen with childe that worche ne mowe,
Blynde and bedredne and broken in here membres,
And alle pore pacient, apayed of Goddes sonde,
As mesels and pilgrimes and parauntur men y-robbed
Or bylowe thorw luther men and lost here catel after,
Or thorw fuyr or thorw floed y-falle into pouerte,
That taketh thise meschiefes mekeliche and myldeliche at herte,
For loue of here lower hertes qoure lord hath hem y-graunted
Here penaunce and here purgatorye vppon this puyre erthe

William Langland, *Piers Plowman*, C Passus IX

[But the old and grey, who are helpless and needy, and pregnant women unable to work, the blind and the bedridden, and those who are crippled, and all the patient poor who accept God's will, such as lepers and pilgrims and sometimes men who have been robbed or tricked by evildoers, and have lost all their goods as a result, or who have fallen into poverty because of fire or flood: out of love of their humility Our Lord has granted all such people, who suffer these tribulations meekly and without complaint, that they may undergo their penance and purgatory here on earth.]

Quite soon after his consecration as bishop of Norwich, in February 1245, Walter Suffield elected to build a new hospital to the north-east of the city near the cathedral. He was assisted in his endeavours by members of the ecclesiastical and mercantile elite, who shared his concern over the growing problem of poverty and homelessness in their community. Yet the hospital was an overwhelmingly personal creation, the realisation of 'a purpose and intent which we have long had in mind, and a desire which surpasses and exceeds every longing of our heart'.[1] Founded by Suffield out of sympathy for the plight of the sick and disabled poor, it was none the less intended first and foremost to secure the remission of his sins.[2] He had, in the words of Pope Alexander IV, a longing for 'those rewards by which the king of eternal clemency repays zeal for mercy', accompanied, no doubt, by an even greater fear of divine judgement.[3]

Between 1201 and 1250 over 160 similar institutions sprang into being in England, adding appreciably to the 250 or so already in existence.[4] Why did Bishop Walter and so many of his contemporaries regard the endowment of a hospital as the surest route to paradise? His project clearly met a pressing social need: Norwich, then a rapidly expanding city, had to make provision for a growing influx of malnourished, destitute and physically disabled paupers. This meant expanding the facilities established by his predecessors during the century after the Conquest. Norwich's Castle and Cathedral still remain spectacular monuments to the Normans who built them, whereas the hospitals founded in this period have been largely forgotten. The stone leper house of St Mary Magdalen, one of the first of a national wave of charitable foundations dating from the last years of the eleventh century, now attracts little attention and few visitors. No memorial commemorates the hospital church of St Paul, which was destroyed in the Second World War after 800 years on the same site. Yet these hospitals had once fulfilled a vital spiritual as well as a temporal purpose. They served, above all, to remember the dead and inspire prayers for their salvation.[5]

St Mary's was run, from about 1119 onwards, by the cathedral monks, who also distributed relief from an almonry and *domus pauperum* in their precinct. This aspect of their ministry attracted by far the greatest support from local patrons, whose gifts of land and rents were generally made in the hope of achieving a celestial reward.[6] Ironically, those who did most to assist the poor had initially intensified their problems by clearing substantial areas of the city and evicting the native population. The Domesday Book, which suggests a late eleventh-century population of between 5,000 and 10,000, reveals that many residents of humble status could not afford to pay any taxes and that certain areas had been devastated to make space for new building schemes. Even so, Norwich must still have seemed a bustling, impressive place, with over forty parish churches and a thriving port on the River Wensum.[7] Commercial success hastened expansion, which in turn attracted more immigrants from the surrounding countryside. Before long, a second hospital, the above-mentioned St Paul's, had been erected for the succour of needy travellers as well as providing about twenty beds for the 'sick, infirm and child-bearing poor of the city'. Although it also distributed food, drink and clothing to the indigent, neither this hospital nor a third, short-lived institution, dedicated to SS Mary and John, offered more than limited assistance. Both, however, addressed the spiritual anxieties of their founders and patrons, which was one of their principal functions.[8]

Over the next century at least four (out of an eventual five) small communities of lepers were established with help from the wealthier citizens on the main roads leading into Norwich [see Map I]. Men and women suffering from other disfiguring diseases may have sought refuge there, too, but no further arrangements were made for disabled, sick or wayfaring paupers until about 1201, when a local merchant named Hildebrand le Mercer set up a shelter 'for poor people wanting lodging' near the Conisford gate to the south-east of the city. An adjacent chapel dedicated to the Blessed Virgin saw to the welfare of their souls, while ensuring that the founder and his descendants would figure constantly in their prayers. Hildebrand was probably responding to a recent appeal by Bishop John Gray, whose efforts to raise money for St Paul's hospital had drawn attention to the heavy demands then being made on its resources. But his hostel remained small and underfunded, with accommodation for only a few indigents at a time.[9] The need for further charitable

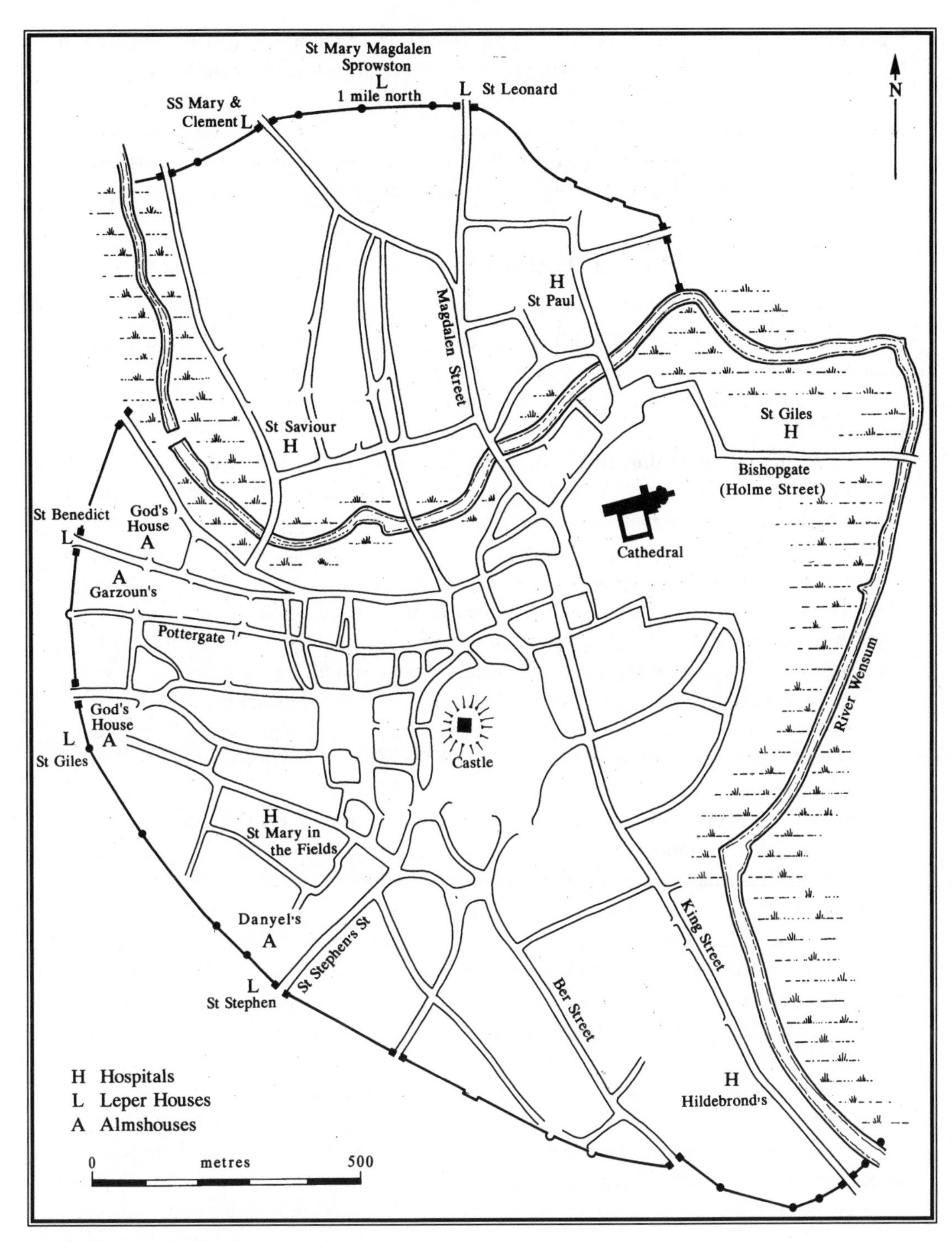

Map I: The hospitals of medieval Norwich.

provision led John le Brun, a priest, to plan another hospital and chapel on this side of Norwich in the 1240s. Probably because of Walter Suffield's decision to embark on a more prestigious project, the buildings were, however, soon converted into a college for secular priests, which many masters of St Giles's hospital later joined.[10] In the long term, the two institutions proved remarkably similar, both being primarily committed to the quest for spiritual health and the propagation of the Christian faith.

AMBIVALENT RESPONSES TO POVERTY

Suffield belonged to a generation of clergy who began their ministry in the aftermath of the fourth Lateran Council of 1215. Described as 'the most important single body of disciplinary and reform legislation ever applied to the medieval Church', its rulings impacted upon almost every aspect of ecclesiastical life, including hospitals.[11] Pope Innocent III's concern to bolster the authority and prestige of the priesthood went hand-in-hand with repressive measures for the extirpation of heresy and other signs of waywardness among the laity.[12] Beside this hefty stick was dangled the carrot of improved charitable provision and solicitude for the fate of the poor. With encouragement from the papacy the mendicant orders, most notably the Franciscans, spread their message of holy poverty across Europe, eliciting an enthusiastic response from men and women at all levels of society. A contingent of Franciscans (the Grey Friars) arrived in Norwich in 1226, along with the Dominican Black Friars, and they were soon established in the heart of the community. Bishop Suffield proved generous to both orders, leaving 66*s* 8*d* to every Dominican and Franciscan friary in his diocese and £20 to the general chapter of each.[13]

Besides contributing two short treatises to the debate on pastoral care and poor relief, Innocent III led by practical example. As custodians of the Church's wealth, his bishops were exhorted to discharge their pastoral duty towards the needy, while he himself gave alms regularly and in person, washing the feet of the poor as Christ's representatives on earth. Walter Suffield almost certainly visited the hospital of Santo Spirito, built by Pope Innocent on the banks of the Tiber for abandoned children, pregnant women and sick pilgrims, when he travelled to Rome on official business. If almsdeeds provided a 'medicine of salvation against all ills', they also constituted a major weapon in the Church's drive for the hearts and minds of men and women who turned to it for help in times of hardship. Innocent went so far as to blame indifferent and avaricious clergy for facilitating the spread of heresy, which was frequently described at this time as a leprosy or cancer of the soul.[14] This aspect of his comprehensive programme for ecclesiastical reform had a profound effect upon the next generation. Many of Suffield's contemporaries, among whom the saintly Louis IX of France (d. 1270) was by far the most celebrated, waged a private battle against spiritual contagion by means of almsdeeds performed, where possible, in person so as to increase their merit. Louis also debased himself before Christ's poor, tending them with his own hands in the *maison Dieu* he built at Vernon, and even welcoming them to his own table.[15] He in turn proved at once an inspiration and a rival to Henry III (d. 1272), whose household at Westminster became a noted centre for the distribution of alms. Besides feeding at least 500 paupers every day, the King observed major festivals by providing meals and clothing for thousands.[16] During Henry's absence in Scotland, in 1255, responsibility for feeding the paupers who flocked there annually on the feast of St Edward and filled two great halls fell, among others, to Walter Suffield, a fitting choice given his long experience of organising relief in his own diocese.[17]

Almsgiving on this scale was an appropriate royal response to Christ's sermon on the Last Judgement (Matthew 25:32–36). On the final day of reckoning, he warned, those who had failed to perform six specific acts of charity would be separated from the heirs to the kingdom of God, 'as a shepherd divideth his sheep from goats', and cast 'into the everlasting fire, prepared for the devil and his angels'. Feeding the hungry, clothing the naked, visiting prisoners and the sick, giving drink to the thirsty and receiving poor strangers thus came to assume an even greater importance beyond the grave than they had done on earth.[18] Although ideas about the value of almsgiving and those best qualified to receive assistance changed quite radically during the period covered by this book, the eschatological drama so often depicted on the walls and altarpieces of European hospitals and parish churches lost none of its terrors. One of the greatest works of art ever executed on the theme of the Last Judgement was painted by Roger van der Weyden in the mid-fifteenth century for the high altar of the infirmary chapel at the Hôtel Dieu in Beaune [see Plate 1]. Its closed state depicts the founder, Nicolas Rolin, chancellor to the duke of Burgundy, who clearly hoped that his soul would weigh lightly in St Michael's scales as a result of his endowment. Not only were hospitals the concrete expression, in bricks and mortar, of Christ's teaching on charity; they promised the donor a constant round of intercessionary prayers and masses for the salvation of his or her soul. Since he was said by Louis XI to have beggared so many people that he was duty bound to care for them in adversity, Rolin needed powerful advocates.[19] As we shall see in Chapter IV, the liturgical functions of European hospitals grew steadily in importance as the Church refined and elaborated its teachings on the tripartite nature of the afterlife. A combination of religious observance and practical almsgiving had long been held to shorten the period of purgation when Christian souls were cleansed of sins which had not been confessed and fully absolved before death [see Plate 18]. Spared the infinite torments of damnation, they would thus slowly and painfully rise to heaven. The Church's acceptance in the mid-thirteenth century of a formal doctrine relating to purgatory, a place remarkably similar to hell in all but the duration of its horrors, prompted a growing and more sophisticated demand for posthumous commendation through 'the suffrages of the faithful'.[20] That the souls of the poor patients would also benefit from the devotional atmosphere fostered by hospital priests and brethren made the patron's generosity seem all the greater.

Concern about the health of their own immortal souls did not blind men such as Walter Suffield to the spiritual needs of the poor. Prominent among these was the desire for a decent burial, which served not only to confirm that all Christians, however wretched, belonged to a community of the faithful, but also to ease the journey ahead. Although Christ had not specifically instructed his followers to perform this act of mercy, medieval men and women came increasingly to value it because funerary prayers, candles, bells and masses were held to promise relief from the pains of purgatory.[21] The guilds of medieval Norwich, and of all other English towns and cities, made funerals a priority, arranging compulsory contributory schemes so that even their poorest members would be 'carried and buried honestly' with the full rites of the church.[22] The city's hospitals were able to offer this consolation to men and women who had neither families nor workmates to visit their sickbed or supervise their burial.[23] In times of plague and other epidemics burying the dead, the last of the Seven Comfortable Works, seemed an act of heroism as well as generosity. It is worth noting that King Louis' desire to assist the nurses who customarily prepared corpses for interment was regarded as a notable mark of sanctity.[24]

Thoughts of the Last Judgement and everlasting fires of hell had for centuries offered a powerful inducement to charity. Suffield's predecessor, Herbert de Losinga (d. 1119), the first bishop of Norwich and founder of the city's two earliest hospitals, had preached eloquently on the redemptive power of almsdeeds. Besides purging the soul 'from the infection and filthy spots of sin', they served to extinguish the incipient flames of concupiscence 'as water puts out fire'.[25] As Christ's representatives on earth, the poor and oppressed would eventually share his throne, helping to determine the fate of those who had hitherto enjoyed the trappings of material wealth. The lesson was clear:

> Know ye, brethren, that the Church's poor are themselves among the saints . . . make them your friends, as the Lord saith, that when you shall fail they may receive you into everlasting dwellings. The holy poor are lean with hunger, and shiver with cold, but hereafter in heaven they shall be kings, and in the presence of God shall sit in judgement upon your crimes, and those of all the wicked.[26]

Dives and Lazarus, the plutocrat and the pauper, were mutually dependent for spiritual and physical health, neither being able to survive alone. Yet, if they were 'too thynges wol nedeful iche to other', the relationship was far from equal.[27] To many theologians the humble and deserving beggar was already sure of his celestial reward, whereas the rich man's soul hung precariously in the balance. The intercessionary prayers of grateful bedesfolk offered a sure hope of redemption to those who feared that they might otherwise be damned outright or else destined for a painful sojourn in purgatory. 'The poor, who spiritually have clear sight', were compared to cripples dependent upon the crutch of alms but none the less capable of showing their blind patrons 'the way to the banquet of heaven'.[28] Such an attitude encouraged individual and institutional charity, while accepting without question that poverty and its consequences were part of the natural order. A healthy society, like a healthy body, showed concern for all its parts, helping those which were 'sike and sore'. 'The membre lesse igreued hath compaciens of the membre that is more igreued', urged the popular thirteenth-century encyclopaedist, Bartholomeus Anglicanus, 'and draweth the matere of the euel to itself'. Yet he none the less envisaged a conventional hierarchy of bodily parts, which prescribed amputation for unruly or diseased limbs and maintained that the nobler and more sensitive organs (such as the eye) would be especially susceptible to pain. The poor ranked around the soles of the feet, and were thus deemed to be more resilient – and inured – to hardship.[29]

Emphasis upon the value of the Seven Comfortable Works mitigated a harsher attitude to poverty and suffering which took its tone from the Old Testament, and in particular from the account of the Fall in the Book of Genesis. All men and women were held to share the Original Sin of their first parents, and were thus heirs to a legacy of pain, sickness and death. In addition to this involuntary burden, lightened by the sacrament of baptism and Christ's sacrifice on the Cross, each individual carried a personal load of sins committed over the years, for which atonement had to be made before he or she could achieve salvation. Punishment might be inflicted collectively and indiscriminately through famine, flood, pestilence and all the other natural disasters which led the Church to urge communal acts of reparation. Prominent among these were almsdeeds. 'Do you want to survive corporal death, epidemics or pain in the side, or the illnesses which beset you day after day?' asked the great Sienese preacher, San Bernardino, during an outbreak of plague in the 1420s. The answer to this rhetorical question was self-evident: charity offered an infallible cure for diseases of the soul, and would, moreover, stay the divine arrows of wrath.[30] But was it enough? As one of the most celebrated of the rulings (cap. xxii) of the fourth Lateran Council recognised, every individual had to assume personal liability in the confessional for the spiritual infirmities which so often gave rise to physical suffering:

> As sickness of the body may sometimes be the result of sin . . . so we by this present decree order and strictly command physicians of the body, when they are called to the sick, to warn and persuade them first of all to call in physicians of the soul so that after their spiritual health has been seen to they may respond better to medicine for their bodies: *for when the cause ceases so does the effect.*[31]

The medieval hospital, whose inmates had little choice but to accept a regimen of confession and prayer devised and implemented by the Church, was in many respects the ideal vehicle for the enforcement of this and other codes for spiritual policing.[32] Had the sick poor, whose health was so often undermined by the dietary and environmental factors discussed below, brought retribution upon themselves?

In a society convinced of the close, symbiotic relationship between body and soul, physical deformity was often regarded as a sign of some deeper spiritual malaise. Disability and disfigurement seemed a just punishment for sin, the misdeeds of the parents being demonstrably visited upon their children. Writing in 1186–7, Giraldus Cambrensis (who twice came near to being made a bishop) observed that he had never seen 'so many individuals who were born blind, so many lame, maimed or having some natural defect' as he had encountered on a recent visit to Ireland. 'No wonder', he concluded, 'if among an adulterous and incestuous people, in which both births and marriages are illegitimate, a nation out of the pale of the laws, Nature herself should be foully corrupted by perverse habits.'[33] Desperation to curtail the pains of purgatory was, in part, driven by a conviction that each of the seven sins would there be punished by the torments of an appropriate disease, such as leprosy, fever or paralysis.[34] On the positive side, this encouraged a widespread belief that the sick and suffering poor had been permitted by God to purge their sins on earth, and would progress more quickly to heaven as a result.

The association between sin and bodily infirmity none the less legitimated a less benign view of poverty, which the conventions of late medieval iconography and literature did little to dispel. Ragged, ugly, diseased and disfigured, the pauper here presents a spectacle which is both pitiful and disturbing, not least because he or she tends to be depicted as a cipher rather than an individual. Torn, filthy clothing and exposed flesh constitute a powerful reminder of decay, sin and the corruptibility of the body – themes developed in the *Testament* of François Villon (1461), the poet laureate of the urban poor:

> Item: I leave to the hospitals
> My window-panes made of cobwebs.
> And to the wretches who sleep under market stalls
> A hearty smack in the eye.
> And freedom to shiver with frozen flesh:
> Gaunt, unkempt and chilled to the bone,
> Clothes tattered, limbs exposed,
> Ice-cold, battered and soaking wet.[35]

Clothing the naked, an act of charity undertaken by many English hospitals as well as private individuals, had a moral as well as a philanthropic imperative. As we shall see in Chapter VIII, distaste at the spectacle of the naked and noisome poor grew even more marked after plague and syphilis became endemic among the urban population. During the fourteenth century, as one crisis succeeded another, many *pauperes Christi* were transformed into potentially dangerous and disruptive outsiders. It is, however, worth noting Bartholomaeus Anglicus' belief, expressed years before the first outbreak of pestilence, that 'the membres of a pure and clene complexioun ben more able to be obedient to the worchinge of the spirit'. Although preachers such as Jacques de Vitry (d. *c.* 1240) were at pains to extol the virtues of spiritual cleanliness over a superficial concern with personal hygiene, appearances still mattered. As he himself noted, one needed the courage of a martyr to tolerate the 'insupportable filth and stench' of hospital patients.[36]

THE CITY AND THE POOR

Always an important consideration for those involved in the ongoing academic debate over poor relief, the question of selectivity assumed greater practical significance in a society preoccupied with the problem of individual merit. As ideas about the best means of escaping purgatory were developed with almost mathematical precision, the moral worth of those in receipt of alms also became a matter of far greater concern. Herbert Losinga had referred specifically to 'the holy poor' (most notably those embracing vows of religion) in his sermon on charity, although the hospital of St Paul, which he helped to found, accepted patients solely on the basis of need, irrespective of any other considerations. Only after successive plague epidemics had taken their toll on the economic, social and religious life of Norwich did it give priority to respectable almswomen whose families could make an initial (and relatively substantial) contribution towards their upkeep.[37] These were the kind of people whom the city's craft guilds and religious fraternities aimed to support during the late fourteenth and fifteenth centuries by setting up schemes for mutual assistance in times of adversity. Recognising that accident, blindness, ill-health or 'sudden and catastrophic misfortune' might reduce all but the very richest citizens to penury, such organisations provided relief for members and other deserving individuals who had fallen into poverty 'thrughe auenture of the worlde'. They were not, however, prepared to assist anyone who might have incurred sickness or destitution 'be his owne foly' or 'rytous lyuyng', or who could still 'helpen him self' in any way.[38]

After more than twenty years in office as an alderman of Norwich, one such unfortunate, the mercer William Welles, was discharged from service in 1494 because of some unspecified infirmity. Along with ill-health came hardship and a humiliating loss of status; shortly afterwards he petitioned the guild of St George for financial support, being then greatly 'afflicted with poverty'.[39] His case provides a telling example of the mutability of fate so dreaded by contemporaries at all levels of society. As one of the 'shamefaced' poor, whose case seemed both salutary and deserving to his former colleagues, Welles almost certainly escaped real penury. His was what historians might term a 'shallow' rather than a 'deep' poverty.[40] It has been estimated that, in mid-sixteenth-century Norwich, approximately 22 per cent of a population in the order of at least 11,000 might, like him, have been considered poor, while a smaller group of about 5 per cent appeared truly indigent.[41] But the margins had always been blurred; for centuries before such precise statistics become available any number of factors, both long and short term, could precipitate a downward spiral from hardship to outright destitution. In times of dearth or epidemic the personal drama was played out on a collective scale, with serious consequences for the city's charitable institutions. Never, at any time during the Middle Ages or early modern period, did the rulers of Norwich intend their hospitals to do more than ease the suffering of a small proportion of the sick poor, who were often drawn from specific, clearly delineated groups, such as pilgrims, the aged, reputable single women and lepers. Although outdoor relief may initially have been provided on a far larger scale than the modest number of beds would suggest, it too, must often have proved woefully inadequate. Given the enormity of the problem, it is easy to see why men and women of substance took refuge in the belief that God had ordained suffering and deprivation as part of the natural order.

While accepting the inherent validity of categorising paupers according to their moral worth, more perceptive commentators, such as the late fourteenth-century poet, William Langland, had long recognised that adverse social and economic circumstances gave rise to many types and degrees of poverty. As the quotation at the start of this chapter reveals, he identified victims of fire, crime, flood and bankruptcy, single mothers, the sick, the old, the blind and the lame as being especially vulnerable.[42] The medieval practice of presenting *ex voto* offerings for sick animals as well as humans at healing shrines made sense in a society where the ownership of a beast or two constituted a family's principal defence against hunger, if not starvation. The old woman who prayed in the 1170s that William of Norwich would cure her ailing pig clearly hovered precariously on the breadline.[43] As will soon become apparent, the living conditions of the urban proletariat fluctuated considerably between the thirteenth and sixteenth centuries, not least as a result of the dramatic impact of successive outbreaks of plague on an overcrowded city. Those fortunate enough to survive benefited from improvements in the quantity and quality of food, growing fitter and more resistant to disease.[44] Yet even in the less testing years of the late fourteenth and early fifteenth centuries, a combination of factors, such as gender, age and the number of dependents an individual had to support, meant that the threat of poverty loomed far larger at certain stages in the life-cycle than at others. As Colin Richmond remarks in an essay on the Paston family and their tenants, 'historians might be more helpful expositors of the past if they presented its mishaps as par for the course . . . death, disease, natural disasters (telling phrase) and bad weather were both too random and too regular for life to have been comfortable or calculable'.[45] How much less secure it was for men and women lower down the social scale. The extent to which chronic disease or disability aggravated the long-term problems of the poor is now fully recognised, but the sudden death of a breadwinner could prove just as catastrophic for his or her surviving dependents. Abandoned or widowed mothers with small children and old people living alone were, for example, demonstrably at risk.[46] Langland wrote movingly of the plight of women reduced to despair by the struggle of earning enough to feed their offspring while they themselves went hungry.[47]

Yet if not all poverty sprang from sickness or disability, it often went hand-in-hand with disease and malnutrition. From a biological as well as an economic standpoint, undernourished women worn down by the strain of repeated pregnancies, the elderly and the very young were once again prime victims. An analysis of the Norwich Census of the Poor of 1570 reveals, for example, that between one third and one half of all the inhabitants over sixty were likely to be impoverished, and that at least one quarter of this substantial group (about 14 per cent of the urban poor) faced serious disability as well.[48] By then, however, the chances of survival into old age appear to have increased substantially. Osteological evidence from the medieval cemetery of St Helen-on-the-Walls, in one of the most deprived areas of York, suggests a high level of infant mortality (estimated at about 50 per cent), as well as a significantly higher death rate among adult women under the age of thirty-five (56 per cent) than men (35 per cent). Only 9 per cent of the 1,041 individuals examined actually reached sixty, the great majority of these being severely crippled. Poor dentition, caused by malnutrition or illness in childhood, low levels of oral hygiene and the consumption of coarse, adulterated bread, compounded the problems of a community plagued by chronic osteoarthritis.[49] The constant low-level trauma of heavy manual work, combined with protracted exposure to cold and damp, exacerbated this painful and eventually debilitating condition. Arthritis of the spine, neck, hands, hips or knees seriously restricted opportunities for employment, and could easily turn the sufferer into one of the destitute and moribund cripples so frequently mentioned in the foundation charters of medieval hospitals and depicted in the iconography of the period.

Skeletal material excavated in the 1970s from a late Anglo-Saxon graveyard in the north-eastern bailey of Norwich's Norman castle and, more recently, from the cemetery of St Margaret in Combusto (*c.* 1200–1468), in one of the poorest parts of the medieval city, brings home the harsh reality of urban life. As well as confirming the ubiquity of dental disorders and osteoarthritis, both excavations disclosed evidence of rickets, caused by a shortage of vitamin D in childhood while the bones are still growing, of hypoplasia, or thinning of the tooth enamel in children exposed to serious illness or protracted food shortages, and of parietal and orbital osteoporosis, common indicators of childhood anaemia.[50] In its extreme form lack of vitamin C led to scurvy: deprived of fruit and green vegetables throughout winter, a significant proportion of the population must regularly have displayed pre-scorbutic symptoms, including general lassitude. Less acute seasonal deficiencies, experienced across the social spectrum, exacerbated the manifold sores and blemishes which constituted a veritable badge or emblem of poverty long before the vicious propaganda of the sixteenth century vilified the idle and pox-ridden pauper.[51] Although they were unlikely to prove fatal in the short term, dietary problems combined with other hazards of medieval life to render the urban proletariat especially susceptible to infectious diseases as well as specific forms of cancer. Low levels of health were, moreover, likely to inhibit recovery from the manifold accidents and injuries which were a fact of life for the labouring classes. Approximately one-third of the 300 or so adult skeletons removed from St Margaret's showed evidence of traumatic injury, most notably to the spine, and several had sustained poorly healed fractures.

If the principal breadwinner was killed or permanently incapacitated, the consequences for his or her dependents could be bleak. Burns, scalds, falls, traffic accidents and, most common of all, ruptures occasioned by lifting heavy weights, occurred with distressing frequency.[52] Medical and surgical practitioners, who customarily charged quite heavily for their services, were exhorted to treat the poor as a work of charity and may often have done so, but their powers of intervention in such cases were strictly limited. The incompetent treatment of broken bones could lead to permanent disability, as also could neglect.[53] Notwithstanding a suggestion advanced by the celebrated fourteenth-century French physician, Bernard Gordon, that new forms of treatment might be attempted first on animals and then on the indigent in hospitals (a telling reflection on their place in the great chain of being), most surgeons were reluctant to risk their own immortal souls by causing the death or mutilation of any patient, however humble.[54] Norwich was celebrated in later centuries for the skill of its lithotomists, who operated quickly and with great precision for the removal of bladder stones. But medieval surgeons were hesitant to use the knife on this agonising condition, which is caused by a chronic lack of vitamin A and an excess of calcium (evident, for example, in a typical peasant diet of bread and cheese). The stone, in fact, showed little respect for status: during the seventeenth century Nicholas Rix, a master of St Giles's (by then the Great Hospital), served 'until the tormenting fits of the stone made him resign that office and afterwards his painfull life'.[55]

Documentary and osteological evidence confirms that leprosy, a disease long associated with poor diet and insalubrious living conditions, still posed problems in later medieval Norwich. Residents of the six extra mural lazar houses remained heavily dependent on public charity, attracting bequests from roughly one-third of those citizens whose wills were proved between 1370 and 1532. Local courts made sporadic attempts to remove suspects who continued to live and trade within the walls, even threatening the master of St Giles's hospital with a heavy fine of 20*s*, in 1440, for allowing a leper named Geoffrey Skinner to lodge in the precinct. Nor was this the first occasion on which the hospital incurred criticism for admitting 'intolerable persons'.[56] Even so, as the population built up resistance to its more virulent, lepromatous strain, leprosy began gradually to retreat. Other diseases took its place. It has been suggested that childhood exposure to pulmonary tuberculosis fosters immunity to leprosy, which is spread by a bacterium (*Mycobacterium leprae*) of the same genus. Heightened vulnerability to the risk of bovine tuberculosis (through increased levels of meat and milk consumption) was once held to account for initial outbreaks of 'the Great White Plague' among the urban poor, and thus to explain the declining incidence of leprosy.[57] Twentieth-century research has questioned the likelihood of widespread cross-infection between beast and man, in recent times at least, while revealing how easily milk can transmit other diseases, such as diphtheria, if it is transported and sold in unhygienic conditions. There can be little doubt, however, that once tuberculosis became established in the human population the environmental conditions of medieval towns and cities provided an ideal breeding ground for rapid transmission. Excavations at the Norwich cemetery of St Margaret in Combusto produced at least four cases sufficiently advanced to affect the spine and ribs, although many sufferers would have died long before this stage was reached.[58]

A significant proportion of the health problems experienced by the urban poor leave no discernible trace on the human skeleton. Whereas the upper and middling ranks of medieval society were probably far cleaner than has often been supposed, the poor commanded few of the resources necessary to maintain a reasonable standard of personal hygiene. Accommodation might be shared with livestock (a cause of many domestic accidents); methods of waste disposal were often rudimentary; and, judging by the evidence of late medieval remedy books, the incidence of fleas, lice and intestinal parasites remained high. In periods of dearth the straw used for bedding and floor-covering would be left unchanged and rotting for long periods, and thus became infested with the vermin which spread potentially lethal infections, such as plague and typhus. Enteric diseases flourish in such conditions: in the early 1470s, for instance, an epidemic of dysentery ('the flux') swept across East Anglia, claiming many lives.[59] It is worth noting in this context the serious risks to health faced by the men and women of humble status who were committed to gaol. In view of the appalling conditions which obtained in many English prisons, visitors displayed considerable bravery as well as Christian compassion. During the mid-1540s, the coroners of Nottinghamshire recorded at least sixteen deaths from diseases (probably gaol fever) contracted 'because of the squalor' in the cells. It may be assumed that the chaplains of St Giles's hospital who, from 1472 onwards, were engaged to hear confessions and celebrate mass 'for the relief and comfort of the prisoners and others incarcerated in the guildhall' more than earned their stipends.[60]

In times of dearth the poor were driven to consume contaminated food, with potentially life-threatening consequences. At least one of the demoniacs described in the twelfth-century *Vita* of William of Norwich may well have been suffering from ergotism, which is caused by poisoned rye and leads also to the loss of limbs through gangrene. As the English climate grew wetter during the early fourteenth century grain crops in general were increasingly liable to fungus and mould.[61] Throughout the late medieval and early modern period, courts in Norwich routinely presented butchers, cooks and other victuallers for selling 'putrid and ill-salted meat', 'full pokky pigges' (which would have spread tapeworm), 'stynkyng makerelles', animals found dead by the wayside, re-heated food and other comestibles deemed 'noutye [naughty] and unholsome for mannes body'.[62] Their vigilance on this score, along with a concern that the city's open drains and sewers should be regularly cleansed, belies some long-cherished assumptions about the squalor of medieval life. It is, indeed, worth noting that in 1445 the master of St Giles's hospital was himself penalised for failing to clean one such 'cokey' which lay just outside the precinct.[63] Yet the poor did not always benefit from this sustained – if sometimes ineffectual – campaign against environmental nuisances, being generally obliged to congregate in the more insalubrious parts of the city and its suburbs.[64] The conviction that rich or exotic fare would tempt paupers into a life of vice may have fostered an analogous belief that 'measly' flesh could safely be given to the destitute in general and 'measles' (lepers) in particular. Scottish borough custom, for instance, decreed that any 'corrupt' pork or salmon offered for sale on the open market should be confiscated forthwith and given to lepers, while the *Leges Forestarum* assigned to 'lepir men . . . to pur folk and to sek' any dead beasts found abandoned in suspicious circumstances.[65] Although many benefactors were anxious to do their best by Christ's representatives on earth, 'Goderyke the Bocher' who grudgingly cast his 'vilest' cuts of meat into the begging bowl of St Bartholomew's hospital in London cannot have been unusual.[66]

The high incidence of blindness among the medieval population and the frequency with which specific provision was made for its victims by the founders of hospitals is also significant. The famous Parisian hospital, the *Quinze-Vingts*, was set up by Louis IX to house 300 blind men and women, and in London the mercer, William Elsing, professed himself so distressed (*viscera mea gravis torquentur*) by the plight of impoverished, blind and paralysed priests that he founded a hospital for them in 1331, hoping to expand its capacity to 100 beds.[67] Low standards of personal hygiene and poor sanitation accounted in part for the spread of conditions such as trachoma. A parliamentary statute of 1542, permitting lay healers to treat paupers free of charge with 'herbes, rotes and waters', notes that the poor were especially prone to ulcerated eyes and conjunctivitis. These complaints must have been aggravated by difficult working conditions and the smoke of turf fires in poorly ventilated rooms, where respiratory diseases also flourished.[68] But vitamin deficiencies were again partly to blame; the prevalence of seasonal ophthalmia no doubt explains many of the healing miracles recorded at shrines, for as the summer diet improved so did the eyesight.[69]

As Walter Suffield recognised when drawing up the statutes of his new hospital, one of the many factors likely to tip the precarious balance between poverty and outright destitution was a poor harvest leading to escalating grain prices. Major urban centres, such as Norwich, had to buy in supplies, which increased their vulnerability. In periods of high population density the market proved remarkably sensitive to even slight fluctuations in crop yields, while floods or famines sent prices rocketing.[70] To encourage almsgiving during the octave of the feast of St Giles, in early September, Suffield offered a perpetual indulgence of forty days' annual remission of enjoined penance to anyone who assisted his foundation. Similar attempts at fundraising were made by Bishops Walton, Middleton and Walpole in 1265, 1279 and 1294 respectively, the last of these indulgences being extended to cover the octave of the anniversary of the hospital's dedication (3 to 8 October).[71]

According to the Bury St Edmund's chronicler, 1294 was a year of 'famine and great want throughout England', when corn prices increased sixfold and new crops were destroyed either in the fields by heavy rains or later by fungus, such as that which gives rise to ergotism.[72] The ubiquity of references to weather conditions and food prices in monastic chronicles is understandable in view of the immediate and often dramatic effect these were likely to have on the demand for alms. The Church's unease on the score of judicial astrology (predicting the future) did not extend to the more legitimate exercise of weather forecasting from the stars. A volume of miscellaneous astrological manuscripts now in the Bodleian Library contains a quire of jottings and calculations bearing the name of Lawrence Somercotes, a member of Bishop Suffield's household, as well as a sheet of notes on how to forecast storms and changing weather conditions from 'a certain book of the year 1249', around the time of the foundation of St Giles's hospital.[73]

Even in good years, the weeks of dearth before harvest when food supplies were running low proved a testing time for the poor and the institutions which helped them. It was for this reason that Suffield initially arranged for extra supplies of bread 'sufficient to banish hunger' to be distributed at the hospital gate each day between 25 March and 15 August, although he later restricted these doles to Saturdays, presumably because of the heavy demand.[74] As we shall see in Chapter III, his insistence that nobody should be turned away empty-handed on such occasions could still place an impossible strain on the hospital's budget. In the year following his death, for example,

> there was a great shortage of everything because of the floods of the previous year, and corn, which was very scarce, cost from 15*s* to as much as 20*s* a quarter. Famine resulted so that the poor had to eat horsemeat [fodder], the bark of trees and even more unpleasant things. Many died of hunger. In the same year all kinds of grain grew abundantly in the fields but were ruined by the autumn rains. In many places the corn remained in the fields after the feast of All Saints [1 November].[75]

Worse was to come. A run of bad harvests from 1310 onwards gave rise to a series of devastating famines and cattle murrains which lasted until 1322. These, in turn, resulted in starvation, epidemics and mass emigration from the countryside. In London over sixty people were reputedly killed in the stampede for alms; similar scenes may have taken place outside St Giles's and the other Norwich hospitals, none of which could have organised relief on the scale required during this exceptional decade.[76] Anticipating San Bernardino's exhortations to the Sienese, Archbishop Reynolds of Canterbury urged the people of England in 1315 and 1316 to seek forgiveness through 'prayers, fasts, almsdeeds and other works of charity'. Not even these measures sufficed: the enormity of coping with such a frightening influx of poor immigrants seems to have provoked a sentiment akin to the 'compassion fatigue' encountered so often in the affluent West today.[77] Well before the first outbreak of plague promoted institutionalised intolerance of the vagrant poor, small town society had begun to equate the unemployed 'stranger' with the 'illdoer'.[78]

The effects of protracted food shortages were all the more acute in a period of chronic overcrowding and land-hunger. The situation in Norwich can be documented in unusual detail because of the survival of an early fourteenth-century tithing-roll for the leet of Mancroft, which covered approximately one-quarter of the city from the central market to the southern walls. An analysis of the entries reveals that, between 1311 and 1333, the number of adult males named in the roll rose by 76 per cent (from 860 to 1,513), and an average of sixty-three newcomers were admitted every year.[79] The great majority of these men had no means of support and were desperate to find work as servants or casual labourers. Norwich then possessed a densely populated hinterland, parts of which may have contained as many as 500 people per square mile. The effects of such intense population pressure on the local peasantry are strikingly apparent on the manor of Hakeford Hall in Coltishall, some seven miles north of Norwich, where the number of smallholders living at, or below, subsistence level increased dramatically. Bad harvests led to panic selling as grain prices more than doubled and starvation threatened. Since the majority of plots thus grew too small to support their tenants, the search for alternative or additional employment became imperative.[80] To this vicious combination of circumstances, which reduced a substantial proportion of the rural population to abject poverty, were added the demands of manorial lords, the Church and the government. The East Anglian peasantry suffered quite lightly from seigneurial exactions, but there was no escaping the burden of taxation, conscription and purveyance imposed by Edward II and his son for the support of their armies in Scotland. Corruption made matters worse: in 1298, for example, a Norfolk official was said to have taken corn 'from the poor and impotent' and 'left the able and powerful alone'. These impositions, which pushed up bread prices while forcing many poor peasants off the land, provided yet another incentive for migration to the nearest town or city.[81]

A steady rise in the population of Norwich, from an estimated 17,000 in 1311 to perhaps as many as 25,000 in 1333, brought into the walls an unprecedented number of men and women who, if not actually paupers, were intensely vulnerable to the reversals of fortune described above.[82] Already, at the beginning of the century, the civic authorities had expressed concern about the influx of homeless labourers who lacked the means to offer pledges for good behaviour or pay fines if they broke the law.[83] The provision of food and housing for individuals whose wage of about one penny a day (when they could find work) was barely sufficient for subsistence placed a further strain upon available resources. Most newcomers appear to have found rented accommodation in existing buildings or in rows of cottages erected speculatively in gardens or waste land in built-up areas. The thatched rows had clay walls and were therefore neither as permanent nor as robust as the timber-framed terraces occupied by the poor in cities such as York.[84] They must also have been colder and damper, especially in a period notable for wet winter weather and gradually declining temperatures. Having neither foundations nor damp courses, they remained exposed to the elements and made scant provision for heating or cooking. Waste disposal facilities were minimal, posing an additional hazard to residents.[85] Although the circumstances of the urban poor improved considerably during the fifteenth century, as population pressure relaxed and food supplies grew more abundant, few significant changes were made in the basic design and construction of Norwich's housing stock. With so many thatched roofs in close proximity the fire risk remained high. One city church was actually known as St Mary 'the Unbrent' (on Brent Lane) in memory of the great fire which had destroyed most of Norwich north of the Wensum shortly after the Conquest, while another in the same quarter bore the name of St Margaret *in Combusto*.[86] Two disastrous conflagrations of 1507 caused even greater devastation, cutting whole swathes through the city and causing widespread depopulation.[87] Fires were yet another of the hazards of urban life which could reduce even the affluent to penury.

It has been suggested that each of these cramped early fourteenth-century dwellings would have occupied approximately 272 square feet, and have contained two or even three storeys. Many families supplemented their meagre incomes by subletting rooms, with inescapable consequences so far as public health and sanitation were concerned. In 1311, for example, thirty-six adult males were living in twenty-seven separate properties in Upper Newport, but by 1333 the number had risen to 112, to which should be added women and children of both sexes under the age of twelve.[88] If, as seems likely, the problem of overcrowding persisted until 1349, it is easy to see why the Black Death claimed so many victims in Norwich. That East Anglia in general, and Norwich in particular, suffered cruelly through infection carried by sea as well as by land was certainly a commonplace among Tudor and Stuart antiquarians. Their propensity for exaggeration (John Stow, for example, estimated over 57,000 fatalities in Norwich alone) should not blind us to the real enormity of the catastrophe.[89] Hitherto dismissed by historians as inherently implausible, assertions that at least half the inhabitants of some English towns succumbed to the pestilence now seem credible in the light of such compelling new population figures. Other sources support this upward revision. Taken alone, episcopal institutions to vacant benefices are a notoriously unreliable indicator of mortality rates. Even so, Bishop Bateman's register provides striking evidence of a rise across the diocese from fewer than twenty institutions per month before May 1349 to 222 in July of that year alone. In October 1350 Bateman secured papal approval for the ordination of sixty young clerks, well below the permitted age, to fill vacancies created by the plague.[90] Perhaps as many as 60 per cent of the manorial tenants at Hakeford Hall died between 1349 and 1359, a figure which rises to 80 per cent if the impact of subsequent epidemics in the 1360s and acute food shortages at the end of the decade are taken into account.[91] In common with that of many other English urban centres, the population of Norwich had probably begun to decline somewhat before the first outbreak of plague. But these statistics may still hold good for the city as well as the nearby manor. The poll tax return of 1377, which supposedly recorded all individuals over the age of fourteen unless they were either beggars or members of a religious order, lists a mere 3,952 inhabitants and that of 1381 a slightly lower total. Even allowing for the inevitable omissions and evasions, the entire population of Norwich may thus have fallen as low as 6,000 and is unlikely to have exceeded 8,000. This represents a loss of between 17,000 and 19,000 inhabitants over a period of just five decades. Relatively speaking, the city then ranked in size after York, Plymouth, Coventry and Bristol, and was not significantly more populous than King's Lynn.[92]

Such a dramatic and lengthy period of dislocation had profound consequences for the city and its poor. The number of parish churches fell from over fifty in the early fourteenth century to forty-six by the early 1520s. Among the casualties of the 1349 epidemic was the parish church of St Matthew, which lay at the west end of Holme Street near the hospital of St Giles, and was in ruins by the 1360s.[93] The striking absence of accounts and ancillary documents in what is otherwise a remarkably full archive, suggests that the hospital itself sustained heavy losses during the third quarter of the fourteenth century. If its infirmary remained open and the brethren continued to distribute alms, the risk of infection would have been overwhelming. Their neighbours in the Dominican friary were 'wiped out almost to a man', while the Benedictines appear to have lost just under half their community in the first outbreak of plague alone. The celebrated 'Apocalypse' cycle of bosses in the cathedral cloister contains several depicting the plagues of the Book of Revelations (Chapters XV and XVI) spread by angels bearing 'seven golden vials full of the wrath of God'. The terror portrayed in the faces of the victims – most notable among whom is a tonsured monk, prostrate in a sea of blood – reflects in graphic detail the 'noisome and grievous sore' inflicted upon the people of Norwich. Trade was seriously disrupted. According to a 1357 rent roll of properties owned by the civic authorities, many dwellings and market stalls remained unlet or had fallen into ruins. A decade later the market was reduced in size.[94]

In the short term, at least, urban life seemed beset by uncertainty and upheaval. If the early years of the century were marked by distrust of a rootless proletariat desperate for employment, the decades after 1349 saw a hardening of attitudes towards men and women who appeared workshy or troublesome. Faced with the associated problem of labour shortages and rising wage rates, the English government attempted to force 'right myghti and strong beggars' back to work by pegging wages and making it illegal to support the able-bodied with alms.[95] The situation in Norwich, where piles of ordure and filth lay uncollected in the streets and the walls had grown dilapidated, led Edward III to reprimand the city governors, in 1352, ordering them to pave their streets and repair the defences. They were to remedy the 'great want of servants and workmen' available for these tasks by forcing 'the many men and women, strong and able [who] roam about the city idle and refuse to work for a sufficient salary' to obey the law.[96] Protracted disagreements between the ruling elite and commonalty of Norwich did little to ease the tension. Six years later the king again intervened to order the arrest of malcontents disturbing the peace and causing civic unrest; and in 1371 further outbreaks of 'grievous strife' threatened to erupt onto the streets as 'certain citizens and the commons' again found themselves at loggerheads.[97]

The flashpoint occurred in 1381, when those who had managed to escape the degrading poverty of previous generations reacted against the escalating demands of royal taxation. East Anglia was briefly but deeply shaken by popular discontent during the Peasants' Revolt. Events at Bury St Edmunds, where the townspeople made common cause with the insurgents and killed the prior, tend to overshadow the disturbances in other parts of the region. But Norfolk, too, was the scene of widespread disaffection. Rebels from the east of the county banded together on Mousehold Heath outside Norwich under the leadership of their 'king', a dyer named Litster. On 17 June they entered the city in triumph 'with pennons flying and in warlike array', only to meet nemesis, in the person of Bishop Despenser, shortly afterwards. The brutal suppression of disorder in the eastern counties won the 'warrior bishop' many plaudits, and marks a further hardening of attitudes towards the unruly poor.[98] Most of the rebels who took up arms in 1381 came from the ranks of taxpaying peasants and artisans. They were men whose burgeoning expectations had been disappointed, rather than downtrodden, hopeless paupers. Inevitably, however, fear of a rebellious underclass tainted by the sin of envy bred on itself and created what Michel Mollat has described as 'a generation frightened by pauperism'.[99] Along with this growing sense of unease went a reluctance to help outsiders who posed a threat to the social order. During the 1380s further repressive legislation empowered local authorities, including 'mayors, bailiffs, constables and other governors of towns', to interrogate and demand securities from 'divers people . . . wandering from place to place, running in the country more abundantly than they were wont to do in times past'. Suspected criminals and those unable to find pledges for good behaviour were to be incarcerated until the next sessions of gaol delivery, which might involve imprisonment for years rather than months.[100] Although, in practice, the statute was not consistently enforced, the implicit assumption that poverty and crime went hand in hand fostered a conviction that only deserving cases incapable of work should be accorded relief. One of the prisoners languishing in Norwich gaol in 1424 was an Irishman seized on suspicion of felony simply 'because he was a vagabond'.[101] As we shall see in Chapter VII, the Church did little either through guidance or example to espouse the cause of able-bodied men and women whose circumstances rendered them unemployed or homeless.[102] Yet the founder of St Giles's hospital had, like so many of his thirteenth-century contemporaries, taken their predicament more closely to heart.

THE FOUNDER AND HIS MILIEU

The statutes of St Giles's hospital reflect the ideals and preoccupations of a reforming bishop whose character emerges today with an immediacy rarely encountered at a distance of over 700 years. The *tabula picta* executed by one Master Peter and bequeathed in Suffield's will to his 'faithful and beloved' companion, William Whitewell, has not, alas, survived. But we are still left with an unusually vivid picture of a remarkable – and extremely complex – individual.[103] The family of Calthorpe, *alias* Suffield, took its name from a village some fifteen miles north of Norwich, not far from the coast, where its principal holdings lay [see Map IV]. Bishop Walter may have retained a childhood affection for this part of Norfolk, as he not only purchased the advowson to settle upon his new hospital but also acquired land in Hevingham and Marsham (on the route between Calthorpe and Norwich) for a park and country seat of his own. He remained on affectionate terms with his brother, Sir Roger, a member of the county gentry, acting as an attorney on his behalf during the 1220s, when he was probably still a university teacher. Sir Roger's interests extended south-eastward into the area now known as Broadland, where the hospital was to acquire some of its most valuable properties. He maintained close links with the Benedictine abbey of St Benet Holme, on the River Yare, and probably married a kinswoman of the house's steward, Peter Obys.[104] Obys, in turn, helped the bishop and Sir Roger make their earliest purchases for the new foundation; and it was probably for this reason that Suffield set aside a substantial sum of money in his will for the commendation of Peter's soul. The two nephews and a niece who also figure in this long and carefully worded document were almost certainly Sir Roger's children. One nephew followed his uncle and namesake into the Church, being the recipient of an impressive collection of books on philosophy and divinity, while the other, William, was left all the bishop's armour and an emerald ring.[105] William inherited and augmented the Calthorpe estates, consolidating his family's somewhat distant links with the aristocratic house of Warenne (their feudal overlords, whose arms the bishop bore) through marriage.[106] Bishop Suffield had used his influence with Henry III to ensure that the young man was exempted from the onerous administrative duties which normally devolved upon a landowner of his status. William also managed to postpone the costly business of becoming a knight, albeit only while his uncle remained at Court.[107] A mixture of affection, gratitude and devotion to the latter's memory made him a notable patron of St Giles's in the years to come.

Such was Suffield's posthumous reputation as a friend to the poor that for a while canonisation seemed likely. It should not, however, be assumed that he was a political innocent, ignorant of the ways of the world. On becoming bishop of Norwich, in 1245, he welcomed his younger brother, another William, into his household and promoted him to the archdeaconry of Norwich at the first opportunity.[108] The preferment of relatives was widely practised at this time, and incurred little censure in cases of genuine ability. Nepotism could, however, lead to other abuses, which reformers were anxious to eliminate. Walter's nephew, the priest, accumulated at least three Norfolk livings (including that of Suffield, a couple of miles east of Calthorpe), which he occupied in plurality during the bishop's lifetime without the necessary dispensation. Another kinsman, Hamon de Calthorpe, held two lucrative benefices in the diocese, as well as serving as the first master of St Giles's.[109] Since the hospital statutes insisted upon almost continuous residence he, too, must have farmed out his parochial duties. Bishop Walter showed rather less concern about supervision at the *domus Dei* in Dunwich, securing the mastership, in 1252, for his domestic chaplain, William Blythburgh, who continued to live in his household. Five years later, a new warden was appointed by royal letters patent, on the significant condition that 'he dispose of the goods and revenues thereof to the advantage of the brethren and poor dwelling therein'.[110] Suffield was the first bishop of Norwich to ratify the endowment of private chantries in the diocese, at least two of his four known confirmations being to foundations supported by his own brother. One, indeed, concerned a chantry at Hales of which Sir Roger (who sometimes used this toponymic) was a principal benefactor.[111] He was, in short, a product of his class. Like many another worldly prelate from the ranks of the county elite Suffield loved hunting, an activity prohibited to priests by the fourth Lateran Council (cap. xv). Most thirteenth-century bishops, however personally austere, kept magnificent households and large stables appropriate to their social and political status, but he took pleasure in his earthly comforts and was devoted to the chase. Perhaps mindful of two licences of 1253 giving him permission to hunt 'the hare, fox and cat' with dogs throughout the king's forests in Essex so long as he lived, he left his pack of hounds and a palfrey to Henry III. He must also have been grateful that attempts by the justices of the same forest to fine him for poaching deer were dropped on the King's orders in 1256, not long before he died.[112]

In marked contrast to several of his friends and mentors on the episcopal bench, Suffield appears generally, if reluctantly, to have accommodated himself to the demands of a difficult monarch. At a time when the King's interests often came into direct conflict with those of reforming bishops, confrontation between Church and State seemed inescapable. Although there can be little doubt where his private sympathies lay during the long dispute between his predecessor, Bishop Raleigh, and Henry III over royal intervention in episcopal appointments, he never personally crossed swords with the King. A man of the world, with a keen awareness of the virtues of compromise, he proved a shrewd propagandist and eloquent preacher, placing his skills at Henry's disposal. The King's piety and concern for the poor may, indeed, have made Suffield more tolerant of his constant meddling in ecclesiastical affairs. When, in 1247, Henry acquired a crystal phial of the Holy Blood of Christ from the Knights Templars, the honour of celebrating mass and preaching to the assembled crowds at Westminster Abbey fell to Bishop Walter. The chronicler, Matthew Paris, provides an eye-witness account of this solemn event, at which the King himself carried the container reverently on foot from St Paul's cathedral to the abbey [see Plate 2]. He also gives a precis of the sermon, carefully crafted by Suffield to strike the right note of pious nationalism. Henry's great rival, Louis IX of France (whom he constantly sought to emulate, if not outdo in ostentatious acts of piety), might possess a sizeable piece of the True Cross and the Crown of Thorns, but the Blood of Christ was surely far more sacred. If the Instruments of the Passion had provided a means for God to redeem sinners, the Blood itself was the price He had been obliged to pay. Just as it had pleased God to make King Henry, 'the most Christian of all Christian princes', the custodian of such a peerless relic, so the realm of England, 'where faith and holiness flourish more than in other parts of the world', was predestined to be its natural resting place.[113]

Suffield's devotion to the cult of the Holy Blood, which accorded well with Innocent III's efforts to uphold the sanctity and power of the Mass, appears beyond question. Yet he was shrewd enough to recognise the political and personal advantages to be gained from so public a profession of faith. Although he was never acclaimed as a teacher or theologian, he had benefited from a sound academic education, and was described in flattering terms by Matthew Paris as a man of letters (*vir eleganter literatus*). His bequest of £5 to 'the poor scholars of Oxford' supports the tradition that he studied and perhaps also taught there. According to the Norwich Benedictine, Bartholomew Cotton (d. 1321/22), he also read canon law at the University of Paris.[114] This was a period when the ablest English graduates sought to complete their education abroad, usually opting to spend a few years in the Paris schools. During the late twelfth and early thirteenth centuries well over a third of the masters teaching there were Englishmen, and it seems more than likely that Suffield followed this well-worn path.[115] Evidence of his continued interest in education, and especially of his commitment, shared with other reformers, to a practical programme for the improvement of standards of literacy among the priesthood, is apparent in the foundation statutes of St Giles's hospital. In them he provided for the support of seven poor boys with an aptitude for Latin grammar, who were to be selected on a rota system by the local schoolmaster and fed in the hospital.[116] They were presumably to be pupils at the neighbouring school, immediately to the west of the precinct and near the episcopal palace, which was then controlled by the Benedictine prior but from 1288 onwards came, like the hospital, under the direct patronage of successive bishops of Norwich [see Map II] Given its proximity to his own official residence, we may assume that Suffield took a personal interest in this establishment, which he may even have attended as a child.[117]

St Giles's possibly served as a model for changes at the hospital of St John the Baptist, Bridgwater. In 1325, Bishop Drokensford confirmed an earlier ruling that, among other things, the master would maintain thirteen poor scholars '*habiles ad informandum in grammatica*', who would study daily in the town.[118] Although long recognised by historians engaged in the ongoing debate over the nature and extent of schooling in medieval England, the contribution made by English hospitals to education has never been explored in depth. Emphasis tends to be placed on fifteenth-century almshouses, such as Ewelme and Holy Trinity, Pontefract, which specifically incorporated schools in the foundation, but many older houses employed schoolmasters or offered exhibitions to deserving cases.[119] Besides enlarging the scope of the Seven Comfortable Works, such arrangements addressed concerns about the calibre of the clergy, while also providing young choristers who could be employed in hospital churches. Arrangements made in 1332 for twelve scholars and their master to be maintained at the hospital of St John the Baptist, Exeter, stipulated that the boys should not only be poor, well behaved and able, but that they should also be familiar with the psalter and plainchant.[120] They were, like the boys at St Giles's, available for services on Sundays and feast days, thus making a valuable contribution to the sound and spectacle of the liturgy.

Suffield's attachment to Richard of Wendover (d. 1252), a 'companion' whom he remembered fondly in his will, confirms that he enjoyed the society of learned men. Wendover was a medical practitioner and canon of St Paul's, London, who may possibly have attended Pope Gregory IX (d. 1241) as a physician. His close connection with the nearby hospital and priory of St Bartholomew is especially relevant, as this was one of the first English hospitals to run a school on the premises, initially for poor children born there, but later for fee-payers, too.[121] It was, perhaps, he who recommended to Suffield that the nursing sisters at St Giles's should be aged fifty or thereabouts.[122] Besides offering a precaution against sexual irregularity, such a measure would have avoided the problems which contemporary medical authorities associated with menstruating females. As the surgeon, Lanfrank of Milan, warned at the end of the century, it was highly dangerous for a woman 'in time of menstrue' even to look upon a sick man, while other writers maintained that her breath would be as contaminating as her gaze.[123] Nor was it desirable that she should then remain in proximity to the Eucharist, which would, of necessity, be regularly elevated before the patients and their carers. Such was Suffield's desire to avoid moral and physical pollution that he refused to allow any other women to lodge in the hospital precinct and insisted upon the immediate suspension of services in the chapel if they had the temerity to do so.[124]

Ideas about the Church's responsibilities towards the poor and the extent of their claims upon society were still inspiring lively debate in academic circles when Suffield began his career. Late twelfth-century canonists, whose work figured prominently in the syllabuses at both Paris and Oxford, had devoted considerable attention to the theological implications of poor relief, an activity which preoccupied Suffield, on a practical as well as an intellectual level, for most of his life. If he did, indeed, spend time in Paris, he would have trodden in the steps of like-minded scholars, such as Peter the Chanter and his pupil, Jacques de Vitry, a propagandist for the Augustinian order and its work in hospitals for the destitute. It was there that Pope Innocent III had refined his views on the role of the clergy – and especially bishops – in assisting the poor of Christ, and Stephen Langton (d. 1228) had extolled the virtues of perfect charity in the priesthood.[125]

Two men in particular exercised a strong personal influence over Suffield during these formative years. He may have attended some of the theology lectures given at Oxford by Edmund Rich (*alias* de Abingdon) between about 1214 and 1222, and certainly came to the latter's attention soon after. We do not know if the gilt cup he describes in his will as once belonging to 'the blessed Edmund' was a gift from the saint himself or his chancellor, Richard Wych, Suffield's dearest friend and second spiritual mentor. Wych himself was said to have performed a miraculous cure upon a paralysed child with a chalice previously owned by his master. Whatever its immediate provenance, the cup became Suffield's most hallowed possession and was bequeathed, appropriately, given its alleged healing powers, to his new hospital in Norwich.[126] As celebrated for his generous almsdeeds as he was for his commentaries on the scriptures, Edmund had been made archbishop of Canterbury in 1233 and died in self-imposed exile at Soissy seventeen years later, during the course of an acrimonious dispute with King Henry. Contemporary accounts of his life contain many references to his concern for the sick and destitute which, allowing for the conventions of medieval hagiography, was manifestly sincere. Matthew Paris mistakenly claims that he gave all his patrimony to a hospital in Abingdon, but he is known to have settled property on that of St John the Baptist in Oxford, and to have run up debts through his generosity to the poor.[127]

Edmund's body was buried, as he had wished, at the Cistercian monastery at Pontigny, near Auxerre, and translated after his canonisation in 1246 to a new and splendid tomb within the abbey. Suffield himself contributed towards the decoration of the shrine, made at least one pilgrimage there and left money in his will to complete the work he had already started. Of even greater interest is his desire to follow the archbishop's example by having his heart removed after his death and placed in a spot 'where his love would ever abide'. Edmund had intended in this way to honour and reward the canons at Soissy who had cared for him in his last illness. His royal, episcopal and aristocratic imitators likewise saw heart-burial as a means of expressing their attachment to particular institutions and religious orders.[128] Suffield was among the first, and his choice naturally fell upon St Giles's hospital. In the event of his dying, and thus being interred, at any distance from Norwich, he asked that his heart should be removed and placed in a cavity made in the wall next to the high altar in the chapel. Other founders and patrons of hospitals followed suit, and perhaps even anticipated the bishop. William Percy's heart was buried before the altar of the Blessed Virgin at his hospital in Sandon, Surrey, at about this time; and Roger, earl of Winchester (d. 1264), ordered that a measure in the shape of a coffin for distributing corn among the indigent should be placed next to the shrine holding his mother's heart at the hospital of SS James and John, Brackley. His own heart was reputedly housed there, too.[129]

Suffield's skills as a canonist had been put to good use by Archbishop Rich and account in part for his rise in the ecclesiastical hierarchy. They also explain the minute and careful attention to detail apparent not only in his will and the two foundation charters of his hospital, but in other *acta* drawn up under his direction. During the late 1230s he served as Rich's Official in the see of Norwich, which lay vacant for three years because of Henry III's refusal to accept Prior Simon Elmham, the candidate favoured by the cathedral monks. The drama was protracted by a second, more serious quarrel between the King and the monastic chapter at Winchester, which wanted William Raleigh rather than a royal placeman as its next bishop. Obliged to stand down and temporarily concede defeat in 1238, Raleigh secured the consolation prize of the still vacant see of Norwich, where he proved a characteristically zealous administrator.[130] Suffield probably remained involved in diocesan affairs, having much in common with a man who, in happier times, had been a royal councillor and judge of outstanding distinction. Both were moderates, whose rigorous legal training was none the less tempered by a strongly developed spirituality, inspired by the late Archbishop Rich. The latter's cult was energetically propagated by Raleigh, for political as well as spiritual purposes. Suffield, meanwhile, undertook in 1244 to give expert advice on the role of future archbishops in election procedures at Canterbury cathedral priory, a contentious issue which had clouded Rich's last years and poisoned his relations with the King.[131] Encounters with this mutinous chapter may well have led Suffield to draft unusually complex – and ultimately unworkable – regulations for the selection of masters at St Giles's hospital, since he was clearly determined to prevent a similar situation arising there. Going far beyond the relatively simple rules 'on making an election by ballot or agreement' promulgated by the fourth Lateran Council (cap. xxiv), he instituted an elaborate system of consultation likely to exacerbate the very problems he was trying to avoid.[132]

For a while, elections nearer home proved even more compelling than those at Canterbury. Raleigh, with the support of Pope Innocent IV and his fellow bishops, had finally forced the King's hand in 1243, and after further prevarications was at last translated to Winchester one year later. As his natural successor in Norwich, Suffield had been elected unopposed by the cathedral monks as soon as the news of Raleigh's triumph broke, but he had to wait until the summer of 1244 for investiture with the temporalities of his see and February 1245 for his consecration, which took place at the spectacular church of Carrow priory, just outside Norwich.[133] Although Suffield's candidacy was never challenged by King Henry, a hint of the problems encountered by the chapter at this time emerges from his will, in which he left the monks an annuity of £5 to compensate for their manifold expenses and labours '*circa electionem meam*'.[134] His gratitude to the monastic community and strong personal identification with his new diocese found more immediate expression in stone and mortar. As the first stage in an ambitious plan for the redesign and extension of the entire east end of the cathedral, he replaced the modest apsidal Norman Chapel built by Herbert de Losinga with a long rectangular Lady Chapel twice its size. It was either finished, or near completion, when he drew up his will in June 1256, as he then asked to be buried before the high altar should he die near Norwich. He also arranged for candles to be burnt there in perpetuity in honour of the Virgin Mary, and for mass to be celebrated daily for the salvation of his soul.[135] It is worth noting that Edmund Rich had dedicated himself to the Virgin as a young man, and that her cult enjoyed great popularity among the more zealous of the reforming bishops. She was, moreover, the dedicatee of John le Brun's projected hospital in the parish of St Stephen.[136] If, as has been suggested, Suffield also hoped to revive the then flagging popularity of William of Norwich (d. 1144), whose shrine lay nearby, there is no suggestion that he himself venerated the boy martyr. On the contrary, he may, as we shall see, have nursed hopes of joining the ranks of healing saints himself; the new Lady Chapel allowed ample space for pilgrims. Protestant reformers destroyed this part of the cathedral in the sixteenth century, but the surviving arch, which leads from the east end of the apse into what is now the regimental chapel, gives some idea of the imposing original design.[137]

In common with many leading thirteenth-century churchmen, Suffield combined a successful administrative career, which sometimes placed him on the international stage, with an inner life of vibrant spirituality. His new hospital in Norwich was dedicated to the Virgin Mary and her mother, St Anne, but first and foremost to St Giles.[138] As the patron saint of lepers, cripples and nursing mothers, St Giles (d. *c.* 710) enjoyed considerable popularity throughout northern Europe. One of Norwich's five civic *leprosaria* bore his name, as did well over a score of other English hospitals. His legend contained many elements destined to attract Walter Suffield: as a young man in Greece he had reputedly given away all his possessions to be shared among the poor, and had devoted himself to caring for the sick and destitute. He subsequently abandoned the world to live as a hermit near Nîmes, where he was sustained by the milk of a hind sent to him from heaven. While out hunting, a local ruler pursued the beast and accidentally wounded Giles, who not only declined the offer of medical treatment, but, 'knowing that virtue is perfected in infirmity', prayed that he might henceforward remain in constant pain. He did, however, agree to become abbot of a monastery built for him in reparation at Saint Gilles de Provence, where his shrine eventually became a major pilgrimage centre.[139] In 1248, not long before the foundation of his hospital, Suffield obtained permission from Henry III to visit the abbey, possibly calling at Pontigny as well, on his way to Rome. Did he wish to make a personal act of dedication? He was later to bequeath the mitre and pastoral staff given to him by Bishop Raleigh, along with a substantial sum of money, as offerings for the decoration of the saint's tomb.[140] The hospital's seal, which may have been designed according to his specifications, depicted St Giles seated beside his hind in a forest. At its base a bishop's mitre surmounting a cross emphasised the house's strong episcopal connections [see Plate 17].[141]

Besides attributing many healing miracles to St Giles, legend maintained that he had successfully sought divine forgiveness for the Emperor Charlemagne, whose soul was infected by a grievous and unutterable sin. The widespread belief that he would intercede on behalf of all poor and frightened sinners, obtaining salvation for men and women who died repentant but unconfessed, contributed further to his popularity among the sick and dying:

> O gracious Gyle, of pore folk chef patroun,
> Medycyne to seke in ther dystresse,
> To alle needy sheeld and proteccyoun,
> Reffuge to wrecchis, ther damages to redresse,
> Folk that were ded restoryng to quyknesse [life]
> Sith thou of God were chose to be so good,
> Pray for our synnys, pray for our wikkidnesse . . .
> And as thou were tryacle [theriac] and medycyne
> To kyng Charlis, whan he is myschef stood,
> Teche us the weye by thi gostly doctryne.[142]

We shall return later to the importance of confession in the regimen of the medieval hospital, but it is worth stressing that senior clergy were not alone in their preoccupation with the spiritual health of men and women near to death. As the poet, Robert Henryson, eloquently explained in his 'Prayer for the Pest', the most terrible aspect of plague was its ability to strike before the physician of souls, or priest, could reach the bedside. To die 'as beistis without confessioun', and thus in a state of mortal sin, seemed to the devout layman a punishment far worse than the disease itself.[143] In providing facilities for those who lacked the ministrations of a parish priest to seek absolution the founder of a hospital made available a potent brand of ghostly medicine.

Archbishop Rich's greatest legacy to Suffield was a strong sense of pastoral responsibility, chiefly manifest in his concern for the destitute of all ages. Many thirteenth-century English bishops, following the lead of Innocent III and the early Franciscans, were notable for their almsdeeds, but Suffield enjoyed a particular reputation for liberality.[144] In his will he left well over £375 in cash to be spent on poor relief in his diocese, as well as instructing his two nephews that they were each to feed 100 paupers every year on the feast of the Assumption of the Blessed Virgin and give one square meal every day to a poor man while they lived. The almoner of Norwich cathedral priory was likewise assigned sufficient capital to provide annual doles worth 20*s* on Bishop Walter's anniversary. A major part of the £100 set aside to pay for his funeral was, in addition, to be distributed among the elderly, sick and indigent, while his new hospital received a promise of £200, together with carts, grain, livestock and part of the residue of an estate which may have been worth even more. Any debts due to him from impoverished clergy, tenants or parishioners were to be written off by his executors.[145] How much of this money actually reached the designated beneficiaries is, of course, another matter. With characteristic foresight, Suffield had obtained royal letters patent in 1251, permitting him to make a will 'without impediment'. But Henry III had, even then, exempted any sums due to the Crown, and within days of the bishop's death, in May 1257, demanded securities from his executors for the payment of such debts 'from the first money coming from his chattels and goods'.[146] Yet, even if his wishes were eventually frustrated, he had clearly *intended* to accord priority to the poor.

Testamentary largesse on this scale might, in some cases, be taken as evidence of a troubled conscience following a lifetime's indifference, but Suffield's past record seems to have been unimpeachable. Enough evidence of his charitable activities survives for us to glimpse some of the reality behind the conventional language of medieval hagiography. His previous expenditure on St Giles's cannot, as we shall see, have been much less than £600, including the cost of the site in Norwich; his own household, moreover, served as an almonry during times of famine. Among the various items left by him to the hospital was 'the cup out of which the poor children drank', which suggests that, like Innocent III, he adopted the practice of feeding orphans and other impoverished children at his own table.[147] Suffield's schemes for practical relief reflect an awareness of contemporary social problems as well as a more subjective concern for the salvation of his own soul. Just as his will reveals solicitude for the welfare of his meanest household servants, who were generously rewarded, so the statutes of St Giles's hospital show genuine compassion for the plight of the destitute. The requirement that every day thirteen paupers were to receive a dole of 'sufficient good bread' and a dish of meat or fish, sometimes supplemented with eggs and cheese, outside the hospital gates was a conventional mark of deference to Christ and his twelve apostles. In the bitter East Anglian winter, however, the recipients were permitted to eat before an open fire; and whenever Suffield or his successors visited the house the number of meals was to be doubled.[148]

Thirty beds or more, if resources permitted, were to be made permanently available for the sick and infirm poor, with only one (albeit major) apparent restriction: the statutes clearly imply that all patients would be male. Warmth and comfort seem again to have been a priority. With sheets and counterpanes, perhaps including the silk coverlets he left to St Giles's in his will, these beds represented a considerable improvement on the straw pallets provided in some English hospitals.[149] It is, indeed, possible that Suffield further ameliorated the lot of patients by allowing each to occupy a single bed, although the common practice of sharing had the perceived advantage of reducing the amount of laundry, making more space available and keeping out unwelcome draughts. Nor was St Giles's the only Norwich hospital to benefit from his support. On becoming bishop, in 1245, he arbitrated in a dispute between the vicar of Marsham and St Paul's hospital over the allocation of tithes, upholding the house's title. It was probably then, before he began planning his own foundation, that he further augmented this hospital's slender income with a gift of additional tithes from three episcopal livings.[150] Such was Suffield's posthumous reputation for philanthropy that centuries later the London chronicler, John Stow (d. 1605), coupled him with St Ethelwold (d. 984), bishop of Winchester, as one who 'sold all his sacred vessels of the church' to relieve the hungry. The physician and antiquary, Sir Thomas Browne (d. 1682), likewise praised him as 'a person of great charity and piete'. Contemporary opinion pronounced a similar verdict. Matthew Paris, who was by no means uncritical of Bishop Suffield in other respects, noted approvingly that in times of dearth he 'expended all his vessels, and even his silver spoons, along with all his treasury on the poor', words which echo Wulfstan of Winchester's panegyric of the Anglo-Saxon saint.[151]

In this respect, Suffield's episcopate closely resembled that of his second mentor, Richard Wych, who had spent many years as a canon lawyer at Oxford before entering Archbishop Rich's household. Not surprisingly, Wych's election as bishop of Chichester in 1244 was strenuously opposed by the King, who none the less came to appreciate his administrative efficiency and ability to raise money – less spiritual attributes he also shared with Walter Suffield. A dedicated reformer, Wych promulgated an influential body of synodal statutes for his diocese, with the aim of improving the moral calibre of his clergy (they were, for example, forbidden to hunt), while impressing upon them the importance of charity.[152] The process of canonisation, which followed quickly after his death, in 1253, drew heavily on reports of his indifference to the trappings of worldly success, and his kindness to the needy. Taking his cue from Innocent III, he used the Seven Comfortable Works as a vehicle for the distribution of spiritual as well as physical nourishment, 'teaching [the poor] patience and counselling them that the hard road of poverty removes all taint of sin'.[153] His confessor, Ralph Bocking, described the effects of this ministry in specifically medical terms, comparing Wych to 'the healing rock that cures those sick from the disease of sin'.[154] A Dominican who espoused the austere ideal of the apostolic life, Bocking knew Walter Suffield well, and cast for him a role as zealous disciple when he eventually came to write Wych's life:

> O how Walter of venerable memory . . . avowed that he became more zealous and fervent for the spiritual life as a result of their association and intimacy! For although [he] blossomed with renowned virtues, holy deeds and devotion to God and the service of God's Church, he nevertheless became 'more watchful in his prayers', more careful in the service of the Lord, more fervent in preaching, 'more lavish in giving alms' . . . Bishop Walter did not blush to confess to me, wretched sinner though I was, that he followed the example of the blessed Richard and thus daily became a better man and more acceptable to God . . .[155]

The debt may not, however, have been entirely one-sided. Wych died before his plans for an almshouse for infirm and elderly priests, at Windham in Sussex, had been fully implemented. It was, predictably, dedicated to Edmund Rich, and served to house clergy who might otherwise bring their calling into disrepute through 'public mendicancy'.[156] Both bishops shared an understandable concern about the welfare of poor clerics who could no longer earn a living because of age or incapacity, and in this instance, at least, Suffield apparently led the way. But there were many examples to follow. Gautier de Marvis, bishop of Tournai, had by the 1240s established one hospital for elderly clergy and another for the sick poor, while also offering generous assistance to students. If the education of ordinands figured high on the agenda of reforming prelates, so too did the provision of decent support for men who could no longer celebrate the divine office in an appropriate and dignified manner. That sick and disabled priests experienced considerable anxiety on this score is evident from their dealings with the medical profession. The ability to say mass and, most notably, elevate the Host in full view of the congregation, was often held to constitute a 'cure' for which at least partial payment could be claimed. In the late fifteenth century, for example, the vicar of Melbourn, Cambridgeshire, who had evidently suffered from a severe stroke, agreed to hand the first half an agreed sum of £10 to his surgeon as soon as he could 'lift his arm to his head so he could say mass and perform his calling'. The size of the fee, which represented more than twice the annual stipend of many clergymen in full employment, is in itself instructive.[157]

The prospects of poorly paid, unbeneficed clergy, whose income derived largely from their work as chantry priests and curates, often deputising on low wages for absentee placemen, could be very bleak indeed. Without wives or children to care for them as they grew old or sick, they enjoyed neither a guaranteed income nor the security of a permanent home. Many must also have suffered from the health problems likely to result from poor diet and the long-term effects of an insalubrious working environment. As they grew blind, sick or arthritic employment became harder to find.[158] A survey of wills made by some 290 members of the secular clergy in Norwich between 1370 and 1532 reveals the existence of a sizeable 'clerical proletariat', whose members barely subsisted on inadequate stipends.[159] Given that clerical mortality was especially high during the plague of 1349–50, and employment prospects correspondingly better during the later Middle Ages, the situation in Suffield's lifetime must have given even greater concern. His insistence that aged or debilitated chaplains incapable of celebrating mass and without other means of support should be received into St Giles's, as funds allowed, decently housed and properly fed, addressed a pressing contemporary problem. It also reflected wider theological concerns about the status of the priesthood. A number of almshouses for destitute clergy sprang up during this period, while existing institutions often reserved a few beds for retired priests. At the beginning of the fourteenth century, for instance, Abbot Northwold of Bury St Edmunds changed the regulations of St Saviour's hospital to give them priority over the poor women who had previously been admitted as patients. The intercessionary prayers of an impoverished priest must have seemed especially effective and his case therefore all the more deserving. Indeed, at the York hospital of St Mary, founded in 1330 for the benefit of six decrepit chaplains, all residents were obliged to celebrate the offices of the dead each day for their patrons, unless they were lying *in extremis*.[160]

That Suffield and Wych conferred closely when planning their respective hospitals seems more than likely. They may also have drawn on the expertise of Lawrence de Somercotes, an authority on canon law who had worked in the papal curia and later served them both. Somercotes spent some time in Suffield's household before becoming a canon of Chichester cathedral during Wych's time as bishop. His authoritative treatise on electoral procedure appeared in 1253, the year of Wych's death, but he had been assembling material for a long time. His hand may certainly be detected in the regulations concerning the selection of masters at St Giles's, and it would be surprising if he had not also advised Richard Wych about the setting up of his almshouse.[161] The relationship between the two bishops remained cordial to the end, and may be said to have survived beyond the grave. Suffield helped Wych to raise money for repairs at Chichester cathedral, and after his death authorised the appropriation of the rectory of Mendlesham in Suffolk to the chapter there. The revenues were to support a chantry next to Wych's tomb, which lay, appropriately, beside the altar he had built and dedicated to St Edmund Rich.[162] In his will, a document remarkably similar in length and tone to Suffield's, Wych left his friend a seal set in a ring and the serpents' tongues (*linguas meas serpentias*) which had decorated his table. It would be tempting to regard the latter as a warning against the dangers of spending too much time at Court, but they were in fact highly prized fossils, believed by contemporaries to possess prophylactic powers. Surprisingly, given the strained relationship between Wych and Henry III, Suffield appears to have presented this remarkable curio to the King, and does not mention it in his will. 'Five serpents' tongues in a silver standard, which reputedly belonged to St Richard, in a painted wooden case' appear in an inventory of Edward I's wardrobe, and remind us that Suffield was no stranger to the royal household.[163]

In one of his sermons Archbishop Rich had preached against 'false counsellors, grasping persons, flatterers, the hard of heart and oppressors of the poor', warning that every monarch was surrounded by such men.[164] His advice to the virtuous was to shun the company of kings and princes, a course of action no member of the episcopal bench could feasibly adopt. Suffield, an able administrator with a close eye for detail, was soon drawn into the net. Already the subject of criticism in 1247 for his activities as an assessor of the tenth of clerical incomes customarily paid by the English Church to Rome, he incurred further obloquy after a 'new' tenth was granted to Henry III by the Pope.[165] His association with a scheme designed both to increase and to spread the fiscal burden placed him in an invidious position, for the money was specifically intended to fund a crusade. Richard Wych had died at Dover in 1253 while urging his congregation to take up arms against the infidel, and there was widespread enthusiasm for such a venture among clergy of all ranks. In practice, however, this was muted by reluctance to carry the financial burden and genuine doubts as to Henry's good intentions. As the senior of the three prelates charged that summer with assessing and collecting the 'new' tenth, Suffield gave his name to the controversial 'Valuation of Norwich', and was widely seen as the principal agent of an unpopular royal policy which would tighten the screws on those least able to pay.[166] Notwithstanding the comparative leniency of the ensuing assessment, his reputation as a friend to the poor was seriously compromised. One of the hospitals to complain vociferously about his 'exactions' was St John's, Oxford, which had benefited from the support of Edmund Rich. That the irony of this situation caused him considerable pain seems evident from the bequest of 20*s* he made to the hospital in his will, it being the only one outside his diocese to receive a legacy. In seeking to accommodate both parties, Suffield pleased neither, for the King, too, professed disappointment at his efforts. It was thus with considerable relief that he stepped down in 1255, to be replaced by papal agents selected for their greater commitment to 'the business of the Cross'.[167]

Bishop Suffield drew up his will at Hoxne, his Suffolk residence, in June 1256, by which time his health may have begun to show signs of the pressures of office. He survived for another year, eschewing any further involvement in the business of government, and was buried, as he had wished, in Norwich cathedral. For a while it looked as if a healing cult to rival those at Pontigny and at Bishop Wych's shrine at Chichester would become centred on his tomb.[168] Yet he was never canonised. His career lacked that element of defiance in the face of secular authority so desirable in a medieval saint, and reveals little of the conspicuous asceticism which characterised his two mentors. Not for him the heroic austerities and mortification of the flesh practised by St Edmund and St Richard; his was a less tormented, but arguably more attractive, brand of spirituality. He may, indeed, have been stout. To his dear friend and executor, William Whitewell, he left his 'great belt to gird himself with as he grew old', which suggests a comfortably spreading waistline or even the ubiquitous problem of an untreated hernia.[169] In the last resort, however, the canonisation process required a substantial investment and a great deal of political lobbying, which Suffield's successors may have been reluctant to undertake.[170] The next bishop of Norwich, Simon Walton, did, however, complete the synodal statutes on which Suffield had evidently been working just before his death. With their emphasis on the quest for spiritual health, the value of education, the sanctity of the Mass and the need to protect the priesthood from moral contagion, they reflect many of the concerns already apparent in the regulations he had so painstakingly drafted for St Giles's hospital.[171]

THE HOSPITAL STATUTES

In October 1248 Bishop Suffield left England for Rome, making a pilgrimage to Pontigny on the way, but chiefly intent on the conduct of 'secret business' at the Lateran. According to the inveterate gossip, Matthew Paris, he returned in the following year 'with an infamous provision for extorting money from his diocese'.[172] He had perhaps also seized the opportunity to discuss plans for his new hospital, which was by then prominent in his thoughts. As a canon lawyer with considerable administrative experience, he naturally gave serious attention to the regulations by which the institution, its staff and patients were to be managed. Many models lay to hand, and the survival of a number of late twelfth- and thirteenth-century English hospital statutes gives us a good idea of the concerns and aspirations of their founders. Some institutions, such as St Paul's, Norwich, and St Saviour's, Bury St Edmunds, came directly under the authority of a monastic house and thus of its rule, but they were not alone in adopting a religious or quasi-religious way of life.[173] So far as we can tell, all but the smallest hospitals and *leprosaria* established during this period functioned as religious communities of sorts, whose members were bound by vows of poverty, chastity and obedience.

The striking diversity in points of emphasis and detail manifest in these documents is, none the less, indicative of the importance of specific local or personal factors, as already apparent from the collaboration between Wych and Suffield. Some statutes, such as those of St John's, Nottingham (1241), and St Margaret's, Gloucester (*c.* 1200), placed particular stress upon the *opus Dei*, minutely cataloguing the intercessionary prayers to be said daily by the brethren and sisters.[174] Others, of which St James's, Northallerton (1244), furnishes a good example, took a brisk, pragmatic approach, concentrating upon matters of commissariat and administration. This hospital, like many others, modelled itself upon an established house (in this case St Giles's, Kepier), although the tendency to look for inspiration in the same diocese or region cannot necessarily be dismissed as narrow parochialism.[175] The belief that 'the horizons of hospital founders and governors were local ones' takes little account of the cosmopolitan environment shared by so many thirteenth-century reforming bishops and senior clergy. Nor is it easy to accept that 'mental restrictions' made them either unaware of, or indifferent to, developments in other parts of Europe.[176] Formal ties were, indeed, often limited, but the close resemblance between an institution such as St Giles's and continental hospitals of modest size suggests that the overwhelming differences were of scale and wealth rather than geographical location.[177]

Like many other founders of the period, Suffield drew heavily upon a model provided by the Augustinian canons, whose work in hospitals had been so zealously championed by Jacques de Vitry.[178] Although the master of St Giles's and his four priests were to be drawn from the ranks of the secular clergy, their rule was closely (and, in some instances, directly) based upon that of an order destined, in R.W. Southern's words, 'to give a new turn to the tradition of organised religion'. Compared less flatteringly by him to 'the ragwort which adheres so tenaciously to the stone walls of Oxford', the Augustinians were soon to become part of almost every English townscape.[179] Emphasis upon the evangelical ideals of poverty, simplicity and absolute obedience combined with a desire for moderation to equip them especially well for a ministry in hospitals and among the urban poor.[180] The almoner of their priory at Barnwell was, for example, urged to make frequent visits to 'old men and those who are decrepit, lame and blind, or are confined to their beds', and to give generously to the poor of Christ. But his task was not merely to execute the Seven Comfortable Works; the sick paupers admitted by him as boarders were constantly to be admonished 'respecting spiritual goods, as confession, communion and the welfare of their souls'.[181]

Discipline and moderation mattered as much to Bishop Suffield as they did to the Augustinians, for a strict but balanced rule offered the best means of achieving his twin goals of tending the sick poor on earth and ministering to diseased souls after death. Specific aspects of his two foundation charters will be discussed in the course of this book, but it is important to note that he paid as much attention to organisation as to liturgy, establishing precise rules for the guidance of the master and his staff of four priests, four lay brothers and four sisters (later augmented to include two clerks). In order to foster an ethic of apostolic poverty and dedication to Christ's poor, Suffield insisted that all the men should live a communal life, sharing the same spartan accommodation, food and drink, and observing the same fast days, in strict segregation from the sisters. The lay brothers were expected to undertake manual work, supervise routine business outside the house and attend most of the services. The bishop specifically banned esquires and 'wanton boys' from the precinct, since they were the most likely to disrupt its tranquil atmosphere with noise and other distractions. Nor, as we have seen, would he tolerate female boarders, whose presence might undermine discipline and disturb the fixed routine of religious observance essential for physical and spiritual health. Although the master possessed wide ranging disciplinary powers, chiefly to be exercised at weekly chapter meetings, he was himself constrained by an oath of office, and warned against the dangers of undue or excessive hospitality. Gluttony, drunkenness and 'unnecessary feasting' among the clergy had been censored by the fourth Lateran Council (caps xv, xvii), which deemed them sufficient grounds for suspension. Ostentatious or unseemly display in the way of servants, horses or clothing had likewise been prohibited (cap. xvi) and clearly exercised the bishop, too. Not only did expenditure on the trappings of worldly success squander resources and demean the priesthood in the eyes of outsiders; it also engendered the sins of *luxuria* and pride and thus constituted a moral pollutant. For this reason clerical dress, a topic which remained contentious throughout the Middle Ages, was carefully regulated in many hospitals. The brothers and sisters at St Giles's were to wear white and grey habits, while the priests were instructed to dress soberly in accordance with canon law.[182]

Suffield soon recognised that one foundation charter alone, however carefully worded, could not address all the manifold questions of discipline, religious observance and administration likely to arise once his hospital actually began to function. It was by no means unusual for the statutes of medieval hospitals to be revised from time to time by patrons or episcopal visitors, perhaps as a result of liturgical developments (St John's, King's Lynn, 1234), or expansion (St Mary's in the Newarke, Leicester, 1356). Union with another hospital (St John's, Ely, 1240) or a highly critical visitation report (St Thomas's, Southwark, 1387) might also result in the promulgation of new rules.[183] Founders themselves may often have wished to develop or modify their initial ideas, but it is unusual to have such a clear impression of the process. A comparison and collation of the texts of Suffield's two charters [Appendix I] reveals every change he wished to make, however minute. It is a testimony to his thoroughness that no further alterations to the hospital's rules were deemed necessary until 1547.

The first, undated charter comprised a short prologue followed by thirty-six separate articles or regulations. At least three copies have survived and, save for a few scribal errors and inconsistencies, are identical. Two remain in the archives of the Great Hospital, one being a neat text of the charter alone in a near-contemporary hand, while the other is a copy of a confirmation and *inspeximus* issued by Bishop Walton, in 1265, together with an additional indulgence of forty days' remission of enjoined penance to anyone assisting the house in its charitable work.[184] The third copy was entered in the late thirteenth-century *Registrum Septum* of Norwich cathedral priory, as also were a few other documents relating to the donation.[185] The charter itself has been said to date from Suffield's first year as bishop, but this unproven assumption probably results from the misreading of papal letters in support of the hospital issued ten years later by Alexander IV, during the first year of *his* papacy (1255).[186] A date around 1249 is generally accepted, being entirely consistent with the bishop's efforts to extend the precinct along Holme Street. This, he notes in his second charter, had been done through the piecemeal addition of properties 'acquired by our industry from the free tenants of the same'. The hospital was clearly well established by 24 July 1251, when Pope Innocent IV bestowed his approval and blessing upon it and its work 'for the relief of the poor coming from all parts', noting that Suffield had already made a substantial donation 'out of his patrimonial wealth'.[187] A bull was issued a few days later, placing the master, brothers and their possessions under the formal protection of the papacy.[188] Suffield again travelled abroad in October 1253, sailing from Dover under a royal safe conduct almost certainly *en route* for Rome to discuss 'the business of the Cross', and quite probably to solicit further support for his foundation.[189] Innocent's death, in 1254, prompted the bishop to approach his successor, Alexander, for new letters of protection for St Giles's, his efforts in this regard indicating clearly enough his concern for the house's future, as well as his determination to exert his own considerable influence on its behalf. An entry in the papal registers records the issue of such letters on 10 March 1255, as does a separate undated *inspeximus* of them by the prior of Bromholm.[190] From the outset St Giles's enjoyed powerful support, being placed under the patronage and protection of all future bishops of Norwich.

Suffield certainly kept a watchful eye on his hospital, which lay only a matter of yards from the episcopal palace [see Map II]. There can be little doubt that he alone was responsible for the additions and amendments made to his first charter. Many reflect his meticulous – sometimes downright pedantic – eye for detail, and had little effect on the substance of what had gone before. Some, such as the addition of two clerks 'to attend chiefly to divine service and worship' and the recommendation that the house should adopt the Use of Sarum (followed in the rest of the diocese) underline the value placed upon its liturgical, intercessionary functions.[191] Others suggest that standards had either grown lax, or, more probably, that Bishop Suffield felt the need to anticipate and forestall any potential lapses. The brethren and sisters were, for example, now prohibited from 'wandering about the city' instead of reading, saying their prayers or tending the sick, and were instructed to 'hear divine service reverently' each day. Not surprisingly, Suffield continued to tinker with the rules for elections, while at the same time the master's disciplinary and managerial roles were somewhat enlarged. So too were the regulations binding him to residence and limiting his autonomy in financial and legal affairs.

The second charter, which incorporated almost all the text of its predecessor, began with a similar short prologue, followed by forty-four articles. Like the first, it was sealed by Walter Suffield in the chapter house of Norwich cathedral priory in the presence of the prior, Simon Elmham (d. 1257). The original has been lost, but at the request of the master and brethren 'the tenor of the said letters . . . written down word for word' was confirmed, along with the foundation itself, by Pope Alexander in October 1257, not very long after Suffield's death. A copy of this important document was kept by the Norwich Benedictines, who maintained a vigilant interest in the affairs of their new neighbours.[192] Alexander's letters were subsequently inspected, in 1272, by Bishop Skerning, and it was this *inspeximus* which the civic authorities chose to have copied into their fifteenth-century Book of Pleas, probably at the time of renewed disputes over the cathedral's exempt liberties during the early 1440s.[193] That the mayor and corporation should pay such close attention to the hospital statutes was inevitable, given St Giles's location in a part of the city over which they had fought, unsuccessfully, for centuries to exert their authority. The situation of many of the larger hospitals of medieval Europe on marginal, suburban land, subject to disputes over ownership and title, reflects their position as brokers between heaven and earth. To this we now turn.

CHAPTER II

THE PRECINCT

And whan y cam to that court y gaped aboute.
Swich a bild bold, y-buld opon erthe heighte
Say i nought in certeine sithe a longe tyme.
I ghemede upon that house and gherne theron loked,
Whough the pileres weren y-peynt and pulched ful clene,
And queynteli i-coruen with curiouse knottes,
With wyndowes well y-wrought wide up o-lofte.
And thanne y entrid in and even-forth went,
And all was walled that wone though it wid were,
With posternes in pryuytie to pasen when hem liste;
Orcheyardes and erberes euesed well clene,
And a curious cros craftly entayled . . .

Than kam I to that cloister and gaped abouten
Whough it was pilered and peynt and portred well clene,
And y-hyled with leed, lowe to the stones,
And y-paued with peynt til iche poynte after other;
With kundites of clene tyn closed all aboute,
With lavoures of latun louelyche y-greithed.

Pierce the Ploughman's Crede

[When I arrived at that noble place I stood open-mouthed. I had certainly not seen such a magnificent building, towering above the ground, for a very long time. I gazed upon it and eagerly observed how the pillars were painted and brightly polished, and cunningly carved with curious devices, with handsomely constructed windows high aloft. And then I entered in, and began to explore: the entire place was walled, despite its size, with private gateways so the inmates could come and go at will;
[there were] orchards and neatly bordered herbers, and a remarkable cross skilfully carved . . . Then I came to the cloister and gaped in amazement at the way it was pillared and painted and beautifully adorned, and roofed with lead, right down to the masonry, and paved with decorated tiles, each one lying squarely against the next; with tin-lined conduits running all around, and exquisitely wrought brass cisterns for washing.]

Almost every facet of life in the hospitals of medieval Europe yielded a rich harvest of spiritual meaning. Many aspects of their topography and location also lent themselves to religious imagery, which drew upon the symbolism of transition, cleansing and marginality. Practical considerations, such as the availability of green space, pure water and building materials, ease of access for patients and patrons, and proximity to local markets dictated where hospitals would be sited. These factors, coupled with medieval ideas about the spread of disease, meant that hospitals were often suburban developments, situated near rivers, major roads, city gates and bridges, at a point where town gave way to countryside.[1] Since many patients were terminally sick or elderly, as well as poor and disfigured, the ambivalence of their position seemed especially poignant: they hovered between sickness and health, life and death, heaven and hell, and were thus liminal in a spiritual as well as a physical sense.[2] The opening paragraphs of Walter Suffield's foundation charter established the boundaries of his new hospital, which conformed to this pattern in every respect. It lay on the road (Holme Street) leading into Norwich over Bishop's Bridge, which still spans the River Wensum less than 100 yards to the east of the present precinct.[3] Before its fortification in the 1340s, as part of a major improvement of the city's defences, the bridge was probably a relatively modest structure with a timber causeway erected over stone piers, but it was the only crossing on that side of Norwich, and thus carried a considerable amount of traffic. The upkeep of bridges ranked as a work of Christian piety analogous to almsdeeds on behalf of the poor. It might, indeed, be argued that without them the creation of wealth, and the concomitant generation of surplus revenues for philanthropic ventures such as hospitals, would have been impossible. There were, however, less immediately pragmatic reasons for the value placed upon them by the Church. For a start, the bridge served as 'an emblem of the Christian life and of the communication of charity within the community'. Theologians variously described mercy as 'the bridge to the glory of paradise', spoke of Christ as a bridge between God and man, and described his mother, the Virgin, as an aqueduct bearing grace from heaven. Significantly, in this context, one of the Latin names for a bishop was *pontifex*, or bridge-builder, his duty being to engineer just such a spiritual highway along which his flock might travel.[4] This duty was taken quite literally by bishops such as Gilbert de Glanville of Rochester, builder of a stone quay on the west side of Rochester Bridge, and founder, in 1193, of the nearby hospital of St Mary, Strood, which was charged with its upkeep.[5]

To medieval men and women bridges presented a constant reminder of purgatory, the transitory state before the cleansed and healthy soul could enter heaven. In the Spanish town of Zamora, confraternities dedicated to the liberation of souls from purgatory placed almsboxes along the stone bridge outside the southern walls, 'converting the roadway into a sacred passage'. Lest any of the thousands of pilgrims and other travellers who traversed this route every year remained blind to the significance of their actions, the brethren also had images of captive souls painted on the walls.[6] It would be surprising if English hospitals, such as St Giles's by Brompton Bridge (Yorkshire), or the Salisbury hospital of St Nicholas, on the Ayleward Bridge, missed the opportunity to solicit passers-by in this way. Both houses initially offered accommodation to pilgrims and other needy travellers, as did the hospital of SS Mary and Julian 'at the bridge foot' on the north side of Thetford, in Norfolk.[7] Pilgrimage, too, represented the long and arduous journey from earth to heaven, which the hospital promised to facilitate. The obligation to maintain the fabric of a nearby bridge was sometimes assigned to hospitals, along with licences to solicit alms for this purpose. From 1202 onwards, for example, the brothers of St John's hospital, Nottingham, which lay just outside the city on the major approach road from the north, were entrusted with the task of repairing the 'great bridge' over the Trent. Royal letters of protection, issued in 1221 and 1229, recognised the value of this charitable activity and urged the citizens to give generously towards it.[8]

The hospital of St Giles was not directly charged with such a responsibility, and thus escaped a potentially onerous financial burden. Since Norwich's only physical defence on its eastern perimeter was the River Wensum, the citizens' concern about the upkeep of Bishop's Bridge had a more urgent, strategic aspect, far removed from questions of spiritual welfare. In 1331, when work was still in progress on the construction of stone walls to the north of the river, they recognised the prior's right to erect gates upon the bridge, which suggests that a more imposing edifice had already been planned. In the event, however, a local merchant named Richard Spynk supplemented taxes raised in the city for the completion of the walls and gatehouses with money of his own, and paid for a substantial part of the building programme. Work completed by 1343 included 'the gate upon Bishop's Bridge, entirely, and all the arches from pier to pier with the drawbridge . . . well and loyally done at his own costs [and] . . . also . . . bars and chains for the gate'.[9] The eastern approach to the hospital must have been impressive, although the new fabric proved costly to maintain [see Plate 3]. Even before successive outbreaks of plague took their toll, the more affluent taxpayers had 'withdrawn from the city' to avoid paying murage, with the result that private individuals, like Spynk, had to dig deeply into their own pockets. Among later benefactors was John Selot, the most eminent of the fifteenth-century masters of St Giles's, who, like so many of his contemporaries, regarded bridge-building as a work of mercy. It was, significantly, as an executor of the late mayor, John Gilbert, that he initially entered a contract with the civic authorities, in 1472, for the repair of Bishop's Bridge. Recognising that the gates and towers were 'gretly wasted and lyke to decaye or hastily come to ruyne without gret costes therupon in al goodly speed be done', Selot and his associates pledged £30 from the deceased's estate. 'Meved and inclyned to accomplissh *a dede of charite*', they agreed that any surplus revenues would help to pay for improvements to the neighbouring riverbank, which by this date bounded the hospital meadows. Selot himself promised an additional £20 'of his good wille' to maintain the embankments between Conisford (to the south) and Blackfriars (to the west).[10] Although, as we shall see, successive masters had a vested material interest in work of this kind, the river, like the bridge, resonated with spiritual overtones.

The simile of compassion running like a river was an ancient one, dating back to Classical times. The early Church fathers, such as St Basil (d. *c.* 379), used it to prick the consciences of the affluent, 'to open the hearts of small-town gentry so that the river of Christian charity might flow again from the doors of the rich into the hovels of the destitute'.[11] Not surprisingly, the image resurfaces in writing about the medieval hospital. To repentant sinners the relics of St Bartholomew's in London were a 'welle of pyte . . . and a streem and ryuer of helth and grace'.[12] Identical metaphors occur in Jehan Henry's *Livre de Vie Active*, a devotional tract composed in the late fifteenth century for the guidance of the nursing sisters of the Hôtel Dieu in Paris. Like the Hôtel Dieu itself, which stood on the Ile de la Cité in the middle of the River Seine, Henry's imagined hospital is an island of grace irrigated with the refreshing waters of mercy:

> On this isle of hospitality, situated on a river of health-giving water, grow trees of charity bearing leaves and fruit which never fall, for throughout all the months of the year, and at every hour of the day, the poor who arrive here find the trees loaded with fruit and leaves. And they are fed and watered with the fruit of food and drink, and made healthy again through the leaves of help and service, namely through my daughters [the nurses].[13]

The latter, he added, were transported as young novices to this island, far away from the world of sin and transition, on the ship of religious profession [see Plate 4].

Preaching on the subject of penitence at a *leprosarium* near Chartres, Bernard of Clairvaux (d. 1153) took as his text the story of Naaman the Leper, who had been cured after bathing seven times in the River Jordan (2 Kings, 5:1–27). He urged upon his congregation the healing virtues of baptism in the waters of penitence, which would wash away the spots and stains of sin, so often described by theologians as leprosy of the soul.[14] Immersion was sometimes real as well as metaphorical: a leper named Ramp, the alleged founder of a *leprosarium* at Beccles in Suffolk, had reputedly overcome the disease by bathing in a sacred spring nearby, and was moved to endow the hospital out of gratitude.[15] And at the appropriately named hospital of St John the Baptist, Oxford, archaeological evidence suggests that healing rituals involving the complete or partial immersion of patients may have taken place.[16] Throughout the Middle Ages, washing the hands, feet and sometimes the limbs of the sick poor figured prominently in the admission procedures adopted by many hospitals. Statutes formulated towards the close of the period (such as those of the Savoy in London) tended to emphasise the hygienic importance of such an exercise, but the desire to emulate Christ's act of humility in washing the feet of his disciples remained paramount.[17] This ritual went hand-in-hand with confession, one cleansing the body, the other the soul. The two activities are depicted side by side in the most celebrated of the murals painted by Domenico di Bartolo in the 1440s for the hospital of Santa Maria della Scala in Siena.[18]

The idea of illness itself as a form of purification drew sometimes upon the biblical imagery of the refiner's fire (as in the *Ancrene Riwle*), but more often on that of water, which is frequently deployed in the context of the confessional. In a famous sermon, delivered in 1375, the Benedictine monk, Thomas Brinton, used both metaphors to advocate a regime of spiritual purity, especially necessary during outbreaks of plague when Death might strike at any moment. Tears brought man closer to God, freeing him of those moist and uncertain humours which might otherwise generate sin. That the best medicine against pestilence (or any other disease) was heartfelt contrition and loathing of evil, mixed into an ointment with the water of tears seemed self-evident.[19] From the wells and subterranean rivers of the heart came a source of spiritual purity, as essential for salvation as clean water was for physical health. Prominent among the Comfortable Works listed by

Christ was giving drink to the thirsty, an injunction taken literally as well as figuratively. The provision of a potable and regular water supply to a hospital certainly ranked as a notable endowment, not least because of the immediate practical benefits it brought. A grant of 1278, made by Bishop Chishull to the new London hospital of St Mary Bishopsgate, not only gave the canons his 'fountain' or spring in the fields of Stepney 'for the recreation, refreshment and profit of the poor who assemble there', but also allowed them to enclose it with a stone wall and pipe the water underground past their garden to the infirmary buildings and thence to other parts of the precinct. The conduit, which supplied the hospital with drinking water, cleansed the kitchens and flushed out the infirmary latrines, appears still to have been in working order in the seventeenth century.[20] A similar gift, permitting the brothers of St Mark's hospital, Bristol, to construct and maintain a watercourse across the donor's land was specifically described in a charter of 1240 as a 'free, pure and perpetual almsdeed'. St Mark's was sited near the river Frome, to which this charter accorded access, and which offered a constant reminder of higher spiritual values.[21] But rivers also constituted real, sometimes dangerous, physical boundaries on the outskirts of towns and cities, where life was often far from pleasant, and a very different frame of reference applied.

LIFE ON THE MARGINS

In a discussion of life on the margins of the towns and cities of early modern Europe, the social historian, Bronislaw Geremek, observed that individuals branded criminous, undesirable, suspect or dangerous by the community invariably congregated in suburban enclaves, near rivers and other places of waste disposal. 'It is thus', he notes, 'that physical and moral refuse is heaped together, material detritus along with human detritus.'[22] Far from being havens of tranquillity, set apart from the bustle, noise and stench of everyday life, hospitals in major urban centres were often to be found at the rougher end of the medieval townscape. The almshouse and hospice of the Holy Trinity, Salisbury, had, indeed, been founded shortly before 1379 in premises reputedly occupied by a brothel, 'next to Black bridge . . . where lewdness, murders and other mortal sins were carried on'.[23] The apparent purity of the water supply at St Mary's, Bishopsgate, offered scant protection against the noisome miasmas arising from the vast quantities of butchers' waste dumped just outside the precinct. This was, moreover, a violent area, attractive to petty crooks and prostitutes, some of whom, including the aptly named Joan Jolybody, ran brothels in accommodation rented from the canons.[24] A government inquiry held in 1403 into abuses at the nearby hospital of St Mary Bethlehem revealed that, among other misdemeanours, the keeper also consorted with women of evil repute. They and a motley crowd of fugitives, thieves and travellers frequented the alehouse which he ran in the precinct, keeping the patients awake with their carousing.[25] Edmund Burnham and his wife, who rented a tenement and garden in Holme Street from St Giles's hospital for a ten-year period ending in 1442, were presented during this period by the local court for, respectively, brewing ale and selling it in contravention of the assize and for harbouring 'common prostitutes' from outside the city.[26] Here was a place very different from Jehan Henry's island of charity.

Concern, expressed by Bishop Wykeham of Winchester in 1387, that dwellings at St Thomas's, Southwark, were being leased by suspect criminals is understandable in view of the hospital's close proximity to the stews. Its situation in an exempt liberty where lawbreakers and other undesirables could gather, beyond the reach of the sheriffs of London, was also a cause for anxiety. Wykeham instructed the brothers to improve levels of security, locking the doors of the church (which also served as an infirmary) at appropriate times, and taking proper care of the keys.[27] Given that many hospitals owned quantities of plate, vestments and other valuables, this was a basic precaution against theft, but the need to avoid moral pollution was even more important.[28] The tall perimeter walls and gatehouses erected by all but the smallest hospitals served not only to keep undesirables out, but also, in theory at least, to prevent the brothers and sisters from being seduced by the secular world. The often quite elaborate ritual which marked a patient's reception at the gate of a medieval hospital highlighted this sense of transition, as did the protective images of patron saints, poised high above on doors, archways or towers.[29] Fifteenth and early sixteenth-century accounts of expenditure on the fabric of St Giles's, Norwich, record a substantial outlay on locks, bolts and keys: in 1477–8, for example, a new bronze key was purchased for the great gate, together with locks and keys for the outer gate, where the poor queued up for food, and for the sisters' chamber, which suggests that fear of seduction may sometimes have been more than metaphorical.[30] The comprehensive rebuilding and repair programmes begun by John Jullys at St Giles's in the early 1500s included what appears to have been a major overhaul of both internal and external security, with the repair or replacement of bolts, locks, keys, gates, walls, fences and doors (especially those giving access to the church).[31]

The calm of the cloister was hard to maintain when laymen could come and go whenever they pleased and do more or less as they wished. Bishop Wykeham had also been alarmed about the distress caused to patients at St Thomas's by craftsmen with workshops in the precinct: the insufferable noise of their 'mechanical arts', practised throughout the night as well as during the day, was so loud as to disrupt the divine service, besides upsetting the sick.[32] Environmental hazards, such as noisy artisans and unpleasant manufacturing processes, which the above-mentioned French physician, Bernard Gordon, had identified as a major threat to health, were often encountered in city hospitals.[33] 'Swart, smoky smiths smirched with smoke' were an intrusive feature of life in suburban Norwich. Such was 'the din of their dints' that a fourteenth-century cathedral monk copied a poem on the topic into one of the priory's volumes.[34] The peace of Holme Street must often have been shattered by John Bush, *alias* Smith, who rented property there from the hospital between 1432 and 1467 and supplied the brethren with large quantities of wrought iron for bolts, locks and keys over these years.[35] With its staithes on the River Thames and ample supplies of water, the hospital of St Katherine by the Tower attracted an even more variegated population of soapmakers, glasswrights, brewers and 'aliens' [foreigners] who hoped to bypass the restrictive commercial practices and avoid the heavy customs tolls of the city of London. Not surprisingly, their claims to exemption, as residents of a royal liberty, caused great resentment: an outbreak of 'riots, routs and unlawful gatherings' at St Katherine's in 1451 was sufficiently serious to prompt the setting up of a royal commission of enquiry; and repeated protests were made in the sixteenth century by members of city guilds who feared the unlicensed competition of 'strangers' living there.[36]

Feelings ran just as high in Norwich. The city's first hospital, the *leprosarium* of St Mary Magdalen, was built on land in a northern suburb acquired by Bishop Herbert de Losinga for the endowment of his cathedral, and thus lay under the control of the Benedictine community. Ownership of this hospital's various franchises, which included an extremely lucrative annual fair, was bitterly contested by the rulers of Norwich, largely for commercial reasons. In July 1441, when the fair was actually in progress, the mayor became involved in a violent affray outside the leper house, leading to the arrest and imprisonment of a clerk in the prior's service. This brazen challenge to ecclesiastical authority was one of several confrontations, culminating two years later in the dramatic events of Gladman's insurrection, when an angry mob threatened (not for the first time) to burn down the cathedral.[37] Antagonism over the exempt status of St Mary's explains why the residents of Norwich gave it so little active support, while enthusiastically assisting the inmates of the five small leper houses which grew up under their protection immediately outside the city walls. Yet even here there were problems, as the lepers and their keepers exploited their freedom from tolls and other regulations to turn a quick, illicit profit. In 1312, for example, one tradesman was accused by his fellow citizens of acquiring twenty combs of wheat and other goods from an inmate of the *leprosarium* at St Augustine's gate, in violation of the rules forbidding attempts to both corner the market and evade tariffs.[38] During the late thirteenth century similar allegations were twice levelled against the residents and staff of St Giles's hospital. On the first occasion, in 1295, Richard de Knapton and his servant, both dwelling in the hospital, were fined 4*s* each for selling oil, shoes and other commodities in Norwich, even though neither they nor the purchaser belonged to the freedom. And on the second, five years later, one of the brothers faced charges of trading in corn 'by night' (a particularly nefarious practice) in order to escape the obligatory market tolls. Such activity ran directly against the provisions of Walter Suffield's first foundation charter, which had specifically prohibited commercial ventures undertaken for crude profit. Not surprisingly, when the second charter was copied into the city records, in the mid-fifteenth century, this clause was reintroduced.[39]

Although they stood well within the city's late medieval defences, Norwich's two largest hospitals – St Paul's and St Giles's – were to all intents and purposes suburban, their position on the margins underscored by their contested legal status. The former lay to the north of the Wensum in open fields which were still relatively undeveloped at the Dissolution [see Map II]. Perhaps because the co-founder, Bishop Everard, had been careful to insist that only layfolk with 'an honest calling' who paid their rents on time might live in the precinct, the house encountered few of the disciplinary problems described above. But 'Spital Lond' none the less ranked among the four exempt jurisdictions claimed by the prior of Norwich as part of Herbert de Losinga's foundation, with the result that St Paul's became another focus for protracted disputes between the citizens and the Benedictines.[40] As in the case of St Mary's, the main cause of friction was the refusal of those living or trading within the liberty to pay commercial dues or taxes to the civic authorities, or to recognise their legal jurisdiction: a matter of some concern in view of this hospital's strategic position on one of the major northern approaches into Norwich, just a short distance from what was then St Martin's Bridge. The other two exempt liberties lay to the west and north of the cathedral, one in Tombland and the other in the area between Holme Street and the Wensum, comprising the parishes of St Helen, St Martin at Palace and St Matthew and the land on which Walter Suffield decided to build his hospital. St Giles's thus became the locus of another battle of jurisdictions fought out for centuries between the monks and the city. Successive priors asserted, with sound supporting evidence, that it (and 'Spital Lond' too) had always been part of the large episcopal manor of Thorpe, and as such fell not within the city boundaries at all, but well outside in Blofield Hundred. Probably as a result of a spate of cases such as the two noted above, the Benedictines conceded, in 1306, that the residents of Holme Street and 'Spital Lond' should pay tolls whenever they traded in Norwich. They did not, however, relinquish any other rights, and throughout the Middle Ages the men and women who lived in and near St Giles's remained under the legal authority of the prior, not the mayor.[41] Although, after further disputes, it was agreed in 1429 that henceforth 'none arreste be made by the officers or ministres of the seid citee in Holmestrete', the mayor and aldermen recklessly defied the ruling. A heavy fine, imposed upon them by the Crown in 1443, followed upon such provocative acts as the arrest of John Everard, the hospital's master mason, at St Martin's church just west of the precinct.[42]

Legal disputes of this kind tended to emphasise the marginal status of many suburban hospitals. So too did the unease inspired by those near to death. Sickness and deformity aroused ambivalent responses, whatever the status of the sufferer: the paupers who sought refuge in institutions like St Giles's were stigmatised by poverty as well as disease and seemed properly to belong on the fringes of society.[43] Here they, and the hospitals or *leprosaria* in which they dwelt, presented a constant reminder of mortality to wayfarers, sometimes literally as well as figuratively reinforced by the proximity of a gallows or gibbet, for the public display of executed criminals.[44] If the hospital was, indeed, an island of Christian compassion, the surrounding waters could seem dank and unwelcoming. Or so it appeared to the chronicler of St Bartholomew's hospital, London:

> Truly thys place aforne his [the founder's] clensynge pretendid noone hope of goodnesse. Right uncleene it was, and as a maryce [marsh], dunge and fenny, with water almost euerytyme habowndynge. And that that was emynente, a-boue the water drye, was deputid and ordenyned to the Iubeit [gibbet] or galowys of thevys and to the tormente of othir that were dampnyd by Iudicialle auctoryte . . . Whoe wolde trowe [believe] this place with so sodyan a clensyng to be purgid, and ther to be sette up the tokenys of crosse! And God there to be worshippid where sumtyme stoid the horrible hangynge of thevys . . . Who schulde not mervel ther to be haunttid the mysterie of oure lordys body and precious blode, where was sumtyme schewid owte the blode of gentyly and hethen peple![45]

Classical and medieval medical authorities regarded rotting carrion and stagnant water alike as prime sources of the fogs and miasmas of epidemic disease, to be avoided where possible.[46]

Clearly, the power of the Mass and sanctity of the relics housed at St Bartholomew's were together deemed sufficient to dispel the threat of earthly contagion. In Norwich the gallows stood near the *leprosarium* of St Leonard's at the Fye Bridge gate, in one of the poorest and most disorderly parts of the city, where lepers and criminals shared a single cemetery.[47] Except on rare occasions, such as the burning of lollards on the riverbank nearby in 1428, travellers passing St Giles's hospital were spared the sight of public executions. But the house had otherwise to face similar problems of 'clensynge' and 'puryfycacion' occasioned by its situation on low-lying, potentially unhealthy, land near the river.

Gentle streams, of the sort beloved by medieval preachers, could turn into dangerous floods. The hospital of St Mary, Bishopsgate, was reputedly one foot deep in water on regular occasions during the late fourteenth century because the complex drainage system had not been properly maintained. Despite constant efforts to counter the problem of building on unstable ground, the fabric sustained serious long-term damage through subsidence.[48] The hospital of St John the Baptist, Hungerford, which was, quite literally, an island surrounded on all sides by river water, must have suffered constantly from damp. Indeed, several other hospitals, including St Bartholomew's, Bristol, St John's, Winchester, and St Mary's, Ospringe, were prone to flooding because of their situation. Strenuous efforts were, however, generally made in these places to keep culverts and gutters clean and well repaired, while also ensuring that supplies of drinking water would not be contaminated.[49] Care was likewise taken at St Giles's: in 1396–7, for example, 'le goter' running from the infirmary was repaired and over 10*s* spent on cleaning out a pond and 'trench'.[50] During the 1430s, when detailed information about the state of the precinct again becomes available, similar measures were implemented, and waste was routinely removed from the various courtyards. References to 'cleansing and purging' ditches and stretches of water, notably the two drainage 'crekes' or canals which fed, respectively, from north to south into the 'pondyerde' near the bakery and from east to west into the fishponds in the great garden, occur from time to time. This was an expensive and labour-intensive process: in 1488–9 alone it cost 26*s* 8*d*, and in 1525–6 kept two labourers (who also removed 'le dunge hill') busy for a fortnight.[51] Fear of disease meant that even comparatively small religious communities paid great attention to the state of privies, open drains and latrines. At St Anthony's, London, for example, regular disbursements were made for 'careyng a wey of dust and fylth owte of the kychen', removing soiled rushes and 'makeyng clene of chambers'.[52] One of the masons at St Giles's devoted a week in 1436–7 to work on the latrine in the cemetery, while a colleague spent the same amount of time clearing the nearby pond.[53]

Less could be done to prevent incursions by the river. Then far wider than it is today, the Wensum was embanked from a comparatively early date along part of the stretch running through Norwich. One of the first landing stages to be constructed on the river lay immediately north-west of what was to be the hospital site, and marked the scene of intense commercial activity from the ninth century onwards. From at least 1274, successive masters of the episcopal school derived a steady income from the quay which they had constructed along the Wensum next to St Giles's.[54] Even so, a considerable expanse of land in the hospital meadows on the bend of the river remained marshy and wet throughout the

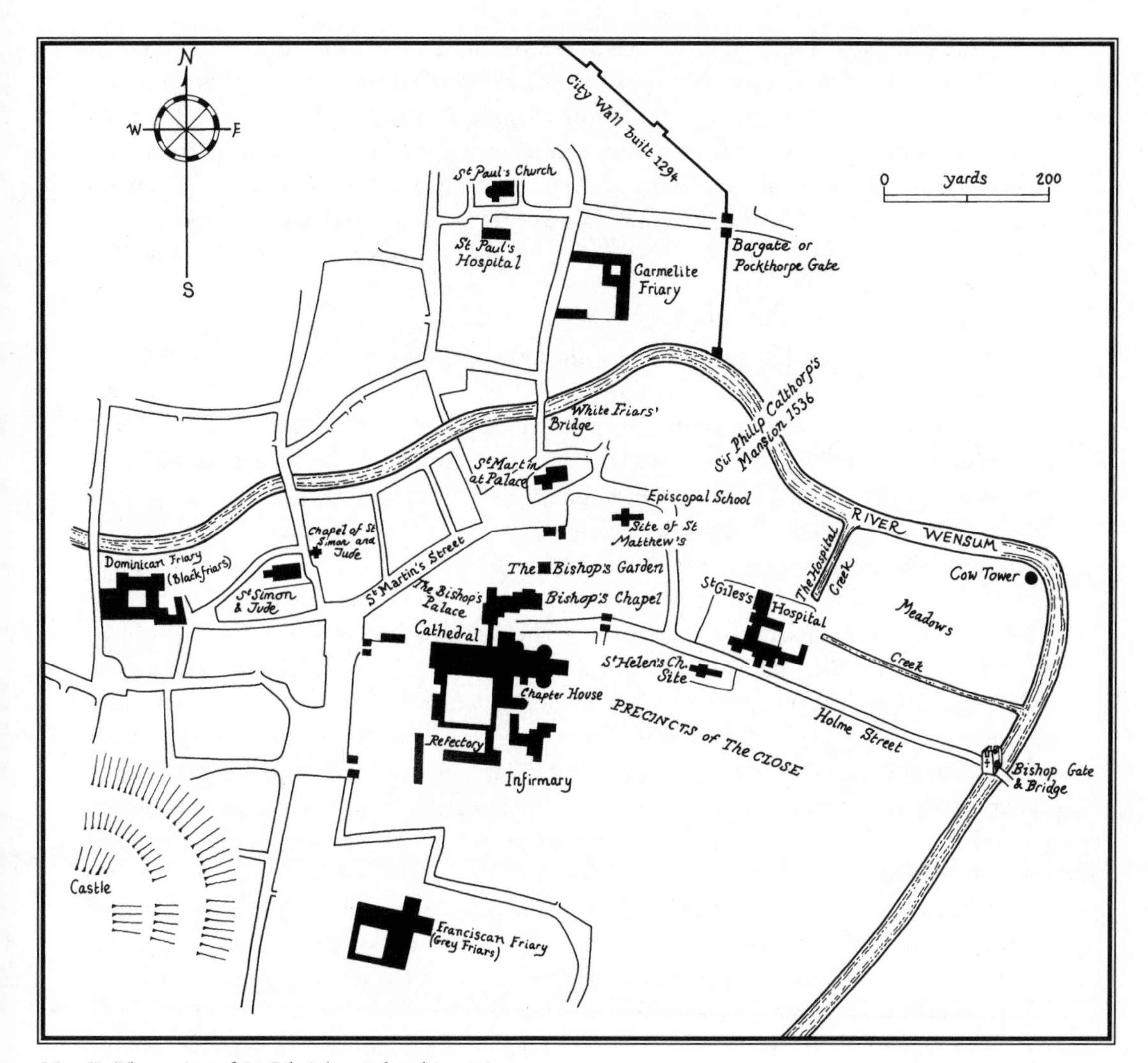

Map II: The precinct of St Giles's hospital and its environs.

medieval period, being given over to reed beds and the cultivation of poplars and willows for use as building material. Sometimes flood water reached as far as the infirmary itself. Shortly after Walter Suffield's death, there was widespread devastation throughout East Anglia, where 'houses, walls and trees were washed away, and hay swept down by the force of the water broke many bridges'. As the climate deteriorated so conditions worsened. According to one eyewitness, the great inundations of 1273 did more damage in Norwich than the Disinherited, who had raided the city seven years earlier, making off with 140 carts of booty.[55] The Benedictine chronicler, Bartholomew Cotton, reported that in January 1290 St Martin's Bridge was actually submerged by a torrent of water which raged as far as the hospital gates, sweeping away houses and transporting them towards the sea.[56]

During the late 1460s steps had been taken at St Giles's to avoid further damage through unspecified work on the riverbank and the construction of stone walls 'next to the water' (but presumably on firmer ground). At a cost of more than £7 (beside the fee of 66*s* 8*d* paid to the above-mentioned John Everard) and requiring seventy-seven carts of stone, this project constituted a substantial investment. Yet neither the walls nor attempts to shore up the bank by 'pylyng', seven years later, could prevent further flood damage. In 1498–9, for example, a handsome payment of 17*s* was made to one William Goodfelawe for disposing of the water then 'coursing through the middle of the hospital'.[57]

Notwithstanding the power of the religious symbolism used to describe its position on the boundaries between heaven and earth, the medieval hospital could sometimes be an unpleasant, even risky place to live. Although St Giles's evidently managed to escape the fires which damaged its Holme Street properties in about 1499 and destroyed almost half of Norwich's housing stock in 1507, large areas of the precinct were devastated during Kett's Rebellion of 1549 and had to be rebuilt.[58] The thatch, plaster and lath of service quarters and lodgings were highly inflammable, and accidents, as well as incendiarism, common. A number of English hospitals, such as St Mary's, Bishopsgate, St Leonard's, York, St Thomas's, Southwark, and St Giles's, Kepier (near Durham), sustained serious fire damage at various points in their histories.[59] The last two houses made a virtue out of necessity and seized the opportunity to move to better sites, but the disruption must have been considerable. The peaceful atmosphere deemed essential for physical recovery and spiritual regeneration (as well, of course, for the proper celebration of the Mass) might be disturbed in a number of other ways. Artisans, such as smiths, fullers, brewers, lime-burners, tanners and potters, whose work posed too great a fire-hazard or nuisance in crowded city centres, made potentially dangerous, as well as uncongenial, neighbours.

So too did the paying guests and other casual visitors who sought short-term accommodation in the large urban hospitals of medieval England. Although, as we shall see, the presence of boarders affluent enough to pay for their lodging offered a welcome source of income, it also brought the temptations of the secular world into the precinct, and in certain cases diverted resources intended for the sick and homeless poor. The hospital of St John the Baptist, Bridgwater, had originally been founded in 1219 as a refuge for humble pilgrims and clerics travelling through the town. Over the years, however, the wayfaring poor of Christ had been demoted to second place. By 1457, Bishop Bekyngton of Bath and Wells felt it necessary to remind the brothers that 'no rich persons, or powerful' were to be entertained or boarded free of charge, allowed to carry off goods belonging to the house or permitted to outstay their welcome.[60] Expense was clearly a contentious issue. The master of St Mary's hospital, Bishopsgate, may have felt it expedient, even prestigious, to welcome Sir Robert Alleyn's wife and her servants as boarders over the summer of 1378, but the trail of unpaid bills she left behind came as an unpleasant surprise. At over £19 (mostly spent on food and drink) her debts gave rise to protracted and costly litigation, pushing the hospital even further into the red.[61] Yet there were some grounds for relief. Neither Lady Alleyn nor her retainers appear to have been drunken, abusive, immoral or violent, or otherwise to have disturbed the quotidian round of religious observance. The failure, in 1470, of the master of St Germinianus's hospital in Tranent,

East Lothian, to admit the sick poor, while at the same time allowing laymen with wives and children to take up residence 'as it were a private house, with occasional bloodshed', suggests that matters might have been worse.[62]

Not even a comparatively well-managed hospital, such as St Giles's, could avoid outbreaks of violence between the scores of artisans, tradesmen and other visitors who passed through its gates every week. In June 1441, for example, a tradesman named William Norwich was fined the sizeable sum of 40*s* for assaulting one John Gegge, fuller, and spilling his blood in the hall of the hospital.[63] Homicides, both planned and accidental, were an unavoidable fact of medieval life. Noblemen and their retainers living in the Tower of London enjoyed practising their archery skills in the nearby gardens of St Katherine's hospital, with predictable consequences.[64] Indeed, the presence of great lords and their retainers generally spelt trouble, and explains Walter Suffield's reluctance to admit squires or 'wanton boys' into the precinct. One of the most notorious murders in fifteenth century England took place at St Saviour's hospital, Bury St Edmund's, where Humphrey, duke of Gloucester, and at least some members of his escort of eighty armed men were billeted during the 1447 Parliament, and where he expired suddenly after being placed under close arrest.[65] The founders of hospitals and the senior ecclesiastics who enforced their statutes were well aware that houses on the major approach roads to towns or cities were vulnerable to corruption if not actual defilement by outsiders. Some guests inspired covetousness, some gluttony and some lust. Concerned lest the presence of such people might undermine his new hospital's spiritual and charitable purpose, Suffield had devised stringent regulations restricting access to the precinct and curtailing the movements of its residents. But could this ideal of quasi-monastic isolation ever be realised? From its inception, the hospital was so closely integrated into the local community, and depended so heavily upon its neighbours for a wide variety of services, that detachment from secular society remained little more than an aspiration, soon forgotten by a succession of increasingly worldly masters.

THE OUTER PRECINCT

Most English medieval hospitals of any size grew organically from small beginnings, the layout and development of their precincts changing in response to the vagaries of patronage and the property market, as well as the amount of space available.[66] At the time of its foundation, in about 1249, St Giles's occupied a much smaller site, and was structurally far more compact than the later medieval hospital, with its massive church and imposing stone-walled precinct. By the mid-fourteenth century, its southern boundary extended along the north side of Holme Street, from Bishop's Bridge (to the east) as far as the lane leading to the episcopal school (to the west). The thirteen or so tenements and messuages which nestled between the highway and the hospital's osier yards and water-courses in a ribbon development at the eastern end of Holme Street also belonged to the brethren, generating a useful income of over £5 a year in rents, and providing additional accommodation for staff or visitors who could not be housed within the walls. The school yard and buildings, along with several other holdings in the adjacent parish of St Martin at Palace, were likewise owned by the hospital, which then encompassed an area of well over ten acres, bounded to the east and north by the river. It contained meadows, gardens, orchards, fishponds, workshops, storehouses, a granary, mill, brewery and other domestic offices, along with a variety of lodgings for men and beasts. In short, it resembled a small village. Almost all this land (except the premises used by the scholars) lay within the ancient parish of St Helen, and had been acquired piecemeal during the second half of the thirteenth century, as plots, meadows and tenements belonging to local people came on the open market or were granted to the hospital in free alms. The parish church itself had, until about 1270, stood directly opposite St Giles's on the south side of Holme Street, within the walls of Norwich cathedral priory. But after a jurisdictional dispute it was appropriated to the hospital, which henceforward opened its own doors to the parishioners, making the old church redundant and leading to its demolition [see Plate 20].[67]

Although this suburban location had obvious drawbacks, there was at least room for expansion. Bishop Suffield must have known the neighbourhood well, since it stood only a few yards from his palace, to the north of the cathedral. As one who customarily welcomed the poor into his own home, he would have been familiar with the sight of passing beggars and pilgrims, exhausted after days on the road and desperate for help. Holme Street had been a busy thoroughfare since Roman times: travellers, relieved to have reached the safety of Bishop's Bridge but still mindful of their impending mortality, would surely prove generous to less affluent wayfarers. To this end, Suffield ordered that a collecting box for the support of the transient poor should be placed in the hospital.[68] A commanding position, as one of the first buildings of any size encountered by men and women entering Norwich from the north-east, gave St Giles's an immediate advantage.[69] The site also permitted access to the river so that heavy goods could be transported more cheaply and with greater ease. Since, with the exception of flint, Norwich was poorly supplied with building materials, facilities for the shipment of stone, either in small quantities from local depots, or up river in bulk from Yarmouth, were essential.[70] It was also necessary to construct a proper drainage system. Water for cooking and drinking may, from the outset, have been drawn from a well sunk near the hospital kitchen. By 1281 some type of culvert or piping had been constructed, diverting a natural stream under the buildings to flush away waste. Early fourteenth-century accounts reveal that the brewery and bakery were already situated near a stone-lined canal, or conduit, which ran due south from the Wensum to the service quarters, probably on the site of one still discernible on the riverbank today.[71]

When Walter Suffield first contemplated his endowment, the north-eastern side of Holme Street comprised a number of small properties fronting on to the road, some barely more than a few yards wide and a score or so in length. On them stood a patchwork of outbuildings, houses and workshops, occupied over the years by artisans and tradesmen such as gardeners, masons, limeburners, tanners, carpenters, innkeepers, foundrymen and smiths – the natural denizens of a medieval suburb. Behind and between these plots, extending northwards as far as the river, lay open meadowland, drained by ditches and owned, from west to east, by Hubert de Morley, Robert de Stanford, Henry de Aula, the Lady Isabel de Cressy, Hubert the Tanner and John and Agnes Herman.[72] Pope Alexander IV's letters of March 1255, confirming the foundation of St Giles's, noted that Bishop

Suffield had used his own assets to finance this work of charity, which began with the purchase of a site.[73] The only property specifically set aside by him for the *construction* of the buildings was a single messuage he had previously bought from Henry de Aula, *alias* de la Salle, a resident of Holme Street. His undated charter granting it in perpetuity to the master and brothers for this purpose contains a pledge of further acquisitions as adjacent, but unspecified, holdings became available.[74] It looks, however, as if Suffield had by then also secured from Robert de Stanford 'all his messuage, buildings and hereditaments' lying between the highway (to the south) and the river (to the north). De Aula had for some time been paying de Stanford a modest assize rent, which the latter subsequently released to the hospital as well, so the two of them may, perhaps, have shared an interest in the same holding.[75] But at most the original endowment comprised no more than two messuages, as a later instrument of the bishop's, sealed with his own seal and that of the hospital, and dated 1251, makes plain.[76]

Both of Suffield's foundation charters describe the eastern boundary of the hospital as a ditch, separating his newly acquired land from that of the widowed Isabel de Cressy, who relinquished her interest to the first master, Hamon de Calthorpe, shortly afterwards.[77] The house's other neighbour is not then named, but must have been Hubert Morley. He and his wife likewise made over to Hamon all their land and buildings to the west of the hospital 'for the health of their souls and the souls of all their ancestors and successors' in free and perpetual alms before 1281.[78] It was then that Edward I granted the master and brethren permission, 'despite the recent provision against mortmain', to acquire two further messuages on this side of the precinct, together with the lane which then constituted its western boundary 'from the gate of the hospital courtyard to the water [a culverted stream] running under the hospital'.[79] St Giles's was now expanding fast, and well able both to exploit a groundswell of support from local *rentiers* and to pressurise reluctant vendors to reach a satisfactory accommodation.[80] William Dunwich, its greatest lay patron, had the funds and influence to accelerate growth. In 1267 the widowed Agnes Herman made over to him rents worth 6*s* 10*d* from five tenements at the east end of Holme Street, as well as all the meadows she then owned on the banks of the Wensum. Since Hubert the Tanner, Isabel de Cressy's neighbour, had already disposed of his land to the hospital, this transaction meant that St Giles's now enjoyed undisputed possession of almost all the available green space lying between the Wensum and the Cathedral Priory.[81] Dunwich planned to use these acquisitions, along with 56*s* annual rent from other city properties, to found a perpetual chantry, which he established at the hospital ten years later.[82] Though welcome, his gift was not an unmitigated blessing. Agnes Herman's meadow stood charged with the payment of 52 gallons of wine a year to the Norwich monks, which in 1306 cost the hospital 17*s* 4*d*. The master evidently tried to economise on quality – a serious miscalculation where his Benedictine neighbours were concerned. By 1348 complaints about the choice and casking of the wine threatened to escalate into a major dispute. The ensuing agreement, whereby the hospital contracted to pay 40*s* a year instead, hardly worked to its advantage.[83]

It is unclear when the hospital assumed responsibility for the large tower, or 'dongon', which stood on the bend of the river in the north-eastern corner of the meadow, and was said by Francis Blomefield to have been built by the prior of Norwich as a toll house [see Plate 19]. The above-mentioned annuity was not, however, levied in return for the right to collect tolls from passing ships, as has sometimes been assumed, for no such receipts appear in any of the hospital accounts.[84] Indeed, the master and brothers continued to pay the troublesome fee long after they disposed of the tower to the civic authorities, in about 1378. They were no doubt glad to be rid of a building which was expensive to keep on a defensive footing, as was required by the Crown, but otherwise of little practical use to their community. The city bailiffs, still reeling under the impact of successive outbreaks of plague, had then received a stern warning from the government 'to view the river on one side of the city, which is choked with grass growing therein . . . and also the walls and turrets which are decayed, and to cleanse the former and repair the latter, and to rebuild the paling on the river bank for the defence of the city'.[85] The case for surrendering the tower to the corporation must have seemed overwhelming, especially as it was by then in a near-ruinous state. Norwich's vulnerability to attack was highlighted during the Peasants' Revolt, as was the need for a complete overhaul of its fortifications. Between 1394 and 1399 alone at least £84 was spent by the city chamberlains on rebuilding 'le Dungeon' virtually from its foundations, which suggests that the master and brothers had not been alone in allowing the fabric to deteriorate. The construction of their great church tower (which cost almost as much to build), was, however, completed at this time through the patronage of Archdeacon Derlyngton, there being no apparent shortage of funds for more appropriate projects.[86] In 1450, Hugh Acton, the then master, confirmed the city's title not only to the 'donjon', but also to a narrow strip of land along the river bank, comprising 'certeyn ground fro the said towre be all the lengthe un to a trench of water that cometh out of the seid hospytall and in brede fro certeyn wylwes [willows] morken and growyng upon the medewes aforesaid, be the said ryuer ageyns the est [east]'.[87]

Indentures of 1423, 1433 and 1435, leasing various hospital properties in Holme Street to three different stone masons, refer to the water course which ran parallel to the highway (from east to west) along the northern boundary of their tenements; and one of 1543 describes in some detail the 'osyer garden' next to the hospital meadow which could be reached 'over a lyttle brydge'. The rivulet below, which was one of two 'creeks' leading from the Wensum into the heart of the precinct, fed into a 'pondeyard' where freshwater fish were kept from the late fourteenth century onwards, if not before [see Map II].[88] In 1500–1 the master restocked these ponds, which had been depleted, with thirty-six pike (and over 2,000 young roach to feed them), presumably for consumption in the refectory. An outlay of 57*s* 6*d* thirteen years later on 251 pike and another 2,000 roach suggests that pike was a delicacy much appreciated by the master and his guests. The new fishing nets, bought at a cost of 4*s* 6*d* in 1519–20, were presumably intended for use in the precinct, as fishing in the river with 'nettes, weares and other engins' was subject to close regulation, along with the dumping of 'mucke or other vilde stuff'.[89] Waste disposal, especially when major rebuilding work was in progress, posed a serious problem with no easy solution. At St Saviour's hospital, Bury St Edmund's, quantities of rubble and other material generated by the extension of the chapel were deposited in the largest of the house's fishponds.[90] The builders working on the new chancel at St Giles's during the 1380s must have been tempted to do likewise, although there was plenty of room for sinking waste pits of the kind found by archaeologists in many medieval hospitals. In 1468, when the corporation of Norwich was again giving careful thought to the state of the Wensum, the master of St Giles's and his neighbour, the prior, were presented before the Assembly for creating 'diverse great nuisances' along the river. A committee of senior officials was set up to establish the hospital's eastern boundaries and arrange for the bankside to be 'cleansed . . . according to the civic ordinances'.[91]

The hospital cemetery was also situated in this part of the precinct, as the stone wall which marked its southern boundary by 1375 abutted on to one of the Holme Street tenements, and a large pond was to be found nearby.[92] A passing reference to the cemetery in Isabel de Cressy's release of meadowland confirms that it must have lain immediately to the north-east of the infirmary chapel, where members of the clerical and civic elite elected to be buried. Walter Suffield had clearly hoped to attract further endowments by offering patrons the right of burial there: a prominent tomb or memorial slab near one of the altars allowed them to retain their superior status after death, while also guaranteeing that they would continue to benefit from the intercessionary prayers of priests and people.[93] Sick paupers dying in the hospital were probably interred in the adjoining cemetery after a modest but seemly funeral. Until 1270 the men and women of Holme Street were not, however, supposed to follow suit, for they came under the parochial jurisdiction of St Helen's church, immediately across the road and within the monastic precinct. Of all the Seven Comfortable Works, the burial of the faithful departed (which earned the priest a mortuary fee) was the most likely to generate ill-feeling between hospitals and nearby parish churches. The canons of St Mary's, Bishopsgate, entered a formal composition, agreeing to compensate their neighbours at a fixed rate for any lost revenues, but some hospitals, such as St John's, Nottingham, encountered far greater hostility from local priests. Quite possibly the bishop of Norwich's decision to grant the church of St Helen to the master and brothers of St Giles's hospital, in 1270, followed a dispute of this kind.[94] Although he specifically exempted the existing burial ground and anchorhold of St Helen's from this award, there was now nothing to prevent the hospital from expanding its own facilities and enlarging the cemetery. Little more can be said about this important part of the precinct, which is rarely mentioned in the surviving accounts. During the 1520s a few testators specifically requested burial in the hospital churchyard, but none were of more than modest means.[95] Their exequies would, none the less, have been decently observed and their last resting place properly tended. As consecrated land, the cemetery was protected from sacrilege by a substantial perimeter wall and a locked gate: a marked contrast to the Bethlehem hospital in London, where the keeper caused a scandal by allowing city bakers to set up an oven and ply their craft at night. That it was quite large and may well have served as an outdoor preaching yard (as did the cemetery at St Mary's hospital, Bishopsgate) is suggested by the presence of a latrine, which was kept in good repair.[96]

The open land which lay between the inner precinct and the Wensum contributed in no small measure to the domestic economy of St Giles's. Trees near the water's edge were used for fencing and building materials as well as fuel, a fortnight or more being set aside almost every year for cutting back willows and binding the wands into bundles. Poplars were regularly pollarded and sometimes felled for timber, their presence being an irritant to the civic authorities who complained in 1511 that the master had committed yet another nuisance by planting 'poples' on ground reclaimed from the water.[97] Beds of reed and sedge were cultivated for thatching, while rushes were scattered on the floors of the master's lodgings, refectory and church. In 1486–7, for example, labourers spent twelve days weeding 'les dokkes and les netlys' around the beds, cutting and cleaning sedge and removing the bundles to a dry place for storage.[98] Hedging, ditching and repairing the earthen walls which ran around the meadows proved even more time-consuming: in the early 1430s such tasks could occupy one of the hospital's workmen for over five weeks.[99] The meadow nearest the river was known as 'paradyse', this evocation of a prelapsarian past providing a further instance of the spiritual connotations of lawns and gardens. The thirteenth-century encyclopaedist, Bartholomeus Anglicus, had waxed lyrical over the health-giving properties of 'meedes'. Scattered with 'herbes and gras and flowers of dyuers kynde', they appeared to laugh with pleasure, promoting a sense of well-being in the beholder.[100]

Rich soil and a regular supply of manure from the nearby stables (as well as from the cattle and sheep which were put out to graze before being slaughtered) were a source of lush pasture and verdant meadows during spring and summer. Until the late fifteenth century, the hospital retained most of this land for its own use, setting some aside for grazing and the rest, including grass in the nearby orchard, for mowing. Two modest harvests a year produced enough hay for the master's horses, sometimes leaving a surplus for sale to boarders. In 1484, however, the master entered a seven-year lease with one John Brown, who agreed to pay an annual rent of 51*s* for the whole of the 'great meadow'.[101] This arrangement, which deprived the hospital of a valuable resource, was not repeated. Instead, it was decided to farm out only a part of the meadow, initially on an *ad hoc* basis, but from 1502 onwards by a contract made for life with one of the hospital's Holme Street tenants and regular suppliers, the limeburner, Richard Nyseham. A prosperous entrepreneur with an eye for speculative ventures, Nyseham also rented a pondyard in the cathedral precinct, as well as a marsh at Carrow and other property belonging to the Norwich Benedictines. He and his widow, who eventually took over all his leases, probably fattened cattle commercially for the local market.[102] This compromise solution left sufficient grazing for the hospital's own stock, kept staff and boarders supplied with hay and augmented hospital revenues to the tune of 16*s* a year. It is now hard to tell how many beasts may have been put out to grass at any one time, as the early sixteenth-century stock accounts cover complete years, during which numbers obviously rose and fell according to the season and demand from the kitchens [see Plate 21]. John Jullys, the first of the sixteenth-century masters, spent at least £50 in building up the reserves of livestock, purchasing sixty-eight head of cattle (including two dairy cows) and 382 sheep in 1502–3 alone.[103] Most of the sheep were kept in the hospital's folds at Cringleford, just outside Norwich, being dispatched on the hoof to St Giles's when required; others were purchased locally as the need arose. Between 1502 and 1512, an average of sixty-six ewes and lambs were killed each year on the premises for consumption, while upwards of twenty or thirty might be sold on. Jullys' hospitality was considerably more lavish than that of his successors. After his departure less beef was eaten, although the herd of cattle may often have contained well over twenty adult beasts at any one time. It was Jullys who ordered the construction of a new 'netehouse' or cattle-shed near the hospital stables.[104]

Gardens, as well as farmland, played a vital and surprisingly varied part in the life of medieval religious communities, although their importance has only recently been fully appreciated.[105] They supplied hospitals with food, fuel and medicinal plants, while also helping in less obvious ways to engender a sense of spiritual and psychological well-being. During the twelfth century the gardens at St John's hospital, Castle Donington (Leicestershire), had produced such 'powerful herbs and roots' that a local physician had gone there in search of a cure for his own ague. Those at the Savoy in London were specifically cultivated 'for the relief and refreshment of the poor who flock to this hospital'. Such a wealthy house could afford the services of a gardener, who worked under the direction of the matron, as well as the medical staff, to grow plants for use in cooking, the preparation of medicines and other 'health-giving purposes'.[106] These last probably included the production of scented candles (of the sort regularly used at St Giles's) and other fumigants for dispelling the noisome miasmas of disease. Rosemary, for example, was carried at funerals, as well as being wrapped around corpses before interment. The fear of unburied bodies so frequently expressed in late medieval tracts on the plague sprang from a conviction that bad odours were themselves pathogenic. In an age before the widespread use of coffins, when all but the affluent were customarily buried in a simple shroud, there must have been a great demand for sweet-smelling plants in hospitals.[107] They were also needed for herbal baths, which offered temporary relief from pain, while also keeping patients relatively clean. The statutes of the Savoy assumed that newcomers would be filthy, bloodstained, ulcerated and verminous on admission, and in need of partial, if not complete, baths before entering the wards.[108] Aromatic preparations, which were used in great quantities during epidemics, were deemed to affect the body's vital spirits more immediately than medicines taken by mouth, and could easily be produced in even the smallest hospital.[109]

At St Giles's, the sisters grew and processed many of the plants required for medicinal purposes. Their walled garden, with its own thatched pentice, afforded complete seclusion, and probably lay near the kitchen complex, to the north-west of the precinct.[110] Such an arrangement is to be found at St Mary's hospital, Bishopsgate, where the nurses enjoyed the benefits of private green space adjacent to their quarters and the kitchen gardens, which lay on the other side of a handsome stone arcade.[111] In accordance with a practice discernible at all levels of society, gardening in hospitals was often undertaken by women, permitting a degree of freedom to professed sisters whose movements were otherwise quite rigidly circumscribed. But they were not the only residents with an interest in horticulture. Like the monastic precinct on the other side of Holme Street, and, indeed, the city of Norwich as a whole, St Giles's presented a patchwork of green space, courtyards, ponds and fruit trees. The sisters' garden was but one of many, including a plot next to the hospital church (quite possibly set aside for meditation and the cultivation of flowers for use on the altars), at least two more by the stables and an enclosed kitchen garden, which in 1444–5 took two labourers ten days to dig.[112] The hospital bakery, too, had its own garden and courtyard, entered through a private gateway near one of the water-courses. Several of the chambers and dwellings leased out at St Giles's also possessed gardens, which appear to have been tended by the occupants or their servants. Between 1438 and 1442, for instance, Master Thomas Welle rented a *domus* comprising a hall, two chambers, a garden and well; and at the close of the fifteenth century some of the chaplains, such as John Dowe and William Crosse, paid for the personal use of gardens and ponds. It is interesting to note that John Jullys's tastes were well developed before he became master; while he was still one of the brethren he rented private rooms and a plot in the precinct.[113] The heavy tasks of weeding, digging, planting and ditching communal gardens were undertaken by jobbing labourers, who were employed, on and off, throughout the year. Some probably lived on the premises, enjoying free accommodation in return for their work. At St Mary's hospital on the Gaywood Causeway (outside King's Lynn) Robert Canteley and his wife were granted a chamber, a garden and membership of the house's fraternity for life, free of charge, in 1529, on the understanding that Robert would do whatever 'dykyng, hedgyng or othere bodely laboure' might be required of him.[114]

How important was horticulture at St Giles's? Information about the gardens derives almost exclusively from the surviving accounts, which are extremely detailed so far as income and expenditure are concerned, but less helpful with regard to the layout or appearance of the hospital. We know that during the fourteenth century the gardens as a whole turned a modest profit of between 78*s* and 40*s* through the sale of surplus produce. Apples, pears, leeks, garlic, onions, hemp, madder and honey from the house's bees were regularly offered on the open market.[115] As was the case at St Saviour's hospital, Bury St Edmund's, a special *domus pomorum* (1458–9) was built for the storage of apples, which suggests that fruit played a more important part in the late medieval diet than some historians have hitherto allowed.[116] Since food constituted 'the first instrument of medicine', and almost every plant was deemed to possess some therapeutic qualities, it is often hard to tell where kitchen garden stopped and herbarium began. Onions, for example, were used in a variety of remedies, notably to reduce the excess of phlegmatic humour likely to accrue in a damp climate where large quantities of fish were eaten. A variety of complaints, from toothache to skin diseases and coughs to indigestion, were likewise believed to respond to garlic, while leeks appeared hardly less beneficial.[117] The saffron and henbane which St Giles's also put on sale featured prominently in the medieval pharmacopoeia: the first as a general prophylactic and the second as a stupefactive for use before surgery.[118] Saffron was widely cultivated as a profitable cash crop, and was still being grown at St Giles's in 1456–7. None of the brothers were, however, tempted to emulate the infirmarer of the cathedral priory, who earned a reprimand in 1492 for pocketing the proceeds of 'one garden with saffron' which had hitherto been grown for the whole community.[119] One of the most commonly used ingredients in popular remedies, honey was recommended for both internal and external use, not least as an antiseptic, so it is hardly surprising that hives were kept in the hospital.[120]

Successive masters clearly sought to utilise all the land available, although drainage remained a problem. By 1396, if not well before, a sizeable area of meadow had been enclosed for cultivation as one 'great' and one 'small' garden. The great garden was aptly named: it contained a woodhouse and lodge (1443–4), a number of mature trees (1455–6), at least one pond (1456–7), a house (1467–8) and a sizeable pasture (1474–5). It was surrounded by earthen and stone walls, which were constantly being repaired, and was entered through a massive wooden gate. The task of replacing the gate occupied a carpenter for twenty-three days in 1450, and cutting the stone for new walls alone took two weeks some five years later. The cost of maintaining masonry on heavily waterlogged soil may explain why hedges (a far cheaper alternative) were planted along part of the perimeter in the 1460s, although over 48*s* was spent in 1475–6 on building a wall next to the 'common stream' which still marked the western boundary, and 30*s* on another wall separating the great garden from the master's stable.[121] Some of these costs were recovered during the later fifteenth century by leasing out all or part of the garden for sums of up to 33*s* a year to a series of tenants (including another local butcher who needed grazing for his animals), but John Jullys had rather different plans for this part of the hospital. He evidently wished to beautify the landscape as well as effecting more functional improvements: ditches in the great garden were repaired and new ones dug; 'wedynyrons' were bought for the removal of docks and nettles; for over a month two labourers transported large quantities of compost and earth by wheelbarrow from other parts of the precinct in order to raise the level of the beds; and three carts of green rushes were planted in the area nearest the water.[122] Expenditure on 'rammyng de lez pales' and the construction of a sluice suggests serious attempts to improve the drainage system.[123] Finally, a reeder was employed to lay cresting (for protection against the elements) along almost 200 yards of garden wall, running from the stream on one side to the gates of the meadow on the other. Henceforward, Jullys and his successors retained the garden in their own hands, using the pasture to feed the hospital's cattle and horses rather than letting it out to others. Masters such as Jullys, who were prepared to place their wealth, influence and position at the hospital's disposal, expected to live in a style and comfort appropriate to their station. Not for them the austere communal life demanded by the founder. By 1464–5 another walled garden had been set aside specifically for their use, although here, too, proximity to the river appears to have caused subsidence. Jullys's schemes included the construction of 'divers boterassez' to shore up these walls: a step already taken at St John's hospital, Winchester, where running water constantly damaged the fabric.[124]

Several of these gardens either supported or accommodated livestock, a common sight among the ranges and courtyards of English medieval hospitals. Indeed, at the Bethlehem hospital in London corrodians were given special permission to construct fences 'for keeping out pigs and other animals'.[125] Notwithstanding Bishop Suffield's desire that the master should live modestly and forgo the ostentation of a mounted escort, stables soon proliferated. Some were attached to private lodgings of the sort occupied free of charge in the precinct by senior clergy, such as Archdeacon Derlyngton and Master Roger Pratt, while others were leased out along with chambers or suites of rooms at a fixed annual or monthly rate.[126] The chaplain who served as surveyor and receiver general of the hospital's estates understandably had his own stable (from about 1481), as did the master (by 1469). A 'great stable' is recorded from 1443 onwards, and almost certainly stood, like that at St Mary's hospital, Bishopsgate, in the outer courtyard, or forecourt, next to the main gates. It soon grew too small to accommodate the horses of all the boarders, guests and visitors congregating in the busy precinct. The new 'great stable', built in 1460, deserved its name: two roofers spent nineteen days repairing the thatch in 1474–5, and almost five weeks in 1521–2.[127] The stable next to the bakery (first noted in 1376) seems to have been used for a cart-horse, while the mill-horse occupied its own thatched stable beside the barn where it was put to work grinding corn and malt prepared in the hospital's copious roasting ovens for home brewing. The equipment necessary for milling demanded a high level of maintenance, and was constantly being repaired or replaced, sometimes under the expert supervision of a millwright, who received an annual retainer of 6*s* 8*d* for his services. During the fourteenth century the hospital used wind as well as horse power to drive its 'old mill', and earned up to 46*s* a year by grinding corn for local people as well as for its own use.[128]

Fresh pork and salted bacon, together with the 'grese' or lard which provided fat for cooking as well as the base for ointments and unguents, were readily available from the hospital's herd of pigs. This generally comprised a few sows, a boar and fifteen or more young males. Once they had been castrated by a farmworker engaged specifically for this purpose, the males enjoyed a short but comfortable life. The stone piggery with its enclosed courtyard and garden probably lay in the same part of the precinct as the mill. After 1430, when the adjacent stable was deemed badly in need of repair, both mill house and piggery seem to have been well maintained: the stone walls around the *ortus porcorum* were replaced by a blackthorn hedge in 1474–5, and new wooden 'swynstyez' [styes] were constructed a few years later. Animals as well as humans benefitted from John Jullys's rebuilding programme, which included a new 'cottage' of stone and thatch for the pigs, complete with 'swynestrowes' [troughs].[129] Many hospitals, including St Mary's, Ospringe, and St Saviour's, Bury St Edmunds, kept a dovecote, usually set apart in a garden or outer courtyard.[130] At St Giles's the 'dove house' (*domus columbarum*) stood, from at least 1467 onwards, on the dormitory roof. It then required extensive repairs involving the labour of a clayman and his servant for over nine days.[131] Some birds were less conspicuous: geese and cygnets remained safe from predators in a 'shudde' near the kitchen, probably living alongside the hens, capons, pullets and cocks which appear in the surviving sixteenth-century stock accounts.[132] In 1502 John Jullys decided to build a new 'haukes mewe', where his falcons could be kept more securely under lock and key. During this period complaints were made at the hospital of St Mary in the Newarke, Leicester, about the visitors and clergy who brought hawks and hunting dogs to church.[133] No such profanities occurred at St Giles's, although it is unlikely that Bishop Suffield would have approved of Jullys's ostentatious lifestyle. The ten peacocks bought by him in 1502–3 were probably intended for the newly landscaped gardens, and may have ended their days as delicacies on his table.[134] Swan was certainly consumed there: like many religious houses the hospital had its own swan mark, and from the 1320s onwards (if not before) had kept several mature pairs on the River Wensum under the eye of a 'swanherde'. The latter was paid a few shillings a year to replenish the game, supervise marking and watch over the cygnets. That the hospital possessed a sixteenth-century precursor of its celebrated swan pit, where birds were fattened for the table, is evident from entries in the accounts for 1589–90. These refer to costs sustained in 'dammyng and fyeng the cryck next the swanyard' and 'pylyng and casting the swanne pond'. As expensive and greatly valued delicacies, swans made acceptable gifts for the bishop and other friends in high places, while also giving aesthetic pleasure to a community which clearly appreciated natural beauty.[135]

THE INNER PRECINCT

A surprisingly large number of service buildings were needed to ensure that even a relatively small religious house could function effectively. Supplies of meat, fish, grain, fodder, fuel and building materials had to be securely preserved; equipment (such as carts, tools and harness) kept in working order; and adequate facilities for malting, brewing, baking, cooking and butchery made available. Practical considerations, as well as a desire to preserve the calm and sanctity of hospital churches and infirmaries, meant that kitchens and other utilities were generally grouped around at least one outer courtyard, giving easy access to carts or boats bearing food and fuel, a constant supply of clean flowing water and plenty of storage space. Archaeological as well as documentary evidence suggests that hospital precincts were not only enclosed by perimeter walls, but commonly fenced or walled off into discrete courtyards or compartments, separating men from women, clergy from laity, boarders from residents, and service areas from buildings devoted to worship or the care of the sick.[136] Although the founders of hospitals such as St Giles's tended to assume that lay brothers would serve as cooks, brewers and stewards, work of this kind was often delegated to married servants, who could not (in theory) be allowed to mix too closely with members of the religious community. From the early fourteenth century onwards, the hospital employed a cook and his assistant, along with an assortment of hired hands, including a laundress, a palfreyman, a boatwright, a smith and a swineherd. Modest retainers were later assigned to skilled operatives such as coopers, barber-tonsors (for the clergy), mole-catchers, bell-hangers, pewterers, clocksmiths, and silversmiths. By 1342 a baker (who also supervised the brewery) had been added to the establishment, which was further augmented, in about 1396, by a butler. Both had their own boys to help with menial duties.[137] It is apparent from later accounts that private chambers were constructed in the two most important service buildings, the bakery and the kitchen, and that both gave on to their own enclosed courtyards where there were additional lodgings (in long-houses) for lay employees. The cook's garden is said to have had a gallery along one side giving access to at least one private chamber.[138] During an episcopal visitation, in 1532, one of the chaplains complained that both the baker and the butler were married and therefore unsuitable employees for a hospital. Their wives may, just possibly, have been active about the precinct, although the objection seems to have hinged more upon the general principle of appointing liveried servants who were not celibate. Some staff, such as the cook, William Haugh, and Richard Frevylle, a lay chorister and organist, had previously elected to rent tenements in Holme Street so they could remain with their families.[139]

As at the hospital of St Mary Ospringe, the bakery was a large building, which also housed a brewery.[140] We have only an approximate idea of the layout of service quarters, lodgings and gardens at St Giles's and cannot pinpoint them with any accuracy, but the bakery's location due north of the cloister can be established with a reasonable degree of certainty, because it shared a common water supply with the chaplains' dormitory. One entrance was approached up a flight of steps, leading from 'le bakhowsbrygg', a structure either first erected or replaced in 1306, when a number of carpenters were paid for constructing a wooden bridge across what must have been the wider (north–south) of the two water-courses leading into the precinct from the Wensum.[141] By 1438 part of the bridge, at least, had been rebuilt in stone, as a mason and his servant spent nine days repairing it. The water fed into another 'pondyerd', which was surrounded by wooden palings (1486–7) and almost certainly supplied the kitchen as well [see Map III]. The hospital possessed its own staithe or landing stage on the Wensum (1524–5) and maintained at least one boat, hiring others as and when the occasion arose. A watergate near the bakery gave access to what may have been an unloading bay for goods transported first by river and thence up the 'creke' to the service quarters.[142] Although it was alleged in 1532 that the roof badly needed repair, considerable sums of money had previously been spent on maintaining the fabric of the bakehouse. Indeed, on at least twelve occasions between 1438 and 1523 the reed thatch was either wholly or extensively renewed; and regular attention was given to the state of the ovens, chimneys, gables, troughs and ironwork, as well as to daubing and whitewashing the clay walls.[143]

The hospital possessed its own malting house, which was probably part of the bakery complex. During the 1460s, upwards of one and a half imperial tons of malt passed through 'le gret masshefatte' each year as part of the brewing process.[144] The decision, taken at some point during the 1490s, to retain a specialist brewer and his servant probably sprang from the brethren's newly acquired taste for beer, which they shared with many other residents of Norwich. Although they were denounced in some quarters as a dangerously effete foreign import, fit only for Dutchmen, hopped brews enjoyed growing popularity as a welcome alternative to ale. They were not only refreshingly bitter, but could be kept for far longer and thus produced in larger quantities.[145] Once again, Master Jullys set the trend, through the purchase of six 'de lez beer glasses' (the accountant's Latin clearly did not run to such exotica), two dozen drinking pots for beer and a variety of hoops and barrels. A consignment of 650 pounds of hops, shipped from the Low Countries *via* Yarmouth, cost 32*s* 8*d* in 1502–3. At a later date domestic brewers allowed one pound of hops for each bushel of malt brewed, which suggests an initial production of around 6,500 gallons of beer, roughly two-thirds of the total output that year from the hospital brewery. In 1505–6 a 'bier leade' and great furnace were constructed there, although henceforward far fewer hops appear to have been used. They were, indeed, a luxury, purchased along with spices and wine as special commodities for the senior clergy.[146]

Cartloads of wheat, rye, barley, peas, beans and oats came into the hospital each year, some paid as rents or tithes, others donated as gifts, and yet more purchased locally in the city. Almost all the barley was either baked into bread for the lower orders or malted and roasted for brewing. It was kept, along with the rest of the grain and pulses, in a granary near the bakehouse. A passing reference of 1415 to one 'John of the granary', who occupied a chamber in the precinct free of charge, suggests that the hospital paid many of its employees in kind, providing accommodation in lieu of wages for the labourers engaged in threshing, winnowing and other manual activities.[147] John Jullys evidently considered the space inadequate, for in 1500 he had a *domus* lying between the bakery and the brothers' dormitory converted into a new grange.[148] Since the stock account for 1502–3 records a striking increase in the annual store of cereals from a total of around three and a half tons (1500–1) to just over five, his concern seems understandable.[149] Far less room was, however, required by his successors. Because of the importance of preserved meat and fish in the medieval diet, it was also necessary to provide proper facilities for keeping large quantities of salt. In 1376 the cost of transporting the hospital's annual supply by cart to and from the Wensum came to no less than 12*s* 2*d*, and it was not unusual for benefactors to offer additional consignments as alms. In 1499–1500 Nicholas Goldwell, the bishop's brother, who had briefly served as master, donated several bushels; and a few years later the fishmonger, William Hecker of Cley, whose family had strong connections with St Giles's, left grey salt worth £20 (in instalments spread over a period of ten years) to the hospital.[150] The salt house which had served well enough during the fifteenth century now seemed unsuitable to Jullys, who ordered the construction of new 'saltbynges' (the size of small rooms) in the kitchen.[151] The kitchen range (with its stone-lined drains, quarters for stock awaiting slaughter and yet another woodshed), was subject to the regular attention of carpenters, claymen, roofers and masons throughout the fifteenth century, as was the larder or slaughterhouse, which must have stood nearby. A new and larger building for the butchering of animals was erected in 1447–8, with a tiled roof, chimney and gutters to facilitate the removal of blood and entrails.[152] Jullys's demands on the catering establishment led, in turn, to increased fuel consumption, which was already high. During the year ending at Michaelmas 1503, some 4,100 bundles of furze (or gorse), 700 bundles of firewood and 1,500 bundles of faggots were delivered to the hospital for heating, brewing and cooking. The gorse was stored in a new 'furzehous' near the bakery, the old building beside the bridge having proved too small, and thus ripe for conversion into private lodgings. At the same time, a thatched 'wodehous' was built against the wall of the master's garden, there already being at least two other wood stores and a turf house (1322–3) elsewhere in the precinct.[153]

One of the primary responsibilities shouldered by the heads and senior administrators of medieval religious institutions was that of maintaining the fabric of the institutions they served. 'As the ruined manor of a temporal lord is the sign that he is generally absent from the place,' argued the Dominican preacher, John Bromyard, 'so ruin in ecclesiastical houses signifies the absence of God, and adversity in external goods signifies the extinction of interior warmth and charity.'[154] Ecclesiastical visitors were expected to report on the state of buildings, and were often distressed by what they found. It was, for example, alleged in 1382 that the preceptor of the hospital of St Leonard at Skirbeck, Lincolnshire, had not only reduced the number of resident paupers by about two-thirds and completely abandoned the distribution of food at the gates, but had compounded his offence by selling off timber from farm buildings and pocketing the proceeds. He had also allowed a valuable mill to collapse, thus occasioning the house further losses.[155] Royal commissioners sent to investigate abuses at St Bartholomew's hospital near Oxford a decade later recorded a sorry catalogue of buildings ruined through neglect and fire, unroofed barns and abandoned outbuildings.[156] There is a tendency to regard such problems as typical of the late medieval English hospital, but the picture was by no means one of unmitigated gloom. A powerful reason for electing affluent masters, such as John Jullys, was their readiness to fund large-scale building projects. Allegations of 1335 that the master of St Nicholas's hospital, Carlisle, had abandoned his charges to pursue a lucrative practice as a surgeon, were soon disproved. Far from alienating the house's possessions, he had used the fees of wealthy patients to repair buildings devastated by the Scots, and had replaced lost oxen, horses, carts, ploughs and seedlings out of his own pocket.[157] In both 1301 and 1340 masters of the hospital of St John the Baptist, Ripon, likewise dipped into their own coffers to replace missing stock, equipment, furnishings and plate. A considerable sacrifice was also made by the warden of St James's, Northallerton, who pledged, after a visitation of 1379, that he would take no salary until all the necessary repairs had been effected and the full complement of patients achieved. Although he had only been in office for year, he had already erected seven new buildings, at no cost to the hospital.[158]

John Jullys's personal outlay of at least £243 on 'upkeep and expenses, repairs and buildings' in the precinct would suggest that the fabric had deteriorated considerably by 1502, although the surviving accounts reveal otherwise.[159] The time, effort and money expended on repairs and maintenance throughout the fifteenth century may, in one sense, be regarded as a further aspect of the hospital's charitable endeavours. In providing regular work for a number of local artisans and labourers, it not only contributed towards the local economy, integrating the house firmly within the community it served, but also kept at least a score or so of men in gainful employment. Workmen were a constant and no doubt sometimes distracting presence in the precinct. Over the year ending at Michaelmas 1448, for example, the accountant responsible for the hospital fabric paid wages to twenty-eight different craftsmen and their helpers, some of whom must have been as familiar to the brethren as the choristers and conducts. Edmund Cauwold, the chief carpenter, then spent over thirteen weeks on a variety of tasks, while James Goos, one of the thatchers, was on hand for ten. All in all, the hospital remunerated 555 days' work in the precinct, while in certain cases providing an allocation of cooked food (*mensa*) from the kitchens as well. Some of the men who were engaged in repairing the Holme Street properties were also entitled to this allowance, which could either be eaten at the common board or taken away.[160] In 1436–7 at least seventy-four meals were provided for workers in Holme Street, as part of their contracted wages, and a further sixty-one for the various masons, sawyers and thatchers employed on the hospital site. Two years later the annual figure stood at 267 individual meals, which does not, of course, include food consumed by the numerous men and boys who were paid only in kind and did not therefore concern the accountant.[161] There is no reason to believe that, as in larger monastic houses, the food was invariably commuted into cash: the prospect of a square meal of meat or fish with a loaf of bread, home-brewed ale and some cheese must have constituted one of the great attractions of employment at St Giles's.[162]

All these workmen required tools and building materials, which were delivered to the hospital and stored ready for use whenever any of its properties in or near the city needed repair. Thus, in 1478–9, part of a consignment of more than 200 bundles of straw was made ready there for thatching a new tenement in the parish of St Martin Coslany, part was despatched to the manor of Costessey and the rest was earmarked for repairs in the precinct itself.[163] Whole areas of the hospital complex must have resembled a builder's yard, so great were the quantities of stone, timber, reed, straw, lead, glass, tiles, lime and sand brought by the cartload for whatever projects might then be in progress. In 1443–4 work on a single chamber previously occupied by one of the chaplains necessitated the purchase of nineteen quarters of lime, five carts of stone and fifteen of sand, and a quantity of timber; the roofing materials were already in store as they came from the hospital's own meadows.[164] Laths, planks and thatch could conveniently be prepared in the relatively open space of the service quarters. So too could the large quantities of clay used to construct many of the hospital's outhouses and domestic buildings, as well as some of the Holme Street properties.[165] Heaps of scaffolding lay everywhere, although the programme was anything but haphazard. The scale of these operations is striking, and demanded a considerable amount of forward planning: the hewing and sawing of 2,960 feet of board in 1522–3 suggests, for example, that a precise schedule of repairs was organised well in advance by workmen as well as auditors and accountants.[166] The preoccupation with security, already observed elsewhere in the complex, was no less evident in the various workshops and stores. Wherever possible, equipment, tools and materials were kept under lock and key in a smithy (1375), a 'tilehouse' (1376), which had the capacity to store over 7,000 tiles at once, a 'werkhouse' (1442–3), a 'storehouse' (1477–8), a carpenters' workshop (1459–60) and a new 'wryghthous' (constructed at a cost of 46*s* 4*d* in building materials and labour in 1475–6).[167]

Throughout the fifteenth and early sixteenth centuries a significant amount of time and labour was devoted to the upkeep and expansion of the domestic quarters occupied by the master, brothers, sisters, hired priests and boarders. As noted above, the sisters' lodgings stood enclosed, locked and separate throughout the medieval period and beyond. One of the overwhelming concerns of ecclesiastical visitors was to prevent unnecessary contact between the sexes in hospitals. Sexual misdemeanours undermined discipline, deterred wealthy patrons, and, most terrible of all, created a miasma of sin, lethal to the spiritual health of staff, patients and benefactors alike. An inspection of St Bartholomew's hospital, conducted by the bishop of London in 1316, revealed general laxity, neglect of patients and insubordination. His response was to recommend far stricter segregation, and the appointment of 'a man of exemplary moral character' as doorkeeper of the sisters' quarters. Only the master could authorise male visitors: he too, eventually succumbed to temptation, being later accused of incontinence with one of the nurses.[168] At St Leonard's, York, the sisters not only sat apart in an 'honest place' to the west of the hospital church when services were being held, but had their own doorway which was forbidden to brothers and priests unless processions were in progress. This arrangement boasted the additional advantage of keeping women well away from the sacred space of the chancel. As strictly segregated in death as they were in life, the sisters and bedeswomen of the hospital of St Katherine by the Tower had a separate walled cemetery near their quarters, which lay on the opposite side of the hospital church, well away from the other lodgings.[169] Free of any serious imputation of sexual impropriety for the best part of 300 years, the brethren of St Giles's hospital respected the founder's injunctions with regard to the admission of female boarders and other undesirables. Such people could, after all, be accommodated along with pilgrims and other travellers in the inn which the hospital owned in Holme Street, just outside the precinct, and leased to a series of local entrepreneurs. Aware of the potential value of a hostelry on one of the principal routes into the city, the master and brothers took the decision, in 1464, greatly to enlarge and improve the premises. Over the next three years almost £27 was spent on labour and building materials, the final touch being provided by the painter, John Parys, who executed an inn-sign depicting one of the hospital's swans.[170]

However anxious they may have been to keep potentially disruptive visitors at arm's length, successive masters of St Giles's were only too glad to accommodate the conducts and choristers whose presence sent exactly the right message to benefactors contemplating the health of their immortal souls. A number of clergy whose rural livings offered none of the opportunities for social and pecuniary advancement available in Norwich found the hospital an ideal *pied-à-terre*, where convenient quarters could be hired while they took on more lucrative employment as mass priests or diocesan administrators. In 1480–1, for example, the rector of Hardingham paid 10*s* a year for a chamber at the east end of a newly built lodging house, along with a stable and a small garden with a pond. Shortly afterwards he acquired another room as well, clearly intending to make himself at home.[171] He was not unusual: the rectors of Acle, Thorpe, Plumstead, Saxlingham, Sall, Heigham and Postwick, and the parsons of Lopham and Wickmere took up residence at various times during the fifteenth century. Because of its situation next to the episcopal palace, the hospital became something of a boarding house for senior clergy, such as the canon lawyers, Master Thomas Dalling (1415) and Doctor John Scarlet (1498), as well as for various bureaucrats on diocesan business.[172] Although the number of semi-permanent tenants was never very high, and the hospital rarely let out all of its more spacious residential quarters at once, there was a regular and profitable turnover of short-term boarders (*perhendinarii*), including the bishops' own servants who stayed for a few weeks or months.[173] In 1500–1, for instance, the not inconsiderable sum of £18 was raised from twenty-three such individuals, including some fee-paying boys, whose parents wished them to study at the episcopal grammar school nearby.[174] In order to make the most of a growing demand, the hospital built at least three new dwelling houses between 1446 and 1456 alone. A row of 'inwarde howses' along the north side of the chancel was probably assigned for use by visiting clergy, although some were given rooms near the gatehouse in the outer courtyard [see Map III].[175] Most of the larger English medieval hospitals of the period were obliged to supplement their incomes in this way. Financial problems at the Bethlehem hospital in London led to speculative ventures whereby tenants on long leases were encouraged to build their own housing in the precinct in return for reduced rents. Chambers were also constructed there for use by affluent corrodians, who purchased or were given sheltered accommodation, and naturally expected a high standard of living. We know little of this aspect of life at St Giles's, although it is unlikely that the men who paid up to £40 for corrodies in the fourteenth century would have been content with a bed in the infirmary. Sir Philip Wem, the most distinguished pensioner at St Mary's hospital, Ospringe, occupied spacious private quarters by a gate leading into the garden.[176]

A number of twelfth- and thirteenth-century hospitals were extensively rebuilt and enlarged in the later Middle Ages, as part of their transformation into collegiate foundations dedicated to the commemoration of the Christian departed. The construction of quadrangles and cloister walks for the chaplains was a natural development as the number of clergy grew, and liturgical functions began to take priority over the care of the sick poor. This layout enabled priests and choristers to process into churches which, as we shall see in Chapter IV, were growing larger and increasingly ornate.[177] It seems likely, however, that at St Giles's the original groundplan had followed a quadrangular pattern of the kind to be found in houses of Augustinian canons, albeit with the cloister to the north rather than the south of the church as was usually (but by no means invariably) the case.[178] Walter Suffield had certainly envisaged that the chaplains and lay brothers would have space to process in copes and surplices from their dormitory to the hospital chapel for matins, returning there after dinner, as they chanted the *miserere*.[179] That St Giles's possessed some kind of cloister by the early fifteenth century is evident from the surviving accounts, the decision to rebuild in stone being part of a far more comprehensive and ambitious programme, which made it necessary to replace the existing structure.[180] During this very same period the open arcading of the cloisters at the hospital of St Mary, Bishopsgate, which must already have impressed visitors, was replaced by glazed screen walls executed to a far higher standard.[181] When work started at St Giles's, in 1447–8, a 'new' suite of guest chambers, a 'new' larder and, significantly, a 'new' thatched hall or refectory (which stood along the west side of the cloister) were also being built.

The hall, in particular, represented a major and therefore protracted undertaking, spread out over a number of years, just like the roofing and paving of the cloister, in order to reduce the strain on the budget and ensure that each part of the project was undertaken in a logical sequence. Masons were still busy on the hall windows overlooking the cloister in 1450; the internal walls were finished off two years later; and it was not until 1457 that the glazing was completed.[182] Regularly strewn with fresh reeds and furnished with a variety of trestles and benches (1472–3), this was, and still remains, a large and impressive chamber (10 × 12 m), which could be made more intimate through the use of tapestry and painted hangings (1476–7).[183] The carved spandrels in the timber roof beams date from the hospital's later association with the city guild of St George (whose dragon they depict), but the handsome kingposts and tie-beams must still have looked imposing even without their decoration [see Plate 22]. Expenditure on a candelabrum, 28 yards of linen for table-cloths and towels, and pewter vessels weighing over 88 pounds (1480–1) suggests that entertaining was done on a lavish scale.[184] Yet the poor were not entirely forgotten: the south end of the hall gave direct access to the infirmary, where food and drink could be distributed to those seeking Walter Suffield's daily alms.[185] John Jullys still found scope for improvement, paying for the construction of a new chimney out of his own pocket. His plans for this part of the precinct included the installation of a pantry, complete with another chimney, along with the refurbishment of the buttery and also of the parlour, where staff were able to entertain relatives and guests.[186] The parlour had been added in the early 1450s, as part of the previous round of improvements, and was clearly in constant use. The laying down, in 1502–3, of a paved entry, complete with a flight of ten steps leading to the 'new pondes'

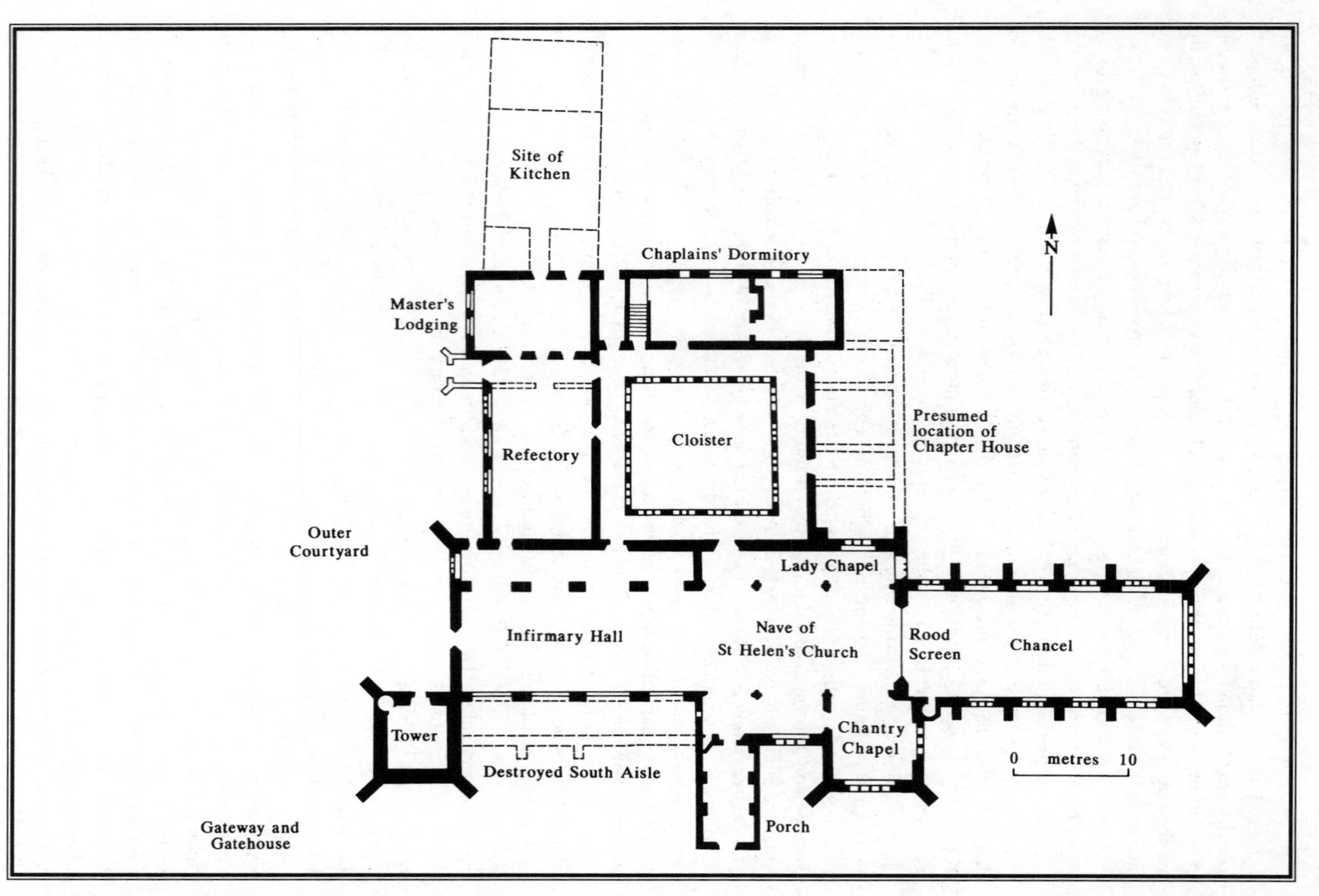

Map III: The inner precinct of St Giles's hospital and St Helen's church.

which Jullys also had made, confirms that it must have been a ground-floor chamber, situated near a supply of running water and probably quite close to the master's quarters in the north-west corner of the cloister. Like the new hospitality room built for the master in 1477–8, it would have been frequented by lay visitors of both sexes, who gained entry through the great gateway and outer courtyard, avoiding the private space of the cloister altogether.[187] The appointment to the mastership, from the 1370s onwards, of careerists with high aspirations led to an increased outlay on rooms which would do justice to their position in the city and the diocese. Thatched in the fourteenth century, but later tiled at cost of no less than £5 to the hospital, this suite of rooms was virtually rebuilt, in 1448–9, as part of the plan to remodel the entire cloister [see Plate 5]. The mason, John Gase, and his apprentice were then paid over 44*s* for twelve weeks spent on both projects, one of the carpenters being called in to partition the master's new chamber with a carved screen.[188]

By this stage, work on the cloister was well under way. Two masons (John Everard and Robert Buchan) had spent a few days in the previous year on preliminary matters of planning and design, while a roofer had been busy for far longer. Serious activity began in 1448, when the carpenter, Edmund Cauwold, was despatched to Yaxham to inspect timber for roofing. Scaffolding was erected for the stone cutters working on the traceried lights in the open arcading, which still runs along all four sides of the quadrangle [see Plate 16]. Large quantities of freestone were shipped by river from Yarmouth, unloaded at the common staithe at Conisford, and then transported by smaller boats over the short distance to the hospital.[189] Roofing, paving and whitewashing the cloister were not finished until 1456–7, by which time the team of masons, plumbers (for the gutters) and carpenters had reached the chapter house on the eastern side. This was also paved with stone, a necessary move given that at least one of the house's patrons, Robert Bosse, later elected to be buried there.[190] The entrance to the chapter house from the cloister, now bricked up, provides a valuable clue as to the source of some of the funding needed to pay for the labour and materials not recorded in the accounts. In a spandrel on one side of the arched doorway appear the arms of John Molet, prior of Norwich (1453–71), and in the other those of Walter Lyhart, bishop of Norwich (1446–70). A badly damaged stone figure in the middle probably depicted St Giles, and provides a further reminder that this part of the building would have been quite lavishly decorated [see Plate 23]. If the hospital church gave the community its soul, the chapter house was clearly the seat of reason. Here, at the weekly meetings demanded by the founder, matters of general interest were discussed, discipline was enforced and staff were reminded of their common purpose.[191] The chapter house was also an appropriate place for electing new masters, examining staff during episcopal visitations and for drawing up, witnessing and sealing important documents, most notably the hospital's surrender to the Crown, which was signed there by the last of the brothers in March 1547 [see Plate 40].[192]

Along the north side of the cloister ran 'the long high house' which served as a dormitory for chaplains and conducts. A 'new' dorter had been built in 1375 to replace the old one and allow staff a degree of privacy not envisaged by the founder.[193] By 1438–9 individual 'cells' or cubicles on an upper floor were available for renting by priests on limited incomes, and within a few years the dormitory below had been similarly partitioned. Lath and plaster walls could be moved with relative ease: in 1456–7 a carpenter spent thirty-one days constructing new ones 'above the dormitory'. All rooms had their own locks and keys, the idea of communal life having few attractions for men accustomed to the comforts of what might best be described as the late medieval equivalent of a gentlemen's club. Similar improvements were effected at St Mary's hospital, Bishopsgate, through the largesse of a lay patron, who left money in 1489 for chambers to be made in the dorter.[194] Like the refectory, the dormitory at St Giles's had a thatched roof, which was completely overhauled at a cost of 25*s* 8*d* in the 1470s.[195] Although it is now difficult to visualise exactly how the service quarters to the north related to the buildings which still stand in the cloister, the accounts contain a few hints about the general topography. Close proximity to the bakery ponds and the 'creke' leading into them ensured that the brothers' latrine (1466–7) could be properly flushed with running water. Indeed, the chaplains had their own 'dorter brygge' (1502–3) which enabled them to cross the hospital 'creke' and enter their lodgings in greater privacy from the north as well as through the cloister. Such developments were seen by critics of the established church, such as the author of the poem quoted at the start of this chapter, as yet further evidence of the collective decline in clerical morality.[196]

Windows on the south side of the dorter gave out on to the cloister, and offered a fine view of the church with its adjacent infirmary. Given the size and complexity of the precinct, it is easy to forget that each and every part served, in theory at least, to support the spiritual and charitable functions which were performed in these two buildings. Both were sacred spaces, where the hospital fulfilled its responsibilities to God, its patrons and the poor, in descending order of importance. These obligations could not be discharged, nor could the precinct be maintained, without adequate funding. St Giles's had been generously endowed by its early benefactors. Would these resources alone enable it to survive the crises of famine, plague and economic decline which brought many late medieval religious houses to the brink of collapse? Its transition into a secular college, increasingly devoted to ritual and liturgy, was a necessary response to indebtedness and falling revenues. To understand the hospital's changing role as a purveyor of spiritual medicine it is first necessary to examine the state of its financial health.

CHAPTER III

ESTATES AND FINANCES

'My other piece of advice, Copperfield', said Mr Micawber, 'you know. Annual income twenty pounds, annual expenditure nineteen nineteen six, result happiness. Annual income twenty pounds, annual expenditure twenty pounds ought and six, result misery. The blossom is blighted, the leaf is withered, the God of day goes down upon the dreary scene, and – and in short you are for ever floored. As I am!'

To make his example the more impressive, Mr Micawber drank a glass of punch with an air of great enjoyment and satisfaction, and whistled the College Hornpipe.

Charles Dickens, *David Copperfield*

Blighted blossoms and withered leaves proliferated in the landscape of the late medieval English hospital. Few, if any, such institutions managed entirely to avoid indebtedness at some point or other, and many were dogged by crippling financial difficulties. The figures are graphic. St Leonard's, York, the largest and richest hospital in the country, experienced a decline in annual revenues from £1,263 net in 1287 to less than £310 gross in 1535, while at St Paul's in Norwich income fell by about two-thirds between 1363 and 1533, leaving the master a mere £24 a year to cover his entire budget.[1] Problems on this scale led, inevitably, to drastic economies and sometimes total collapse. It was, for example, reported in 1532 that the hospital of St Leonard, Lancaster, had distributed no alms to the poor for the past sixty years and that many buildings were either in ruins or had already been demolished.[2] Complaints about poverty appear so frequently in the history of English religious communities as to suggest that the currency had become somewhat debased. Allowing for the hyperbole characteristic of such appeals, there is, even so, good reason to suppose that real and prolonged hardship often occurred. This phenomenon has been widely viewed as an inevitable consequence of economic dislocation following the first outbreak of plague in 1348–9.[3] Yet, as more evidence emerges about the crisis years of the early fourteenth century, it becomes apparent that the writing was already on the wall for many small hospitals well before this date.[4] In his study of the great famine of 1315–22, Ian Kershaw notes that over 100 hospitals and religious houses were placed under royal protection during the first year of dearth alone, while many others experienced serious upheavals.[5] Some never fully recovered: the case of St Bartholomew's, Bristol, which in 1344 was said to be 'greatly decayed' and unable to continue without assistance, is by no means unusual.[6]

Institutions which survived the testing first decades of the century faced further trials from the mid-1370s onwards, as the cumulative impact of successive national and local epidemics began to bite. A contemporary chronicler, writing at the Grey Friars, King's Lynn, observed that the plague of 1361, although less virulent than the first great pestilence, took a particular toll of children and adolescents. This, as we have seen in Chapter I, undermined replacement rates, leading to a steady fall in population and an attendant rise in wages.[7] Over 100 years after the first outbreak of plague in East Anglia, the nuns of Thetford identified it as the root cause of their misfortunes; and other female monastic houses, which, like hospitals, operated within the tightest of financial constraints, were badly affected by this long-term phenomenon.[8] Straitened circumstances do not, therefore, necessarily imply dishonesty, weak stewardship or mismanagement. To pursue the comparison with poor nunneries, sweeping generalisations about the intrinsic decline of late medieval English hospitals are often based upon a few, justifiably notorious, cases of inefficiency and corruption, whereas external factors were often to blame for persistent financial problems.

Changes in the law posed another obstacle, albeit one which could generally be circumvented. The promulgation, in 1279, of the Statute of Mortmain made it illegal for the Church to secure land in such a way as permanently to deprive the chief lord of any attendant feudal rights or revenues. Resort to leasehold, exchanges, collusive lawsuits and the creation of trusts (forbidden in 1391) enabled religious houses to continue acquiring property despite the ban against unregulated alienations. Such stratagems were, however, risky. Although St Giles's deployed them all over the years, it also pursued the safer, if more expensive, policy of soliciting royal approval for licensed amortisations. This involved the award of broadly worded royal letters patent allowing purchases or gifts of land up to a certain value, and then, at a later date, of others for the acquisition of specific property.[9] Whether or not the Crown chose to levy a fine depended upon the political exigencies of the moment and the persuasiveness of the petitioner. Less than three years after the passage of the statute, Edward I agreed, 'for the salvation of his soul' and evidently without payment, that the brethren of St Giles's might enlarge their precinct, notwithstanding any impediment posed by the new legislation.[10] The support of influential episcopal patrons, as well as a reputation for probity, certainly helped them avoid heavy financial penalties when they were building up their estates in the fourteenth century. But they still had to find over £60 in 1410 for permission to set up John Derlyngton's chantry in the hospital, and a further £31 for a licence, awarded in 1451, when substantial purchases were being made in Mundham.[11]

KEEPING THE ACCOUNTS

The widespread impression, derived from visitation reports and government inquiries, that the majority of medieval hospitals were lax in matters of administration and record-keeping has been reinforced by the wholesale destruction or dispersal of muniments during the 1530s and 1540s. Whereas several of the great monastic houses of medieval England, including Norwich cathedral priory, have left substantial archives from which it is possible to reconstruct a detailed picture of financial affairs, hospitals remain less well documented and thus open to sweeping generalisations about indifference and lack of vocation.[12] Yet, just as bodily health required the maintenance of a delicate humoral balance, so an institution like St Giles's depended for its survival upon the careful management of an often inadequate budget. There was, in reality, no margin for malversation or incompetence. Only through a very public display of efficiency was it possible to attract the new endowments which helped to arrest, if not reverse, the process of decline. In a city such as Norwich, where many religious houses and parish churches competed for patrons, the fittest alone survived. As Simon Langham, bishop of Ely, stressed during a visitation of St Leonard's, York, in 1364, stringent economies and strict accountability were essential in a period of recession, not least to reassure potential benefactors that their charitable provisions would be put into effect.[13]

The persistent failure of St Mark's hospital, Bristol, to feed 100 paupers each day, as the statutes required, led, in 1279, to an episcopal mandate ordering two receivers to present a full statement of annual profits to 'the wiser brethren'.[14] As a general rule, however, hospitals, in common with most other English landowners, drew up their accounts according to a system whose principal purpose was not to establish profit or loss but to monitor the probity of the officials involved. The first section, or 'charge', recorded in minute detail all the sums (including arrears or uncollected debts carried over from past years) for which the accountant was responsible, while the second, or 'discharge', comprised an equally exhaustive list of payments and expenses. In the latter instance, any 'surplus' or overspending in the previous year would be added to the final total [see Tables A and B below]. Although the auditor sometimes made a rough note of the current *proficium*, or profit, after the final balance had been calculated, his principal aim was, quite literally, to account for every farthing. This practice made it hard to assess relative productivity, but gave a very clear picture of who owed what.[15] The principle of personal liability was certainly no empty fiction: in 1478–9, for example, the steward of St Giles's noted that unpaid arrears of £15 charged to his predecessor, Robert Tounour, would be raised 'out of his own goods and chattels'.[16]

From the early fourteenth century, if not before, the administrative structure at St Giles's followed a model traditionally adopted on most lay estates of any size. Each of the hospital's appropriated rectories, manors and other substantial properties was placed under the control of a bailiff, reeve, rent collector or farmer, who answered, in turn, to the receiver general. As his name implies, the latter took delivery – on paper at least – of whatever money remained once local expenses had been met, and used it to run the hospital. Being either a chaplain of some years' standing or even the master himself, he was, as we shall see in Chapter V, almost always a seasoned bureaucrat with considerable administrative expertise. From the 1420s onwards, as direct management was abandoned on the hospital's manors and rectories in favour of leasehold, either he or the steward (who took charge of provisioning) accounted personally for properties which had hitherto been supervised by a layman or resident chaplain. But the same principles of personal responsibility still obtained. The survival of hundreds of accounts drawn up by these officials testifies both to the importance of the annual audit and the comparatively high levels of efficiency maintained at St Giles's. These documents are, indeed, no more than the tip of an archival iceberg, since they represent the end of a complex process requiring quantities of supporting evidence, working notes and rough drafts, almost all of which have now been lost. Staff such as the steward, the sacristan of the hospital church, the keeper of the granaries and almost all employees who handled money or stock were expected to produce journals recording every transaction in minute detail. Along with bills of sale, receipts, contracts with workmen and tradespeople, tallies and other documentation, these provided the raw material from which the accounts were synthesised, and are often mentioned in them. We know, for example, that the sacristan, who collected gifts of alms as well as altarage, routinely presented a sheaf of paper bills at the annual audit.[17]

One of the principal duties incumbent upon the master of a hospital was to ensure, either personally or through a deputy, that accounts were regularly compiled and submitted to outside inspection. Not even the leprous were exempt from this requirement: on assuming office, the warden of the *leprosarium* at Buckland by Dover had to swear that he would render a full statement of finances whenever necessary, even though he was himself a patient.[18] Canon seventeen of the Council of Vienne, which met in 1311, had introduced practical measures for the reform of hospitals, insisting upon the presentation of annual accounts and inventories. Some bishops, such as William Bateman of Norwich (d. 1355), actually cited this ruling when new appointments to masterships were entered in their registers.[19] The outcome of such close scrutiny was not invariably negative: in 1437, for instance, allegations of corruption levelled against the master of St Giles's hospital, Kepier, led Bishop Langley of Durham to order a comprehensive investigation, after which the suspect was acquitted of all charges and confirmed in office for life. Conversely, among the many sins of omission committed by the warden of the hospital of St Mary Bethlehem, London, in the late fourteenth century, was his failure to keep accounts for a period of thirteen years, during which he made off with large amounts of money donated as alms.[20]

The systematic preservation of deeds of title, preferably in the accessible format of a cartulary, such as the composite *Liber Domus Dei* kept at St Giles's hospital (and known also, significantly, as '*le Domesday*'), was no less important. Here, on a topographical basis, are recorded some 260 grants, purchases, exchanges and quitclaims whereby the masters and brethren consolidated their holdings in Norwich and Norfolk, mostly during the second half of the thirteenth century and early 1300s.[21] In addition, the hospital maintained a collection of hundreds of individual conveyances relating to its country estates. Although it is not known how these were stored, references to a registry (*domus registrarum*) in the precinct suggest that considerable care was taken to safeguard them and all the copious administrative and financial records generated every year. Storage was certainly important. An extent of hospital property in Cringleford, copied into the manor court roll for 1479, was reputedly 'wretyn owte of a papir of maister [John] Smythes hande whiche bille remayneth in the chest with evidences of the hospitall'.[22] Standards of record-keeping in English medieval hospitals varied considerably, and were of pressing concern to visitors, not least because of the attendant financial implications. The absence of any coherent *registrum* of charters belonging to St Thomas's hospital, Southwark, irritated Bishop Wykeham during his inspection of 1387. He ordered that one should be compiled immediately, along with a detailed rental noting the current value and location of all hospital properties.[23] His instructions presuppose the existence of some form of archive; and enough material was, indeed, available to make possible the production of a cartulary recording the provenance of holdings in London and Surrey not long afterwards.[24] A number of hospital cartularies, such as those made for St John's, Bury St Edmunds, St Bartholomew's, Dover, and St Mary's, Yarmouth, incorporated rentals as well as copies of statutes and charters. But rentals had only limited value unless they were regularly revised, which could prove a difficult and laborious process. Despite strenuous efforts in the fifteenth century to collect and record evidence, including wills, on a parochial basis, the brothers of St Giles's still accumulated spectacular arrears of uncollected rents in Norwich.[25]

Like Bishop Suffield, who had specifically drawn attention to this matter in the foundation statutes of St Giles's, Wykeham was no less exercised about the safe-keeping and supervised use of the seals which authenticated documents of title. Here, his underlying concern was that land, rents or franchises would be alienated by St Thomas's hospital, thus reducing its income even further.[26] Overt corruption apart, the temptation to sell or mortgage property in the hope of paying off debts or raising essential capital must have been hard to resist. For this reason, the seals belonging to St Leonard's hospital, York, were supposed to remain in a box with three locks, each key being held by a different official. And, although it was often disregarded, a rule of 1364 forbade the master to use his personal seal for hospital business.[27] Anxiety on this score was clearly justified. Royal letters patent of 1376, ordering an inquiry into the management of St Lawrence's hospital, Bristol, drew attention to the 'misrule' of past masters, their alienation of lands and other possessions, the indiscriminate award of pensions in return for short-term financial gain and other abuses. By 1400, further depredations had occurred, resulting in the sale of assets and leasing of property at well below the market rate. Since the king was himself a direct beneficiary, in spiritual terms, of the hospital's good works, and his own soul was placed at risk by the attendant threat to divine worship, it is easy to see why the government wished to improve standards. How this was to be achieved on a net income of less than £15 a year remained an unanswered question. Once sufficient to support the hospital's needs, resources had declined in value, and morale had, understandably, fallen too.[28]

Given the number and diversity of the institutions themselves, striking extremes of efficiency and neglect are to be found, sometimes within the very same organisation. In marked contrast to the majority of early large-scale foundations, the London hospital of St Mary, Bishopsgate, experienced a dramatic revival during the early sixteenth century. This was thanks largely to the entrepreneurial instincts of Prior Cressall, who tightened up administrative procedures and secured royal support for a programme of investment in new property. He was thus able to achieve a degree of solvency which had seemed impossible during the previous century, when plummeting land values and managerial incompetence together threatened to undermine the house's charitable activities.[29] Even greater miracles were wrought at St Anthony's hospital, another London house, said in 1441 to have formerly been 'beautiful, wealthy and very handsome', but then described as 'melancholy, squalid and almost desolate, and stripped to the verge of poverty'. Once again, through royal and civic patronage and the efforts of an energetic master, a failing institution was transformed, in this instance acquiring a successful school and confraternity.[30] That St Giles's, Norwich, not only preserved its territorial possessions, but actually managed to consolidate its assets in town and country consistently throughout the later Middle Ages was likewise due in no small measure to the calibre of its senior staff and the support of successive bishops of Norwich. But the hospital was, none the less, still beset by financial problems. As will soon become apparent, a combination of dwindling receipts and rising wages conspired to frustrate the efforts of the most conscientious bureaucrats.

Even during more prosperous times, the endowment of a modestly sized hospital required a substantial commitment of capital or property and was not a venture to be undertaken lightly. Ecclesiastical patrons, such as Walter Suffield, aimed to attract a steady flow of donations through the offer of indulgences, enabling benefactors to purchase relief from enjoined penance.[31] They also hoped that their initial generosity would be matched by wealthy landowners and merchants. But a regular, secure income was essential from the outset to support the requisite number of paupers and other beneficiaries of charity specified in the statutes. Staff had to be fed, clothed, housed and paid, the fabric had to be maintained, and if – as was usually the case – the premises contained a chapel or church, additional funds would be needed to provide vestments, service books and other furnishings. Bishop Richard Wych's modest foundation for aged, blind and debilitated priests at Windham in Sussex clearly cost more than expected. His will of 1253 contained a bequest of £20 to the house, besides 'the debt for which I am bound to them'; and it was probably out of a sense of obligation to his predecessor that Bishop Climping stepped in to complete the endowment.[32] Other prelates left less to chance. It has been estimated that, to generate an annual income of just under £30 for his almshouse at Clyst Gabriel, Walter Stapleton, bishop of Exeter, made over episcopal property worth about £560 on the open market, in 1309, and spent more than £360 of his own money on buildings and equipment.[33] Walter Suffield's endowment upon St Giles's was just as generous. Besides purchasing the actual site of the hospital, described in the previous chapter, he appropriated to it no fewer than six Norfolk livings, with a capital value of approximately £570, and planned (but did not live to accomplish) the transfer of two more. With characteristic thoroughness, he also set in train a policy of piecemeal acquisitions in and around Norwich, thus establishing a pattern for territorial expansion which was sustained over the next three centuries. For ease of reference, a chronological list of all accessions may be found in Appendix II. The following section deals with the management of properties acquired before the crisis years of 1315–22, and addresses some of the long-term problems encountered by ecclesiastical landowners. It then examines in greater detail the contribution made by individual manors and rectories to the economy of St Giles's.

BUILDING UP THE ESTATES: THE INITIAL ENDOWMENT

Both the first and second drafts of Suffield's foundation charter and a separate conveyance of 1251 confirmed the new hospital in possession of the advowsons and temporal profits of the parish churches of Calthorpe, Costessey, Cringleford, Hardley, Seething and St Mary in South Walsham [see Map IV].[34] During the early 1320s, the receiver general collected a minimum of between £30 and £40 a year in cash from this core endowment of six livings,

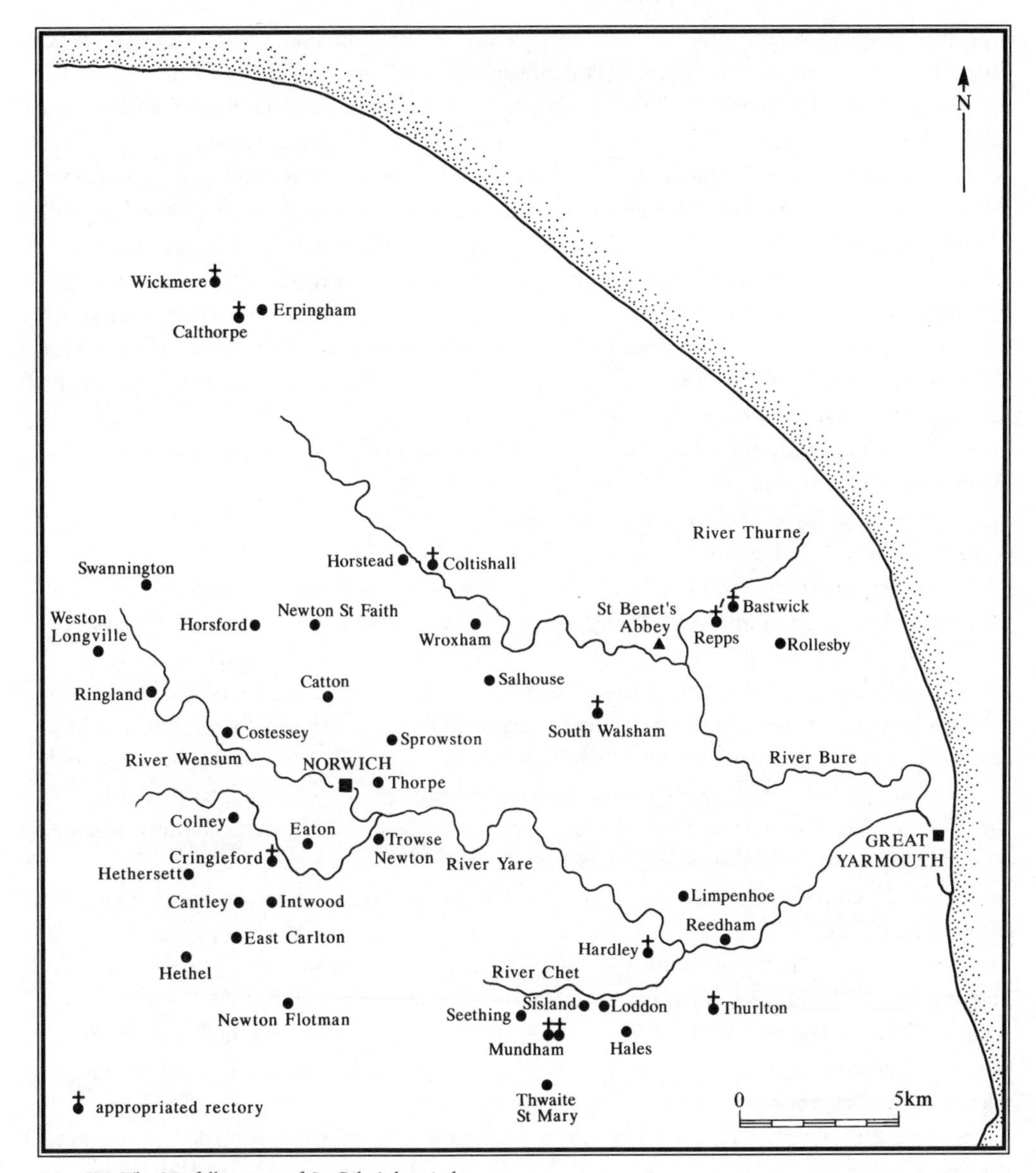

Map IV: The Norfolk estates of St Giles's hospital.

which by then constituted well over half the hospital's net income from its expanding country estates. A significant proportion of this money came from the sale of cereals (notably barley) and other crops grown on the hospital's own demesnes and glebe land, or paid by parishioners as tithes. East Norfolk, in which all but one of St Giles's medieval holdings lay, was blessed with richer and more fertile soil than the west. The flourishing trade in locally produced cloth boosted other aspects of the regional economy; and a far higher proportion of the county's 140 market towns was concentrated in this area. Easy access by river to the coastal ports of Yarmouth, Cley, Wiveton and Blakeney meant that surplus grain could be shipped along the coast or overseas – an important consideration at a time when war with Scotland and France generated a constant, sometimes onerous, demand for provisions.[35] Thanks to the high levels of agricultural productivity sustained throughout the county, large consignments of grain were also dispatched to the hospital's Holme Street granaries during the thirteenth and fourteenth centuries. These fluctuated in size and value from year to year, but could be worth considerably more than any monetary payments made directly to the receiver general. All receipts and disbursements of stock, from black peas to piglets, were itemised in a separate section on the dorse of the rectorial accounts and clearly added appreciably to the total profitability of each holding. Although, in cash terms, it appears rather high, the tax assessment of £57 a year returned for these six Norfolk livings at the time of the Valuation of Norwich, in 1254, may actually represent a significant underestimate.[36]

Concentration on monetary transactions alone can, indeed, give a misleading impression of an economy based as much on kind as on hard cash.[37] During the famine years of 1315–16 sales of barley from Calthorpe, made judiciously as prices spiralled from 6*s* 8*d* to an unprecedented 15*s* a quarter, raised £27 for St Giles's, while an additional 70 quarters of malt (then fetching 14*s* each on the open market) were despatched by cart to the hospital. Fifteen years later, by which time prices had returned to normal, the bailiff of Calthorpe sent his employers 99 quarters of wheat, barley, malt and peas worth just over £24 at current prices, and thus still of great value to the community.[38] Once the grain was safely stored, sales could be staggered to take optimum advantage of an unpredictable market. At the close of the accounting year 1414–15, for example, the bailiff of Seething retained 63 quarters of malt, waiting as prices climbed from 4*s* to 6*s* a quarter during the winter before finally clinching a more profitable deal for the brethren.[39] Direct management thus offered flexibility, while guaranteeing a regular and high quality supply of grain for consumption by the household and distribution to the poor. The receiver general concluded the charge section of his account for 1318–19 with a note that 110 quarters of wheat, 67 of barley, 55 of rye, 35 of peas and oats, and 260 of malt had arrived in the precinct that year from the estates. The volatility of prices makes it difficult to compute precise monetary equivalents, but there can be no doubt that the contents of the hospital's barns were then worth far more than the net cash income of £115 recorded in the same document.[40] Any surplus produce could, moreover, be sold quickly and efficiently in central Norwich, where an expanding population ensured a constant demand for comestibles before plague first struck in 1349.[41]

As labour costs began to rise and profits fall, however, the prospect of stable money rents payable for a fixed term became increasingly attractive. Tithes (which were rendered in kind, and thus had to be threshed and winnowed along with crops harvested from the demesnes) could be included in the lease, farmed separately for a period of years or sold piecemeal, on an *ad hoc* basis, to local dealers. At Seething, for instance, the demesnes were leased in 1464 for a period of seven years to a husbandman named John Calf, while another entrepreneur continued, as he had done for some time, to buy up all the tithes at a price negotiated annually with the master of St Giles's. A few grain merchants, such as Robert Chandeler of Yarmouth, Thomas Iryng of Ranworth and Oliver Cubyte of South Walsham, bought wholesale from more than one rectory at once.[42] Whatever the circumstances, the gradual move from direct management saw a pronounced decline in revenue, but had the dual advantage of eliminating overheads and curtailing the administrative responsibilities of senior staff. As Bruce Campbell has shown, 'the most immediate and enduring effect of the reversal of population trends', evident in eastern Norfolk even before the Black Death, was upon farming practices. The concentration of agricultural property in far fewer hands led to the rise of a small group of affluent tenant farmers anxious to extend their holdings through leasing and speculation on the grain market.[43] It was they who benefited from the financial difficulties experienced by religious houses both great and small. Although many such institutions opted for the security of extremely conservative long-term leases, and consequently suffered as prices began to rise again in the early sixteenth century, St Giles's had always maintained a more pragmatic approach, perhaps following the example of the cathedral priory.[44] The enterprising John Jullys was thus able to commandeer almost all the hospital's tithes for consumption in the precinct or sale in Norwich between 1500 and 1505, briefly cutting out the middleman altogether.

Appropriated livings, in particular, presented the ecclesiastical landowner with a variety of options, which St Giles's exploited to the full. Many hospitals derived a substantial part of their revenues through appropriation, a process which conveniently side-stepped the barriers to expansion set up by the Statute of Mortmain. Not only did it bestow valuable reserves of patronage, and thus allow the institution to appoint a vicar of its own choosing to serve the parish; it also earmarked for the house in question whatever tithes, altarage, glebe rents and other spiritualities had hitherto been enjoyed by the rector. In livings such as Calthorpe and Seething these were obviously worth having. But the practice was not without its drawbacks, as twelfth- and thirteenth-century reformers, including Walter Suffield, clearly recognised. In an attempt to husband resources, patrons were inclined to ignore their pastoral responsibilities, implementing economies which antagonised parishioners and deprived incumbents of the one-third share of revenues to which they were legally entitled.[45] The practice of diverting this money to pay the stipends of some of the hospital brethren may have worked well enough when, like John Senster, vicar of Seething (1412–16), they actually took personal charge of running the demesnes. It is, however, unlikely that Robert Treswell's busy life as steward, receiver general and supervisor of the hospital's estates left much time for his parochial duties at South Walsham, a living he occupied briefly in the 1520s.[46] Perhaps like Peter Goos, who served the hospital's free chapel at Bastwick for many years in the mid-fifteenth century, he arranged for one of his colleagues to cover during his long absences on estate business. Late medieval accounts from Cringleford certainly suggest that the hospital was punctilious with regard to the cure of souls there entrusted to its care. The brethren or conducts who ministered to this particular parish were customarily in residence for at least 110 days of the year, and would thus have been able to serve the living conscientiously.[47]

Although it did not, apparently, ever engage in the notorious abuse of leaving vacancies unfilled in order to economise, the hospital of St Giles certainly incurred criticism in other respects. Responsibility for the upkeep of ecclesiastical buildings (especially the chancels of appropriated churches) imposed a heavy burden. One solution, deployed at Bastwick throughout the 1460s, was to allocate altarage worth up to 40*s* a year directly to the parishioners so they could maintain the free chapel themselves, hiring labour when they saw fit [see Plate 24].[48] As we have already seen with regard to developments in the precinct, careful forward planning might help to spread the financial load, but essential structural repairs could not be postponed indefinitely. It is sobering to reflect that, between 1441 and 1463 alone, the hospital spent a total of at least £60 on large-scale projects mounted one immediately after the other for rebuilding the chancels at Hardley, Thurlton (acquired in 1334) and Repps.[49] To their credit, the brethren evidently appreciated that the refurbishment of parish churches constituted an important work of spiritual charity. They engaged their best workmen and used high-quality materials. But this had not always been the case. In 1330, the people of Seething indignantly withdrew some of their offerings because the hospital had not only failed to repair the bell-tower, but had also neglected its obligation to feed thirteen paupers each day in Easter week, a breach of faith which understandably caused particular resentment.[50] At this date parochial discontent in Cringleford focused upon the question of repairs to the dilapidated cemetery wall and neighbouring vicarage.[51]

This was a testing decade for St Giles's, which had by then to cut expenditure elsewhere in order to discharge its responsibilities to the poor of Norwich. Shortly after the living of Mundham St Peter had been appropriated as an emergency measure, in 1340, another quarrel erupted, this time over the allocation of a decent stipend and living quarters to the vicar, who submitted his case to arbitration and evidently won.[52] Nor was this the first occasion when the master and brethren had faced a disgruntled incumbent: during a metropolitan visitation in 1304, the archbishop of Canterbury had intervened at Calthorpe to negotiate a fairer assignment of revenues for the parish priest, whose portion had become a matter of contention between him and his patrons.[53] At this point the hospital had less justification for such stringent economies. The productivity of the demesnes and the value of the tithes there and in the other five livings which constituted Bishop Suffield's original endowment seemed initially to promise a secure future. During the years after his death, a plentiful, mobile and relatively cheap supply of labour, combined with innovative farming methods, placed Norfolk landowners among the most successful and prosperous in England.[54]

Some fifteen miles due north of Norwich, and a short distance from the coast, the living at Calthorpe, together with several acres of woodland, heath, arable and pasture, one half of a knight's fee and the neighbouring manor of Erpingham, had been acquired by Bishop Suffield between 1246 and 1248 from his kinsman, Peter Obys. Whereas the estates which he held to the south, at Hevingham, were intended for his own sport and recreation, he earmarked these properties for the new hospital.[55] His nephew and heir, Sir William, who had been a party to the transactions, later released his title, but other members of their family retained a shared claim on the estate. In 1309, after a legal wrangle over the number of clerks and paupers then being maintained at St Giles's, the bishop's kinsman, Walter de Calthorpe, finally made over his own interests in Calthorpe and Erpingham to the community.[56] By then the master and brothers had acquired a number of smaller plots of land and rents in the area, which enabled them to consolidate their demesnes. Despite the disastrous consequences of a lengthy drought during the 1350s (which seriously affected the barley producers of south-east England, where dearth followed hard on the heels of plague), returns from Calthorpe held up remarkably well. A dairy herd produced cheese and butter for the hospital; hens and geese supplied as many as 3,000 eggs a year; and, between 1323 and 1388, annual deliveries of grain to the storehouses in Holme Street rarely fell below 75 quarters (mostly malt) and occasionally exceeded the hundred mark.[57]

At first glance, evidence from a run of accounts for almost the entire fourteenth century suggests that the living not only remained prosperous, but that net profits paid into the hospital's coffers actually rose somewhat during the late 1380s and 1390s, when they twice reached £15. But this was because a far larger proportion of surplus agricultural produce was by then going directly to market, and a correspondingly smaller one to St Giles's for consumption by the community. In 1394–5, for instance, the hospital took delivery of a mere 9 quarters of wheat and peas, while almost the entire yield of malt (80 quarters) was purchased for £19 by local factors, quite possibly for shipment at Blakeney, Cley or Wiveton. After running costs had been met, just over £9 was left for the receiver general: a sum which contrasts tellingly with the value of the grain despatched to the precinct earlier in the century.[58] In absolute terms, then, both yields and profits appear to have fallen at a time when the full impact of successive outbreaks of plague was finally beginning to take its toll on most ecclesiastical landowners, whatever their wealth and the ingenuity of their responses to adverse economic and climatic conditions.[59] It was only a matter of time before the hospital opted for the security of a steady income by putting both the tithes *and* the demesnes out to farm on fixed leases. In 1429 the annual rent was set at £15 for an initial term of ten years, and then increased by a further 20*s*.[60]

The wisdom of such a policy became apparent during the lean years of the mid- and late fifteenth century, when areas of intensive barley production failed to benefit from the general upturn in the national economy. Supply far exceeded demand, forcing East Anglian farmers to seek more distant markets and thus reduce their profit margins even further. None the less, landowners who had prudently opted to let out their demesnes for cash still encountered problems. As a tenant of the Paston family explained when his rent fell due in 1440, he could 'not yet gete monay, for his cornes arn at so litell price that he can not vtter them, and yet ther is noman wole bye it for al the gret chep'.[61] By the 1470s net profits from Calthorpe had slumped by 75 per cent to a mere £5 a year or below and never recovered.[62] This was a pattern repeated across the hospital estates, prompting a brief but essentially impractical return to deliveries in kind rather than cash. The depressed state of the grain market spelt trouble for *rentiers* as well as farmers, forcing them to make the most of other assets. Useful sums could, for instance, be raised through the sale of kindling and timber. A visitation of St Leonard's hospital, York, made in 1399, criticised one of the masters for devastating woodland, notably 'several green oaks' of great value, in order to turn a quick profit. Since this hospital consumed over 30,000 faggots a year, the depletion of such a vital resource had potentially serious consequences.[63] On the other hand, the careful management of woods and coppices gave a significant boost to otherwise declining revenues, as well as guaranteeing regular supplies of fuel for domestic use. In 1438–9 alone, 'Uphalleyerd' at Calthorpe yielded over £8 through sales of 'lez stubbes de whitthorn', alder and timber.[64]

A careful eye on logistics as well as the economics of the market place clearly influenced the decision to rent out the Calthorpe demesnes, since other properties, nearer Norwich, continued to supply the hospital's dietary needs for longer. The livings at Costessey and Cringleford, on the immediate outskirts of the city, together provide a good illustration of the pragmatic approach adopted by the hospital to the management of its resources. Like so many of the grants made to medieval religious houses, the gift of Costessey came burdened with earlier obligations, in this instance necessitating the annual payment of a pension of 66*s* 8*d* to the abbot of Sawtry and of tithes to Rumburgh priory in Suffolk. In 1282, the tithes were commuted to a cash sum of £4, which partly explains why the accountant so often found himself in the red.[65] The assumption, then made in an archiepiscopal confirmation of this arrangement, that almost £7 would be left for the support of 'decrepit chaplains, elderly brethren and other paupers who are beggars staying and seeking alms [at the hospital]' soon proved wildly optimistic – at least if *cash* payments to the receiver general are any guide.[66] Although, between 1362 and 1395, sales of produce from tithes and demesnes rarely raised less than £10 a year, and sometimes exceeded £20, almost all this money was consumed by labour costs, the not inconsiderable expense of keeping ploughs and carts in working order and the maintenance of buildings. Escalating wages posed a universal problem: although the government did its best to peg them as the population fell and labour became increasingly scarce, landowners had to operate in a seller's market, especially during the aftermath of local or national epidemics. The Costessey ploughman who, in 1372, demanded 39*s* a year in cash may technically have remained within the letter of the law, although his reluctance to accept payment in kind (as had previously been the case) added an extra 25*s* to the wage bill. Building costs also rocketed. During the 1390s, work on the stables, hall, bakery and grange exceeded £8 and repairs to the chancel for which the hospital, as we have seen, bore full responsibility, accounted for over £16. Far from making a profit, the master was obliged by the end of the decade to subsidise expenses to the tune of £23 allocated from his own resources.[67]

Despite the cost of keeping them on the road, the hospital's carts still proved a worthwhile investment. They were used to convey produce, fuel, manure and building materials around the estates, as well as carrying supplies of fish from the coast. In an age when transport by land was both difficult and increasingly expensive they constituted a valuable asset, and could be hired out to other landowners. They were, moreover, needed to deliver the sizeable quantities of up to 100 quarters of grain which were dispatched from Costessey each year to St Giles's during the fourteenth century, compensating in kind for what the rectory rarely paid in cash.[68] It has been estimated that transportation costs on the estates of Christ Church priory, Canterbury, escalated by as much as 40 per cent between 1349 and 1370. In 1375 alone, St Leonard's hospital, York, spent £78, or one-tenth of its budget, on carriage: the brethren of St Giles's were clearly well advised to retain a modest labour force for work of this nature but had to pay heavily for it.[69] The value of grain contributions more than offset any local cash deficit, however, and quite substantial deliveries of malt continued to be made for many years. Indeed, as late as 1454–5 the keeper of the granary at Costessey sustained expenses of over £4 on the cost of a new malt kiln, where barley from tithes and the 35 acres of demesne still under cultivation was processed before being sold or sent to the precinct.[70] Even so, the transition to a *rentier* economy proved inevitable. Caught between the pincers of high labour costs and falling grain prices, the hospital eventually opted to buy more of its supplies direct from city markets and abandon the farm at Costessey altogether.

Walter Suffield's purchase of the advowson of Cringleford and a small amount of land in this area from Alexander de Vaux had stimulated a number of sales and donations from neighbouring landowners, such as the Baruns and the de Cringlefords, whose endowments upon the hospital included a valuable watermill (known as 'Beckmill') and a fishery on the banks of the River Yare just outside Norwich. Along with these grants, often made in free and perpetual alms in return for spiritual services, came land in the adjacent vills of Cantley and Intwood.[71] Widows, such as Joan de Cringleford, were prepared to make over dower rights in return for practical support: in this case a lifetime's supply of grain, readily available from the rectory.[72] In order to consolidate and better exploit its holdings, the hospital effected a number of exchanges and purchases. It drove a hard bargain with Henry de Heylesdon, who leased Beckmill in 1293 at an annual rent of 26*s* 8*d*. Securities of no less than £20 were required as a guarantee that he would maintain the fabric, and when his son objected to the additional powers of distraint demanded by the master, an exchange of property was effected instead.[73] Mills were an invaluable asset during times of high population density, but as the demand for corn fell and the cost of wages and maintenance rose they became less productive. The answer was to rent them out, insisting, as St Giles's generally did, that the miller or farmer should undertake all reasonable repairs. In 1453, for example, Richard Wyreham, a miller from the neighbouring village of Keswick, contracted with the master to rent a more recently acquired mill at Cringleford, along with its pool and a fishery, for five years, on the condition that he would maintain and replace all equipment, as well as seeing to the upkeep and 'dammyng' of the pond. Once again, pledges of £20 were demanded as an earnest of good faith.[74] Given that the hospital spent at least £21 in the early sixteenth century on building a new mill on this stretch of the Yare, such heavy securities were clearly warranted.[75]

Because its soil was so varied, ranging from sandy heathland to rich riverside pasture, Cringleford presented a truly mixed agrarian economy. The less fertile commons and fold courses could support a sizeable flock of up to 500 sheep, which supplied local butchers as well as the hospital kitchens with fresh meat, while also producing the characteristic light wool used locally to make worsted. In 1427–8 sales of 38 stones of wool (some paid as tithes) and eighty sheep together raised over £8, which was promptly invested in new stock. At this date the hospital's flock comprised about 450 beasts, although it had not always been so impressive. A few decades earlier, when the wool market was over-supplied by landlords who had opted for pastoral farming as a more profitable alternative to arable, numbers had been allowed to dwindle.[76] It was then that St Leonard's hospital, York, which had previously relied on wool as a staple source of income, moved over to cattle production, reducing its flocks from over 7,000 in the 1280s to fewer than 2,000 a century later in direct response to the changing demands of the market.[77] At St Giles's, however, the brethren reacted to worsening financial circumstances by temporarily abandoning commercial animal husbandry altogether. Like the monks of Ramsey Abbey, near Cambridge, they may have sold stock in an attempt to raise capital as more traditional sources of revenue failed.[78] For them this was a period of retrenchment. The bailiff of Cringleford accounted for about 100 sheep in 1364, seventy or so in 1365 and fewer than forty in the early 1380s, by which time the outlook as a whole gave cause for concern. As at Costessey, the rectory and demesnes at Cringleford had rarely shown a cash profit during the fourteenth century, but had regularly provisioned the Norwich precinct: some 58 quarters of malt, rye and wheat had, for instance, been despatched in 1342, and 67 quarters in the following year. By the 1390s, however, the picture looked bleak. Yields from tithes and demesnes declined steadily; no grain deliveries of any consequence were made to the hospital; and the deficit between income and expenditure was running at £18. As we shall see, the acquisition of the manor of Cringleford in the early fifteenth century helped to reverse this trend. Fortunately, too, there were other useful resources. From the neighbouring woods came cartloads of fuel, available in large quantities right up to the Dissolution. Over 4,000 bundles of firewood and 1,500 faggots were made up for the hospital's kitchens in 1502–3 alone, and no fewer than 7,675 faggots (at a cost of over £4 for carriage) in 1519–20.[79]

From the outset, the hospital was understandably anxious to extend its holdings in the immediate environs of Norwich [see Map V]. Besides supplementing the pastures, reed beds and meadows which constituted such a valuable part of the precinct, piecemeal acquisitions of woodland and heath to the north-west of the city provided another welcome source of fuel, including almost limitless supplies of the furze and gorse essential for cooking and heating. During and just after Bishop Suffield's lifetime a messuage, woods and at least 33 acres of land in Sprowston, where William of Norwich's body had been retrieved in 1144, were added to the hospital's rental.[80] In the early fourteenth century these properties, along with land in Catton, turned a modest cash profit, but their greatest value lay in the quantities of kindling which they produced. Regular expenditure on the upkeep of hedges and ditches, and investment in the making and planting of new enclosures more than paid off: as late as 1522 some 5,000 faggots were transported from Sprowston woods across the Wensum to St Giles's.[81] Riverside property in the old episcopal manor of Thorpe, to the south-east of the hospital, was acquired during the time of Hamon de Calthorpe, the first master. Later known as 'Fyssheresclos' or Fishers' Meadow, it supplied hay, thatch and timber to the hospital, as well as providing additional grazing for cattle and sheep before they were slaughtered there.[82] Further to the south, near the Benedictine nunnery at Carrow, lay two other riparian meadows, described in the hospital accounts as 'Gloton' and 'Paradyse'. Both had been recovered at law in the 1280s from Agnes and John Herman, in what may have been a collusive suit intended to circumvent the Statute of Mortmain. References to a dispute over the land which they had already granted to St Giles's along Holme Street suggest, however, that some pious benefactors may have required a sharp reminder of their continuing obligations to the sick poor.[83]

The Hermans were also prevailed upon to donate property to the north of Norwich, just outside St Augustine's gate. Early on in his mastership, Hamon de Calthorpe had shrewdly

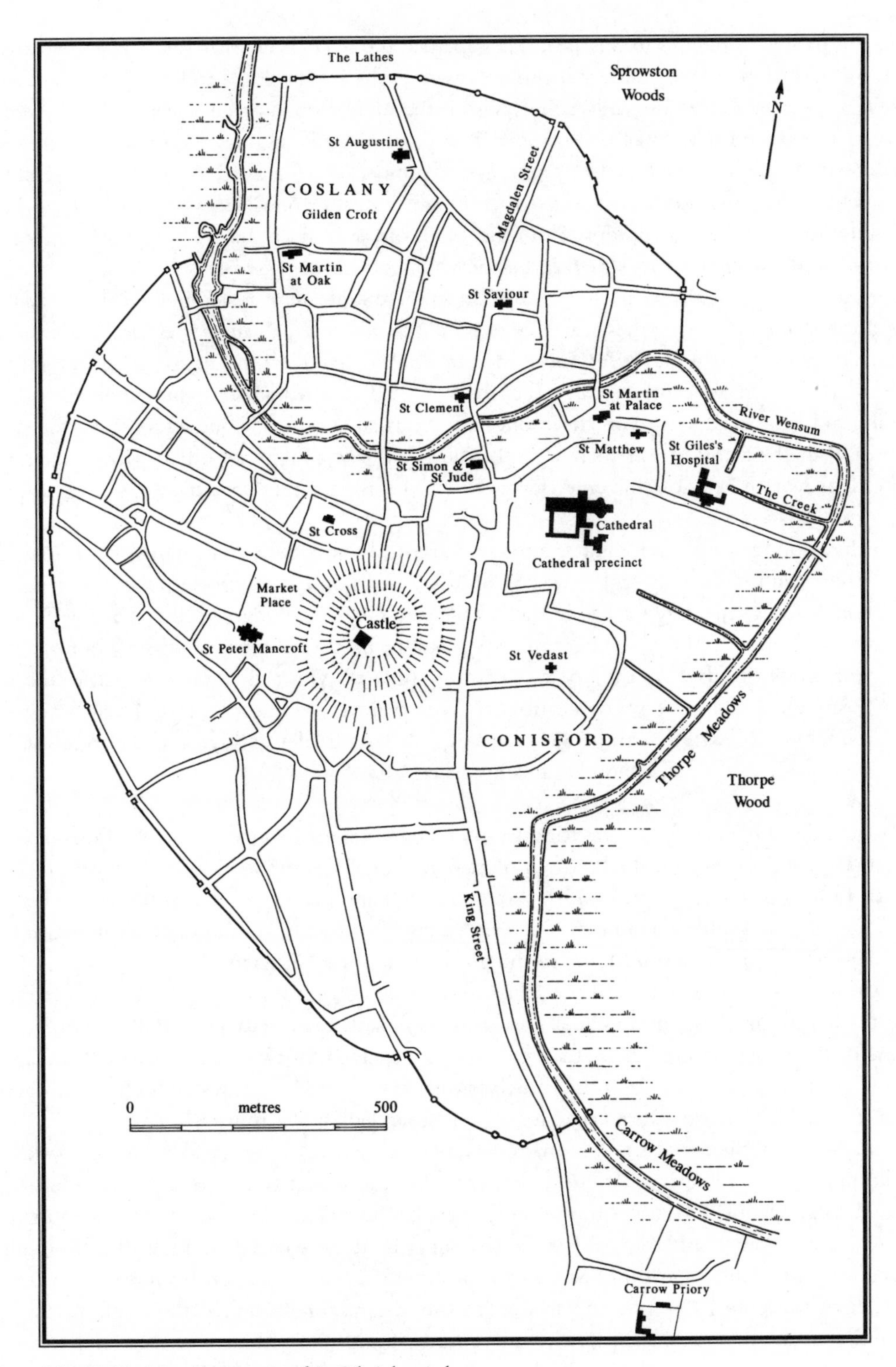

Map V: The Norwich properties of St Giles's hospital.

begun to amass holdings in this area. They formed the nucleus of what was later to become 'le Lathes', another hospital farm complete with granaries, stables, a mill, fold courses and several plots of arable. Just within the walls, in the undeveloped green space of the Coslany district, a second substantial endowment, known as Gildencroft, was acquired by Hamon's successor in about 1284.[84] With no shortage of prospective tenants from among the wealthy merchant elite, the hospital managed to maintain a steady annual income of about £5 by leasing some of these acquisitions from the 1330s onwards, if not before. The profits helped to subsidise a second small carting business which was managed for the hospital by its serjeant of the ploughs. During the early fifteenth century, sums of around £7 a year were regularly raised by hiring these carts, horses and ploughs to local landowners and tradesmen on a daily basis when they were not needed by the hospital. Kept in English in an extremely rough hand, the serjeant's weekly journal for 1428–9 records all the work undertaken by him and his men, along with the money they earned as private contractors. Save for the loan of the best horse to the master so that he could ride along with other civic dignitaries in the mayor's procession, the entry for 23 to 29 May is fairly representative:

> The Munday we leddyn sand and marle al day to here renteris [tenements] in Holme Strete. On the Tuesday xijd in ledyng of sonde and ston aforn non – no more at aftur non by cause the mayster hadde the hors to the meyres rydyng. On the Wedenysday we leddyn marle al day to the masunnys [masons] in Holme Strete. On the Thursday, Corpus Christi day. On the Fryday to Cossey [Costessey] for xij combe of malt to the hospytal; the same day xij combe of malt from the same place to Frostys the broughster [brewster]. On the Saterday xvd in ledyng of cley and lyme aforn none. At after none, j lod of cley and j lod of sond price viijd.[85]

Being reluctant to continue investing in stock and equipment once the retreat from direct management had begun, the brethren of St Giles's finally abandoned this enterprise in the late 1430s.[86] An account for 1435–6 refers to bonds and indentures drawn up for the lease of the carts and other equipment 'for term of years' to two of the hospital's Holme Street tenants (a mason and a smith), but nothing is known of the terms involved.[87] Carters at the nearby hospital of St Paul, who had previously earned upwards of £13 a year for the cathedral monks, had, meanwhile, sub-contracted with their erstwhile employers for the use of their wagons and beasts at a fixed annual rate. Henceforward they provided haulage on a commercial basis for other institutions, including St Giles's, which no longer maintained the infrastructure necessary for full-scale demesne farming.[88]

Although Suffield and the first masters were constrained by the vagaries of the market, the policy of building up a ring of properties on the outskirts of Norwich was pursued with some vigour. Five miles to the south-west of the city lay the two adjacent manors of Hethel and East Carleton, held in fee by the Bigod earls of Norfolk. Bishop Suffield acquired an estate there from Earl Roger, and in 1252 settled it upon his hospital 'for the relief of the poor'. Over the next twenty years the brethren secured their title to these holdings and augmented them with piecemeal acquisitions.[89] Net revenues paid to the receiver general fluctuated considerably, from about £4 in the 1270s to a few shillings in the 1320s, but, once again, the real value of these properties lay in the amount of brushwood and faggots they produced.[90] Comparatively speaking, the hospital's land in Hethel and Carleton made only a modest contribution to its coffers. Yet great vigilance was none the less exercised in the matter of leasing. Before permitting the son and heir of the previous farmer to renew his contract for another five years, in 1445–6, Hugh Acton, the then master, took securities for the settlement of outstanding arrears of £5, and recorded all the payments due in a separate account. A sustained effort was made at this time to keep track of the small sums owed by the tenants of the more scattered properties (such as those as Horstead, Catton and Sprowston) which did not come under the direct supervision of a bailiff or reeve and were thus easily forgotten.[91]

Seething, the next of Walter Suffield's appropriations, was situated about nine miles to the south-east of Norwich on heavier clay soil, which meant that wheat, as well as barley, could be grown as a staple crop. In 1311, sales of produce raised no less than £24, and in 1389 tithes alone comprised 120 quarters of barley, 20 of wheat and 23 of oats. The advowson had been acquired in two parts: the first from Norwich cathedral priory, whose almoner claimed an annual rent of £7 for the support of the poor, and the second from the neighbouring house of Premonstratensian canons at Langley. Roger Bigod, earl of Norfolk, and the previous owners, the de Seethings, duly confirmed the hospital in possession of a living which Bishop Suffield specifically reserved, in 1253, for the support of his annual obit in the hospital church and the distribution of food and drink to 100 paupers on the anniversary of his death.[92] In light of the complaint, frequently voiced, that hospitals failed to implement their benefactors' wishes, it is worth noting that the brethren scrupulously observed these conditions at a cost of about 20*s* a year until 1535, if not later, and that the priory collected its rent until alternative arrangements took effect in the mid-fifteenth century.[93] A few other endowments were settled upon St Giles's in this area during its early years, most notably a gift made in perpetuity by the widowed Mary de Attleburgh, in 1309, in return for a corrody of board and lodging for life, as a hospital sister.[94] As we shall see, such arrangements were often deployed to raise money, and had distinct pecuniary advantages over the proffer of a single lump sum, which might run out before the death of the corrodian. But it proved impossible to reverse the pattern of diminishing yields and falling rents which made the transition to direct management inexorable. At some point between 1441 and 1460, the tithes, herbage and demesnes at Seething were leased to the first of a succession of farmers, together yielding the receiver general a consistent net annual profit of about £10 until the Dissolution. Perhaps since this represented such a marked decline from the previous century, the hospital proved a strict landlord. In 1465, for example, prompt action was taken against John Osberne, the current farmer, who was summoned to appear in the Court of Arches and then replaced, presumably because he had been unacceptably slow to settle his account.[95]

During the fourteenth century, receipts from Seething were sometimes conflated with those from Hardley, which lay about four miles to the north-east, on the marshland between the rivers Chet and Yare. Twice, in 1256 and 1268, Hamon de Calthorpe, the first master of St Giles's, took the precaution of securing his title to the advowson and one acre of land there by fines sued out in the Court of Common Pleas at Westminster.[96]

Thanks to the generosity of local landowners, it soon proved possible to build up a sizeable demesne and avoid the squabbles with disgruntled incumbents which occurred in other hospital livings. In 1335, for example, the vicar was granted a generous amount of arable for life, along with an allocation of seed corn at appropriate times of the year. An annual rent of 6 quarters of barley was reserved for the support of the local poor, the upkeep of the church tower and, significantly, as a supplementary stipend for another of the hospital's many vicars. The next incumbent actually made over a tenement in Hardley to the hospital, in return for membership of its burgeoning spiritual fraternity.[97] Proximity to the Yare meant that grain could easily be transported up river to Norwich, or, as was more often the case, seawards to Yarmouth and other local markets. But Hardley proved no exception to the general trend. Although the hospital brethren could rely on substantial deliveries of up to £20 a year in cash from the sale of produce and tithes during the early fourteenth century, it proved impossible to sustain such a high level of profitability. Significantly, too, the flock of between 100 and 500 sheep, recorded in stock accounts for the early 1330s, appears to have been run down, and is not mentioned after 1335, perhaps because the fold courses at Cringleford were so much more convenient for supplying the precinct. During the fifteenth century the same familiar pattern of declining revenues emerges: rents from the demesnes remained fairly steady at around 30*s*, but sales of tithes never rose above £11 and eventually slipped to about half this sum.[98]

The last of the six appropriations made by Bishop Suffield lay in Broadland, in the rich alluvial valley of the River Bure. The living of St Mary's, South Walsham, was potentially one of the hospital's most lucrative holdings [see Plate 25]. Because the rectory lay some distance from Norwich, produce was, once again, generally sold in nearby market towns, with the result that substantial cash sums were paid direct to the receiver general. During the early fourteenth century he sometimes collected as much as £24 a year, although for reasons described below revenues could fluctuate unpredictably and sometimes fell as low as a few shillings. Barley and malt sales were the most variable but also the most important, alone raising over £17 in 1398–9, and thus contributing over 80 per cent of net profits from this part of the estates. Occasionally, as in 1408–9 and 1411–12, when prices were low and the local market seemed to be over-supplied, consignments of malt (42 quarters and 38 quarters respectively) were sent to the hospital instead. But for most of the fifteenth century the rectory and tithes were farmed either separately or together by grain merchants or local *rentiers*. Fresh contracts were initially negotiated every year for sums ranging from £14 to £19 according to the state of the market. Because of the continuing slump in barley prices, the master failed to attract a buyer in the early 1460s, and revenues fell dramatically. A new farmer (the vicar) was found in 1467, but between then and the Dissolution the brethren had to rest content with rents of just £12 a year. Spared all but the most basic running costs, they contrived to keep outgoings at a minimum; yet, even so, net annual payments to the receiver general had, as elsewhere, fallen by more than half since the beginning of the century.[99]

Archdeacon William Suffield had been involved in the acquisition of St Mary's, which he confirmed to the hospital on the death of his brother, the bishop, in 1257. The looming presence directly across the Bure of St Benet's abbey, one of the most powerful religious houses in medieval Norfolk, proved oppressive, in a real as well as a metaphorical sense. Violent disputes over grazing rights on the marshes and access to turbaries, reed beds and other valuable local resources often broke out between Broadland farmers, and constant vigilance was called for in the proximity of such a predatory neighbour. It not only seemed expedient to secure Bishop Skerning's exemplification of the original appropriation, but also to have it ratified, in 1269, at common law.[100] The Suffield family had previously enjoyed a far happier relationship with St Benet's abbey, acquiring the advowsons of St Peter's church, Repps, and the neighbouring free chapel at Bastwick from the monks in the late twelfth century. In 1238 Walter (the future bishop) and his elder brother, Sir Roger, went to law against a neighbouring landowner to strengthen their title. Thoughts of a charitable foundation may already have been forming in their minds: ten years later their sibling, William, a safe pair of hands, was presented to the two livings.[101] These stood a couple of miles to the north-east of the abbey on some of the most fertile and densely populated land in Norfolk. Barley grew in abundance; the marshland along the banks of the River Thurne supported flocks of sheep and herds of cattle; and the peaty fens provided almost inexhaustible quantities of fuel and building materials.[102]

Since it was acquired as early as 1247, William's reversionary title to additional property in this area may have been intended by Bishop Walter Suffield to supplement a seventh major endowment upon St Giles's, besides the six listed in his two foundation charters, but he died before the arrangements could be completed. So it was his successor, Bishop Walton, who issued an *inspeximus* in 1261 confirming the appropriation to St Giles's of the advowsons of Repps and Bastwick upon the death or resignation of the then incumbent. The prior of Norwich gave his approval three years later. An undated entry in the hospital cartulary records that the two livings and other holdings in Repps came as a personal gift from Archdeacon Suffield, made in return for burial and perpetual commemoration in the new hospital.[103] Other donations followed, most notably a release of their own title to the estate by Hugh and Agnes Caly, relatives of the founder, who likewise sought reception into the spiritual community.[104] The acquisition of Repps and Bastwick gave a valuable boost to cash profits, since during the early fourteenth century between one quarter and sometimes even a half of the receiver general's net receipts from the hospital's country estates came from this part of Broadland. Occasionally the proportion was even higher. The loss of local accounts before 1437 makes it impossible to tell exactly how the unusually large sums of £42 and £51 were raised in 1320–1 and 1322–3, respectively: even during less productive years clear profits could exceed £25. But this encouraging state of affairs was not destined to last. In 1332 net receipts slumped to a mere 20*s*, with disastrous consequences for St Giles's.[105] The year 1331 had been one of dearth for barley growers, but dramatic fluctuations in profitability reflected other, long-term problems inherent in an area vulnerable to heavy flooding. During the fifteenth and early sixteenth centuries payments to the receiver general never exceeded £9, and were often far lower. Such fertile conditions had been purchased at a heavy price.[106]

CRISIS AND CONSOLIDATION

Notwithstanding the generosity of its early patrons, by the third decade of the fourteenth century St Giles's lacked the financial resources to withstand the combined onslaught of climatic change, economic dislocation and a concomitant rise in the demand for poor relief. Four receiver general's accounts from the famine years of 1315–22 [Table A] reveal that net annual income from the hospital's estates, including about £18 a year from property and rents in Norwich, then fluctuated between £75 and £105, largely because the contribution from Repps and Bastwick could vary so much. Casual revenues, which comprised profits from the sale of surplus produce, payments for masses, obits and lights in the hospital church and a variety of legal dues, were naturally unpredictable, although they netted a minimum of £20 throughout the fourteenth century. Only during the 1320s are the brethren known to have raised appreciable sums by selling corrodies thus greatly augmenting their casual receipts. This practice is discussed at greater length in Chapter VI, but it is worth noting here that one corrody alone fetched £40 in 1321–2, and two others slightly more in 1326–7. Since several accounts for the period are either badly damaged or missing, we may reasonably assume that similar transactions were recorded in other years.[107] The money was badly needed. Even allowing for the fact that grain rarely had to be bought in significant quantities, food and the cost of preparing it still constituted by far the largest item of expenditure. This rose from £56 in 1318–19 to £82 in 1321–2, as stock prices escalated because of murrain, and greater demands were made upon the hospital's charity.[108] Pensions to other religious houses, which the brethren considered a serious drain on resources, came to £20 a year, and were thus quite onerous, while the stipends of priests and conducts not paid directly from the appropriated livings consumed a further £10 or so. Repairs, the cost of additional fuel supplies and other incidental expenses also ate into the budget, leaving the receiver general with an annual deficit which, by 1323, stood at £26 and threatened to mount far higher.

In order to escape this dilemma, the hospital had resort to a stratagem traditionally adopted by most beleaguered religious houses: that of augmenting its holdings. One solution, adopted with increasing frequency as the Middle Ages progressed, was to offer commemorative and intercessionary prayers and masses in return for specific endowments. In November 1318, for example, while the country still suffered the depredations of famine, John Cursyn of Norwich secured a royal licence permitting him to alienate 100 acres of arable and pasture in Earlham (just outside the city) to the brethren for the support of a chantry.[109] Although welcome, such a modest acquisition had little impact upon the overall budget; and, in February 1321, the hospital obtained permission from Edward II to purchase additional land to the value of £10 a year. During this period of financial and economic crisis, the king was as happy to sell licences as anxious communities were to bid for them. A loan of £13 was duly raised in 1321, and, in the same year, Henry le Speller offered £40 for one of the above-mentioned corrodies specifically so that St Giles's could buy more property. Almost all of this money was spent at once: £10 went on holdings at Reedham (on the Yare near Hardley) and £23 on unspecified 'land and marsh' acquired from Matthew Palmer. But the brethren did not seek approval for these individual transactions for another decade, possibly because the original letters patent provided a

Year	1315–16	1318–19	1319–20	1320–1	1321–2	1322–3	1326–7	1327–8	1330–1	1332–3
Estates	75	80	84	105*	81	?	50	68	89	84
Casual	53	21	21	23	72	?	77	29	47	20
Loans/gifts	0	14	10	0	13	?	0	17	27	0
TOTAL CHARGE	128	115	115	128	166	96	127	114	163	104
Overspent last year	?	4	7	14	8	13	40	5	?	?
Current expenses	?	107	110	121	171	109	92	125	137+	?
Loans repaid	?	11	13	1	0	0	0	0	13	?
TOTAL DISCHARGE	138	122	130	136	179	122	132	130	?	280
Overall balance	-10	-7	-14	-8	-13	-26	-5	-16	?	-176
This year's balance	?	-3	-8	6	-5	-13	35	-11	?	?

Year	1333–4	1334–5	1335–6	1336–7	*c.* 1338	1341–2	*c.* 1372–3	1374–5	1396–7
Estates	?	97	83	?	?	?	140	149	?
Casual	?	?	72	?	?	?	32	32	?
Loans/gifts	66	50+	33	74	?	60	0	0	28
TOTAL CHARGE	?	211	188	131	156	149	172	181	143
Overspent last year	176	132	76	89	?	0	5	6	16
Current expenses	?	155	201	111	?	96	163	175	164
Loans repaid	?	0	0	7	44	56	0	0	0
TOTAL DISCHARGE	?	287	277	207	201	152	168	181	180
Overall Balance	-132	-76	-89	-76	-45	-3	3	0	-37
This Year's Balance	?	56	-13	13	?	-3	9	6	-21

Table A: The Finances of St Giles's Hospital 1315–1397 (NRO, NCR, 24A, Great Hospital accounts, 1306–1398)

All sums are rounded up or down to the nearest pound sterling. Accounts run from Michaelmas to Michaelmas [29 September], except for 1396–7, which runs February–January

* The totals in this account are incorrect: these figures offer a readjustment.

'safety net' or blanket insurance against prosecution.[110] By then other deals had been struck. In June 1331, Edward III formally sanctioned the acquisition of property worth 17*s* 4*d* a year in Norwich and eight Norfolk villages. Some of the new purchases (in Hardley, Repps, Seething, Cringleford and Hethel) consolidated existing estates, but the hospital also extended its interests to Limpenhow (north-east of Hardley) and Wickmere (near Calthorpe). Marshes in Reedham and Limpenhow produced no more than 10*s* annual rent in the sixteenth century, but proved a useful source of thatching material, marsh hay, alder wood and grazing for sheep and cattle. Further additions to the value of 20*s* were authorised in March 1334, this time in Seething, Repps, Cringleford and Norwich, as well as Mundham and the neighbouring parishes of Thwaite and Sisland (which lay to the west of Seething).[111] Here again, the aim was to create compact units of land, which either augmented existing demesnes or could be leased *en bloc* to tenants. Benefactors, such as Geoffrey and Maud de Salisbury, who sought perpetual commemoration in the hospital church in 1331, donated sums of money – in this case over £5 – so that the brethren themselves could make the most suitable and advantageous purchases.[112]

Piecemeal additions were, however, only a partial solution. Appropriation offered an even more effective and immediate answer to pressing economic problems, not least because the necessary licences could be secured with relative ease from the house's episcopal patrons. But first the hospital had to obtain the advowson of a living or livings within convenient distance of its existing property; and this, in turn, involved the not inconsiderable expense of suing out further letters patent at Westminster. The process from acquisition to appropriation was lengthy, expensive and bureaucratic. In October 1331, Thomas de Preston, rector of Colby, 'donated' a sum of £100 for the purchase by St Giles's of the advowson of St Peter's church in Mundham, which was to fund another chantry in the hospital. The receiver general had, however, already handed over £69 for the advowson and £6 to buy out the rector's interest in the previous year, the money being raised partly by loans, including a widow's mite of £4 from the hospital sisters and an earlier advance of at least £14 (then repaid) from Preston himself.[113] The fluid state of the local land market at this time made it easy for institutions such as St Giles's to invest in plots near their own estates, and the brethren took full advantage of a situation which, in lean years at least, favoured buyers.[114] Their outlay on property was, indeed, so high as to suggest that they ignored the financial restrictions stipulated in Edward II's letters patent.

No less than £54 was also spent in 1330–1 on 'debts and expenses over Rollesby', most of this sum (£47) being assigned to the rector, John Skyryng, who later lodged in the hospital. A receiver general's roll for 1341 records an intriguing, but now illegible, payment of revenues from the manor, which lay just to the east of Repps. Expansion in this direction would clearly have been administratively convenient, even though it had not yet been approved by either of the royal licences. In 1332 further expenditure on unspecified 'land and marshes of the bishop' came to £89, pushing annual disbursements up to £280, over twice the customary level. One year later a damaged and partly indecipherable account records that the deficit of £176 created by these unprecedented expenses had been somewhat reduced to £132, but only through the expedient of borrowing another £66. In all, between 1321 and 1342 the brethren raised (and contributed personally to) loans well in excess of £380 and spent a bare minimum of £257 on augmenting their estates.[115] They were thus disposing of capital sums worth two years or more of the hospital's entire net income. Since the cost of buying land was then generally calculated at a commercial rate of about ten times clear annual profits, this would suggest an investment aimed to increase revenues from property by about £25: that is by just over one-quarter, which was approximately the size of the discrepancy between income and expenditure noted above.

Although beset by pitfalls, this strategy seems to have paid off. By the early 1340s the backlog of debt had been completely cleared, and by the 1370s the financial prognosis seemed correspondingly brighter [Table A]. In this instance there is no evidence to support Sandra Raban's belief that religious houses rarely acquired property to the full value specified in royal licences because of inflated assessments and hidden fines imposed by the Crown. On the contrary, St Giles's appears to have spent well beyond the limits imposed.[116] The brethren were certainly able to raise quite large sums of capital, and clearly inspired confidence. Whether or not all the loans were fully repaid – or whether creditors even expected to be reimbursed – remains a debatable point. Perhaps the promise of intercessionary prayers was recompense enough; donors were well aware that, by helping the hospital to continue its pious works, they were storing up treasure in paradise. There was far less cause for optimism at the hospital of the Holy Spirit, Sandon, which, like St Giles's, had secured a royal licence in 1331 for the acquisition of property worth £10, only to sink further into irreversible debt and decay.[117]

Meanwhile, concern lest the government might suspect them of fraud led the 'poor chaplains' of St Giles's to petition Parliament in 1334 for its support with regard to the appropriation of Mundham St Peter. Their bill stressed the cost of maintaining *thirteen* priests and 'many poor', and confirmed that, since the living was worth no more than £7 6*s* 8*d* a year, St Giles's would still not be in breach of its original letters patent. Royal assent was duly given.[118] The way was now clear for Bishop Ayermine to approach Edward III on the brethren's behalf for formal permission to acquire and appropriate St Peter's. The living was then finally released by the trustees who had previously occupied it on behalf of the hospital, and a fine of £5 paid at Westminster. As was so often the case, the king's letters and the subsequent episcopal licence simply acknowledged a *fait accompli*. Although Ayermine had already by then established precise conditions of employment for the new vicar, it was not until 1340 that his successor, Bishop Beck, officially authorised the appropriation. From start to finish the process had taken a decade.[119]

As the next parish to Seething, St Peter's constituted a convenient but not especially lucrative addition. Together, the two livings produced £31 net in 1376, St Peter's alone turning a profit of about £5 a year at the close of the century, over and above modest, but regular, deliveries of wheat, peas, oats and barley made to the precinct.[120] Further acquisitions were clearly necessary if the manifold problems described in Beck's licence were to be solved. This document paints a gloomy picture of flooding, dilapidation and oppression by powerful neighbours, which rendered the hospital even less able to cope with a growing influx of paupers clamouring for relief.[121] The phraseology is repeated, almost *verbatim*, in petitions addressed to the papacy at this time by the monks of St Benet Holme and the Premonstratensian canons of Langley (near Hardley, on the river Yare).[122]

Both communities had also suffered from the storms and floods which caused widespread devastation on both sides of the North Sea between 1250 and 1348. And both found it impossible to succour those who had been made destitute as a result. John of Oxnead, a monk at St Benet's, recorded a catalogue of disasters, dominated by the great inundations of 1287–8, when hundreds of people had been killed, houses and crops throughout Broadland had been destroyed and the abbey outbuildings had been accessible only by boat. At Hickling priory, not far from Bastwick, the great altar had been completely submerged at least a foot below the flood, and horses had been led to safety in an upper dormitory.[123]

Although the barley growers of East Anglia were, as a whole, less vulnerable to the damper and cooler conditions which followed a general deterioration in the climate at this time (and, in any event, farmed on higher ground above the flood-plain), owners of turbaries lost a valuable resource once the pits became waterlogged. References to 'brodingge' (the creation of broads or lakes) as early as 1315 on the marshes belonging to South Walsham suggest that the problem of extraction, made worse once the diggers began to charge a competitive rate for their labour, had already become acute. By 1379 the monks of St Benet's could not even exploit their reed beds because of rising water levels.[124] It is by no means certain when the hospital acquired its first properties at Salhouse and Wroxham on the river Bure, but some were probably among the 'land and marshes of the bishop' noted above. By 1385, they comprised well over 50 acres of arable and marshland, the latter being perhaps already partially submerged, and thus of declining value.[125]

That Bishop Ayermine recognised the gravity of the situation is evident from a second appropriation initiated by him in 1334. While Parliament was still sitting, in September that year, he approached the Crown for permission to alienate to St Giles's the advowson of Thurlton parish church, which lay across the Chet, to the south-east of Hardley. He had recently acquired the living, hitherto shared by two local families, in order to fund a chantry of three priests in the episcopal palace at Norwich. This he expected to cost £12 a year in salaries, leaving any surplus revenues and agricultural produce for use by the hospital, which could also appoint the vicar.[126] The arrangement worked well enough at first: in 1342, for example, the receiver general netted almost £9 in clear profits, over and above any payments made to the hospital in kind. But, by 1369, three outbreaks of plague in the vicinity had caused wholesale depopulation, accompanied by an equally dramatic fall in rents and tithes. Accepting that St Giles's now supported much of the cost of Ayermine's chantry, Bishop Percy then agreed to economise by removing one priest and cutting the wage bill. Once again, the hospital benefited for a while, but, although net receipts from Thurlton were as high as £13 a year in the 1370s, it proved impossible to sustain such good returns. By 1437 the cost of supporting one chantry priest in Norwich, paying a parochial chaplain and repairing the rectory was too much for the diminishing resources to bear. Four years later the hospital had to find no less than £13 for the construction of a new chancel, about half this sum being paid to the master carpenter, John Durant, for his labour. Faced, in any event, with a persistent deficit of between £6 and £8 a year, the master of St Giles's had no choice but to surrender the living to Bishop Lyhart, who, in 1449, acknowledged that his predecessor's act of generosity had compounded rather than alleviated the hospital's financial difficulties.[127]

The history of Thurlton provides a good illustration of the problems encountered by any religious house which hoped to attract endowments in return for spiritual services. From the institutional point of view, a long-term commitment to support a chantry could prove counter-productive, resulting in unwelcome financial liabilities, especially when property values were sinking. The effects of plague in Norwich and its hinterland have already been discussed in Chapter I, but it is worth emphasising that, as rental income and profits from demesnes fell, so also tithes, upon which St Giles's depended for a substantial part of its income from appropriated livings, were seriously depleted. Endowments, such as those made by Suffield himself, which had once generated quite handsome profits became progressively less viable. Not surprisingly, the search for affluent patrons whose sense of impending mortality had been sharpened by pestilence assumed an added intensity, and the brethren energetically exploited their liturgical resources. The hospital's earlier connections with her family, along with its reputation for financial probity and increasingly elaborate ritual, attracted Mary de Brotherton, the widowed countess of Norfolk, who obtained permission from Edward III, in July 1351, to found a perpetual chantry there. Her advowson of St Laurence's church in South Walsham was to be appropriated to the hospital, thus putting it in possession of both livings in the Broadland township. Opposition from Edward and Alice Montacute, who successfully challenged the brethren's title in the following September, sabotaged all these costly plans, which came to nothing.[128] Fortunately for the hospital, this temporary reversal occurred at a time when long-term financial prospects seemed about to improve. Thanks, in part, to acquisitions made in the 1330s and 1340s, the receiver general's net annual receipts rose as high as £181 in the early 1370s, and should have stayed at this level had it not been for the onset of another recession.

A commission of inquiry set up to examine the finances of St Leonard's hospital, York, in 1375, reported a shortfall of £143 between income and expenditure, debts of £278 and a lack of resources for the completion of essential repairs. Of especial significance is the complaint that stock and grain production had fallen by 50 per cent, necessitating increased expenditure in local markets.[129] The cumulative effect of the decline already observed on individual rectories and manors across St Giles's estates was just as serious. By the late fourteenth century, as net annual receipts fell by over £40 and payments in kind decreased at a similar rate, it seemed as if the brethren were swimming hard against the tide. How could they stay afloat? Being conditioned to regard property as an unsinkable life-raft they again gave thought to expansion. Dated 1381 and 1392, two new royal licences allowed further acquisitions to the value of 53*s* 10*d* in Calthorpe, Hardley, Loddon, Mundham, Norwich, Repps and Sisland, apparently because the previous accessions had proved less profitable than they at first appeared.[130] Given the scale of the problem, these new properties made little appreciable difference. Although it is dangerous to generalise on the basis of single accounts, which may be unrepresentative, comparisons are at least suggestive. At the end of the century, in 1396–7, the receiver general's income from property and casual receipts combined stood at just £115, by which date several of the hospital's appropriated livings were selling off a far higher proportion of their tithes to local markets, and should thus have been much more productive in cash terms [Table A]. At about £16 a year, overspending once again threatened stability, even though outgoings had been cut to the bare minimum. The one exception was building, for this year saw the completion of a new bell-tower and the construction of more properties for leasing in Norwich. In this way the brethren hoped to tap other sources of income: they were speculating to accumulate.[131]

FRIENDS IN HIGH PLACES

A different and potentially more enterprising solution to this worsening financial predicament was proposed by Archdeacon John Derlyngton, sometime master of the hospital and intimate of Bishop Despenser, who recognised that St Giles's would have to employ more radical measures to avoid a lingering and painful decline. His vision was of a grand collegiate foundation, where liturgy and the ritual of the Mass would take pride of place in majestic surroundings. He almost certainly masterminded and helped fund the rebuilding of the nave and infirmary and the construction of a new chancel (described in the next chapter); he donated almost £50 during his lifetime for the erection of the great stone-faced bell-tower; and in his will he made substantial provision for a chantry in the refurbished church. In 1410 the late archdeacon's executors paid heavily for royal letters patent sanctioning the appropriation to St Giles's of the parish church of Wickmere and the alienation to the hospital of the manor of Cringleford (sometimes known as Berford's).[132] The manor had recently been released to them by a local landowner named Simon Sampson and an influential group of feoffees, but despite the involvement of such distinguished figures as Derlyngton's old friend, the Norwich alderman William Setman, the question of ownership still proved contentious. As late as 1430 John Sampson of Harkstead in Suffolk pledged unusually heavy securities of £666 to the hospital that he would relinquish whatever claims he might have inherited. Had the archdeacon himself purchased the manor for St Giles's? Or was he merely anxious to strengthen a potentially uncertain title to a recent, perhaps legally questionable, acquisition, while also providing for the good of his own immortal soul? It was not unusual for senior clergy to use the estates of religious houses in this way, in an arrangement devised for the benefit of both parties, the one spiritual the other temporal. In this instance, however, it looks as if Derlyngton, a long-standing patron of the hospital, had invested yet more money from his own coffers for its long-term support. But once again not everything ran smoothly. As had happened in 1351, when steps had been taken to appropriate another living at South Walsham, the issue of a royal licence was no guarantee that all the property described in it would actually change hands. In the event, Derlyngton's plans for the rectory at Wickmere were frustrated, and the brethren had to rest content with their acquisitions at Cringleford.[133]

Profits from the new manor helped to cushion the fall in revenues described above, the demesnes initially being managed directly by St Giles's. The area under cultivation in Cringleford increased from 75 acres (1395) to 190 (1414); and the flock was gradually built up again, already numbering some 182 sheep and lambs in 1414 and rising to 450 or more over the next fourteen years. The manor was subsequently farmed out at a rent which, in 1450, stood at just £10 a year. The lease then negotiated for a term of five years with a local husbandman shows that the hospital gave meticulous attention to detail, stipulating exactly what crops were to be grown, drawing up a detailed inventory of seed corn, beasts and implements, and reserving sizeable amounts of land for pasturing 300 of its sheep.[134] Rents later fell to £8, although the acquisition of the neighbouring manor of Heylesdons more than offset this decline. Sold to St Giles's by the executors of Robert Spenser (master 1412–30), who had instructed them to ask for no more than £20 purchase price, this property was firmly secured thirty years later, after a long and bitter legal battle, described in Chapter V.[135] By the 1470s, the two Cringleford manors, along with the sale of tithes from the rectory and the profits of the hospital's flock, netted the receiver general an average of about £16 a year, and maintained their value up to the late 1520s.

The assistance of powerful patrons made it easier for comparatively small institutions, such as St Giles's, to acquire property. They smoothed the way through a tangle of bureaucracy at Westminster, offered protection at law, helped to raise money, and brought subtle pressure to bear on vendors whose mercenary instincts might otherwise have overwhelmed their charitable impulses. The 'cruell and vengible' Norfolk knight, Sir John Fastolf, was notoriously unsentimental in this regard. Being, as his servants claimed, 'for the most parte withoute pite and mercy', he proposed to drive a hard bargain with the hospital over the sale of the manor of Mundham and advowson of the parish church of St Ethelbert.[136] The involvement of Bishop Lyhart, a royal favourite, and his chancellor, John Selot (who later became master of St Giles's), in the negotiations clearly expedited matters. The letter which Fastolf wrote in 1450 to the incumbent of his living at Castle Combe, in Wiltshire, suggests that he held the hospital in some regard, and was thus, perhaps, more open to persuasion:

> Syr parson, wolle ye wete that the maister of seint Gylys wyth my lord Norwych Chauncellor hath be wyth me for the purchase of Mundham maner wyth appurtenaunce yn Cyselond [Sisland]; and so I am accorded, and hafe promysed hym to make astate to such as he wolle name, [he] payeng me iiC marc [£133 6*s* 8*d*] there as he and I shall accord. And I shall do scende the new evidens home to yew, in haste, how ye shall be demened. Sende me word whethyr I hafe made a gode bargeyn. I was not avysed to sylle it, *except it goth to a goode use*: for it clere gode [makes a profit] and ys wyth avouson. And he wold I shuld hafe do almesse on hem and relessed hem som money. But ye may sey hym the untroth of the pryor of Hykelyng [Hickling] drawyth awey my devocion in such causes . . .[137]

Because the new manor and advowson were administered together with the appropriated rectory of Mundham St Peter, which had proved something of a financial disappointment, it is hard to tell exactly how much this purchase was really worth. Since St Peter's showed a clear profit of only £5 a year in the 1370s, and the receiver general could usually expect to raise approximately £15 from all the Mundham properties in the late fifteenth and early sixteenth centuries, it looks as if Sir John asked just over twelve times the net value of the estate, which would then have seemed a fair price. On top of the money paid by the hospital – or its well-wishers – for St Ethelbert's, came an additional sum of £31 demanded by the Crown in January 1451 for permission to acquire unspecified holdings to the value of £20 a year. This licence allowed scope for further accessions, besides those in Mundham, and probably owed a good deal to Lyhart's influence over the impressionable King Henry, for whose soul the brethren gratefully undertook to pray. The bishop was by then acting as a trustee of the new acquisitions, which remained in the hands of a powerful group of local landowners until 1478.[138] Friction between the two parishes of St Peter and St Ethelbert had previously been a regular feature of life in Mundham. To combine both under a single ecclesiastical patron made for social as well as administrative harmony. It also eased financial pressures.

Given what we know about the extensive rebuilding programme then in progress at St Giles's, the brethren's complaints of destitution cannot be taken too literally. Having itemised their financially burdensome works of charity – including the upkeep of eight chaplains – they claimed to be

> so poorly endowed in tithes, oblations and income from churches, which are daily declining, that there is not enough to support all these charges, and undertake this work, and pay the great sums in annual rent, portions and pensions demanded of the house, besides [funding] the other responsibilities incumbent upon it, *especially the divine service, which must be celebrated daily in the hospital church.*[139]

Yet, allowing for a degree of special pleading, the ongoing transition from direct farming to a *rentier* economy was far from painless. It certainly strained the hospital's already declining capacity for poor relief, increasing the brethren's dependence upon outside support, while greatly restricting their ability to help others. The one surviving annual valuation (*valor*) of rectories and manors compiled by the receiver general dates from this period (1441–2), and records an outlay of at least £38 on grain which now had to be bought from local markets, in order to feed all the house's dependents. Since current receipts then stood at £105, this represented over one third of a considerably reduced net income.[140]

The budget was further stretched by the cost of providing an appropriate setting for the increasingly elaborate liturgical observances without which it was impossible to attract affluent patrons. Whether or not the irascible but shrewd Sir John Fastolf had in mind acts of spiritual or temporal charity when he wrote of 'the good use' to which his estates in Mundham would be put, he clearly believed that St Giles's had much to offer. So, too, did John Selot, who vigorously defended its territorial interests in Cringleford during his mastership, and also secured for it an additional 288 acres of land and rents worth over £4 in Hethel and Carleton. Having entrusted this property to feoffees from 1455 onwards, Selot used it, along with the manor of Heylesdon's in Cringleford and certain tenements in Norwich, to endow a personal obit for eighty years at the hospital, thus side-stepping the legislation with regard to alienations in perpetuity.[141] Although the land in Hethel and Carleton was almost certainly managed as a single unit along with the estate which the hospital had owned there since the thirteenth century, it rarely showed a clear profit. Once the cost of the obit had been met, there was seldom much left; and, as Hugh Acton had found in the 1440s, the accumulation of unpaid arrears (running at £28 in 1516–17) posed a constant problem. Yet the estate did provide the salary of a conduct or chaplain, and in this respect – along with its rich supply of timber – proved a worthwhile acquisition.[142]

Rather more valuable was the advowson of the rectory of Coltishall, which John Selot, a figure of considerable foresight as well as authority, acquired for the specific purpose of funding the master's annual stipend of £4, thus relieving the receiver general of a recurrent charge. Since the cost of fees and liveries for resident priests and choristers had more than doubled since the early fourteenth century, such help was clearly needed. Selot used his close connections with Bishop Goldwell to secure a papal bull, in February 1465, permitting the appropriation of the living to St Giles's. The validity of this procedure was successfully challenged by the college of St Mary in the Fields, Norwich, at a time of increasing hostility towards papal pretensions, in 1522, and the hospital had to relinquish Coltishall after a tenure of fifty-seven years.[143] By then at least 63 acres of land in this area (on the river Bure, just seven miles north-east of the city) had been settled upon St Giles's by Selot's successor, John Smyth, to support *his* own annual obit. Hoping that it would eventually be possible to amortise the property in question, Smyth adopted Selot's stratagem of setting up a trust for a term of eighty years. In accordance with his will of 1489, the revenues were paid directly to one of the hospital chaplains, who supervised the obit and may have derived some of his stipend from this source.[144] In addition, Smyth planned a chantry, which was to be financed by income assigned on similar terms from the manor of Rollesby and other property in the western part of Flegg Hundred. There can be little doubt that he aimed in this way to strengthen the hospital's title to land acquired much earlier, in the 1330s, and now subject, like so many other unauthorised purchases, to the unwelcome scrutiny of an avaricious monarch. In 1413–14 St Giles's estates in Rollesby had produced just over £6 in net profits, which was exactly the sum described as coming from 'the farm of land late of John Smyth' in 1498–9.[145] This particular chantry cannot have augmented the hospital's existing revenues, then, but it did serve to put an acquisition of dubious legality on a firmer footing.

In 1529, the farmland in Coltishall which funded Smyth's obit was leased by the master to a new tenant at 26*s* 8*d* a year. His deed refers to a more detailed rental or terrier of property there, which was kept 'in a payre of papre bookes indentyed'.[146] The preservation of such *minutiae*, along with the accounts rendered annually to the receiver general for property supporting the hospital's larger late medieval chantries and obits, serves as yet another reminder of the gravity with which the brethren approached their responsibilities to deceased benefactors. Confidence that the fate of his immortal soul would be in safe hands, as well as a desire to ease the hospital's financial difficulties, led Bishop Goldwell to entrust the brethren with the task of managing no fewer than three new chantries and an obit. Revenues to support these foundations were secured upon the annual income from estates with a minimum capital value of £456, to be bought by his executors. The first purchases, of the manor of 'Rokelles' in Trowse and other property near the hospital's riverside meadows to the south-east of Norwich, were made in 1498, soon after he died. Along with them came a large area of grazing known as 'Blackes Hilles' and a 'marke of swannys called . . . by the name of Blakes Swane Marke', as well as all the birds bearing it. Not until 1503, however, did the executors obtain Henry VII's formal approval for

St Giles's to acquire new holdings worth up to £38 a year. Although some of this money was reserved for the upkeep of cantarists at Norwich cathedral and the college of St Mary in the Fields, the brethren could still anticipate a substantial profit after they had paid another chaplain to celebrate for the bishop's soul in their own church.[147]

In 1510 Goldwell's surviving executors confirmed the hospital in possession of additional land in the Norfolk villages of Horsford, Newton and Swannington. John Jullys's brother then took advantage of the royal letters patent to grant the executors an estate in Salhouse and Wroxham, which was intended to fund the late master's obit, but netted a few shillings more in clear profits. All these acquisitions lay within a relatively short distance of Norwich, and augmented the hospital's supplies of hay, straw and fuel. In 1507–8, for example, the receiver general recorded a delivery of thirty-two cartloads of timber from the woods at Swannington alone.[148] The most valuable of the new purchases was, however, the most distant, being the only property owned by the hospital outside Norfolk. Two large marshes and their appurtenances in Fobbing, Essex, were leased for over £13 a year to local wool producers, bringing the net annual value of the whole endowment up to just under £35.[149] As had so often proved to be the case, though, there was a world of difference between potential and real profits. The property near Norwich was expensive to maintain, but had to be repaired (at a cost of no less than £17 in 1525–6 alone) in order to attract and keep reliable tenants. There was, moreover, the ubiquitous problem of unpaid arrears of rent which had risen to over £30 by 1527. During the 1520s the receiver general might be charged with a superficially impressive net income of almost £40 a year, but little more than £8 accrued from Goldwell's foundation once all the overheads had been met and the backlog of debt deducted.[150]

Notwithstanding the very obvious success of this sustained campaign to expand the hospital's territorial base, the combined effect of falling profits from the sale of tithes and escalating arrears was indeed corrosive. The accumulation of unpaid debts was a blight afflicting most late medieval landowners, albeit one now liable to misunderstanding and misinterpretation. Because of the stress placed, year after year, on an accountant's personal liability, large arrears could grow over the decades from relatively modest beginnings, giving a false impression of impending bankruptcy.[151] Nor was it unusual for the farmers of tithes to run a year behind with their payments, sometimes, as at Hardley in 1506–7, or Bastwick throughout the early sixteenth century, with the full agreement of the master.[152] On the other hand, as successive Norwich rent collectors discovered, the continuous failure to raise a significant proportion of the annual charge *did* have serious long-term consequences for all concerned.

ACQUISITIONS IN NORWICH

This chapter has so far concentrated upon sales and donations of property in the Norfolk countryside made to St Giles's by senior clergy and leading members of the county gentry. But many modest holdings and even smaller rents came from men and women of limited means, who were no less anxious to help the sick poor while securing their own place in paradise. This was especially the case in Norwich. As might be expected, Walter Suffield's initial generosity and reputation for sanctity, the hospital's commanding position and, perhaps most of all, the influx of destitute men and women pouring into the city during the late thirteenth and early fourteenth centuries, stimulated a significant number of donations. No lay benefactors came near to rivalling William Dunwich and his wife, who systematically acquired over the years a rental income of just under £9 in twenty-two city parishes. This, along with three messuages in Norwich, they conveyed to the hospital in the 1260s, in order to support a chantry and obtain membership of the house's spiritual fraternity. Their joint endowment was followed, in 1271, by William's bequest of the meadowland described in Chapter II, and of additional rents worth 62*s* 10*d* per annum.[153] Other gifts, from men such as Thomas Spynk and Edward de Hovethorpe, both of whom made over annual rents of 4*s* for the provision of lights in the hospital church, had a collective rather than an individual impact on the house's finances.[154]

Revenues from Norwich, which constituted approximately one-fifth of the receiver general's net income during the fifteenth century, were used to fund repairs and building works in the precinct and were thus vital for the upkeep of the fabric. They fell into two distinct categories. On the one hand were the messuages, tenements, market stalls and gardens owned and maintained by the brethren, and leased to tenants at competitive rates. On the other were the more numerous but much smaller fixed assize rents scattered across the city. By 1423, the start of a long run of accounts compiled by the hospital's rent collector, gross income from urban leasehold stood at £24, of which just over £10 came from eighteen separate properties running the entire length of Holme Street, in the hospital's own parish of St Helen. The rest derived from tenements in four main areas of the city. Immediately to the north-west were holdings in the adjacent parishes of St Martin at Palace, SS Simon and Jude, St Clement and St Saviour; further west on the other side of Norwich lay tenements and gardens in the parishes of St Martin Coslany and St Augustine; nearer the centre were market stalls and other premises in the busy parishes of St Peter Mancroft, St Cross and St Andrew; and to the south-east, near the Wensum, lay a messuage in the parish of St Edward Conisford [see Map V].[155] Keenly aware of the need to invest in bricks and mortar, the brethren had erected two substantial new houses near the church of St Martin at Palace in 1397, at a cost of £15, henceforward deriving at least 50*s* a year from that parish alone.[156]

Four other significant acquisitions were made in the city during the later Middle Ages. Through an arrangement reached in 1470 with the abbot of Sawtry, John Selot bought out the latter's annual pension charged upon the living at Costessey, while also securing from him possession of a messuage and tenements in Holme Street. Although these dwellings were said to be 'ruynous and . . . of littell yerely value and verisembleable to growe of lesse value', repairs were soon put in train. In 1483–4 the hospital steward, to whom revenues from Norwich were ultimately paid, received over 38*s* from 'tenements in Holme Street lately purchased by Master John Selot'.[157] At some point over the next twenty years, property known as 'Skypwythys', comprising an osier yard, a garden and closes, was also added to the rental. The net profits of between £4 and £6 a year were sufficiently high to merit the completion of separate accounts, drawn up by the receiver general rather than the rent collector.[158] Further expansion along the Conisford riverside occurred in 1512,

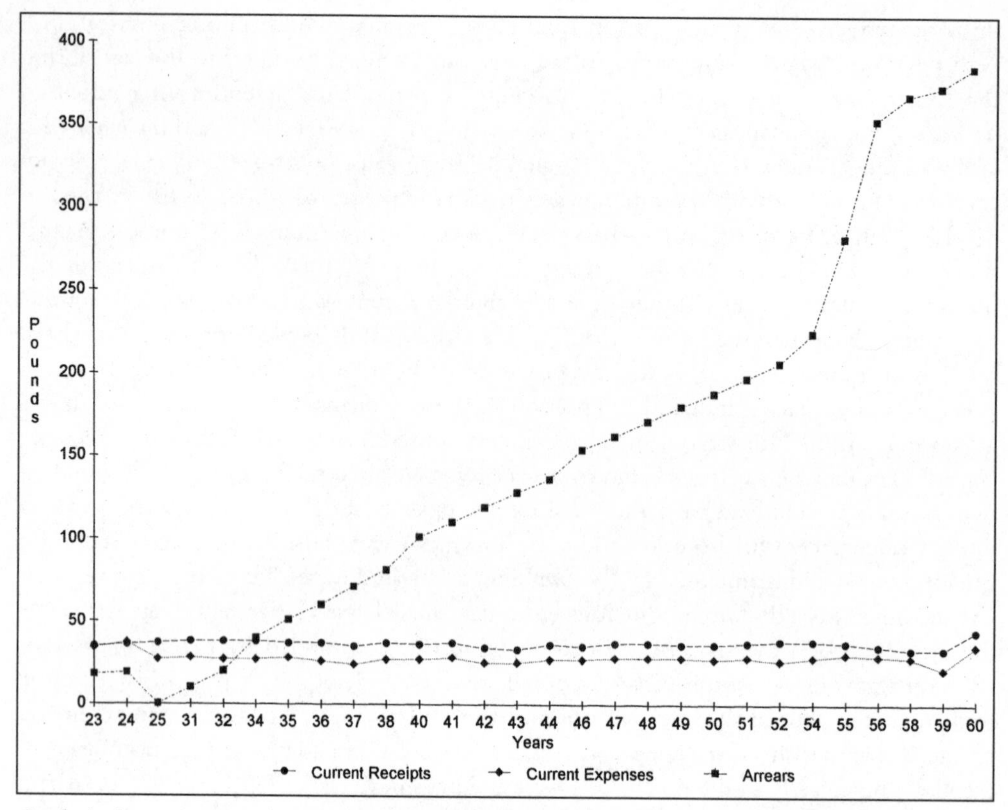

Graph A: Arrears, receipts and expenses, Norwich properties of St Giles's hospital, 1423–60. (NRO, NCR, 24A, Great Hospital Norwich Accounts, 1415–60)

when Robert Godfrey, a chaplain and senior administrator, made over an adjacent close in the parish of St Vedast to fund his obit. In 1526 the master and brethren leased some of these new holdings, along with a fishery in the river, to a group of local tradesmen, specifying in considerable detail how the 'greate creke' leading from the Wensum was to be used, cleansed and repaired, how many 'osyers' were to remain at the end of the term, and how any buildings to be erected by the tenants might eventually be purchased by the hospital at a reduced rate. In 1515 John Hecker, then master of St Giles's, paid £16 for yet another message in Conisford, which suggests a deliberate policy of consolidation in this area, where members of the mercantile community were constantly on the look-out for property.[159] The brethren were certainly not lacking in business acumen.

Problems over the collection of the hospital's fixed assize rents made such a policy all the more necessary. It was through the gift of these quite modest sums that men and women with only a few shillings, or even pence, to spare were able to endow charitable institutions. Since they and their heirs retained full ownership of the freehold, which could still be bought, sold or devised at will, only the basic rent charge levied upon it passed out of their control. Although the recipient could, theoretically, distrain in cases of non-payment, it proved extremely difficult to monitor changes of title. Another efficiently managed hospital, God's House, Southampton, encountered even greater obstacles in this regard, being driven as a result to compile a new cartulary in order to marshal its evidence. But this was only the start. The expense and effort involved in litigation for the recovery of comparatively small sums of money deterred institutions with limited budgets. During the first half of the fifteenth century, the brethren of St Giles's hoped to raise £16 a year in assize rents from properties in no fewer than thirty Norwich parishes, but generally succeeded in collecting only about a third of this sum. For many years their officials were hampered by the lack of an accurate rental; by the time one had finally been produced, in 1455–6 (noting the past, present and currently untraceable occupants of the properties in question), arrears spanning over two decades had climbed to £234, with no realistic hope of settlement. Indeed, debts continued to mount at a steady rate of about £10 a year, so that by 1461 (when they stood at no less than £384) it was decided to write off the entire deficit and start afresh [Graph A]. Henceforward, the accountant was charged with just £4 a year in assize rents – a reduction of 75 per cent – although, in the long term, three-quarters of this sum also failed to materialise. From 1502 onwards arrears again began climbing steadily, reaching a high of £64 in 1528 [Graph B].

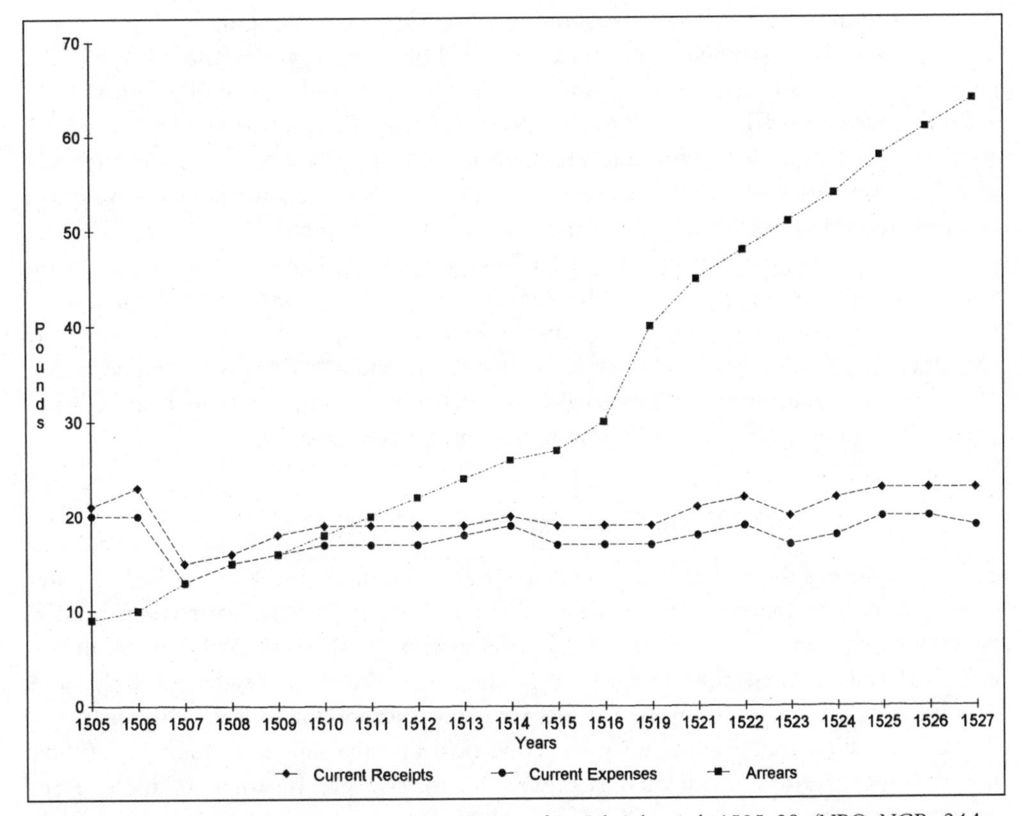

Graph B: Arrears, receipts and expenses, Norwich properties of St Giles's hospital, 1505–28. (NRO, NCR, 24A Great Hospital Norwich Accounts, 1485–1509, 1510–28)

Genuine poverty as well as intransigence led, inevitably, to debt, especially during times of hardship. Perhaps taking a lead from the monks of Norwich cathedral priory, who adopted a similar policy, the brethren attempted during the early fourteenth century to resume into their own hands properties which their predecessors had let out at fixed rents, often through an arrangement with early benefactors. Capitalising upon the apparently insatiable demand for rented accommodation, they hoped to convert these dwellings to leasehold.[160] But even here they encountered problems. In June 1317, when famine was gripping the city, Agnes and Richard Colman surrendered their tenement held at an annual rent of 16*s* in the parish of SS Simon and Jude, 'not being able to maintain the same, pay the rent or settle the arrears'. Within a matter of months, the next occupant, a widow, had encountered similar difficulties and likewise abandoned her tenancy.[161] By the fifteenth century, when they had grown more accustomed – if not resigned – to the consequences of economic stagnation, the brethren bowed to the inevitable: in 1464–5, for example, a man and woman were excused arrears of 6*s* 4*d* 'because they are destitute and have nothing upon which they may be distrained'. Over the next few years one Robert Munforth was similarly classed as 'insufficient'; and another 'beggar' (*mendicans*), Hugh Spycer, who owed 16*s* 4*d*, obtained a full pardon.[162] Lest it be assumed that the brethren lacked persistence and were unbusinesslike in managing their affairs, we might note that the corporation of Norwich also wrote off uncollectible rents at this time, as their revenues from city property dropped significantly in the 1460s and again in the 1490s.[163] The problem of urban poverty grew even more acute during the early sixteenth century, when a slump in the worsted trade combined with the effects of two disastrous fires, in March and June 1507, to cause serious dislocation. At just under £5 a year during the aftermath of the conflagrations, the hospital's losses in leasehold income were certainly not as serious as those sustained by the cathedral monks, but they compounded existing financial problems.[164] Improved and expanded facilities for paying boarders, described in the previous chapter, usually generated sums of between £5 and £14 a year for the hospital at this time, but neither they nor the rents from newly acquired properties sufficed to compensate for falling profits. Whereas during the previous century sums raised by the Norwich rent collector for building work and delivery to the receiver general had only twice fallen below £20, from 1499 onwards they never once rose above £19.

PROBLEMS AND SOLUTIONS

Although, during the fifteenth and early sixteenth centuries, the hospital had acquired urban and rural property worth on paper about £93 a year net, annual receipts from its estates were not much higher than they had been before the Black Death [Tables A and B]. Could more have been done to improve productivity? When, in September 1479, John Smyth assumed the mastership, he was permitted by Bishop Goldwell to postpone taking the oath of office until a full inquiry had been held into the house's finances.[165] Without the relevant steward's accounts it is impossible to give precise totals of income and expenditure at this time, although there was clearly some cause for concern. In 1478–9, the receiver general, a priest named Robert Blythe who had only recently been engaged as a

Year	1465–6	1483–4	1486–7	1488–9	1499–1500	1500–1	1502–3	1505–6	1506–7	1507–8	1509–10	1510–11	1511–12
Arrears	15	18	0	0	0	0	0	85	91	91	85	74	80
Estates	74	79	91	94	98	99	69	51	111	98	93	91	62
Casual	28	10	15	15	8	40	14	35	30	62	17	16	17
TOTAL CHARGE	117	107	106	109	106	139	83	171	232	251	195	181	159
Overspent last year	5	10	22	19	39	53	0	0	18	0	9	7	0
Current expenses	145	117	108	98	111	151	177	106	103	130	107	98	97
TOTAL DISCHARGE	150	127	130	117	150	204	177	106	121	130	116	105	97
This year's balance	-43	-28	-24	-11	-5	-12	-94	-20	38	30	3	9	-18
Overall balance	-33	-20	-2	-8	-44	-65	-94	65	111	121	79	76	62

Year	1512–13	1513–14	1514–15	1515–16	1516–17	1519–20	1521–2	1522–3	1523–4	1524–5	1525–6	1526–7
Arrears	114	114	116	123	130	117	125	138	144	172	174	185
Estates	70	100	95	102	93	111	100	98	102	90	93	107
Casual	24	27	22	20	24	24	33	24	17	27	9	40
TOTAL CHARGE	208	241	233	245	247	252	258	260	263	289	276	332
Overspent last year	37	57	55	61	18	33	78	75	76	50	62	88
Current expenses	114	124	123	130	112	134	125	121	90	122	118	120
TOTAL DISCHARGE	151	181	178	191	130	167	203	196	166	172	180	208
This year's balance	-20	3	-6	-8	-13	1	8	1	29	-5	-16	27
Overall balance	57	60	55	54	117	85	55	64	97	117	96	124

Table B: The Finances of St Giles's Hospital, 1465–1527 (NRO, NCR, 24A, Great Hospital general accounts, 1465–1501, 1485–1508, 1510–25)

Because of adjustments made at the close of the account, which might entail contributions by the master, figures for overspending are rarely consistent from one year to the next.

conduct, raised just £65 from the holdings in his charge. This was, indeed, a low point in the hospital's financial history; even if the steward had (as later) contributed a further £25 or so from various sources in Norwich, Blythe's efforts to keep within a strict budget would still have been hampered by his colleague's current overspending of £22 on the household. The stagnant grain market was partly to blame for such disappointing returns, and no doubt also for the accumulation of arrears of around £28. We should also recall that Norwich was then devastated by another 'great plague', which may have disrupted life at St Giles's, delaying the audit. But a firm hand at the helm also paid dividends. John Selot's final years saw a decline in net income of at least £10 a year, which may reflect a weakening of his iron grip through advancing age or sickness. His successor's decision to assume the receiver generalship in person on becoming master was quickly followed by a corresponding rise in receipts, which would suggest that vigorous management could make an appreciable difference.[166]

John Jullys, another energetic master, likewise opted to combine the two offices. His drive to reduce a backlog of arrears which again showed signs of escalating out of control led him to conclude his account for 1502–3 with an itemised list of *all* unpaid rents and other sums of money, however small, due from no fewer than ninety-two individual tenants and officials. The urgency of the situation was intensified by his desire to recover some of the £243 he had spent 'of his own money . . . to the honour of God and St Giles, and towards the benefit and improvement of the hospital'; and he successfully raised about two-thirds of the £95 or so due. It is also worth noting that, although he diverted large amounts of produce into the hospital's granaries, income from property was still higher than it had been in the late 1470s. Yet, despite repeated efforts to keep them at a manageable level, arrears remained a constant problem throughout the estates. Never less than £74 during the years between 1505 and 1528, they were often higher than current receipts and began mounting quite dramatically from 1523 onwards [Table B]. This explains why the total 'charge' laid to the accountant during this period seems so high. Because overspending in one year was, by the same token, included among outgoings in the next, total annual disbursements during the difficult early years of the century also seem grossly inflated. An analysis of *current* receipts and expenditure, stripped of inherited accretions, reveals a rather different picture of careful housekeeping, as the receiver general struggled to remain within the constraints of a shrinking budget [Table B]. He ought sometimes – as in 1513–14 and 1521–2 – to have ended the year with a few pounds in hand, but since he was charged with sums that could no longer be raised and obliged to pay off a backlog of old debts, his position appeared far more precarious than was really the case.

Was it possible to tap alternative sources of income? John Jullys's ambitious plans for the further development of the hospital in the early sixteenth century did more than simply affect the way the accounts were presented. A larger and more prestigious establishment needed a reliable supply of fresh meat, and to this end he ordered the construction of a warren on the dry, sandy soil around Cringleford. By so doing, he probably hoped to utilise land of otherwise minimal value. That he also had his eye on the expanding regional market for flesh and fur seems more than likely; several East Anglian warrens made a notable contribution to the regional economy. Rabbit was at this date still something of a delicacy, as the considerable expenditure on the thatched coney-house (*domus cuniculorum*) and construction of the artificial burrows between 1499 and 1501 reveals. With free board and an annuity comprising five barrels of ale, a robe and 26*s* 8*d* in cash, the warrener was clearly a figure of consequence. His skill in nurturing and protecting animals which were neither as robust nor as prolific as their modern-day descendants merited a generous reward. Probably because of the heavy costs involved, William Soper, the next master, decided to lease the warren at an annual rent of £4, together with sixty pairs of rabbits to be delivered in time for the festivities at Christmas and on St Giles's day. The experiment proved highly successful: after the first seven-year contract expired, in 1512, some 1,300 rabbits were culled, earning the receiver general almost £9 and thus recouping some of his earlier expenses.[167] Culling on this scale (which also made 200 rabbits available for the hospital kitchens) suggests a rapid growth on a par with some of the larger Breckland colonies. Yet, in 1524–5, the then farmer of the warren, Thomas Davy, contracted with the master to demolish it and sell off all the stock.[168]

The evident profitability of the venture makes this decision hard to understand. It seems unlikely that John Hecker, a master noted for his abrasive character and litigiousness, had paid undue attention to complaints voiced by his tenants, in January 1519, about the damage caused to their crops by the hospital's rabbits and sheep. He did, however, authorise an inquiry into the extent of the problem, and perhaps eventually acceded to pressure from below. Poaching was certainly rife and may, as elsewhere, have been occasioned by these grievances. Kett's rebels were later to protest over the abuse of seigniorial privilege by Norfolk landowners with large flocks and warrens; and the hospital may have been considered oppressive. It was sacked during the insurrection of 1549, partly because of a more recent association with Norwich's ruling elite but perhaps also as a result of long-remembered injustices.[169] Hecker's determination to acquire more grazing for the hospital's flocks on the pastures at Thorpe, just outside Norwich, led to his appearance before the court of Star Chamber, on a charge of intimidation.[170] His campaigns, waged in the ecclesiastical courts against the parishioners of Seething and Bastwick for the payment of tithes and the enforcement of other legal rights, are fully described in Chapter V. They constituted yet another attempt to arrest the apparently irreversible process of financial decline, the extremity of Hecker's response reflecting the gravity of his situation.

The early sixteenth century also saw a return to intensive pastoral farming at Cringleford. During the 1460s the hospital had kept between 300 and 446 sheep on its fold courses there, raising about £11 a year from the sale of wool and livestock.[171] Low levels of ovine fertility throughout the region were compounded by what, for breeding purposes, was an unfavourable ratio of wethers (castrated rams) to ewes. This gave a heavier wool crop, but demanded continuous investment in order to maintain numbers.[172] As had been the case at the close of the fourteenth century, the overheads sustained by paying a shepherd, shearing and tending the sheep and repairing enclosures were harder to bear when there was a slump in the wool market. Numbers fell quite dramatically in the 1470s from 440 to 147, perhaps also reflecting some of the financial and managerial problems evident during the last years of John Selot's mastership. Although his executors hoped to rebuild the flock with a gift of ninety-seven sheep, in 1479, many beasts were sold and it was not until 1487, when £18 was allocated from the hospital's 'common chest' for expenditure on some 393 lambs, ewes and wethers, that real recovery began. Grazing land which had been let out to other farmers was once again retained for the hospital's use and the fences needed to enclose the fold courses were repaired. The hospital may have followed the example of the Norwich Benedictines, who recognised the commercial potential of sheep farming at a time of otherwise declining revenues. Expanding rapidly in size from about 1,000 sheep in 1475 to 8,500 in 1515, the monastic flocks represented an incisive response to the growing demands of regional and national markets.[173] Not even John Jullys could hope to emulate a commercial enterprise on this scale, although his personal investment in 156 new animals in 1502–3 pushed numbers up to an unprecedented 518 (of which a significant number were destined for his table). His successors were content to maintain a flock of around 400 in the first decade of the sixteenth century and of 240 or so in the second. Only after 1525 did numbers fall well below 100, as the hospital, in common with many other religious houses, appears to have abandoned any attempt to seize the economic initiative and liquidated its investments.[174]

By 1526, the cumulative shortfall between income and expenditure at St Giles's stood at £88, which constituted a heavy, but by no means intolerable load for the hospital to bear. It represented less than one year's revenue, and, more tellingly, approximately a third of the sum which John Jullys had spent out of his own coffers on improvements and renovations at the beginning of the century. Hitherto a wealthy friend, master or benefactor had invariably appeared in times of need with an offer of financial help. Thomas de Preston had pledged £100 for the purchase of St Peter's church in Mundham, and John Derlyngton had given half this sum for the new bell-tower alone. Indeed, he probably donated hundreds more when the nave, chancel and infirmary were being rebuilt. We will never know how much Bishops Lyhart and Goldwell sank into bricks, mortar, prayers and masses. Nor can the contributions made by less eminent clergy and lay patrons ever be computed. St Giles's had always managed, one way or another, to attract the practical support of men and women whose concern for spiritual health made them generous patrons and occasionally even friends to the poor. That it might soon be denied these vital subventions must have seemed as unthinkable as the fate awaiting the magnificently ornamented church which had hitherto constituted its greatest spiritual and material asset.

CHAPTER IV

THE HOSPITAL CHURCH

> As Christians we know that there are two kinds of medicine, one of earthly things, the other of heavenly things. They differ in both origin and efficacy. Through long experience, earthly doctors learn the powers of herbs and the like, which alter the condition of human bodies. But there has never been a doctor so experienced in this art that he has not found some illnesses difficult to cure and others completely incurable . . . The author of heavenly medicine, however, is Christ, who could heal the sick with a command and raise the dead from the grave.
>
> Fulbert of Chartres, 'Hymn to St Pantaleon'

Although it underwent many changes during the 400 years before the Reformation, the medieval English hospital remained chiefly concerned with the promotion of spiritual rather than physical health. If the salvation of wealthy benefactors eventually took priority over that of the patients, the emphasis upon 'heavenly medicine' remained constant.[1] Such a scale of values was inevitable, given the pre-Cartesian view that body and soul were inextricably linked, the one affecting the condition of the other, and the attendant assumption that sin would be punished by physical suffering, either in this world or the next. For this reason a ruling of the fourth Lateran Council of 1215 (cap. xxii) threatened medical practitioners with excommunication if they treated anyone who had not first made a full confession, or had at least sworn to do so.[2] The priest, aptly described in this decree as a physician of the soul, had at his disposal a pharmacopoeia of potential cures, the best and most powerful of which was the medicine of Christ's body and blood as revealed in the sacrament of the Mass.[3] Innocent III had described how the Eucharist washed away sin, bestowing eternal life and health through its redeeming grace. Such was the potency of this *medicina sacramentalis*, that the mere sight of the Host at the moment of elevation was deemed to ease the torment endured by all sinners, and also to relieve the more immediate symptoms of earthly disease.[4] How could the late medieval medical profession, hampered by its limited knowledge of human physiology, compete with this propaganda? In the East Anglian *Play of the Sacrament* (known to us through a unique copy produced at Croxton, Norfolk, in the late 1460s), a drunken and incompetent quack serves as a comic foil to the Christ, the Divine Physician, who appears miraculously at the climax to effect a cure. His promise of health and redemption to penitent unbelievers, guilty of desecrating the Host, underscores the powerlessness of any earthly practitioner to deal with the physical symptoms of sin. It cannot have escaped the local audience that the spiritually bankrupt charlatan, with his 'therde-bare gowne and a rent hoose', has his home just *outside* St Saviour's hospital at Bury St Edmunds: a telling juxtaposition of profane and sacred medicine.[5]

The theme of *Christus Medicus*, Christ the Physician, first elaborated at length by St Augustine of Hippo (d. 430), is a recurrent one in the art of the medieval European hospital.[6] The painfully realistic late fifteenth-century lime-wood carving of the tortured Christ, crowned with thorns, which still stands at the west end of the salle des pauvres in the Hôtel Dieu, Beaune, recalls Augustine's description of the Passion as a 'bitter cup' of medicine tasted by the physician to reassure his patient.[7] Because so many English medieval hospital buildings have been destroyed or damaged over the years and almost all their contents have been lost, it is easy to forget that the very meanest would also have been decorated with Christian iconography designed to heighten the devotional atmosphere. The painted chamber at St Wulfstan's hospital, Worcester, with its images of healing saints, the Trinity, Crucifixion and (significantly) Last Judgement, serves as a reminder of the importance accorded to visual imagery in these buildings. Even the small leper house at Wimborne in Dorset boasted a painted chapel, and it seems likely that portable icons, as well as crucifixes, were available in the larger hospitals, such as St Giles's, Norwich, for use in the infirmary.[8] Patients near to death in the Florentine hospital of Santa Maria Nuova were comforted by nurses bearing pictures of Christ on the Cross, a practice which was almost certainly universal.[9]

Attendance at deathbeds was an appropriate activity for these women, since in the wake of the Divine Physician came his nurse, the Virgin Mary, a ubiquitous presence in the wall paintings, statuary and altarpieces of hospital chapels and infirmaries throughout Christendom. Her role as a mediatrice between sinful humanity and God ensured a special place for Marian devotions in the liturgy for the dead. The sight of her image offered reassurance to the sick. She decorated the fourteenth-century beds of the Ospedale del Ceppo in Pistoia, watched as a Madonna of Mercy over the patients in the Heiligen-Geist Hospital in Lübeck, and stood on a pillar beside the crucifix in the main ward of the Hôtel Dieu in Paris.[10] A statue of the Virgin and child still occupies a niche high in the gatehouse of the hospital of St Cross in Winchester;[11] and the story of her life is recounted in the roof bosses of the Lady Chapel at St Giles's in Norwich [see Plate 10]. Marian imagery may also be found, *inter alia*, on the seals of William Elsing's hospital for the blind in Cripplegate, London, the hospital of St Thomas the Martyr at Beck (Norfolk), the *leprosarium* of the Holy Trinity in Knightsbridge (Middlesex) and the hospital of St John the Baptist, Bridgwater (Somerset).[12]

Henry, duke of Lancaster (d. 1360), son of the founder of the hospital of the Annunciation of St Mary in the Newarke, Leicester, composed a lengthy tract on the subject of sacred medicine shortly before remodelling the hospital statutes in 1356. The prospect of convalescence in the care of a nurse as tender and loving as the Virgin gave him courage to face the painful remedies needed to treat his seven 'putrefying and dangerous wounds' (the seven deadly sins). Among these, the 'sacred ointment' of confession loomed large, offering him an opportunity to 'ease the foul wound in my mouth and thereby cleanse it of its encrusted filth'.[13] Duke Henry spoke on behalf of all medieval sinners, rich or poor, but his words assume particular significance in the context of the contemporary English hospital. Since the services of physicians and surgeons were only occasionally available to the sick paupers who found refuge there, the quotidian round of meditation, prayer and liturgy came to dominate their lives. In theory, if not in practice, the Spiritual Works of Mercy, with their emphasis upon counsel, correction, solace and forgiveness, provided balm for injured souls.[14] Confession and absolution of sins were deemed essential before any member of the laity could receive communion. As the prerequisite of a 'good death', they figured prominently in the ritual for the visitation of the sick.[15] At the duke's own hospital, for example, the original foundation statutes of 1330 stipulated that every newcomer was to confess before gaining entry. Once admitted, he was to lie in the body of the hospital church so that he could hear 'all the divine offices' and witness the elevation of the Host at a special mass to be celebrated each day in full view of all the bedridden inmates [see Plate 6].[16] The statutes of St Leonard's hospital, York, made provision for two chaplains to tour the wards at night, urging the patients to repent and confess, while also providing reassurance that the last rites could quickly be administered in case of need.[17] As might be expected of a foundation modelled upon one of the largest and most impressive hospitals in Italy, the Savoy in London planned to employ no fewer than six priests 'to hear confessions within the hospital of all who are ill there, and to absolve them from sins however grave, even if forgotten, both at the point of death and when death is expected'.[18]

The idea of hospital patients as 'unseen congregations whose white rows lie set apart above', lingers on in Philip Larkin's powerful poem, 'The Building', in which he speaks of men and women 'all here to confess that something has gone wrong', and admit their 'error of a serious sort'.[19] The admission of error, of moral shortcomings which might occasion poverty and disease, was a matter of great concern to medieval patrons as well as to the more devout patients.[20] By cleansing the soul of the spots and stains of sin, regular confession made the penitent – and his or her prayers – more acceptable in the eyes of God and man. It is important to remember that the poor inmates of medieval hospitals were not the only hopeful beneficiaries of what, in practice, constituted the spiritual equivalent of intensive care. Founders and patrons, too, hoped to derive lasting merit from intercessionary prayers and requiem masses said or sung to speed the passage of souls through purgatory.[21] And it was they who set the agenda for change. The sick poor had to play their part, and were increasingly required to do so in a formal, precisely regulated fashion. As a Spiritual Work of Mercy, prayer infinitely surpassed the Comfortable Works undertaken so conspicuously by the rich, although it, too, became a commodity to be bargained and sold.[22] An agreement of 1386 between the prior of Norwich and the townspeople of Yarmouth stipulated that, in return for their upkeep, the poor brothers and sisters of the hospital of St Mary Magdalen were to be present in chapel every day for each of the canonical hours, as well as attending a mass from start to finish. They were also to say the Lord's Prayer and the *Ave* 'with devotion' for the souls of past patrons.[23] It was, no doubt, considered fitting that paupers, who depended upon a regular issue of loaves for their physical survival and the sight of the Host for spiritual well-being, should beseech

God for daily bread in the *Pater Noster.* But their welfare was not necessarily the first priority. Many of the almshouses founded in the next century imposed far heavier burdens upon inmates carefully chosen from the ranks of the respectable poor, on the assumption that prayers said by individuals of unimpeachable moral character would find greater favour with God. Such an arduous round of devotion would necessarily have precluded the moribund or severely disabled, who were not always welcome in institutions of this type.[24] Older hospitals, such as St Giles's, Norwich, also became more selective. By 1492 the brethren were supporting a 'poore man that helpith the preste to syng'; and during the early sixteenth century at least one inmate was known as the 'bedeman', his primary duty being likewise to pray for the souls of past benefactors.[25]

As we have seen, the endowment of a hospital gave devout Christians the opportunity to perform some or all of the Seven Corporal or Comfortable Works, and thus obtain 'helth in bodye, grace in sowle and everlastyng joy' through the manifold benefits of almsgiving.[26] Patrons could further improve their spiritual condition by purchasing indulgences. Sold on the open market in return for charitable donations, they offered a share of the celestial treasury accumulated by an almshouse or hospital through good works, prayer and, most notably, the celebration of masses. This, in turn, served as a currency to be traded against weeks, years or even decades of enjoined penance, thereby reducing the debt which would have to be discharged, with interest, after death. Fear of purgatory, where atonement would be made for any sins not fully expiated on earth, was real and earnest. As medieval preachers frequently reminded their congregations, its pains differed only in duration from the unending torments of hell, and were beyond even the most vivid imagination.[27] Few indulgences were as generous as one reputedly issued in the 1320s by the leper house of St Mary Magdalen at Liskeard in Cornwall, which promised to remit a hefty fourteen years and 400 days of penance.[28] When helping to found the hospital of St Paul in Norwich, Bishop Everard (res. 1145) had promised just forty days' remission to men and women visiting the house each year on the feast of the patron saint 'with oblation of alms or pious disposition of heart'; and similar indulgences were extended by Walter Suffield and his successors to benefactors of St Giles's.[29] In an attempt to solve its worsening financial problems, the London hospital of St Mary, Bishopsgate, secured a papal indulgence in 1391 for anyone who provided alms during the major festivals of the ecclesiastical year, and was inundated with crowds attending mass in the church and the annual 'spital sermon' outside in the preaching-yard.[30] Although by the end of the Middle Ages the currency had grown somewhat debased, there can be little doubt that the practice of awarding indulgences, especially to pilgrims and other visitors, proved a further stimulus to liturgical developments in the larger English hospitals.[31] Whatever sums of money came to St Giles's in this way seem to have been earmarked for its church rather than the infirmary, not least because music and ritual attracted more worshippers.

Patrons also embraced the opportunity to join a Christian brotherhood staffed by priests and clerks, whose task was to commend the living and remember the dead. In late medieval London, for example, the pledge of a fixed annual contribution towards its religious and eleemosynary work earned patrons of the Bethlehem hospital a place in the confraternity of St Mary the Virgin, which had been set up in the mid-fourteenth century as part of a fundraising drive. The promise of a generous indulgence (endorsed by no fewer than six popes), participation in 'all the privileges, intercessions and benefits of the hospital' and perpetual commemoration by the choristers and chaplains must have seemed well worth the price.[32] In the eyes of the Church, and, indeed, of a substantial part of the laity as well, such an exercise in compassion for the faithful departed took priority over corporal acts of mercy, however laudable. 'Among the different works of piety and service of divine majesty', wrote one fifteenth-century clergyman, 'solemn masses shine forth as Lucifer among the stars.'[33] The failure of the canons of the hospital of the Annunciation of St Mary in the Newarke to celebrate mass regularly thus seemed especially shocking. In a visitation report of 1440, Bishop Alnwick warned them that 'you ought to pray and make oblations for them whose alms you receive daily; and there is no sacrifice can be greater than the Body and Blood of Christ'.[34] The masters and brethren of St Giles's hospital needed no such prompting. As we have seen in the previous chapter, royal letters patent of 1451 allowing them to acquire additional estates worth £20 a year described the principal claim on their resources as 'the divine service which has to be celebrated in the hospital church every day . . . for the praise of God and His honour and the love of St Giles'.[35] Even after the first wave of protestant reform had led to the dissolution of several of the larger English monastic hospitals, Robert Codde (master 1536–46) stubbornly upheld the terms of Henry VI's grant. When suing Robert Wace in Chancery for 'unlawfull and crafty practyse to lete and hynder the celebracion of . . . devyne servyce and deades of charyte' at St Giles's, he emphasised that religious observance had been the chief and most serious casualty. It was in this way, he reminded the court, that the hospital not only praised God, but also brought 'relyffe and comforte [to] a greate noumbre of the kinges hyghnes faythfull subyectes, *both pouer and ryche*'.[36] His words echo those of the disciples of Thomas Aquinas (d. 1274), written a few decades after the foundation of the hospital, which describe the Eucharist as 'the origin and bond of charity', uniting the dead as well as the living in the body of Christ.[37]

The rich were constantly exhorted to abase themselves as spiritual beggars at the feet of their dependents, but most felt it expedient to purchase additional insurance, in the way of elaborate funerals, masses, annual obits and commemorative prayers. In attacking what they perceived as a pernicious waste of resources which properly belonged to Christ's poor, reformers inevitably turned a spotlight upon the liturgical excesses so conspicuous in English hospitals. Propaganda circulated by the followers of John Wycliffe in the late fourteenth and early fifteenth centuries claimed that many such institutions had been 'full nyh distroyed' by avaricious clergy bent on accumulating treasure for ostentatious display.[38] The transformation of many hospitals into collegiate churches or glorified chantry chapels was by no means unusual, and reflects a common response to the pressures of economic and social change.[39] It is also indicative of a genuine desire on the part of patrons – both lay and ecclesiastical – for new and elaborate liturgical practices. In certain cases, as at St Giles's, some of these innovations may also have been prompted by a lingering fear of heresy, which gained widespread support in East Anglia, even though Norwich itself remained staunchly and flamboyantly orthodox.[40] The widespread destruction of English hospitals and the loss of their archives at the Dissolution now makes it hard to envisage their prominent place in the army of the Church Militant and the range of spiritual services which served them as ammunition. The survival of a unique combination of documentary and architectural evidence concerning the layout, furnishing and liturgy of the church at St Giles's hospital suggests that here, at least, critics of the ecclesiastical establishment had some cause for alarm as well as complaint. It is certainly apparent that written records alone, however full, present only a very limited picture of the buildings themselves, and thus of the important role played by many hospitals in the religious life of the wider community. Stone and flint rather than parchment can best help us to understand this aspect of their history.

THE HOSPITAL CHURCH BEFORE 1270

Walter Suffield's concern that due attention should be paid to the physical as well as the spiritual requirements of patients and pensioners in his new hospital led him to adopt certain features of the Augustinian rule, which accorded a relatively modest place to the *opus Dei*, and thus allowed time for other activities, such as ministering to the sick or distributing alms. But ritual still dominated the quotidian round. Suffield's first foundation charter instructed the master and his four chaplains to say the eight canonical hours with 'due chant and measured delivery' (*cum cantu et tractu moderato*), celebrate the Mass of the day solemnly and dress soberly in black copes and surplices during services. The requirement that two additional masses (a requiem mass and a mass of the Blessed Virgin) should be offered daily and that all the staff, including four lay brothers, should process each evening to the chapel chanting the *miserere* (the fifty-first psalm) gave additional scope for ceremony.[41] The Lady-Mass had been celebrated each day at Salisbury cathedral from 1225 onwards with great solemnity and an elaborate ritual which changed throughout the ecclesiastical year, but the custom was at this point largely confined to secular cathedrals and larger collegiate foundations.[42] Another innovative aspect of liturgical practice at St Giles's was the weekly celebration of a full service of the patron saint, to whom Bishop Suffield was especially devoted, unless Lent or a major festival made this impossible. As we have already seen, the cult of St Giles traditionally attracted the sick poor, as well as those who feared that they might die unconfessed; and Suffield clearly wished to place the patients under his powerful protection.[43] But Giles was also an abbot, famous for his intercession on behalf of the Emperor Charlemagne during the celebration of mass. An imposing statue of him tonsured and dressed in full priestly robes, hand raised in blessing, survives from the hospital of St Giles near Lincoln, which was founded in about 1280. It serves as a reminder of his close connection with the Christian liturgy.[44] Similar representations of the saint almost certainly decorated the Norwich precinct, too [see Plate 23].

Suffield's provision of support for seven poor scholars, who were to have their keep throughout term-time while they learned Latin grammar at school, also had important implications for the religious life of his foundation. Once classes were over they would have been available to act as altar boys, read the lessons and possibly assist in the choir. Quite a few of the larger hospitals of this period employed their pupils as choristers.[45] After its refoundation, in 1273, the London almshouse of St Katherine by the Tower paid six poor boys to serve in the chapel; and in 1298 St John's hospital, Bridgwater, was enlarged to maintain thirteen such boys 'who shall be excused from full ritual so they may attend school each day in the town'.[46] At St Mark's hospital, Bristol, where three solemn masses (including a Lady-Mass) were celebrated daily from 1259 onwards, the precentor assumed responsibility for twelve choristers, as well as directing other services of commemoration 'especially for the benefactors of the house'.[47] The boys of St Giles's were not officially described as choral scholars until 1451, although by then the hospital had long been a centre of musical excellence. That Suffield may himself have envisaged developments along these lines seems probable from his revised statutes, in which, as noted in Chapter I, he ordered the brethren to adopt the highly ritualised Salisbury Use and added a deacon and sub-deacon 'dedicated to divine worship' to the existing staff. He also specified that the canonical hours were henceforward to be sung rather than said. His insistence that everyone should devote time not spent in church to prayer, study or visiting the sick is, however, significant, as is the emphasis placed by him upon the charitable aspects of his foundation.[48] Suffield's concern with both spiritual and physical health is evident from his grant to the hospital of the advowson of Seething, made towards the end of his life in 1253. Some of the revenues were to go to the almoner of Norwich cathedral priory for the support of the poor, while the hospital itself was to feed 100 paupers every year on the anniversary of his death. This event was also to be marked by a solemn, sung service in the church, each of the chaplains being required to celebrate mass for the salvation of his soul. Suffield's anniversary, which fell on St Dunstan's day (19 May), remained one of the great landmarks of the hospital year until the Dissolution, and must have set the tone for the many other services of commemoration which followed.[49]

The promise that regular intercession would be made on their behalf clearly attracted the hospital's early patrons, whose concern for their own salvation may already have proved a more potent inducement to charity than sympathy for Christ's poor. Suffield's readiness to offer burial rights and facilities for the upkeep of oratories to anyone who wanted them inspired further grants of land and rents, and initially helped to support the house's philanthropic activities. His brother's endowment of the livings at Repps and Bastwick was offered in return for burial and commemoration at St Giles's, while the local landowners who joined in the transaction requested a more modest share in its 'spiritual benefits'.[50] These, of course, included the celestial treasury laid up by the founder. Bishop Walter's tomb stood at the east end of Norwich cathedral, but his posthumous presence in the hospital was, as we have seen, tangible. Besides leaving twenty marks (£13 6*s* 8*d*) for requiem masses to be celebrated there, he had also arranged for his heart to be preserved in a niche beside the high altar. Although he never became the focus of a permanent cult, there is reason to suppose that the relics which earned the sacristan sums of up to 23*s* a year in the late fourteenth century included parts of his own body.[51]

Benefactors may quite often have given sacred objects, charged with therapeutic powers, to hospitals. John de Lacy (d. 1190), constable of Chester and reputed founder of St John's hospital, Castle Donington, placed there a piece of the staff owned by St Gilbert of Sempringham. At least two individuals are said to have been healed by it soon afterwards: the master, himself a victim of paralysis, and, significantly, a local physician suffering from tertian fever.[52] A twelfth-century account of the foundation of St Bartholomew's hospital, London, lists a far greater number of miraculous cures attributed to the famous collection on display in the neighbouring priory, which included a piece of the True Cross and remains of the patron saint (who had been skinned alive).[53] The ownership of relics aroused fierce competition among the religious houses of medieval England, largely because they attracted substantial donations from visitors. In 1391, an investigation into abuses at another hospital dedicated to St Bartholomew, this time near Oxford, found that the fellows of Oriel College had removed a comb owned by St Edmund, a piece of the skin of the patron saint, the bones of St Stephen and a rib of St Andrew the Apostle 'which had remained from old times as relics for the adornment and honour of the chapel'.[54] Even though it lacked such covetable items, those on display at St Giles's hospital must likewise have been a focus of devotion, especially after the great rebuilding programme of the next century.

Very little is known of the original layout of the hospital chapel, which probably occupied the east end of an open-ward infirmary, in full view of the patients. This was an arrangement often adopted in twelfth- and thirteenth-century foundations, such as the leper house of St Mary Magdalen at Sprowston, which still survives on the outskirts of Norwich.[55] Close proximity to the hospital's various altars gave the sick poor an active role in its religious life, soon to be lost because of expansion. In 1271, their most generous lay patron, William de Dunwich, endowed a perpetual chantry of one priest, who was solemnly to sing a mass of the Blessed Virgin every day, while calling upon the patients lying in bed to remember him when they prayed.[56] As his will of the following year reveals, Dunwich intended to support another priest as well, probably to celebrate a similar votive mass at the altar of St Katherine, beside which he asked to be buried. To this side altar he left money for four lights, together with silver plate for reworking into 'phials' for rinsing out the vessels used in the Mass. His better pieces were added to the collection of decorated goblets begun by Bishop Suffield, and probably adorned the high altar.[57]

It was at this time that the hospital acquired the fabric and parochial rights of St Helen's Church, which then stood on the other side of Holme Street inside the precinct of Norwich cathedral priory [see Map II].[58] Friction with the Benedictine community over the vexed question of burials may have been compounded by squabbles about ritual and liturgy of the kind which so often arose when a hospital chapel threatened to usurp some of the functions (and divert the revenues) of a nearby parish church.[59] Perhaps the decision to demolish St Helen's and either find or create additional space to accommodate the parishioners had already been taken when Dunwich set up his chantry in the hospital. The insertion of a nave between the infirmary and the chapel was but one of several developments which served to favour outsiders at the expense of the patients. Some masonry in the south porch of what is now the parish church of St Helen appears to have escaped the comprehensive rebuilding programmes of the later Middle Ages and early modern period, and suggests that the original layout may have allowed direct access to the infirmary chapel from the street. This was itself provocative. A long-standing dispute between the hospital of Saint-Simon, Douai, and the cathedral chapter there concerned the celebration of mass by secular priests, the ringing of bells, the use of elaborate ritual and, worst of all, the admittance of lay worshippers into the hospital church. Here, as in many other European houses, fear that congregations and their financial support might be lost lay at the root of the problem. Not for nothing was the hospital of St John the Baptist,

1. The Salle des Pauvres of the Hôtel Dieu, Beaune, was dominated by Roger van der Weyden's magnificent rendition of the Last Judgement, painted in the 1450s, just after the hospital's foundation. The centre panel depicts St Michael weighing souls in the balance. The heavier of the two, having demonstrably failed to perform the Seven Comfortable Works, is destined for hell. To reinforce the point, lettering in black records the words of Christ [Matthew 25:41]: 'Descend from me ye cursed into everlasting fire prepared for the devil and his angels.' Imagery of the Last Judgement, intended to inspire charity and elicit the prayers of grateful patients for their patrons, dominated the iconography of the medieval hospital. St Giles's even possessed a detached chapel, dedicated to St Michael. (Museum of the Hôtel Dieu, Beaune)

2. *Illustrated by the author himself, the* Chronica Majora *of Matthew Paris contains an eye-witness account of Henry III's procession to Westminster abbey in 1247 bearing the Holy Blood of Christ in a reliquary. Among the prelates who received him was Goffredo de Preffeti, bishop of Jerusalem, a leading supporter of the Order of Bethlehem and its charitable work, who was then involved in setting up the London hospital of St Mary Bethlehem. Bishop Walter Suffield, the future founder of St Giles's hospital, preached the sermon on this occasion, being himself a keen advocate of the aims of the Order, which included the defence of religious orthodoxy. (Corpus Christi College, Cambridge, Ms 16, fo 216r)*

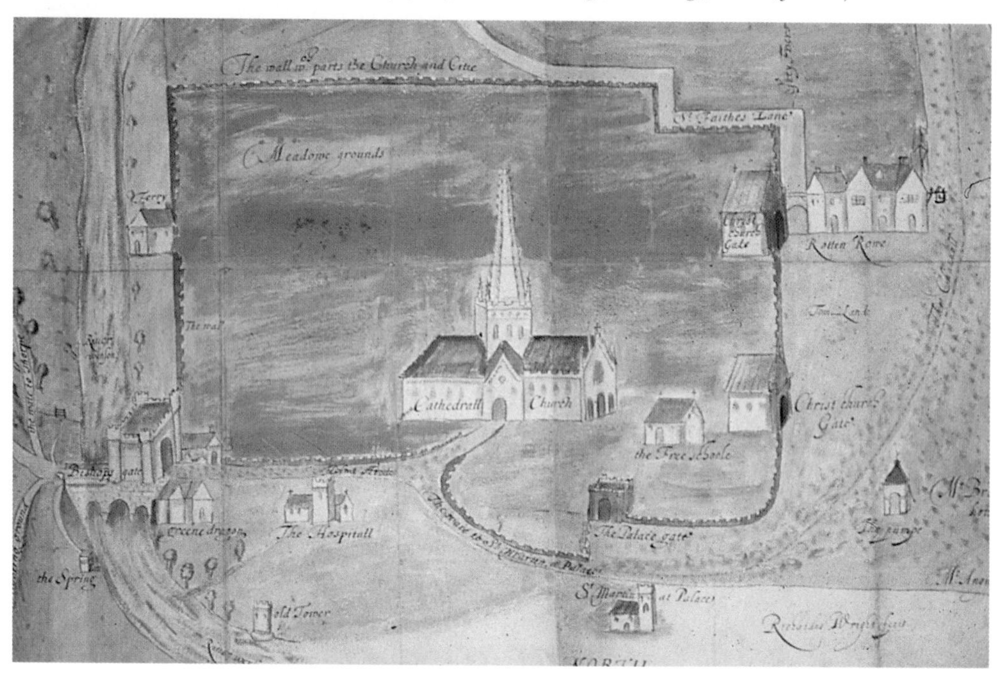

3. *Situated on the north-eastern boundary of Norwich, on waterlogged, marginal land near the River Wensum, St Giles's hospital offered a refuge to sick paupers entering the city over Bishop's Bridge, then the only crossing to the east. Its patrons, the bishops of Norwich, lived a matter of yards away in the episcopal palace and the cathedral monks occupied a large precinct on the other side of the street. The whole of this area was, indeed, an exempt liberty, directly under their jurisdiction. The turrets and gatehouse of the bridge, built in the 1340s, were burnt along with many of the hospital buildings in Kett's rebellion of 1549, when Holme Street became a focus of heavy fighting. (NRO, ACC 1997/215, a c.1630 map of Norwich reproduced by permission of Mr Peter Hornor)*

4. *The frontispiece to Jehan Henry's* Livre de Vie Active, *produced in the late fifteenth century for the sisters of the Hôtel Dieu, Paris, draws upon the metaphor of the hospital as an island of charity in a troubled sea. It also contrasts the contemplative and active aspects of the nurses' lives. A young novice, dressed in white, disembarks from the ship of religious profession (accompanied by Poverty, Chastity and Obedience) to be received by Contemplation. The arrival of a stretcher-borne patient at the door of Active Life suggests, however, that many physical demands will be made upon her, as does the scene to the right, depicting the hospital laundry. (Musée de l'Assistance Publique, Paris)*

5. *Constructed during the late 1440s and 1450s, the new stone-built cloisters of St Giles's reflect its transformation from modest hospital for the sick poor into an imposing college for secular priests. As benefactors demanded more elaborate spiritual services, the clerical establishment expanded and facilities grew increasingly impressive. Senior staff also expected a higher standard of living appropriate to their status. This view shows the master's lodgings in the north-west corner of the cloister, with the refectory (finished* c. *1457) on the west side and the brothers' dormitory on the north. (Photograph Carole Rawcliffe)*

6. Religious life in hospitals throughout medieval Europe focused upon the celebration of the Mass, the most important of the Seven Sacraments. The mere sight of the Host, which was elevated regularly before the patients, was deemed to bestow physical as well as spiritual health, while the offering itself helped to speed the immortal souls of patrons and benefactors through purgatory. This early sixteenth-century depiction of a nursing sister about to take communion comes from the Potterie Hospital, Bruges, which also housed a number of important relics and a healing shrine to the Virgin Mary. (Museum of the Potterie Hospital, Bruges)

7 and 8. An outstanding feature of St Giles's hospital was its great chancel, built in the 1380s as a long-term investment during a period of financial crisis [see Plate 28]. The aim was to create more space for the liturgy and thus attract a greater number of wealthy patrons. The chestnut ceiling, with its 252 wooden panels bearing the stencilled arms of Richard II's Queen, Anne of Bohemia, was probably completed after a royal visit to Norwich in 1383. It may well have been paid for by the King, who was always anxious to advertise his imperial connections. The ceiling of the chancel also boasts 232 painted and gilded bosses, once clearly of remarkable beauty but largely neglected for the 400 years during which the building functioned as a ward for elderly women. Major renovations were effected in the 1950s, revealing the extent of the deterioration. (Photographs Richard Tilbrook)

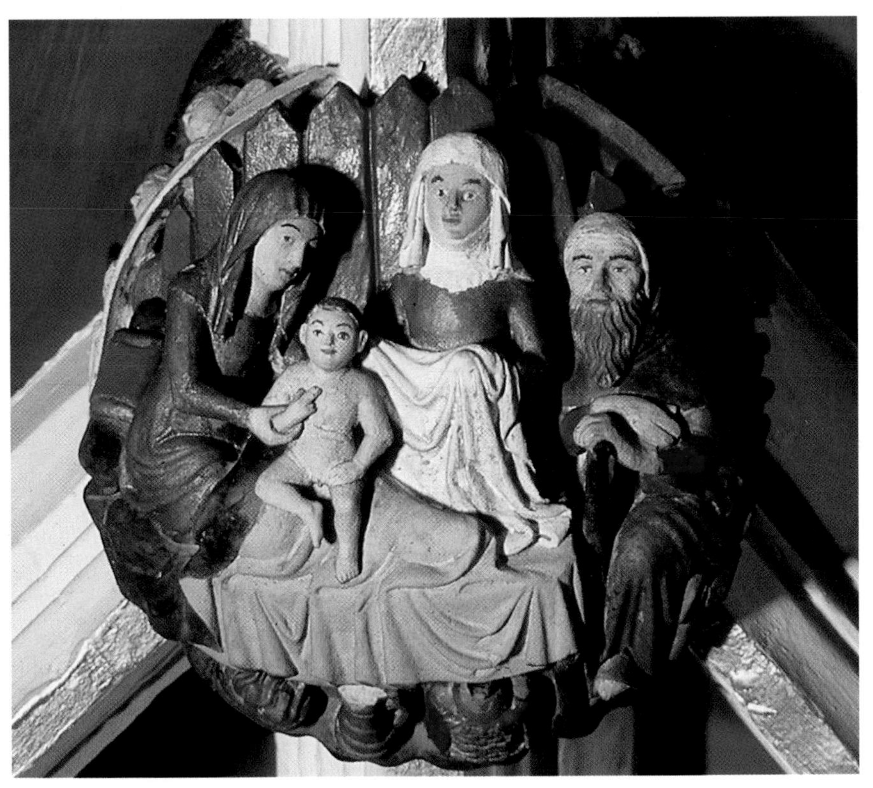

9. Built at the close of the fifteenth century, Bishop Goldwell's chantry chapel in the south transept of the hospital church contains a number of roof bosses depicting incidents in the life of Christ and his mother, the Virgin Mary [see Plate 15]. This distinctly domestic portrayal of the Christ Child with his parents and grandmother, St Anne, reflects the popularity of the cult of the Holy Kindred in the region, where affluent tradespeople and merchants espoused a comfortable and familial brand of piety. Anne was a co-dedicatee of the hospital, which by the close of the Middle Ages had placed an 'ymage' of her in the chancel, next to one of the organs. (Photograph Carole Rawcliffe)

10. The coronation of the Virgin after her assumption into heaven stands at the centre of two circles of bosses in Bishop Goldwell's chantry chapel. As an intercessor on behalf of sinful humanity, and, indeed, as the nurse serving Christ the Physician, the Virgin was frequently depicted in the paintings, sculpture and seals of medieval hospitals, offering reassurance to patrons and patients that they would have a powerful advocate on the Day of Judgement. (Photograph Carole Rawcliffe)

11. Displaying the high quality line drawing for which East Anglian workshops were famous, this illuminated processional (or guide to the performance of liturgical ceremonies) belonged to St Giles's and was probably commissioned by one of its patrons in the late fourteenth century, just after the building of the chancel. As might be expected, the feast of St Giles, which normally passed without undue ceremonial, was accorded great prominence at the hospital, becoming a highlight in the ritual year. Decorated initials in the chant for the day include a picture of an archer drawing his bow, recalling the celebrated incident in the life of the saint depicted on the hospital's seal [see Plate 17]. (BL, Department of Manuscripts, Add. Ms 57,534, fo 123v)

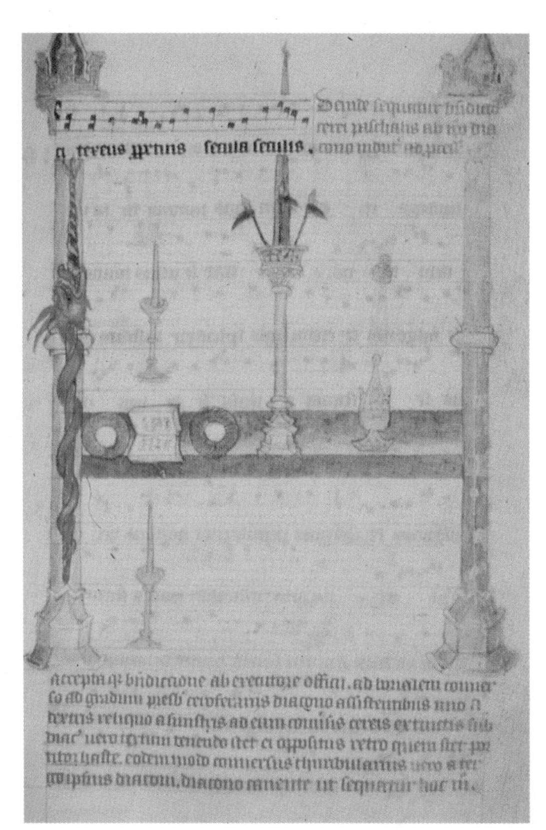

12. The St Giles's processional is now unique among medieval service books in providing coloured diagrams explaining how nine major liturgical ceremonies should be performed. Like the rest, this depiction of the blessing of the paschal candle on Easter Saturday identifies officiating clergy and other participants synecdochically, an appropriate symbol denoting their place in the procession. Here, a deacon and subdeacon are represented by tonsured heads (seen from above), two taperers by candles, the censer by a thurible and others by a book and holy water stoup. Of interest, too, is the holder encircled by a red dragon, bearing the three lenten candles twisted together, and the elaborate candlestick for the paschal candle, which is decorated with spears and flags. (BL, Department of Manuscripts, Add. Ms 57,534, fo 57r)

13. The blessing of branches on Palm Sunday was another of the Easter ceremonies to be marked by lavish displays of ritual. This diagram from the hospital processional shows the flowers and foliage given by the clergy on the high altar and the offerings of the laity on its steps. The officiating priest, designated by a blue tonsured head above a red and gold cope, is flanked by his deacon and subdeacon. Other participants are denoted by the relevant symbol – service book, candles, crucifix, holy water stoup, wand and censer. These diagrams were later to be used in the first English printed processionals produced at the beginning of the sixteenth century. (BL, Department of Manuscripts, Add. Ms 57,534, fo 32r)

*14. Developing his metaphor of the Church as a hospital for diseased souls, the French mystic, Jehan Henry, describes how penitents are admitted into the infirmary, where, 'lying on the low beds of humility' they are nursed by four professed sisters, Prudence, Temperance, Fortitude and Justice (designated by their appropriate symbols: rod, bridle, tower and scales). The accompanying illumination depicts the layout of any sizeable open ward infirmary: the shared beds are well furnished with covers and pillows; draughts are excluded by hangings; and a number of novices learn their craft by observing their superiors. (*Livre de Vie Active, *Musée de l'Assistance Publique, Paris)*

15. The hospitals of medieval England depended upon the continued support of wealthy patrons. James Goldwell, Bishop of Norwich (1472–99), almost certainly endowed this magnificent chantry chapel, where mass was to be celebrated daily for the health of his immortal soul. His younger brother, Nicholas, served as master of St Giles's, as did a number of his senior diocesan administrators, and he had the greatest confidence that his fate in the hereafter would rest in safe hands. The elaborate design of the vaulting followed that recently adopted in Norwich cathedral by Bishop Lyhart, whose rebuilding project was then being completed by Goldwell, his successor. The hospital's master mason, Robert Everard, who also worked on the cathedral, probably supervised the construction. (Photograph Richard Tilbrook)

Nottingham, forbidden, in 1243, to open its chapel doors to the people of the town, or, indeed, to have an entrance giving on to the main street.[60] As it now stands, the porch of St Giles's is a substantial structure with a vaulted roof of three bays and an upper room, which functioned as a private chapel during the fifteenth century [see Plate 26].[61] All these developments, which brought laymen and women into the hospital on a regular basis, were contentious but not unusual. Other hospitals, such as St Mark's, Bristol, and St John's, Bridgwater, welcomed lay congregations, who paid the customary parochial dues, assumed responsibility for maintaining their part of the church (the nave) and could, moreover, be approached for alms.[62] But their presence inevitably proved yet another impetus for change.

THE DEMAND FOR SPIRITUAL SERVICES

Evidence from the late thirteenth century reveals tantalising glimpses of embellishment and ornamentation at St Giles's. A gift of rents by one of the chaplains in the 1270s provided candles to illuminate the mass of the day and the Lady-Mass, which was then still being celebrated *submissa voce* (with a low voice). Before too long, however, the money was assigned to keep a lamp burning by the Crucifix at night instead, and thus, perhaps, bring comfort to the patients. By 1286 the house possessed an Easter sepulchre, surrounded by candles at passiontide; and other lights had been donated by benefactors to the high altar, the altar of the Blessed Virgin and the altar of St Nicholas. Roger de Tybenham, who, like the founder, left 20 marks for the celebration of requiem masses, also donated 50 ells of cloth to decorate the church and arranged for his anniversary to be observed there in perpetuity.[63] During the later Middle Ages up to 100 pounds of wax were purchased annually by the sacristan, who had some perfumed with flowers for use on special feast days. Since many more candles were donated or left over from the funerals which regularly took place in the church, it must already have seemed bathed in light. The altar of St Helen meanwhile served as a focus of parochial loyalty, where tithes were paid and some leading local figures were buried. The Lady Chapel, which by 1331 is described as standing to the north of the church, on the side traditionally occupied by female parishioners, may have been maintained with funds donated by the women of Holme Street.[64] There were many other devotees in the city. Some twenty-five years later, Robert de Bungay left a valuable messuage in Cordwainer Row to the hospital on the understanding that money from the rent would support a weekly mass of the Blessed Virgin to be celebrated there for his soul.[65]

As we have seen in the previous chapter, St Giles's managed to cushion itself against successive financial crises by attracting a steady flow of new endowments. Despite the threat to solvency posed in the later fourteenth century by falling land values, rising wage rates and urban decay, a degree of financial equilibrium was maintained through the support of local patrons. Yet this came at a price. Almost all of them wished to share in the spiritual benefits of the house in ways appropriate to their wealth or station. Although some were sufficiently generous to make surplus funds available for the sick poor, their first, overriding priority was to ensure that their souls would be fittingly commemorated after death. A few, such as Thomas de Preston, financed the purchase and eventual appropriation of new livings, which in turn were to bear the cost of perpetual chantries. In return for his gift of £100, in 1331,

Preston stipulated that his chantry priest was to be accorded exactly the same treatment as one of the hospital chaplains, so the house would have been obliged to feed, clothe and accommodate him, as well as paying him an annual stipend of up to 40*s*. Given the size of his initial endowment, which enabled the hospital to acquire the advowson of Mundham St Peter, this is unlikely to have placed undue strain upon the budget.[66] But it brought yet another priest and quite possibly another altar into St Helen's church.

The endowment of a perpetual chantry was a time-consuming and costly exercise, not to be attempted lightly. Neglect, incompetence or corruption on the part of the priest or the patrons might jeopardise the founder's hopes of salvation, and for this reason religious corporations, including the larger English hospitals, were extremely popular with potential donors.[67] In theory, if not always practice, they offered an effective level of supervision, a reliable promise of continuity, fitting surroundings and a plentiful supply of suitably qualified personnel. Any spare revenues could be reassigned for charitable uses, while the priest himself might prove a valuable addition to the choir or serve as church organist. Cantarists were, moreover, expected to assist their superiors by hearing confessions and administering the sacrament – duties which assumed especial importance in a hospital.[68] But, just as the injudicious sale of corrodies could place a financial millstone around the neck of any institution which thought in terms of immediate profit rather than long-term investment, so too the proliferation of chantries and chantry chaplains carried a certain element of risk. What if the original endowment proved contentious or insufficient? In response to a petition of 1350 from the master and brethren of St Giles's, Bishop Bateman of Norwich absolved the hospital of any liability to support a perpetual chantry of three priests for the benefit of the immortal souls of Hugh and Agnes Caly, who had been parties to Archdeacon Suffield's gift of land in Repps and Bastwick some eighty years earlier. Since the couple had never secured an episcopal licence, it proved relatively easy to shed this onerous burden. Justificatory claims that 'the goods of the hospital were to be expended for the sustenance of Christ's poor and especially of chaplains in poor health, for the sake of the souls of the late Bishop Walter . . . and his successors, *and for no other work*' were, however, soon forgotten once a richer and more prestigious patron appeared on the scene. Another perpetual chantry, to be funded out of the profits of a living at South Walsham, was planned by the widowed countess of Norfolk at St Giles's within a few months of Bateman's ruling and eagerly welcomed by the brethren. To their intense disappointment, as noted above, it never materialised.[69] The vogue for perpetual endowments had already begun to decline, being further affected by the imposition, in 1391, of even tighter restrictions on alienations in mortmain.[70] Instead, wealthy donors opted for alternative forms of commemoration, often with a greater liturgical component.

Men and women with limited budgets had long spent what they could afford on annuals (short-term chantries lasting just one or two years), requiem masses and special prayers.[71] In 1323, for example, the executors of John de Staving paid 30*s* for a funeral service at the hospital and a similar sum for commemorative masses; bequests for the spiritual health of Simon de Belton came to about 57*s*; and occasional receipts worth a few shillings were set aside by the sacristan for anniversaries (or obits).[72] Drawing upon the sombre and dramatic liturgy for the office and mass of the dead, obits were celebrated annually, often on or near the date of death of the donor or of any other named person. They could be tailored to personal needs and financial circumstances: the least expensive, but also, relatively speaking, the least efficacious, were performed on a collective basis by a single priest, while the most lavish might extend over a whole octave (eight days in all), with elaborate musical interludes and processions.[73] It is evident from the will of the Norwich notary, John Blomfeld (d. *c.* 1506), that St Giles's kept a bede roll, or obituary, recording the names of men and women whose deaths were to be remembered with varying degrees of solemnity in this way. One such, from the hospital of St Mary Magdalen, King's Lynn, comprises a long list begun in about 1296 of hundreds of individuals from across the region, and provides a powerful testimony to contemporary anxieties about the next life.[74]

The reckoning at St Giles's cannot have been any less impressive. Some donors were meticulous about details, reaching a careful agreement with the master before they died. Beatrice Godale's gift of rents in Holme Street was, for instance, made to the house in 1347 on the strict understanding that an annual would be celebrated for the health of her soul, and that perpetual obits would take place on the vigil of All Souls for Beatrice herself, her parents and her late husband, each of whom was to be received posthumously into the house's spiritual confraternity.[75] Sir John Orreby's release of rights in Mundham, finalised a few years earlier, is by contrast a short, workmanlike document concerned solely with legal technicalities. It is, however, endorsed with a note in a different contemporary hand to the effect that prayers were to be said for Sir John, his wife, his mother, *Dominus* Geoffrey le Scrope, *Dominus* John Orreby and other kindred.[76] Evidently uncertain as to the precise value of his estates, John Blomfeld cautiously requested that his name might be recorded in 'the obite bok to be prayd for among the brodrin and fraternyte of the said hospitall . . . as it may be born of my goodes comyng to myn executors handes'.[77]

Not surprisingly, members of the clergy showed an especial interest in such matters. John Smyth, who died in office as master in 1489, made his grant of an eighty years' lease of the manor of Coltishall conditional upon the proper performance throughout this period of an obit in the chancel of the hospital church (where he was to be buried) involving all the priests, conducts, clerks, choristers and bedesmen. Like the canon lawyer and hospital chaplain, Robert Godfrey, who arranged for a service of perpetual commemoration in 1512, he insisted upon a full ceremony of '*placebo*, *diryge* and masse of requiem be note', which was to extend over the customary period of two days.[78] So too were the services held each year in memory of Bishop Goldwell (d. 1499), one of the hospital's leading benefactors. As befitted a senior dignitary of the Church, whose generosity had extended to the citizens of Norwich, his *placebo* and *dirige* on 7 January, and the requiem mass on the following day, were attended, albeit sometimes reluctantly, by the mayor, sheriffs and at least six aldermen of Norwich, along with seven 'discrete persons' chosen from members of the common council.[79] Not to be outdone, one of John Jullys's surviving brothers settled an estate in Salhouse and Wroxham upon St Giles's for the celebration of the late master's anniversary. This fell in August, and cost about 19*s* a year in payments to priests, choristers and up to thirteen boys brought in from outside to swell the ranks of the choir. We have already seen how scrupulously the hospital discharged its obligations to the dead.[80] These must have been onerous. The chance survival of an arrangement made during the mastership of John Selot for the annual commendation, again over two days, of the souls of his patron, Bishop Lyhart, his friend, the notorious John Heydon, and his own parents suggests that the chancel often echoed with the sound of requiem masses.[81]

In common with the college of St Mary in the Fields, to which some of its staff were closely connected, St Giles's may have maintained a separate guild or fraternity for secular priests, or at least have admitted local clergy into the brotherhood of the hospital in return for their help and patronage. No mention of any formal organisation appears in the very full and numerous guild returns made for the city of Norwich in response to a parliamentary inquiry of 1386, but individual benefactors and some masters were accorded special privileges.[82] Within a few days of relinquishing office, in the summer of 1412, Roger Pratt, a figure of considerable local influence, was unanimously welcomed into the confraternity of St Giles's, there to share in all the 'alms, suffrages, prayers and spiritual benefits' accumulated by the hospital since its foundation. He was also promised the solemn and perpetual obit customarily reserved for a master who had died in office.[83] A neatly written entry at the very back of the hospital processional records in an early fifteenth-century hand the ritual to be followed when the master himself admitted a new brother. Its inclusion suggests that others, besides the chaplains and almsmen, may have knelt in St Helen's church as the master received them into this exclusive community of souls, invoking the blessing of the Holy Ghost and the merits of fraternal love.[84]

The demand for spiritual services, however welcome, placed an increasing burden upon the clerical establishment, which had to be augmented with hirelings as and when the need arose. Since priests were not supposed to celebrate mass more than once a day, extra 'conducts' were recruited from a local pool of unbeneficed clergy. As noted above, these men were customarily required to perform other duties, such as visiting the sick, and may have been selected at St Giles's because of their musical ability. If necessary, they could be accommodated in lodgings in the precinct, sometimes at the expense of the hospital, but more often as a charge on the estate of the deceased. It seems likely that many of the boarders listed in the accounts from the fourteenth century onwards were serving on a temporary basis as cantarists in St Helen's church. Occasionally, as in 1524, when Richard Wells rented a chamber for three months so that he could 'celebrate for Edward Norwich and his wife', the reason for their presence is clear. The two chaplains, Peter Hall and Henry Curle, who appear as boarders in 1483–4, and George Virly, who is first mentioned as a chaplain-chorister and occasional boarder shortly afterwards, probably fell into this category. Virly later joined the permanent staff, having evidently made a good enough impression by 1498 to be offered secure employment as a full-time chaplain and sacristan when a vacancy occurred.[85]

That senior clergy might call in old favours to secure accommodation for their cantarists is evident from the will of William Soper, who died in 1519 while serving as master. In it he made provision for two priests 'of reputable conduct and known reputation' to celebrate the exequies of the dead every day for his soul in the hospital church for two years. He hoped the brothers would agree to give them free board and lodging, and as a douceur he spent lavishly on his funeral in the Lady Chapel, while also ensuring that a cash sum of

£40 would eventually be paid in instalments to the house. His bequest of 13*s* 4*d* to each chaplain and 6*s* 8*d* to each additional priest present at his funeral suggests that he expected a number of conducts to attend.[86] The proliferation of hirelings is better documented during this period, but was certainly no recent phenomenon. Nor was the expansion of the regular establishment. Since no fewer than nine priests were named in the account for 1306, it looks very much as if Bishop Salmon's decision to double the original complement of four chaplains at the end of the decade was made in recognition of a *fait accompli*. One of the lay brother's places was assigned shortly afterwards to support a chantry priest, bringing the roster up to ten and necessitating the purchase of a new gradual. During the 1320s the number of priests on the payroll fluctuated between eight and eleven, each receiving a modest annual stipend of 20*s*, with robes and board.[87] To this basic fee would be added the gifts of money, clothes and even books made with increasing frequency by the men and women who sought burial or commemoration in the hospital church.

THE NEW CHANCEL

John de Ely, who died in 1383 leaving a missal to the hospital and 3*s* 4*d* to each of the chaplains in return for their prayers, was one of the first to be interred in the spectacular new chancel.[88] Over 25 metres and five bays in length, it constituted a major extension to the existing building, and was reserved as sacred space for the clergy and choristers. The east end of the old church, where the high altar had previously stood, could thus be incorporated into an enlarged nave, making more room for the congregation and the constantly growing number of tombs and side altars [see Plate 26]. Yet, because both the east and west ends of the nave were completely walled off during the sixteenth century to create a far smaller post-Dissolution church, it is easy to underestimate the impact of the original design and its effect on liturgical practices. Sweeping alterations undertaken by the civic authorities at various points after 1548 resulted in the construction of two discrete upper-storey wards for the sick poor: one (for men) in what had been the medieval infirmary to the west of the nave, and the other (for women) in the chancel. Today's visitors often remark upon the unusual height of the present parish church in relation to its length, being unaware that their late medieval predecessors worshipped in a building which was approximately three times as long [see Map III]. Light must also have intensified the sense of airiness and space: a tall, perpendicular-style window at the west end of the infirmary (the central aisle of which was then open to the nave) and another at the east end of the chancel (separated from the rest of the church only by the customary carved rood screen) then illuminated the entire building [see Plate 31].[89] The insertion of an ingle-nook and chimney against the great east window and the erection of partitioned chambers for the elderly women living on the upper floor of the chancel make it even harder to imagine what this part of the hospital would have been like in the later Middle Ages. Nevertheless, despite the cumulative effects of long neglect and extensive rebuilding, some of the splendour of the painted ceiling with its 252 surviving wooden panels, of the elaborate tracery, and of the lofty proportions still remains.[90]

On a purely practical level, the new chancel provided space for the choir stalls, processions and elaborate ritual which some hospitals, such as St John's, Cambridge, simply could not find. Others, including St Mary's, Bishopsgate, in London, and St Bartholomew's, Bristol, occupied large enough sites to permit wholesale restructuring. In both these cases, the original infirmary buildings were given over entirely to ecclesiastical use, while the sick poor were removed to separate, more private quarters.[91] Rebuilding at St Giles's clearly represented a calculated investment, designed to assert the political connections and spiritual authority of the hospital, and thus elicit the continued support of influential patrons. The cynical, but undeniably realistic, response to complaints by lollard polemicists about reckless expenditure on 'heye chyrchis' was that 'people take no account of the poor and impotent . . . either to honour or obey them'.[92] In short, it paid to advertise. Towers and gatehouses of the kind still visible at the Kepier hospital outside Durham and at the hospital of St Cross, Winchester, offered a reassuring display of earthly as well as spiritual power, of investments shrewdly and profitably made.[93]

Even if, as the surviving accounts for the late 1390s suggest, the construction of the chancel and almost complete rebuilding of the nave and infirmary were staggered over a long period, a project on this scale would still have placed an intolerable burden on the hospital's already strained finances. Chronic debts at St Saviour's hospital, Bury St Edmund's, which in the mid-1380s was overspending to the tune of between £235 and £283 a year, were almost certainly occasioned by expenditure on the new chapel and its lavish furnishings, together with a bell-tower 'of considerable altitude as well as magnitude'.[94] A review of finances at the London hospital of St Thomas Acon, made in 1518, recorded total annual receipts of £317, a backlog of £719 overspent in previous years and an additional deficit of no less than £1,431 occasioned by recent building works. That the master succeeded in reducing this formidable burden of debt to a manageable £80 was due in no small part to the support of the Mercers' Company, which had by then stepped in to offer the hospital its help and protection on an official footing.[95] St Thomas's had long enjoyed a mutually profitable association with this rich and powerful city guild. Its members held business meetings in a hall above their own private chapel at the west end of the hospital church, and spent lavishly on vestments, plate and fittings of the highest quality.[96] In 1517 they began rebuilding the hall and chapel, 'to the enlarging and beautifying of the said church and increase and maintenance of God's service'. On completion, the bill stood at £2,736, over and above the £50 spent on a carved Flemish altarpiece.[97] Labour costs accounted for well over two-thirds of this outlay, as they may well have done in Norwich during the late fourteenth century, when the wages of skilled craftsmen soared because of the dramatic slump in population. Yet to be financially viable at any time, large-scale building programmes needed the support of wealthy patrons. St Giles's had only limited connections with the mercantile elite of Norwich at this stage in its history, but it could rely on powerful friends in the Church.

A substantial part of the initial cost of the new chancel was probably underwritten by Bishop Henry Despenser, who is said (without any supporting evidence) to have commissioned it as an act of thanksgiving for the collapse of the Peasants' Revolt. His own part in the brutal suppression of the uprising of 1381 is well known, as also is his remarkable talent for fund-raising, especially from pious women, anxious to secure absolution for themselves and their relatives.[98] He was certainly rich and ambitious enough to contemplate an undertaking on this scale at St Giles's in the early 1380s, although the fiasco of his crusade in Flanders, his impeachment before Parliament in October 1383 and the subsequent confiscation of his temporalities as bishop of Norwich would have brought his financial involvement to an abrupt and inglorious end.[99] The burden may then have fallen upon his archdeacon and trusted counsellor, John Derlyngton, who had briefly served as master of St Giles's in the 1370s. Derlyngton was the first of a long series of diocesan officials with impressive academic credentials to hold this office, and he retained a set of rooms in the precinct for most of his life. That he continued to nurse grandiose plans for the hospital seems beyond doubt. His donation of £24 (following an earlier gift of £28) made possible the completion of the massive new bell-tower in 1397; and an endowment of 1410, with which he intended to support a perpetual chantry in the hospital church, was sufficiently generous to generate an annual income worth six or seven times the cost of a chaplain's stipend.[100] Other benefactors from the ranks of the Norfolk clergy included Roger Eaton, the parson of Yelverton, who donated large quantities of paving stone for the chancel and nave as late as 1396. Eaton had been a hospital chaplain in 1375; he appears as overseer of its estates in Costessey a decade later; and in his will of 1405 he asked to be buried in the church which he had helped to beautify. Like so many of the hospital's former employees, he also set aside money (in this case 10*s* out of rents worth 20*s* a year) for the celebration of his anniversary.[101]

Whoever settled the bill, there can be no doubt that the construction of the chancel was an exercise in architectural patronage at the highest level. The decorated perpendicular style, especially evident in the flamboyant, variegated tracery of the windows, had been developed on major royal building projects by Edward III's master masons, and was still something of a novelty in East Anglia [see Plate 27]. John Harvey has argued that John Wodhirst (d. 1401), who rose to become a specialist stone-carver at Westminster during the 1350s and probably directed work on the presbytery of Norwich cathedral throughout the following decade, executed the design. By 1385 he was personally supervising operations in the cathedral cloister, just a few hundred yards from the hospital, so the circumstantial as well as stylistic evidence seems persuasive. Wodhirst's hand may also be detected at the parish churches of Swanton Morley and North Walsham and at Ingham priory in Norfolk, at St Gregory's church in the centre of Norwich, and at Ely cathedral, where, between 1387 and 1393, he earned the substantial annual fee of £4 (with robes) as master of the work on the reredos of the high altar.[102] During the fifteenth century glaziers were called in from time to time to work in the hospital church. Its windows almost certainly displayed the fine craftsmanship for which Norwich glass-painters were famous, and of which many examples still survive elsewhere. Members of the Hadesco family and other local glaziers, who had been employed at St Stephen's chapel, Westminster, during Wodhirst's time there, may possibly have been retained at St Giles's too, but we can only speculate on this point.[103]

As it stands today, the most striking and original feature of the chancel is the chestnut ceiling, divided by intersecting ribs into 252 rectangular panels with foliated bosses at each corner [see Plate 28]. On every panel was first stencilled and then painted a black eagle with outspread wings, arched claws, a red beak and a long tongue [see Plate 7]. This was evidently done at ground level, since some of the wooden boards still bear the Roman numerals used to facilitate re-assembly *in situ*.[104] The 232 bosses were originally painted and gilded, but, like that of the eagles, the intensity of their colour has faded [see Plate 8]. Some of the larger, more ornate ones towards the centre of the ceiling are decorated with male, female and leonine heads, leaves and flowers, while three on the north side once bore shields displaying emblems of the Passion, the *Arma Christi*. Tradition maintains that the ceiling was installed by Bishop Despenser to mark the visit of Richard II and his young bride, Anne of Bohemia, to Norwich in the early summer of 1383. But he was then in Flanders, with more pressing business in hand, and the eagle motif may, in fact, have been proposed by Richard himself. The royal progress through East Anglia, which took in the great abbeys of Ely and Bury St Edmunds, was not an unmitigated success. With his accustomed asperity, the monastic chronicler, Thomas Walsingham, attacked the predatory foreigners who accompanied the queen, while blaming Richard for his failure to curb their extravagance. Vanity and self-indulgence blinded the spendthrift monarch to the extortions committed in his name.[105] Richard certainly used his artistic patronage to advertise the powerful connections which marriage to the daughter of one Holy Roman Emperor and sister of another had brought him. The imperial eagle (which at this point was still depicted with a single rather than a double head) was an obvious and unmistakeable device: it decorated the tomb which Richard himself designed for Anne in 1395; and appears on the monumental brass of the Norfolk knight, Sir Simon Felbrigg, who was Richard's standard bearer and an intimate of Archdeacon Derlyngton's.[106]

Some members of the royal party may have been accommodated at St Giles's hospital in 1383; and there is a strong possibility that Richard and his queen inspected the new chancel, then still in the process of construction. Although the house was dedicated to St Giles, Walter Suffield had placed it under the special protection of St Anne, whose cult was naturally dear to her namesake, the queen. A papal mandate ordering the official observance of her feast in England had been issued in 1382 on the occasion of the royal marriage; and we know that the hospital maintained an altar and lights dedicated to the saint.[107] By the close of the fifteenth century, and probably long before, her image stood in the chancel. Suitably transformed into 'ryght ryche folk', leading comfortable, bourgeois lives similar to their own, Anne and the Holy Kindred inspired particular devotion among the affluent East Anglian middle classes. Women especially identified with a saint who, in the course of her three marriages, had accumulated a large extended family and had personal experience of the travails of pregnancy and childbirth [see Plate 9].[108] So both Richard and his queen had good reason to favour the hospital with their patronage. Two of the heads carved on the crowns of the wall arches in the side-chapel to the south of the nave are traditionally said to depict the couple.

Here was an appropriate setting for the full panoply of ritual which both lay and ecclesiastical patrons required, and which the older English hospitals had to provide as insurance against the looming threat of bankruptcy. Even those hospitals, like St Giles's, which continued to help the poor, had to adapt to changing circumstances. Not least was a growing sophistication on the part of potential benefactors, whose desire for salvation led them to emphasise the *quality* as well as the quantity of prayers offered on their behalf.

Successive outbreaks of plague had, moreover, engendered a heightened sense of vulnerability. 'The shortnes and unstablenes of this lyf, the hastynes of deth [and] the ferefulnes of dome' preyed upon the collective imagination. Intimations of mortality must have been especially strong in a city whose population had fallen by almost two-thirds in the space of sixty years. Thoughts of *mors improvisa* concentrated the mind with unusual clarity upon the importance of spiritual health.[109] The consequences were predictable. It is no coincidence that the London hospital of St Mary Bethlehem, a house badly affected by the loss of patrons during the first plague epidemic of 1349, turned to the sale of indulgences and the establishment of a confraternity to ease its financial difficulties.[110]

LITURGICAL DEVELOPMENTS

At St Mark's hospital, Bristol, the fifteenth-century masters and brethren may actually have gone so far as to falsify their early charters in order to justify a greatly enlarged clerical establishment and corresponding reduction in almsgiving. Almost half the poor inmates were, in fact, choristers, whose principal duty was to enhance the daily round of worship with votive antiphons, sung masses and other musical embellishments. As one of the hospital's many patrons noted, in 1351: 'they who assist the work of a house of the Lord by increasing its opportunities to perform its blessed commerce of changing the earthly into the celestial and the transitory into the divine deserve reward'. The reward in question was nothing short of eternal salvation, which hospitals such as St Mark's and St Giles's, Norwich, 'moved by the desire to provide their benefactors with a safer reckoning before their eternal judges', promised to secure.[111] In an age notable for its pervasive culture of 'good lordship', clientage and protection, they performed a vital role as spiritual intermediaries, whose function was to 'labour' the almighty on behalf of miserable sinners, just as a courtier might agree to solicit a royal pardon for one of his retainers.[112] Success did not, however, come without expenditure and effort. Hand-in-hand with a desire to improve the fabric and furnishings of hospital churches (discernible at St Giles's in such carefully itemised purchases as 'silkfrenges' and thread bought in 1397 for the repair of vestments), went concern for proper liturgical practices.

Reforms at St Saviour's hospital, Bury St Edmunds, in 1385, led to the refurbishment of the chapel and the provision of new service books.[113] A few years later, William of Wykeham's investigations into the state of the former *leprosarium* of St Mary Magdalen outside Winchester revealed an even more abundant provision of crucifixes, banners, chalices, relics, vestments, embroidered altar cloths and hangings, as well as at least fifteen service books, one being worth the substantial sum of £5. These, in turn, were eclipsed by the contents of the sacristy, treasury and library of the London hospital of St Mary Elsing, which in 1448 also included more than sixty volumes on theology, canon law, history and natural science, and testify to the generosity of its well-wishers[114] Some institutions were, however, found wanting. High on the list of abuses which came to light at the Bethlehem hospital, in 1403, was the master's failure to celebrate mass for the patients. Their chapel was poorly equipped, its stock of one silver chalice and four 'unsuitable' volumes being deemed grossly inadequate. Matters had improved considerably by the close of the century, when the master, Thomas Denman, made bequests of jewellery and plate to the image of the Blessed Virgin and her altar there.[115] Patronage of this sort was essential if hospitals were to discharge their proper function in serving the dead as well as the living, and, indeed, compete for benefactors with handsomely endowed parish churches. At the hospital of St Giles, Kepier, well over thirty liturgical volumes and an impressive collection of ecclesiastical furnishings had been accumulated by the early sixteenth century. The library then possessed four graduals, two lectionaries, three processionals, two manuals, an ordinal, five mass books, five psalters, seven antiphonals, a hymnal, one book of epistles and two of gospels, a bible illuminated with gold, selections from the writings of St John Chrysostom, a book called '*Catholicam*' (a Latin dictionary) and a copy of *The Golden Legend*.[116] At least five of these volumes had been acquired through the largesse of Robert Wycliffe (d. 1423), chancellor and receiver general of Bishop Langley of Durham, who had lived in some state at the hospital during his years as master.[117] Wycliffe was a contemporary of John Derlyngton, a remarkably similar figure, whose attachment to St Giles's proved so influential at this time. Derlyngton's patronage manifested itself in bricks and mortar, but he may also have commissioned the illuminated processional, now in the British Library, which dates from the late fourteenth century and belonged to the hospital before the Dissolution.[118]

Medieval processionals were small, portable books containing the music for the responsories and anthems sung in the increasingly elaborate processions made in some English churches before mass on Sundays, after evensong in Easter week, on Rogation days and at other special festivals [see Plate 29]. They also provided clear directions to the participants, who would have included choristers, vergers, candle-bearers, censers and crucifers, as well as the officiating priest and his assistants.[119] As we have seen, St Giles's followed the Salisbury Use, with modifications to allow for the observance of synodal feast days. A rubric in the hospital processional notes that the 'Norwich Use' is to be followed on the feast of the translation of St Edmund, an East Anglian saint.[120] As might be expected, the feast of St Giles, usually marked by nothing more elaborate than the all-purpose chant, *miles Christi*, is here given particular prominence. Two chants, one in rhyme, the other in prose, are recorded, and it appears, moreover, from the text that a special office was customarily sung or said on this important day in the hospital calendar.[121] The players who performed 'at various times' at the hospital in 1375 almost certainly enlivened the feast day celebrations, which on subsequent occasions were marked by visits from the city waits and the bishop's minstrels, as well as a lavish banquet involving the hire of catering staff, servants, female dish-washers and quantities of extra pewter vessels.[122] Suffield's own synodal statutes had forbidden clergy from indulging in such frivolous activities, but times had changed. Since reformers now accused church choirs of singing in a 'fascyon more convenyent to mynstrellys then to devoite mynystyrys', sacred and profane may have sounded remarkably similar.[123]

The ownership of a processional – and the hospital had at least two – presupposes an interest in ceremonial which was by no means universal.[124] Ninety-six of the 358 churches visited by the archdeacon of Norfolk in 1368 did not possess one, whereas only sixteen lacked an ordinal, which was considered essential for divine worship.[125] The relatively high quality of penmanship and illumination displayed in the hospital processional (which measures a handy 140 mm × 220 mm) further reflects the value placed upon it. The text, in black ink with extensive rubrics, is interspersed with ornamented initials. The largest and most impressive are decorated with carefully painted red and blue leaves and exuberant sprays of foliage; others in gold leaf on a blue and pink ground stand squarely against the margins. The style is remarkably similar to that of two large fifteenth-century annotated breviaries from the diocese of Norwich, also now in the British Library, although the line-drawing in the processional is infinitely more delicate and imaginative.[126] Many capital letters incorporate lightly coloured sketches of human heads, foliage and figures. Appropriately, given Walter Suffield's love of the chase, the latter include hunting dogs, as well as a harpist, a lion and a dragon. An archer, drawing his bow, points upwards from one of the capitals in the chant for the feast of St Giles: a reminder of the incident of the fugitive hind depicted on the hospital seal [see Plate 11].[127] Of even greater interest are nine unique diagrams showing how the processions were to be conducted. These adopt the unusual approach of identifying participants synecdochically, an appropriate symbol or garment serving to denote where the priests (tonsured heads and copes), crucifer (a processional cross), censer (a thurible) and so forth should stand.

No other such diagrams are known to survive in manuscript form, although early sixteenth-century printed editions of the Salisbury Processional contain sets of up to thirteen, which, it has been argued, may well derive from the St Giles's volume.[128] There is no means of telling if the artist who executed the diagrams ever saw the inside of St Helen's church and depicted the altars, images and furnishings as he saw them. Some of the candle-holders, encircled with coiled red dragons, are particularly intriguing, given the hospital's subsequent connections with the influential city guild of St George [see Plate 12].[129] But they, too, may represent no more than a flight of fancy, inspired by the practice (adopted at both Westminster abbey and Hereford cathedral) of decorating the spear which carried the new fire in Holy Week with the effigy of a serpent.[130] Passiontide processions were among the most lavish and theatrical of the ecclesiastical year, and St Giles's may have been tempted to ape many larger churches by mounting an extravagant display. The depiction of the blessing of palms, when offerings of foliage from the priests (on an altar bearing an elaborate frontal and large image of the Crucifixion) and congregation (on the steps) were sprinkled with holy water, raises the interesting possibility that the full Salisbury rite was followed on such occasions [see Plate 13]. This would have made considerable demands upon the choir, which, by the fifteenth century, at least, possessed sufficient resources (tenor, trebles and bass) to perform the Passion according to St Matthew. Crosses made from the branches were deemed to offer protection against disease, and may have been distributed among the almsmen.[131] That each of these diagrams was added shortly after the text is evident from the positioning of the borders, and the empty space at the start of the entry for the feast of Candlemas, which was presumably intended for a tenth diagram. Processionals did not, however, *need* such plans to be intelligible and useful. We may assume that the book was made for an institution which valued the liturgy for its own sake and could now, after the late fourteenth-century rebuilding programme, provide an appropriate setting for the choir and priests to process in splendour.

Because criticism of the high cost of such ceremonies frequently went hand-in-hand with protests about indifference towards the deserving poor, hospitals, like friaries, presented an easy target. 'Special preyeris for dede men soulis mede in oure chirche . . . is the false ground of almesse dede', ran one complaint, which asserted that 'alle almes houses of Ingelond' owed their survival to a wicked act of deception 'nout fer from symonie'.[132] During the late fourteenth and early fifteenth centuries the question of reform became a matter for political debate, as the House of Commons began to agitate for improvements in hospital provision.[133] Although plans for a nation-wide enquiry into abuses came to nothing, the staff and patrons of hospitals like St Giles's clearly felt vulnerable to attack, and tended as a result to adopt an even more entrenched position.[134] The response of John Malvern, a doctor of theology, royal physician and commissioner at a series of important heresy trials held in 1393, 1397 and 1410 provides a good example of the general reaction. While master of the hospital of St Katherine at Ledbury, Herefordshire, Malvern used his considerable influence a few years later to secure a papal licence for 'a bell, which may be sounded at hours convenient for the celebration of divine offices . . . and to have mass and other services celebrated in the chapel even solemnly and *alta voce* (with a loud voice)'.[135]

At St Giles's the bells pealed from Derlyngton's tower, which from 1397 stood four-square and powerful against the west end of the church, and now provides a dramatic contrast on the skyline to the elegant cathedral spire. Bells played a prominent part in the ceremonial life of the hospital, welcoming important visitors and tolling the exequies of the dead.[136] Their presence could prove another cause of friction with parish clergy, jealous of their rights and revenues. It was agreed in 1283 that the hospital of St Thomas, Southwark, might bury 'outsiders', as well as its own staff and patients, but only with the approval of the nearby rector, and on a strict understanding that no more than two bells weighing under 100 pounds could be rung. St Giles's was not fettered by such restrictions, the size of the tower, with its stone-faced buttresses, testifying to the weight of the four large bells which hung there [see Plates 26 and 31]. The chime was carefully maintained: in 1488–9, for example, Edmund 'le Belhanger' of Elsing spent five days in the hospital supervising necessary adjustments.[137] Lollard tracts and sermons inveighed against the cost and ostentation of funerals, with their elaborate liturgy and sounding bells, rung to elicit the prayers of the faithful and hasten the souls of the deceased on their way through purgatory. A number of heretics tried at Norwich between 1428 and 1431 had denounced the use of church bells as yet another pretext for lining 'prestes purses', some going so far as to equate them with 'Antecristes hornes'.[138] Philip Repingdon (d. 1424), sometime bishop of Lincoln and a lollard sympathiser, had insisted that there was to be no clamorous bell-ringing at his funeral, but that all his money was to go to the poor. Spiritual abnegation on this scale was not, however, practised by the staunchly orthodox elite of medieval Norwich, whose members regularly made detailed arrangements for prayers and requiem masses to be sung or said at St Giles's during the fifteenth and early sixteenth centuries. Some, such as the alderman William Norwich

(d. 1470), left money to each of the priests, clerks and choristers on the condition that they marked his passing with 'solemn exequies and masses with ringing of bells and other appropriate solemnities'.[139]

THE CHOIR

With an establishment of about seven chaplains, various conducts and seven or more boy choristers in the late 1390s, St Giles's hospital possessed musical resources superior to many collegiate foundations of the period. The greatly enlarged chancel was equipped with canopied choir stalls, which were probably fitted at this time. Accounts drawn up in January 1397 record a payment of £4 12*s* 1*d* on paving and tiling the chancel and church and on wooden boards for 'les stoles'.[140] The 'stoles' or seats in question may, however, have been pews: the laying of a new stone floor in the newly enlarged nave would have offered an ideal opportunity for the provision of formal seating for at least some of the congregation.[141] Laymen of high status might retreat with their 'cosshyn, carpet and curteyn, bedes and boke' into the chancel of a cathedral or parish church, to sit alongside the clergy, but other worshippers often had to stand, sit on the floor or bring their own stools. Lounging, loitering, wandering about from one altar to the next and even flirting were common, and caused growing concern to an ecclesiastical establishment already exercised about the problems of lay ignorance and heterodoxy.[142] Fixed pews not only delivered a captive audience for sermons; they also ensured a degree of quiet and concentration during long, and potentially challenging, musical interludes. The pews in St Helen's church survived the Dissolution, but the choir stalls were ripped out by the civic authorities almost as soon as they took control of the hospital. In May 1549 the assembly 'enacted and agreed upon divers consideracions that the lede of the same chauncell, the pathement and the stalles or deskes with the selyng [canopy] annexed to the same stalles or deskes' should be sold.[143] By an irony clearly not lost upon alderman Thomas Codde, who supervised the new poor house, at least two statements of account compiled during this period were bound in pages torn from one of the hospital's fifteenth-century missals. Illuminated in blue and red, they record the notation for sequences from four different votive masses, including that of the Blessed Virgin as sung during full services in Advent [see Plates 42 and 43]. Other volumes were no doubt used by the governors 'to serve theyr iakes . . . to scoure theyr candelstyckes and . . . rubbe their bootes'.[144]

The acoustic of the new chancel at St Giles's had almost certainly encouraged experimentation with polyphony from the outset. This required specialist training, and was a regular feature of worship in such hospitals as the former *leprosarium* at Sherburn in County Durham (four chaplains, four clerks and two choristers) and St Leonard's, York. The latter could boast by far the largest choir in England, with more boys in the mid-fourteenth century than the two cathedrals of Exeter and Salisbury combined. Then numbering no fewer than thirty, as specified in the hospital statutes, the boys were taught singing as well as Latin grammar, their tuition being grounded to a notable extent on the liturgy they would have performed on an almost daily basis.[145] Not surprisingly, ecclesiastical reformers of the period took particular exception to such 'gret criynge and joly chauntynge', which they denounced, along with other manifestations of secular pomp, as an instrument of the devil. Exposure to the 'abhomynable blastis and lowd criynge . . . of song, as deschaunt, countre note and orgene [formal polyphony]' was, they maintained, a certain incitement to lust and vainglory, whereas an honest sermon or reading from the gospel would foster a spirit of pious humility.[146] Even worse, the money spent on such excesses deprived poor children of education and took bread from the hungry:

> Thes worldly prelates . . . don not here sacrifices bi mekenesse of herte and mornynge and compunccion for here synnes and the peplis, but with knackynge [caterwauling] of newe songs, as orgen or deschant, and motetis of holouris [whoremongers]; and with worldly pride of costy vestymentis and othere ornementis bought with pore mennus goodis. And suffren hem perische for meschef, and laten pore men haue nakid sidis and ded wallis haue grete plente of wast gold.[147]

From the 1420s onwards, testators leaving cash or goods to St Giles's for requiem masses or other acts of commemoration generally made a clear distinction between priests serving in the hospital on either a temporary or permanent basis and 'them that occupie the quere daily'. Legacies of a few pence customarily went to 'euery chyld of the chapell', while the choristers of 'mannys age' received slightly more.[148]

By the third quarter of the fifteenth century, at the very latest, staffing arrangements had been regularised to set the choir on a yet more formal footing. This involved a reduction in the number of priests, and the creation of three permanent choral posts. Six priests (described as brothers of the hospital), were joined in 1478–9 by two chaplain-choristers and a layman named Robert Dunne, whose role was to 'sing divine service'. All drew the same salary of 40*s* a year, and all were provided with food and clothing. Other clerks and laymen were recruited on an *ad hoc* basis when additional voices were needed, and if necessary extra surplices could be made 'for outsiders when they celebrated in the choir'. Dunne left after a few years, but laymen remained a permanent feature of the hospital choir.[149] Disapproval of this trend, which reflects the growing complexity and demands of late medieval English church music, was not confined to neo-protestant reformers. At the hospital of St Thomas Acon the presence of lay choristers was deemed subversive, although it would have been difficult to maintain the high musical standards of the house without them. An account of the installation of John Young as master, in 1510, describes an elaborate ceremony, 'the hole quere syngyng *te Deum laudamus*', with much bell-ringing and processing about the church.[150] Laymen were, however, not always to blame for disruptive behaviour. In the close, sometimes unwelcome proximity of the choir stalls, petty quarrels and displays of temperament among the clergy could get out of hand. The circumstances which led Thomas Sweyn to depart 'voluntarily' from his chaplaincy at St Giles's half way through the year in 1487 remain unknown. But in 1526 bickering in the choir between William Hecker and John Bredenham threatened to disturb the celebration of divine service.[151]

Study and rehearsals now loomed large in the daily routine of choristers. It would be interesting to know what role John Scarlet, who served as a priest of St Giles's in 1430, played in coaching the boys and chaplains, since he was later retained as master of the song school at Norwich cathedral priory. There he was responsible for the elaborate ritual of the Lady-Mass and probably gave the monks lessons in polyphony.[152] Similar duties appear to have been undertaken at the hospital later in the century by Robert Godfrey, whose salary as a priest was augmented in 1480 'for keeping the organs'. His replacement as organist in 1486, by a chorister specifically hired for this post at an extra 13*s* 4*d* a year, suggests that the authorities now recognised the importance of engaging a skilled professional, unencumbered by administrative duties, for at least part of the year.[153] Before long, in 1500, a layman named Richard Frevylle found employment as both organist and master of the choirboys. Such a step had already been taken at the London hospital of St Anthony, which had received a handsome legacy in 1449 for the support of a clerk to instruct the scholars in both polyphony (*in cantico organico*) and plainsong (*plano cantico*). St Anthony's was so famous for its choir that in 1469 the royal minstrels set up a fraternity there; and the boys studied music as part of their general education.[154] By 1505, Frevylle was described as 'master of the boys', his other duties being to 'help in the choir', which he did, with occasional absences, until 1523.[155] His contribution to the musical life of the hospital may well have been considerable, as he had an impressive and unusually well-documented early training, first as a chorister (1486–9) and then as senior boy (by 1494) at St George's Chapel, Windsor, an establishment famous for the quality of its musicianship. One of his compositions, a *nunc dimittis*, perhaps sung at St Giles's, still survives, having passed into the hands of the bibliophile, John Smith (d. 1563), who collected material in East Anglia.[156] The intruiging possibility that Frevylle may have been supported in his early studies by the hospital is raised by the presence on the staff of the baker and brewer, Roger Frevylle, in the late 1480s. There can have been few more auspicious places in the region for a talented young chorister to begin his musical career, quite possibly as a protégé of Oliver Dynham, whose dereliction of his magisterial duties was in part due to the rival attractions of a canonry at Windsor.[157] It is not known if another putative kinsman, Humphrey Frevylle, who began reading for a doctorate in music at Cambridge University, in 1495, after five years' study *in patria*, shared this connection with St Giles's. Two other relatives, Nicholas and Edmund, certainly did, the latter rising to become a senior chaplain just before the Dissolution.[158] On his return to Norwich, Richard Frevylle may have worked alongside John Whetacre, the master of the episcopal school, who was allocated premises in the hospital after the fire of 1507, and taught the charity boys grammar in return. Whetacre also helped out as a chorister, before being engaged in 1512 at an unusually generous stipend of 60*s* (with robes and board) to teach singing as well. One account notes that he coached 'men and boys residing in the hospital', which suggests that, like John Scarlet, he trained adult voices, too.[159]

By this date the hospital possessed impressive instrumental resources, Frevylle's arrival having coincided with, and possibly prompted, a donation made by the master, John Jullys, of a 'pair' (that is a single box) of organs acquired by him from Hoxne, the country seat of the bishops of Norwich. Many parish churches bought second-hand organs as wealthier institutions commissioned new ones, and the episcopal chapel is likely to have maintained exacting standards. The organ from Hoxne was placed next to the image of St Anne in the chancel of the hospital church, while the 'great organs' and 'small organs' already *in situ* were overhauled at a cost of 66*s* 8*d*, likewise at Jullys' expense.[160] The smaller instrument probably stood in the Lady Chapel, where it would have been used to accompany the elaborate votive antiphons sung in masses of the Blessed Virgin. A raised gallery or 'organ perke' may subsequently have been constructed in the choir to improve the acoustic. In 1525 Richard Nyseham, one of the hospital's wealthiest tenants, left 6*s* 8*d* to pay for the repair and gilding of the 'perke', but it is possible that he was describing the carved rood screen at the west end of the chancel rather than an organ loft.[161] St Jerome had compared the human body to an organ, which might be played upon by good works to produce a melody in praise of God, and Jullys's gift was in fact described in the records as an almsdeed. So too was the sum of 110*s* raised by him in donations for the replacement, repair and tuning of three of the hospital's bells 'in honour of St Giles'. The various organs were subsequently overhauled at the same time as the clocks and 'le clokkewhele', which serves as a reminder that mechanical chimes, as well as the bells in the tower, were used during special ceremonies to heighten the sense of occasion and increase the cheerful noise.[162] An inventory of goods in the chapel of the Kepier hospital, made at about this time, listed the clock, organs and 'sacryng bells' (rung at the consecration of the Host) together; and this was how they were often played.[163]

PUBLIC ORTHODOXY AND PRIVATE DEVOTION

The hospital's priests, choristers and instrumentalists would have made a great effort to mark the ordination services which were held there from time to time by the bishop of Norwich's suffragan. Over the year ending March 1447, for instance, all but one of the seven services recorded in Bishop Lyhart's register for the ordination of priests, deacons and subdeacons in the diocese of Norwich took place in St Helen's church, the other being at the church of the Friars Minor not far away.[164] Locations later favoured in the city were the chapel of the episcopal palace, the cathedral, the newly enlarged parish church of St Peter Mancroft and the collegiate church of St Mary in the Fields, each of which could provide an appropriate setting for the reception of ordinands.[165] Of greater interest, however, is the frequency with which the latter named St Giles's as their 'title' or guarantor of financial viability. Canon law required that every candidate for the higher orders should be able to support himself in a fitting manner without bringing the priesthood into disrepute through poverty. Confirmation, in the form of a testimonial from a lay patron, or, more commonly during the later Middle Ages, an undertaking from a monastic house, collegiate church or other religious institution that the person in question held a salaried post and would not prove a drain on the resources of the Church, was demanded before the ceremony.[166] Larger hospitals situated at or near diocesan centres provided such titles on a regular basis: two-thirds (forty-seven) of those issued by the bishop of Bath and Wells between 1443 and 1464 came from St John's hospital, Wells; and over 100 ordinands gave the name of St John's hospital, Exeter, between 1497 and 1534.[167] Yet even by these standards the evidence for St Giles's is impressive: between 12 March 1446 and 4 March 1447 alone, the hospital guaranteed twenty-five subdeacons, twenty-seven deacons and twenty-one priests – that is well over one-third of the total number (184) recorded.[168]

A recent analysis of the (incomplete) ordination lists preserved in the registers of six bishops of Norwich between 1413 and 1486 shows that, even when ordination services were held in other parts of the city or diocese, the hospital continued to issue far more titles than any other institution. Against an overall figure of 287 from Ixworth priory, a moderately prosperous house near Bury St Edmunds, and 183 from the College of St Mary in the Fields, stands St Giles's total of 754, an average of about ten a year.[169] A variety of explanations have been advanced to account for the involvement of religious houses in this activity, which at St Giles's was clearly an established bureaucratic procedure. The suggestion that titles were sold for a modest fee seems implausible, in this instance at least, for besides risking the charge of simony, commercial transactions on this scale would surely have been noted in the hospital accounts. And although St Giles's may occasionally have wished to help poor candidates for the ministry, it is unlikely to have undermined both the spirit and the letter of the law in such a systematic and deliberate fashion. Perhaps high mortality rates among the secular clergy during successive outbreaks of plague had turned the procedure into little more than an empty formality. Yet vetting of sorts may still have been carried out. The character and calibre of ordinands remained an important matter, albeit one which could now be established by testimonial rather than examination before a senior official.[170] Was it also necessary to ensure that they were doctrinally sound? Fears of a priesthood infected by the contagion of lollardy were certainly running high in Norwich for part of this period, which saw the implementation by Bishop Alnwick (trs. 1436) of sweeping measures designed to extirpate heresy in the region.

St Giles's certainly occupied a place at centre stage, standing as it did next to the episcopal palace, where most of the 120 heretics examined by the diocesan authorities between 1428 and 1431 were detained, and only a few yards from the spot where the ringleaders were burnt. Four of these men had been priests, notorious both for their extremism and the apparent strength of their following.[171] The two waggon-loads of wood, bought in Norwich market at a cost of 4*s* 8*d* for burning the 'eretycs', were transported past the hospital by a local carter, the reek of burning flesh serving to dispel the miasmas of heresy. That hospitals were expected to protect society against the poison spread by such individuals is evident from the writings of the French reformer, Jean Gerson (d. 1429), one of the leading opponents of the Hussite heresy. His long connection with the Hôtel Dieu, Paris, probably led him to recommend that basic religious instruction should be provided in hospitals, as well as schools and parish churches. Although it clearly reflects the wider theological concerns discussed at the beginning of this chapter, his insistence upon confession by all hospital patients may likewise be seen as part of a campaign begun by him in the early fifteenth century to instruct, educate and discipline the poor.[172] Chaplains in English hospitals are known to have kept a vigilant eye on potential suspects. As late as 1540, a cantarist at the Eastbridge hospital in Canterbury swam against the evangelical tide by censuring 'common readers of the Bible in service time' and others sympathetic to the new regime.[173]

The appointment during the fifteenth and early sixteenth centuries of senior diocesan officials as masters of St Giles's may reflect no more than a desire on the part of successive bishops of Norwich to find convenient and suitable lodgings for their advisors. Hugh Acton, a notary public who had been a regular attender at the Norwich heresy trials, was preferred to this post by Bishop Alnwick in 1437.[174] Yet even if it was not the primary intention, such a policy certainly helped to preserve the hospital as a bastion of orthodoxy. Here is evidence in abundance of that 'confident, coherent religious leadership . . . consistent in the forms of public cult it wished to impose, and systematic in its attempts to control opinion', which Jeremy Catto has identified as one of the strongest features of the early fifteenth-century English Church. The formal adoption by the ecclesiastical authorities of a style of worship already popular with 'doubtful and troubled laymen' provided a safe conduit for religious enthusiasm which might otherwise have flooded into dangerous channels.[175] Since it ranked, along with the collegiate church of St Mary in the Fields, as one of the liturgical showcases of the city, St Giles's hospital naturally attempted to satisfy the demand for new rites and rituals. In 1500, for example, a Master Ryder was paid 8*d* for writing out the lessons to be read on the feasts of the Transfiguration and of the Holy Name of Jesus; and the respond and versicle for the ninth lesson of the feast of the Holy Name were added, along with a section of the *Magnificat,* to the processional at about this time.[176] Both feasts had been proclaimed throughout the English Church during the late 1480s, but tended to be observed only in the larger parish and collegiate churches. Votive masses of the Holy Name, on the other hand, had been celebrated in Norwich from the beginning of the century, their appeal resting largely on the belief that anyone who commissioned a trental (one sung each day for thirty days) would die in a state of grace. By 1466 the city had two confraternities dedicated to the Jesus Mass, and St Giles's clearly hoped to attract the support of pious and affluent layfolk by promoting 'wyrshyppe of thys name gloryows'.[177] The hospital's reputation certainly extended beyond Norwich, prompting Margaret Paston to leave it 20*s* in 1482 for a *dirige* and mass in commemoration of her soul.[178]

The hospital also offered masses of the Five Wounds of Christ, which were usually requested in multiples of five for the commemoration of the dead. The chaplains themselves appear to have fostered this widespread and popular cult. John Veryes, who made his will in 1521 after twenty years' service at St Giles's, left no less than 10*s* to the master, 6*s* 8*d* to each of his colleagues and 5*s* to every conduct and chorister specifically for singing twenty-five such masses.[179] Identification with the suffering Christ has often been described as a manifestation of the introspective piety and obsession with death so characteristic of the period; the depiction of the instruments of the Passion on the ceiling of the chancel has already been noted. But, as we have also seen, the Passion had long carried a freight of medical imagery, which seems especially relevant in the context of the English hospital and its role in the cure of souls. At the Crucifixion, *Christus Medicus* had placed himself in the hands of the surgeon, or so the author of the *Ancrene Riwle* (*c.* 1200) reminded his female readers. He was let blood on the Cross, 'and not merely on the arm, but in five places, in order to heal mankind of the disease to which the five senses had given rise. Thus the living, healthy part drew out the bad blood from that which was diseased, and so healed that which was sick'.[180]

As the legendary discoverer of the True Cross, St Helen was also associated with healing miracles, although the prominence accorded to her feast at St Giles's reflects the more personal devotion felt by the parishioners of Holme Street for their patron saint. The will of John Bettyns (d. 1462), who leased the hospital's principal messuage there for almost thirty years and undertook a variety of administrative tasks for successive masters, shows how strong this attachment could be. Having committed his soul to the Virgin Mary, St Giles and St Helen, he requested burial at the altar of St Helen, left money for a vestment to be bought for use in daily masses there, and also set aside 13*s* 4*d* for the painting of its screen or frontal. A chantry chaplain was, moreover, to be retained for one year to assist every day in the choir at each of the canonical hours, as well as celebrating mass on Bettyns's behalf. One of his executors was Richard Braunche, the priest then in charge of collecting dues for the upkeep of the parochial altar, so there is every likelihood that his wishes were scrupulously observed.[181] The plainchant for the office of St Helen, transcribed in a rather poor early sixteenth-century hand, appears in the back of the hospital processional, suggesting that Bettyns was not the only devotee of her cult. It is, indeed, no coincidence that this volume eventually came into the possession of a family noted for its connection with the church of St Helen at Ranworth in Norfolk.[182]

It is impossible to discover exactly when many of the altars, images and fittings noted in fifteenth and sixteenth-century sources first appeared in the hospital church, but all testify to the same continuous process of embellishment. A new cloth was purchased for the altar of St Michael in 1397, and at some point over the next sixty years a detached chapel (with a thatched roof) was dedicated to him.[183] As the archangel responsible for weighing souls at the Last Judgement, when the poor would at last reap their eternal reward, St Michael figured prominently, if not without irony, in the iconography of the medieval hospital [see Plate 1]. Quite possibly this chapel, like one excavated on the site of St Saviour's hospital, Bury St Edmunds, stood next to the gatehouse and was reserved for special use, although a more appropriate site (as at St Bartholomew's, London) would have been in the cemetery.[184] During this period the nave of St Helen's church also underwent some striking changes. Although it was necessitated in part by the construction of the new chancel and the growing demand for spiritual services, the enlargement of the nave should also be seen in the wider context of architectural developments in Norwich. The refurbishment, and in some cases complete rebuilding, of the city's forty-six parish churches set a high standard. The patrons of St Giles's hospital and the parishioners of Holme Street were not to be outshone. By the early fifteenth century the nave and infirmary shared a lofty, central aisle which was even taller than the chancel. Its height permitted the insertion of a clerestory, with traceried windows in the perpendicular style. This ran immediately above the north and south aisles, and, like them, extended from the east end of the nave to the west end of the infirmary. The sense of airiness and symmetry thus created was lost as a result of the damage caused by Kett's rebels in 1549, when the south side of the infirmary was destroyed [see Map III].[185]

The nave was divided into three bays by clustered columns, which allowed ample space for the proliferation of altars, tombs and the heraldic trappings of wealthy patrons, such as Bishop Goldwell. His arms are still prominently displayed in St Helen's church on a shield borne by one of the stone angels whose task was to advertise the hospital's powerful connections [see Plate 30]. The richly decorated side-chapel, which extends like a transept beyond the first bay of the south aisle of the nave (and now houses the altar of the parish church), seems to have been one of his many gifts to St Giles's. For although he was buried in the cathedral, to which he left £400 for the support of a magnificent chantry, he evidently harboured some reservations about the monks' readiness to perform the charitable works necessary for his salvation. Goldwell had already criticised their failure to honour the wishes of local testators in this respect, and was perhaps reluctant to risk the welfare of his own immortal soul by leaving them to supervise all six of the cantarists he planned to employ in Norwich. Managed by clergy he knew and trusted, the hospital offered a reassuring prospect of security. Its staff were, moreover, ideally placed not only to choose the twenty poor bedesmen who were to receive alms on a permanent basis from his estate, but also to ensure that the paupers in question discharged their part of the bargain by attending all the necessary services and assiduously saying their prayers. In return for an even more substantial endowment, the master and brethren undertook to fund an additional chantry priest in the cathedral, another at the chapel of St Mary in the Fields and a third in their own church, quite possibly in a separate chantry built specially for the purpose.[186]

Stylistic evidence suggests that Goldwell himself commissioned this chapel. The external walls of high-quality knapped flint and lavish interior decoration would have been far beyond the hospital's limited budget, but represented no more than a relatively modest outlay on his part [see Plate 26]. It probably cost a fraction of the money spent by him on a major rebuilding programme at the cathedral, and almost certainly utilised the manpower and materials already concentrated there. His predecessor, Bishop Lyhart, had paid for the vaulting of the cathedral nave after the fire of 1463, adopting a complex pattern of ribs, tiercerons and liernes to display to the best advantage a magnificent sequence of bosses recounting the entire history of the world, from the Creation to the Last Judgement. A combination of personal vanity and aesthetics led Goldwell to deploy the simpler motif of his own rebus when he came to decorate the choir and presbytery.[187] The didactic possibilities of a series devoted to Christian iconography, especially in the more intimate surroundings of a hospital, prompted him (if, indeed, he was the patron) to return to more traditional religious imagery at St Giles's. Here, an elaborate vault, modelled upon the design of the cathedral masons, provided a geometrically patterned background for two concentric circles of, respectively, eight and sixteen bosses, with a larger boss, depicting the coronation of the Virgin, at the centre [see Plate 15]. Along with incidents from the lives of Christ, his mother and grandmother, St Anne, were represented each of the twelve apostles and four other saints (Edward, Edmund, Katherine and Margaret) chosen because of their popularity in the region [see Plates 9 and 41]. Robert Everard, who designed the new spire and worked on other parts of the cathedral throughout this period, had a long-standing connection with St Giles's, and may well have been the architect.[188] It is interesting to compare the roof bosses of the hospital chapel with those in the Bauchun chapel on the south side of the cathedral presbytery. William Sekyngton, who was master of St Giles's in the early 1430s, had chosen to be buried there in 1460, probably because it was where the consistory court, in which he played a prominent part, customarily met. Like the main body of the cathedral, the Bauchun chapel was re-vaulted and 'richly adorned with carved bosses' during the third quarter of the fifteenth century.[189] The central boss of the south bay depicts the Assumption of the Virgin, and that of the north bay her coronation in heaven. Although the hospital bosses are stylistically more accomplished, it seems likely that the two chapels, both strongly associated with the cult of the Virgin, were being vaulted at roughly the same time [see Plate 10].[190]

Only the shell of the chapel at St Giles's now survives, making it easy to forget how lavish the decor and furnishings would have been.[191] Sir Robert Poyntz (d. 1520), who did not live to see the completion of his chantry at St Mark's hospital, Bristol, had instructed his executors 'to garnish the same chapel and certain images and the altar of the same with altar cloths, vestments, book and chalice, and all other things thereunto necessary'.[192] Goldwell's chantry probably utilised the service books and silver left to St Giles's in 1489 by John Smyth, who had been the bishop's Official and owed his appointment as master to his patronage.[193] Smith's own cantarist may even have shared an altar with the bishop's chantry priest, a suitable arrangement given the close and mutually profitable connection he and Goldwell had enjoyed for many years. Between them, the two priests would have accounted for a substantial share of the 5,000 communion wafers and fourteen gallons of wine which were bought in 1510–11 for the celebration of mass at St Giles's.[194] The Lady Chapel, to the north of the hospital church, also continued to attract bequests, not least from Thomas Shenkwyn, the last of the fifteenth-century masters and another of Goldwell's protégés, who left a pair of silver candlesticks to the altar. On it already stood an image of St Nicholas (his patron saint), near which he asked to be buried, and, if his wishes were carried out, here also would have been placed a second picture, executed to the highest possible decorative standard.[195] The proliferation of chantries in English hospitals accounts in part, at least, for the impressive collections of books, plate and vestments many were able to accumulate. So too does investment on the part of wealthy masters, such as Jullys, Smith and Shenkwyn, who could simultaneously purchase a place in paradise while advertising their status on earth. Even John Hecker, who had risen over a period of more than twenty years from the ranks of the chaplain-choristers to become master in 1519, and was evidently not as affluent as some of his predecessors, used his own resources to beautify the church.[196] A few of the exquisitely carved bench-ends commissioned during his mastership still survive, and testify to the decorative splendour of the nave at this time. One, depicting him 'on his knees in priest's habit', was recorded in the early nineteenth century, but has since disappeared. His name is carved beneath another which portrays St Margaret and her adversary, the dragon [see Plates 33 and 34].[197] Her presence in the one part of the hospital church regularly frequented by married women assumes particular significance in view of the popularity she enjoyed as the patron saint of childbirth.[198] Like that of St Anne, her cult would have appealed to the prosperous artisans of Holme Street and their wives, who sought in religion a mirror of their own experiences. Offerings may have accompanied their devotions: women in the town of Newbury, who had recently been churched after giving birth, would traditionally visit the hospital of St Bartholomew with their midwives and present wax, candles and money in thanks for a safe delivery.[199] It was in this way that larger urban houses tapped a rich vein of popular piety.

By the early fifteenth century, the hospital of St Giles exhibited the unusual combination of strict doctrinal conformity and baroque exuberance so characteristic of religious life in pre-Reformation Norwich.[200] Its proximity to the city's great Carmelite friary, the episcopal palace, the cathedral church and the magnificent chantry chapel erected next to what is now the Erpingham Gate by Bishop Salmon in 1316 rooted it firmly within a powerhouse of prayer [see Map II]. Given such surroundings, the process of transition into an imposing collegiate foundation now seems inexorable. Salmon's chantry may, indeed, have provided the inspiration for the rebuilding of the hospital church in the 1380s, not least because it, too, had been designed by a royal architect and modelled upon work then in progress at Westminster. Although very different in style from St Giles's, it also served to advertise the spiritual and temporal power of a bishop of Norwich, while commemorating the souls of the Christian departed [see Plate 35].[201] Regulations of 1322 described in meticulous detail the daily round of masses and prayers to be undertaken by the chapel's six priests, who can have had little time for any other activities. The addition, a century later, of a perpetual chantry dedicated to Henry V's esquire, John Woodhouse, is notable for the founder's requirement that alms should be distributed to the poor in memory of the Holy Trinity and the Five Wounds of Christ. They, in return, were to attend each mass and intone the requisite number of 'orisons and salutations'.[202] In discharging its own heavy burden of suffrages for the dead, and thus performing what contemporaries would justify as a laudable work of compassion, St Giles's likewise responded to the demands of influential patrons. Chief among these were the senior diocesan clergy who came, increasingly, to view the hospital as a secular college devoted to ritual and liturgy, with limited commitments for the support of a few debilitated almsmen and non-resident dependents. As ambitious careerists, whose fear of purgatory was rarely incompatible with a desire for preferment on earth, their influence extended far beyond the chancel and the cloister, lending even greater weight to their authority.

CHAPTER V

POLITICS AND PATRONAGE

> For many, many years – records hardly tell how many, probably from the time the founder's wishes had been first fully carried out – the proceeds of the estate had been . . . divided among the bedesmen . . . Times had been when the poor warden got nothing but his bare house . . . and in those hard times [he] was hardly able to make out the daily dole for his twelve dependents. But by degrees things mended . . . and the wardens, with fairness enough, repaid themselves for the evil days gone by. In bad times the poor men had had their due, and therefore in good times they could expect no more. In this manner the income of the warden had increased; the picturesque house attached to the hospital had been enlarged and adorned, and the office had become one of the most coveted of the snug clerical sinecures attached to our church. It was now wholly in the bishop's gift, and though the dean and chapter, in former days, made a stand on the subject, they had thought it more conducive to their honour to have a rich precentor appointed by the bishop, than a poor one appointed by themselves.

Anthony Trollope, *The Warden*

A symbiotic relationship between the rich and powerful and those with skills or services to offer is characteristic of all but the most primitive societies. Thanks largely to the wealth of the surviving records and the assiduity with which they have been studied by generations of post-war historians, late medieval England appears notable for its complex networks of patronage, which extended downwards through Church and State to enmesh the humblest clerk or meanest domestic servant. This culture of 'mutual convenience and profit', of lordship and friendship, has been eloquently described by K.B. McFarlane, whose memorable account of the busy letter-writers of fifteenth-century England, 'one after another ladling butter, rolling logs and scratching backs' has proved an enduring model.[1] The detailed reconstruction by his disciples of interconnecting relationships of clientage and protection throughout society, may, in some cases, have led to an oversimplification of the motives and ideals of members of the ruling elite. By concentrating on the minutiae of social and familial connections rather than the wide sweep of political or religious ideas, we cover only part of a far broader canvas.[2]

Even so, there remains much to be said for the *pointilliste* approach, especially when it can be used in new ways to enhance our knowledge of social structures, rather than simply providing a few more examples of individual greed and ambition. Hitherto, prosopographical surveys of the masters and senior staff of medieval English hospitals have been undertaken almost exclusively in the misguided hope of discovering cases of medical practice among the sick poor, similar to those found in the larger charitable institutions of France, Italy and Byzantium. Most of the evidence is, however, conjectural, and few, if any, of the examples cited hold up under close examination.[3] But such an exercise *can* demonstrate how patronage networks of a distinctly secular nature, as much as those linking heaven and earth, could influence the changing priorities, and even the very survival, of houses like St Giles's. It is unlikely that Christine Carpenter had hospitals in mind when she urged McFarlane's heirs to 'look at public institutions, and at how private power and private interests focused around them'.[4] Yet a study of this kind can provide valuable insights into the interaction between urban and ecclesiastical elites, and the aspirations of both.

The accumulation of biographical information about the twenty-seven men who ran St Giles's between 1249 and 1546 is an interesting undertaking in its own right, but its real value lies in the way that an analysis of their careers, wealth, education and connections can help to explain why this hospital (and others like it) changed so radically between its foundation and its acquisition by the civic authorities just over 300 years later. Only in this way can we understand how effectively the late medieval masters integrated themselves into urban life, providing influential citizens with the spiritual services they so earnestly desired, and ensuring an unusual degree of support for the purchase and refoundation of the house after its surrender to the Crown at the end of Henry VIII's reign. As this chapter will show, St Giles's continued to flourish because its governors demonstrated as shrewd a grasp of political reality as the patrons who turned to them in hope of salvation after decades of log-rolling and back-scratching. Indeed, the latter also sought, and received, more immediately practical advice. It was John Smyth, one of the late fifteenth-century masters, who spelt out the harsh facts of life to John Paston I, during the course of his protracted struggle for ownership of the Fastolf estates. Writing in 1461, he urged the merits of a negotiated settlement, achieved through the support of influential friends, rather than a Pyrrhic victory in the courts:

> And thow ye recuuere in the lawe, as I am enformyd, ye schall recuuere of hard, and but a part, the qwech [which] schuld be dere [costly] of the sute. Qwere it semyth to me yt were necessarye to you to se [sue] remedy for thys mater, and eyther putt it in award [arbitration] or ell that my lord of Warwyk, *the qwech is your good lord*, may meue that the Kyng or hym-sylf or my lord Chawmbyrleyn or sum othyr wytty men may take a rewle betwexe you and youre aduersaryes; for yf ye may not holde the forseyd landys there schal growe great losse bothe to the dede and to you . . . It is better to bere a lyttell losse than a gret rebuke.[5]

Whatever the spiritual authority exercised by institutions like St Giles's, there can be no denying their subjection to the vagaries of earthly politics. The effects of that system of clientage known since Victorian times as 'bastard feudalism' extended far beyond the castles and manors of medieval England into the cloisters and chapels of the larger hospitals. This was primarily because the mastership of such houses bestowed considerable reserves of power and patronage, and was thus a marketable commodity to be solicited, exchanged and exploited as coinage in the currency of 'good lordship'. As chancellor to Bishop Lyhart and a pluralist on a grand scale, Smyth knew whereof he spoke.[6] The clergy of later medieval England were no less avid for preferment than any other members of the body politic. Although certain avenues of promotion were clearly denied them, they could accumulate benefices, canonries and other ecclesiastical appointments which paid handsome dividends and might, in practice, be discharged by deputies.[7] Preaching at the start of the sixteenth century, the celebrated humanist and dean of St Paul's, John Colet, bewailed the avariciousness of his colleagues. 'For what other thinge seke we nowe a dayes in the churche than fatte benefices and hygh promotions?', he enquired with a rhetorical flourish. 'Ye, and in the same promotions, of what other thyng do we passe vpon than of our tithes and rentes?' The fact that Colet was then vigorously lobbying Cardinal Wolsey to provide one of his staff with just such a prosperous living adds a note of unintentional irony to a complaint which had long been voiced by satirists and reformers alike.[8]

Hospitals were no less vulnerable to this scramble for earthly preferment, the consequences of which have generally been viewed by historians as almost invariably detrimental. Medieval men and women certainly recognised the harm cynical exploitation might cause. Condemning the widespread 'negligence and abuses' to be found in *leprosaria* and hospitals, the senior clergy who attended the Council of Vienne, in 1311, blamed the practice of treating them as benefices for the reward of ambitious seculars. 'But let these institutions be governed by prudent, suitable men of good repute, who have the knowledge, good will and ability to rule them, to take care of their property and defend their rights to advantage', ran the seventeenth canon of the Council. The need for financial probity was also emphasised; too many wardens had lined their own pockets at the expense of the sick poor.[9] Yet, as the authors of this ruling, themselves the recipients and dispensers of patronage, must surely have realised, such vulnerable institutions could not function effectively without powerful friends and influential masters, whose authority depended upon the strength of their connections in the secular world. It was hard to strike a mutually advantageous balance.

The masterships of hospitals and *leprosaria* were commonly used by kings, noblemen and prelates to reward their physicians, domestic chaplains, administrators and kinsmen.[10] At some point in the 1440s, the hospital of St Andrew, Ness (on the Wirral), was entrusted by Bishop Booth of Coventry and Lichfield to his nephew, a fourteen-year-old boy in minor orders. The latter's 'scruple of conscience' on the score of pluralism rather than extreme youth was rapidly allayed by a papal dispensation: one of several issued during the later Middle Ages to permit what was effectively the syphoning off of hospital revenues to pay the salaries of well-connected clergy.[11] Masterships could be bestowed and withdrawn like any type of preferment, hardly differing from the other perquisites with which lords attracted retainers and just as vulnerable to abuse. In 1522, for example, the earl of Westmorland, who exercised the right to appoint to the mastership of Staindrop hospital, county Durham, evicted the current incumbent (actually confiscating his keys) so that he could institute one of his own placemen.[12] Nearby at Kepier, the bishops customarily appointed their own officials as masters of St Giles's hospital, but during a vacancy, in 1504, Henry VII put in the young son of his personal physician and astrologer, the Italian, Giovanni Baptista Boerio. The post of royal physician required constant attendance upon the King, so three years later father and son leased out their prize, at a rent of £120 a year, to a consortium of local landowners.[13]

St Giles's, Norwich, was never mismanaged in this way, although several of its senior clergy engaged in such practices elsewhere. The bishop of Norwich's decision, made in 1419, that the erstwhile pilgrim hospital of St Thomas Becket at Beck (near Walsingham) should rank as compatible benefice without cure meant that it could be used to boost the income of clergy with other livings and priorities. He and his successors were thus able to appoint their senior administrators as wardens, among them being no fewer than four of the late medieval masters of St Giles's.[14] One of them, John Selot, also shared an eighty-year lease of the Augustinian *domus Dei* at Great Massingham, Norfolk, which was farmed out to him and other entrepreneurs by the prior, in 1460, at a fixed annual rent of £13 6*s* 8*d*.[15] Fifteen years later, the buildings of the hospital were pronounced 'so much decayed' and its emoluments 'so small' that it was appropriated by the bishop to the priory at West Acre, and used to support the surviving rump of two resident bedesmen. Were Selot and his friends little more than asset strippers, or had the house already entered an irreversible process of redundancy and decline? Although pluralism and greed did much to undermine the charitable purposes of the English medieval hospital, the issues at stake were not always quite so black and white. The main argument advanced in favour of the appointment of John Brereton as master of St Bartholomew's hospital, London, in 1532, was that a man possessed of so many benefices would surely be able to relieve its poverty.[16]

John Jullys was already rector of Blickling when, in 1497, his patron, Bishop Goldwell, made him master of Hildebrand's hospital, Norwich, and rector of the city church of St Giles on the Hill. Hildebrand's was then worth very little and had effectively ceased to receive the itinerant poor, as the founder had intended, so the award hardly constituted an abuse of episcopal patronage.[17] Nor did Jullys's subsequent appointment as master of the hospital of St Giles, where he had previously served as a chaplain and senior administrator. As we have seen in Chapter II, his term of office was marked by a costly and ambitious rebuilding programme, funded in the short term, at least, out of his own pocket. Bishop Nykke's decision to institute him as warden of the *leprosarium* or 'sickhouse' of St Mary Magdalen, Sprowston, was likewise a pragmatic measure designed to make the most of its fast diminishing resources.[18] Such an impoverished institution with revenues of less than £10 a year could no longer survive alone, but might help to support another, more viable hospital.[19] Throughout Europe it was recognised that small, underfunded houses should either merge together or be absorbed into more effective administrative structures. In 1469, for example, the master of the hospital of SS Mary and Edward the Martyr, Limerick, petitioned the Pope for permission to acquire another living so that he could better care for the sick poor, repair the buildings and extend the hospital's charitable role.[20] At Ipswich the two leper houses of St Mary Magdalen and St James were merged after the Black Death, the combined endowment being further augmented with revenues from the free chapel of St Edmund and the parish church of St Helen, two livings henceforward occupied by the keeper.[21]

Such steps seemed inevitable in a period of social, demographic and economic upheaval, when leprosy was disappearing and the itinerant poor were seen as dangerous subversives rather than objects of compassion. Worth little more than £5 at the time of the Dissolution, in 1535, the hospital of St Thomas at Beck constantly hovered on the brink of financial collapse. Even so, William Soper used his undoubted influence as master of St Giles's and friend of Bishop Nykke in the early sixteenth century to take a stand against John Curson, 'a cruell man of his covetowse mynde', whose family had been attempting to wrest control of the estates of St Thomas's for more than a century. His claim to have been prevented from performing the 'dedes of charitye' and spiritual services required by the founder and to have been personally subject to 'daly manesse and threte' by the defendant suggests that he, at least, took his responsibilities seriously.[22] He was, on the other hand, a far more flagrant pluralist than Selot, with livings as far away as Lincolnshire, Wiltshire and Somerset. It was through the patronage of Bishop Nykke that he had first come to Norwich from the south-west, his arrival at St Giles's, in 1504, involving him in one of the most serious legal battles fought – and won – by the house before the Reformation. His readiness, once again, to stand his corner, and his subsequent generosity to St Giles's, where he was buried, provides one of many instances of the ways in which clientage and 'good lordship' conferred benefits as well as causing problems.

ECCLESIASTICAL PATRONS

It is hardly surprising that Walter Suffield should appoint a member of his own family as the first master of St Giles's. Trustworthiness and reliability were the main desiderata influencing his choice of senior subordinates, and though the preferment of his brother, William, as archdeacon of Norwich in 1246 smacks of nepotism, his decision to entrust his new hospital to Hamon de Calthorpe seems to have been determined by more than familial ties. The survival of a project so dear to his heart, upon which the fate of his immortal soul depended, made it essential to select the right man. To Calthorpe fell the additional responsibility of executing his kinsman's will, and performing a number of pious works on his behalf. In order to implement Suffield's long-term plans for the hospital, it was, moreover, essential that the new master should command respect in the wider community. This he manifestly did; long after the bishop's death he continued to attract enthusiastic support among the leading citizens of Norwich, greatly augmenting the original endowment.[23] The unusually elaborate rules for the election of new masters set out in the foundation statutes of 1249 may well reflect the presence in Suffield's household of an authority on this aspect of canon law, but they also demonstrate a pressing concern about the calibre and general acceptability of candidates for office.

Within three weeks of a vacancy occurring, the prior of Norwich was to summon the archdeacons of Norwich and Norfolk to meet him at the hospital in order to make a new appointment. During the interim period the three men were to examine each of the brothers diligently under oath regarding the merits of their own colleagues or, indeed, of any suitable outsiders. Once a decision had been reached, the successful candidate was to be presented by letters patent to the bishop or his Official promptly over the next seven days. If any of the designated clerics happened to be absent, or their offices vacant, provision was made for the dean of Norwich and the Official to take appropriate action either together or individually. The bishop himself was empowered to intervene if delays or disagreements held up the proceedings for more than five weeks, thus avoiding any serious hiatus in the house's administration.[24] As Hamon de Calthorpe recognised, these complicated and potentially divisive arrangements threatened the hospital's autonomy and purpose. They were modified by Bishop Skirning at his personal request, in 1272, by which time he had been in office for twenty-three years and was probably contemplating retirement. He clearly envisaged trouble if the brothers were not given a freer hand in the choice of his successor, and may with good reason have been worried about Archdeacon Alan de Freston's desire to interfere. The new regulations empowered the clergy of St Giles's to hold their own elections without deferring in any way to outsiders who might be unfamiliar with the house and its ways.[25] They had still, however, to make their presentation to the bishop, whose influence over the selection procedure was greatly strengthened by the removal of any discordant voices. As was the case in many other hospitals, such as St John's, Cambridge, the brothers were now technically autonomous, while at the same time dependent, in the last resort, upon their patron's approval.[26] The bishop continued, moreover, to exercise his right to appoint a temporary warden from among 'the more discreet priests of the hospital' as soon as a vacancy was announced, which meant that a man of his own choosing would be responsible for holding the election. Reference is specifically made to a presiding officer (*presidens*) of this modest assembly on five occasions between 1431 and 1489, which suggests that the practice continued throughout the Middle Ages. In 1436 (when John Walpole, an episcopal nominee, was elected) Bishop Alnwick's vicar general sent along a representative to ensure that 'any objections or contradictions' to the candidate would be properly heard, although his presence may well have intimidated rather than reassured the brethren.[27]

Calthorpe relinquished the mastership in 1274, and was succeeded by Robert de Branford, the unanimous choice of the priests and chaplains. He had already been instituted by the bishop, had taken full possession of the temporalities of the hospital and had received oaths of obedience from the brethren, when de Freston, as archdeacon of Norfolk, moved to challenge his title. During the course of proceedings heard in the court of the papal judge delegate, William de Langtoft, in the summer of 1277, de Freston's proctor tried, unsuccessfully, to assert the rights accorded to successive archdeacons of Norwich and Norfolk in Walter Suffield's foundation charter. But there was no turning back. Whatever influence they may have exerted behind the scenes (and some of them actually became masters in the later Middle Ages), none ever played an official part in elections.[28] It is, however, worth noting that de Branford and his immediate successors were confirmed in office by the prior of Norwich; the support and approval of such a powerful neighbour had still to be secured.

For the best part of a century the new selection procedure favoured local men, familiar to the community at St Giles's. At least three, and quite possibly all, of the six masters appointed between 1274 and 1372 had already lived in the hospital as chaplains or boarders. Peter de Herlyngflete is known to have been involved in its affairs long before becoming master, and his successor, Roger de Mettingham, had previously played a part, as one of the brethren, in managing its estates. Both appear to have risen through the ranks, and both discharged remarkably long terms in office, of, respectively, thirty-two and twenty-six years.[29] To Roger de Erpingham's two decades of service should be added the fourteen or so years previously spent by him as a hospital chaplain and administrator, during which he acted as surveyor and receiver general. Indeed, for the first 123 years of its history St Giles's enjoyed great stability in this respect, each master remaining in place for an average of just over seventeen years (between 1372 and 1546 the average fell sharply to somewhat less than eight years). Appointments seem to have been made when the successful candidates were comparatively young and energetic, it being presumed that they would stay at the helm until they died or, as in the case of Hamon de Calthorpe, wished to retire. Little is known of their careers or personal connections outside the hospital: none appear to have been flagrant pluralists, to have studied at university, or, significantly, to have arrived in the region as members of the episcopal household.

All this changed with the appointment, in 1372, of John Derlyngton, a graduate of Oxford University who later received a doctorate in canon law from Cambridge. Originally from the north-east, he came to Norwich in the retinue of his patron, the formidable Bishop Despenser (1370–1406), who seized the opportunity offered by Mettingham's death to provide his friend and counsellor with comfortable quarters next to his palace. Derlyngton was the first of at least eleven masters to possess a university degree,[30] of ten to occupy a senior position in the diocese[31] and of twelve (besides Hamon de Calthorpe) to enjoy a close personal relationship with the incumbent bishop.[32] He likewise set a trend by combining the mastership with a senior position in the diocese: he appears to have been Despenser's vicar general (with responsibility for pastoral and administrative business) at the time of his appointment in 1372, but soon after he is described as his Official (in which capacity he presided over the consistory court). Although his term as master was relatively short, he retained a keen interest in the affairs of the hospital, keeping a suite of rooms there throughout his life and, as we have seen, endowing it with a chantry when he died.[33]

In this context, the physical location, accessibility and relative spaciousness of the hospital were crucial in determining its future. Notwithstanding the various drawbacks described in Chapter II, residency seemed an attraction rather than an unwelcome imposition. Ambitious careerists, lodged so near the episcopal palace and the cathedral, sought to enhance their earthly status as well as their chances of salvation by embellishing and beautifying the fabric. A telling comparison may be made with the London hospital of St Katherine by the Tower, which despite its insalubrious surroundings provided a agreeable home for clerks with posts in the royal household. John de Hermesthorpe, master in the late fourteenth century and keeper of the king's privy wardrobe, was a notable benefactor of the house. He built the new chancel and nave of the hospital church, provided vestments, plate and furnishings, ran the estates with remarkable efficiency and improved standards of discipline. These measures, in turn, attracted new patrons from among the royal family and the rulers of London, who were dissatisfied with the poor behaviour apparent in some London hospitals.[34]

Hardly less spectacular, in a provincial context, the rebuilding programme begun at St Giles's during the last two decades of the fourteenth century should be viewed in a similar light. Indeed, as noted in the previous chapter, almost the entire cost of erecting the new bell-tower was met out of Derlyngton's own purse, and he quite probably subsidised the construction of the chancel, nave and infirmary too.[35] That he persuaded Despenser to contribute towards this ambitious programme seems almost certain, for the two men were extremely close. When Despenser left for his 'crusade' in Flanders, in 1383, he authorised Archdeacon Derlyngton to act in his place, and, on his death twenty-three years later, the spiritualities of the see of Norwich were entrusted to his former counsellor. Thomas, Lord Morley, had, indeed, described Derlyngton respectfully as one of his kinsman's 'principal advisers'.[36] The archdeacon was himself a notable patron, and it looks as if John de Thornham owed his election as master of St Giles's, in 1395, to his support. Some ten years earlier, Derlyngton had offered securities at Westminster on behalf of the priest, who then stood in danger of being arrested on an unspecified charge. Thornham later acted as a trustee of the estates in Cringleford which were to support Derlyngton's chantry in the hospital, having by then established himself as a figure of consequence in his own right. As an executor of the will of Bishop Totington (d. 1413), a friend of the prior of Horsham St Faith's and a pluralist on a modest but profitable scale, Thornham exemplified the new breed of master. Neither he nor his successor, Benedict Cobbe, held office for very long, however, although Cobbe had already spent some time as receiver general and was thus familiar with the daily round of administrative affairs.[37]

Both Roger Pratt and Robert Spenser, the next two masters, are notable for their assiduous cultivation of Norwich's wealthy mercantile elite, which itself presumes almost constant residence. Although each of them acquired livings in other parts of Norfolk, they, too, became personally involved in the minutiae of life at St Giles. As the only one of the hospital's twenty-seven medieval masters to serve two terms of office, Pratt, in particular, seems to have been an able and conscientious administrator. The brethren's decision, unanimously reached in 1412, just after the end of his first mastership, to grant him spacious living quarters in the precinct free of charge for life and admit him into their spiritual fraternity speaks for itself. The ensuing indenture refers to the 'many subsidies and benefits' already 'given out of charity' by Pratt, whose contacts among the aldermanic class clearly increased his attractions as a lodger.[38]

Bishop Alnwick's appointment of his commissary general, William de Sekyngton, as master on Spenser's death, in 1430, may have been influenced by a desire to improve the intellectual calibre of diocesan appointments and thus, *inter alia*, strengthen resistance to heresy. It was certainly an overt act of episcopal patronage: the ceremony took place at the bishop's palace and Sekyngton was preferred to at least three other benefices in Alnwick's gift shortly afterwards. Like John Derlyngton, he was an outsider (from Huntingdonshire) who had moved to Norwich with his bishop. He could also boast degrees in both canon and civil law. No fewer than ten of the masters appointed between 1430 and 1546 had attended university, five having been to Oxford, three to Cambridge and one (Nicholas Goldwell) to both.[39] Two others, Hugh Acton and Thomas Simmondes, were almost certainly graduates, while Robert Codde, the last of the pre-Dissolution masters, had been prior of the Augustinian house at Pentney, and was reputedly a learned man. The remaining two, John Jullys and John Hecker, had both been chaplains and senior administrators at St Giles's for many years before their election, which suggests that they had given sufficient proof of their ability to cope with the demands of office.

The need to raise educational standards among the English clergy became a pressing concern in the late Middle Ages, and the close connection between the episcopal school, the hospital choristers and the bishop's palace was one of many considerations now influencing appointments.[40] The recruitment of 'fast stream' careerists with academic qualifications into senior administrative positions in the diocese of Norwich certainly created a pool of suitable candidates. It is significant that more than half of the masters (at least nine out of sixteen) appointed between 1430 and 1546 held such offices. But did the hospital really benefit from these developments? Sekyngton served for only six months, Roger Pratt (who did not apparently have a degree) being brought back to replace him in May 1431. Had he been called in as an experienced hand to deal with administrative or financial problems? After five years during which he assumed personal responsibility for drawing up the hospital's accounts, Pratt was replaced by another graduate and bureaucrat, John Walpole, who departed abruptly seven months later because of his patron's translation to the see of Lincoln. Whereas Sekyngton remembered the hospital fondly in his will, Walpole soon forgot his brief association with one of many institutions encountered on his climb up the promotional ladder. In short, Bishop Alnwick's active intervention may have caused more problems than it solved, disrupting the administrative continuity which had previously been a hallmark of the hospital.

The arrival, in 1437, of Hugh Acton, a notary public who had participated in the Norwich heresy trials of 1428–30, brought a return to equilibrium. Throughout his thirteen years in office he too compiled the annual accounts, toured the hospital manors assiduously and was resident for most of the time. Besides putting in train the first round of improvements to the inner precinct described in Chapter II, he managed to persuade Sir John Fastolf to sell his estates in Mundham to the hospital. Although the stubborn old knight resisted his appeals on the subject of almsdeeds to the poor (having perhaps seen the new refectory), Acton was clearly a man who mixed easily in county society and could speak the same language as the gentry whose support the house so badly needed.[41] This important attribute was shared by the next master, John Selot, who, as episcopal chancellor, had accompanied Acton on his visits to Sir John, and helped to negotiate the purchase. Selot is in many respects the most interesting and best documented figure to hold office before 1546. Born in Twickenham, Middlesex, in 1412, he became a scholar of Winchester College at the age of twelve, moving on, as a good Wykehamist, to Oxford University, where he graduated in both canon and civil law. Doctor Selot owed his promotion to Bishop William Lyhart (1446–72), whom he served loyally and well throughout his episcopate, even travelling with him overseas on diplomatic missions. A pluralist and dedicated careerist, Selot possessed the authority, drive and ability necessary to protect the hospital in a turbulent period. He was a political animal, his politics being unequivocally those of his patron. The latter was, significantly, named along with him, in November 1450, as one of the trustees of the hospital's newly acquired estates in

Mundham. The bishop's direct involvement in these transactions was not entirely auspicious, however, occurring as it did not long after Cade's Rebellion and the outbreak of popular disturbances in Norwich specifically directed against Lyhart himself.

As one of a small but powerful group of courtier-bishops, Lyhart had been closely associated with William de la Pole, first duke of Suffolk, who probably secured his appointment as confessor to the Queen, Margaret of Anjou, and certainly engineered his subsequent elevation to the episcopal bench.[42] Suffolk's murder, in May 1450, occurred within a few months of that of two other close friends, Bishops Ayscough of Salisbury and Moleyns of Chichester, whose cloth offered them scant protection. Having fled in terror from London to the diocese which he had so far conspicuously neglected, Lyhart himself faced an angry mob, further inflamed by hatred of the late duke's East Anglian henchmen.[43] Suffolk's most notorious counsellors, Sir Thomas Tuddenham and John Heydon, were profoundly unpopular in Norwich, where the factionalism of civic politics during the previous two decades had been exacerbated by their intervention on behalf of a minority party led by the alderman and local landowner, Thomas Wetherby.[44] A vicious satire circulating just after Suffolk's death listed Tuddenham and Lyhart among the courtiers, pluralists and placemen who were to perform his obsequies by singing 'for Jake Napes sowle *Placebo* and *Dirige*'.[45] The lampoon also named Thomas Daniel, whom Selot and his bishop were later said to favour. Writing in about 1460, one of John Paston I's correspondents complained that the episcopal council, which then included both Tuddenham and Heydon, was blatant in its support of insolent lawbreakers, citing, as a case in point, the blatant favouritism accorded to Daniel by Doctor Selot.[46]

It is worth noting that Sir Thomas Tuddenham, one of the least congenial figures in fifteenth-century East Anglia, had employed two sometime masters of St Giles's, Hugh Acton and John Walpole, in 1436, as proctors in his divorce case while it was being heard before Bishop Alnwick's commissary.[47] Predictably, when members of the Norfolk gentry attempted to have Tuddenham and Heydon indicted on a variety of charges after the duke of Suffolk's death, Doctor Selot's name appeared on the list of men who sat firmly on the fence.[48] His attachment to the de la Poles remained constant, at least if the less than objective opinion of Margaret Paston may be believed. She wrote indignantly to her husband in September 1465 about Selot's 'demenyng and parcialte' towards the second duke when he was attempting to settle a dispute between them and Suffolk in the ecclesiastical courts. Her claim that even Bishop Lyhart was displeased with Selot's flagrant partisanship ('the seyd Master John . . . is not grettly in conseyt at this tyme') is harder to credit, however. Seen through other eyes, his insistence upon a thorough search of the legal records seems both reasonable and just, although his past history suggests that he did, indeed, favour the duke.[49]

As will be apparent from the next two sections of this chapter, Selot's skilful manipulation of local patronage networks made him a powerful advocate of the hospital's interests, and, in the end, earned him the respect, if not the affection, of the civic elite. Well before he assumed the mastership of St Giles's, he shared a gift of 18*s* 4*d* made by St Paul's hospital for the 'benevolence' of senior diocesan officials in the ongoing dispute over exempt jurisdictions. His expenditure of £5 in 1465–6 on 70 yards of cloth to provide liveries for the '*gentlemen*, yeomen and boys' of St Giles's likewise speaks volumes.[50] He clearly impressed Bishop Lyhart's successor, James Goldwell (1472–99), who kept him on as his chancellor and through him became one of St Giles's greatest medieval benefactors. Not for nothing were the arms of the two prelates prominently displayed there, Lyhart's appearing on the east side of the new cloisters, the design of which was almost certainly influenced by William Wykeham's school at Winchester and the Oxford colleges where he and Doctor Selot had spent so much of their youth [see Plates 23 and 30].[51] Lyhart's help was invaluable in other ways, too: when, in 1465, Selot sought to appropriate the rectory of Coltishall to the hospital so that the revenues could be used to pay his successors' stipends, papal approval was easily secured. The bishop's success at Court owed a good deal to his interest in education, which he shared with many members of Suffolk's circle, as well as with the King himself. In 1444 Lyhart had left Oriel college, Oxford, to become master of St Anthony's hospital, London. Although he spent only two years there before being made bishop of Norwich, he was later recommended by Henry VI to serve on a papal commission for the reform of its statutes. He was thus involved in shaping one of the country's most celebrated grammar schools, and turning St Anthony's into a centre of educational and musical excellence. There seems little doubt that he and Selot together wished to see similar developments at Norwich's largest hospital.[52]

Just as John Derlyngton had used his influence to select his successor, so Selot was almost certainly instrumental in choosing John Smyth, who became rector of Coltishall and master of St Giles's on his death, in 1479.[53] A bachelor of canon law who had, like Selot, initially prospered in the service of Walter Lyhart, Smyth was by then Bishop Goldwell's Official. Because of his heavy burden of administrative duties, and perhaps also through his personal attachment to Selot, he had retained rooms in the hospital from 1455 onwards, and had been a party to various conveyances of its property. He therefore slipped comfortably into Selot's place, sharing his obvious affection for an institution which had become his home. Like him, he made generous endowments of land for a chantry and obits, and also left quantities of plate, cash and vestments to embellish St Helen's church.[54]

This fifty-two-year period of stability and good stewardship maintained by Acton, Selot and Smyth came to an end on the latter's death in 1489. His successor, Oliver Dynham, was a flagrant pluralist, with a clutch of valuable canonries and rectories from Devon to Derbyshire. The only master of St Giles's with blue blood in his veins, he was the younger brother of John, Lord Dynham, treasurer of England under Henry VII, and thus potentially in a position to wield enormous influence on the hospital's behalf. He had, however, begun collecting benefices at the tender age of nineteen, in 1457, and was disinclined to spend any time in Norwich when far more attractive prospects, such as his canonry at the royal chapel of St George, Windsor, beckoned.[55] Significantly, though, he was removed from the mastership not very long after an episcopal visitation of 1492, when complaints about his absenteeism had been voiced by the brethren. Unlike their peers at St Leonard's hospital, York, they evidently did not relish the prospect of manning a rudderless ship.[56] Dynham's replacement, Thomas Shenkwyn, Official and chancellor to Bishop Goldwell, came armed with a newly awarded papal indult permitting him to occupy three incompatible benefices with cure of souls at once, but he none the less elected to reside in the hospital. Unlike Dynham, he proved a generous benefactor to the inmates, as well as the fabric, and requested burial in the Lady Chapel, which he helped to beautify.[57]

Shenkwyn's early death, in 1497, must have come as a blow to the brethren, and led to the temporary appointment of Bishop Goldwell's own brother, Nicholas. The continuing strength of the episcopal connection with St Giles's is evident, not only from this short-lived 'caretaker' regime, but also from the fact that the next two masters, Doctor Robert Honywood and John Jullys, had been chosen with Nicholas to serve as executors of Goldwell's will and trustees of the estates which were to support his chantry at St Giles's. Nicholas himself gave generously to the hospital, but it was his work as an executor which proved of lasting benefit. So far as we can tell, Honywood left the senior chaplain, Robert Godfrey, in charge of day-to-day administration. He was certainly absent when the hospital was visited, in April 1499, by the archbishop of Canterbury's Official, and has left scant trace in its records.[58] This seeming neglect was more than remedied by Jullys, a native of Norwich who had lived and worked at St Giles's for the best part of twenty-four years before becoming master, and was dedicated to its improvement. Perhaps some of the money which financed the building schemes described in Chapter II came from Goldwell's estate, for it seems unlikely that he alone could have raised so much capital. Yet his long-standing connection with Bishop Goldwell, followed by an equally profitable relationship with Richard Nykke (1500–35), enabled him to forge some useful links of his own with such august county families as the Boleyns, the Skipwiths and the Hobarts. Far from being a humble priest with narrow horizons, he appears to have been in constant demand as a trustee of landed estates around the region.[59] The appearance in the hospital accounts for the first time in 1505–6, and annually thereafter, of entries recording receipts of between £4 and £6 a year from 'Skypwythes', in Norwich, suggests that Jullys was well able to capitalise upon his connections.[60]

Newcomers to the diocese, who may best be described as episcopal placemen, were just as likely to develop a permanent attachment to St Giles's as long term residents. They were, moreover, often better placed to defend it from attack. This was certainly the case with William Soper, who had travelled to Norwich from Wells in Somerset in the entourage of Bishop Nykke. In 1505, a year after succeeding Jullys, he occupied livings in both parts of England, being excused residence in either, so he could continue his studies at university and attend the Roman curia. Despite this less than promising start, he proved a zealous champion of the hospital's rights, remained in office for fifteen years and elected to be buried in the Lady Chapel of St Helen's church. He was fortunate in being able to entrust much of the house's routine business to John Hecker, the steward, receiver general and surveyor, whose expertise was such that Bishop Nykke employed him from time to time as an auditor. It thus seemed natural that he, in turn, should occupy the mastership, although not even he could arrest the insidious process of financial decline which was beginning to affect the fabric. He too, devoted much time and energy to husbanding resources, but was fighting a losing battle. Perhaps he had lived so long in the hospital that sweeping change seemed unpalatable. In common with his two successors, Thomas Cappe and Thomas Simmondes, he shared his bishop's arch conservatism, and thus found himself vulnerable to the chilly wind of protestantism already sweeping across East Anglia from the North Sea.

For the first time in its history, St Giles's appeared to suffer rather than benefit from its intimate connection with the incumbent bishop. But there were other strings to its bow. From the days of Hamon de Calthorpe, the masters had fostered ties with the ruling elite of Norwich. These Robert Codde, the brother of an alderman, was effectively able to exploit, capitalising upon 300 years of close and generally harmonious contact between his predecessors and members of the civic hierarchy.[61] It was, however, the support accorded to successive masters by bishops from Walter Suffield onwards which had previously given the hospital such an advantage at common law, as well as in the ecclesiastical courts. Here was an acid test of 'good lordship' at work, and to this we first turn.

THE HOSPITAL AND THE LAW

However great their desire to achieve spiritual health, few of the men and women who endowed and helped to maintain the hospitals of medieval England thought much of the hereafter where their own territorial interests were concerned. Friends as well as enemies could employ underhand tactics and were all the more valued as a result. Attempts by Philip de Poitu, bishop of Durham, to secure sweeping concessions for the hospital of St James, Northallerton, in the late twelfth century may have been morally dubious, if not illegal, but they underscored his usefulness as a patron at a time when ethical considerations often came a poor second to the prospect of material advantage.[62] Other religious houses, fighting hard to overcome the problem of falling revenues and competing for a declining share of the patronage market, made dangerous adversaries, as did neighbouring parish churches, jealous of their lucrative rights and franchises.[63] Disputes with the monks of Norwich cathedral priory over the parochial rights of St Helen's church and subsequent quarrels about rents payable from the hospital meadows have already been examined in Chapter II. Although relations between the brethren and their powerful neighbours seem otherwise to have been relatively peaceful, occasional hints of trouble may be detected, perhaps exacerbated by friction at a higher level. There was, for instance, a significant rise in the master's legal expenses during the late 1390s, as Bishop Despenser's conflict with the Benedictine community over a variety of issues, including his rights in the controversial exempt liberties, came to a head.[64] An undated composition drawn up in the mid-fifteenth century between John Selot and Prior Molet suggests some contention over the upkeep of a 'cokey', or open drain, in Holme Street, as well as the annuity pledged by Walter Suffield from the hospital's manor of Seething. But serious disagreement was averted, the prominence of Molet's arms in two different parts of the precinct testifying to the respect in which he was held [see Plates 23 and 32].[65] Relations were more variable at a local level, as evidence from the manor of Cringleford reveals. A potentially acrimonious dispute arose in 1497, for example, because of the diversion of a water-course from one of the hospital's mills towards land owned by the priory. The poaching of game by monks and their greyhounds constituted a further irritant, to which the masters evidently grew resigned.[66] As so often proved the case, the payment of tithes became the real bone of contention, resulting, in 1525–6, in the award of damages of £20 against the hospital in the ecclesiastical courts.[67]

Gifts of property, such as the manor of Cringleford, could prove a mixed blessing, demanding heavy legal expenses and constant vigilance. Shortly after acquiring the advowson of the church of Mundham St Peter, for example, the brethren of St Giles's were sued by the vicar of the nearby parish of Thwaite St Mary over the allocation of tithes, as well as by the incumbent, who demanded better support.[68] The appointment of a weak, negligent or incompetent master had disastrous effects when a hospital was threatened by marauding neighbours intent on vexatious litigation or worse. But administrative efficiency – especially during periods of economic upheaval or political unrest – also brought its own problems. Already subject to physical attack by resentful townspeople, the master and brothers of St John's hospital, Bridgwater, were confronted by a local mob during the Peasants' Revolt of 1381 and obliged to surrender financial securities previously taken from the burgesses. At the close of the century another hospital of St John, this time in Bristol, was besieged by 'malefactors assembled in large numbers and warlike array', who forcibly removed 'divers bags containing charters and writings'. Anger over agricultural dues traditionally claimed by the hospital of St Leonard, York, likewise spilled over into violence when a rising, ostensibly mounted in favour of the Percys, broke out in Yorkshire in 1469.[69] Each of these houses was seen, in its different way, to have combined rapacity with indifference to the poor. Such a charge was never openly levelled against the masters of St Giles's in their official capacity, although the hospital's close connection with Bishop Despenser, whose brutality towards the insurgents of 1381 became the stuff of legend, must surely have alienated that significant proportion of the local community which had welcomed the rebels into Norwich.

William Lambarde's entertaining account of a brawl between the monks of Rochester abbey and the brothers of St Mary's hospital, Strood, who ambushed their adversaries 'with clubbes and battes' while they were 'merily chanting their latine letanie', was no doubt embroidered in the telling.[70] Yet, even allowing for the exaggeration commonly deployed by medieval litigants as well as Tudor antiquaries, confrontations of this kind were not unusual. The staff, tenants and retainers of hospitals and other religious houses were as culpable as any in a society where individuals of all classes and conditions tended to take the law into their own hands. During the late 1280s, for example, 'the men of the abbot of St Benet Holme' embarked upon a sustained campaign of intimidation, attacking the flocks and devastating crops on farms belonging to St Giles's hospital at Hardley. Cattle, horses, poultry and sheep were stolen by night, some being maimed and killed, others detained for long periods. Beasts were even driven into the cemetery of Hardley church, where they caused considerable damage during vespers. The then master, Martin de Brunstead, took prompt action at common law, as did Peter de Herlyngflete when similar offences were perpetrated by retainers or tenants of the abbey three decades later. On this occasion, the full authority of the ecclesiastical courts as well as that of the State was brought to bear on the hospital's adversaries, who were excommunicated on the orders of the bishop.[71] Meanwhile, in 1306, another local dispute, this time with the Premonstratensian canons at Langley, just across the parish boundary, over the payment of tithes to the rector of Hardley, was submitted to arbitration.[72]

During the early sixteenth century a farmer at Bishop's Thorpe, whose land lay next to the demesnes of St Giles's hospital, claimed that the master, John Hecker, and another landowner had stopped at nothing to acquire his property. 'Accompanyd wyth dyverce persones to the nombere of xij [twelve] . . . yn ryotus manere arrayd, that ys to say wyth swordes and buckleres, byllys, bowys and arroys and othere wepyns ynvaysyve contrare to the pece' they had reputedly attempted 'to haue myschevyd, murdrid and slayn hym'. Finding him gone, they stole his cattle and released large numbers of their own sheep on his pastures, confident of the support of the bishop's steward and the local tenantry, who were too frightened to help him.[73] Whatever the truth of these allegations, there can be little doubt that Hecker's display of strength and promotion of the hospital's interests would have earned the warm approval of his subordinates. Nor was this the only occasion on which he appears to have overstepped the mark. During the course of a protracted dispute over the payment of tithes to the hospital's rectory at Seething, which had dragged on since 1512, he was said to have used his influence with the bishop's Official to have the defendant excommunicated. Although the sentence was evidently repealed, he allegedly intervened again, in 1521, to engineer the removal and excommunication of a neighbouring clergyman who had permitted his adversary to take the sacrament.[74] Not long afterwards, Hecker turned his attention to the parishioners of Bastwick, suing them in the ecclesiastical courts because of their resistance to the hospital's demands.[75] Far from turning the other cheek, a successful master was always ready to assume the offensive. Excommunication, which not only placed the offender outside the Christian community but also brought with it loss of reputation and the prospect of social ostracism, was a powerful weapon in the hospital's quiver.[76]

So far as the brothers of St Giles's were concerned, the most unfortunate result of Bishop Goldwell's decision to appoint Oliver Dynham to the mastership, in 1489, was the fact that their enemies exploited his frequent absences both in and out of the law courts.[77] Absentee masters were common enough in English hospitals, but not at St Giles's, where the spirit, if not the precise letter, of Bishop Suffield's ruling on the subject of near-continuous residence was generally upheld.[78] Dynham's offence must, moreover, have appeared all the more reprehensible when set against the diligence shown by some of his predecessors in defending and augmenting the hospital's estates. Notable among them was John Selot, whose intimate connection with Bishop Lyhart and the de la Poles rendered him a formidable opponent at law. His mastership was punctuated by a number of property disputes, during which he proved a redoubtable and tireless opponent. The most revealing, from a political as well as legal standpoint, was with the prominent Norfolk lawyer, John Jenney of Intwood, who in about 1457 seized 200 acres of land occupied by the hospital in Heylesdon's manor, Cringleford. As the younger son of an even more distinguished lawyer (John Jenney of Knoddishall in Suffolk), brother of a future judge, and son-in-law of Thomas Wetherby (d. 1445), the Norwich alderman whose faction the duke of Suffolk had so effectively supported in the 1440s, Jenney boasted some impressive connections. He was also extremely able. John Knyvett, another leading figure in the county, had engaged him as an attorney during his epic struggle to recover the Clifton estates in the early 1450s, and subsequently employed him as his chief steward.[79] Besides sitting as an MP for Norwich in 1453–4 and serving on numerous royal commissions, he later became steward of the Norfolk estates of George, duke of Clarence, an appointment which likewise testifies to his professional and personal standing.[80]

On the death of the first duke of Suffolk, in 1450, Jenney appears to have joined the vociferous East Anglian lobby agitating for a formal indictment of his henchmen. By the time of the parliamentary elections in October of that year he was being suggested as a possible MP for Yarmouth who could be relied upon to 'seye well' in the cause. His appointment as legal adviser to the king's chamberlain, Ralph, Lord Cromwell, also strengthened his hand. Even so, he trod carefully. Sir John Fastolf criticised his apparent failure to defend Cromwell's interests in the region against John Heydon and Sir Thomas Tuddenham.[81] This was a wise move in view of their formidable capacity for grudge-bearing, but also, more immediately, because all the estates in Cringleford which Jenney's wife then stood to inherit on the death of her widowed mother, Margaret Wetherby, were held by Heydon in trust on her behalf. Curiously, in view of later developments, the late Thomas Wetherby had also employed Roger Pratt as a trustee, and had enjoyed cordial relations with Hugh Acton, Selot's immediate predecessor. This was no doubt because he acknowledged both men as feudal overlords, a concession to the hospital which neither Heydon nor Jenney were initially prepared to make.[82]

By the time of Margaret Wetherby's death, in 1457, Heydon had recovered much of his former power, having been pardoned and reappointed as a justice of the peace in Norfolk. However sound his personal relations with Selot and other members of Bishop Lyhart's circle, he would clearly be anxious to defend his own and Jenney's territorial interests. Selot therefore faced a daunting challenge, and prepared to stand his ground. He promptly denied Jenney's claim (made, significantly, in his capacity 'as bailiff of the said John Heydon') that the hospital was no more than a tenant of the 200 acres in question, and thus liable for substantial arrears of rent. Asserting that the land belonged instead to the hospital's manor of Cringleford, Selot countered that Jenney owed *him* a slightly higher rent of 45*s* per annum, as well as unpaid arrears of no less than £40 for the lease of a water mill.[83] By February 1459 the dispute had been referred to arbitration, almost certainly after a round of litigation in either the mayor of Norwich's court or at the local assizes. The survival of an indenture whereby Jenney (and presumably Selot as well) offered securities of £66 to accept the award of the two chief justices of England, reflects the problems both sides had encountered in negotiating out of court.[84] Despite the obvious skill and experience which the mediators brought to their task, so much bad blood now existed between Selot and Jenney that the likelihood of reaching an amicable settlement seemed increasingly remote. During the summer of 1459 Jenney scored a shortlived triumph by having his adversary committed to the Marshalsea prison of the court of King's Bench on a charge of trespass against the Statute of Maintenance. The evidence was too flimsy to survive close inspection, but none the less suggests that Selot had been exploiting all the networks at his disposal. He stood accused of covertly attempting to prejudice the outcome of another lawsuit over land in Cringleford, this time brought against Jenney, in March 1459, by the prior of Horsham St Faith. Selot was said to have incited the prior to proceed against his enemy in the previous January by plying him and his attorneys, Nicholas Ovy and John Fyncham, with lavish entertainment in the hospital. A meal of bread, ale, wine and fish, implausibly priced at 20*s*, served in the privacy of his lodgings, constituted the 'reward' or bribe offered for their compliance. Selot strenuously denied having 'laboured' anyone in this way, protesting that the prior had done no more than ask him to recommend a suitable attorney, and that his choice had dispassionately fallen on Ovy, 'then learned in the law in Norwich'. It was, he added, with the sole intention of seeking advice in his own dispute with Jenney that he had invited the three men to his table.[85]

The case never reached a verdict, and was probably no more than a tactic on Jenney's part to intimidate his opponent. He knew well enough that both attorneys had long-standing connections with the hospital, and were busy stirring up trouble on its behalf. Ironically, under the circumstances, Ovy had also served, from 1444 onwards, as a trustee of the manor of Trowse, along with the unholy trinity of Selot, Sir Thomas Tuddenham and John Heydon.[86] But Jenney was a resourceful man, and had another shot in his locker. Following his charges of bribery came allegations made in the same court of King's Bench that Selot and a gang of ruffians had broken, *vi et armis*, into his fishery at Cringleford, and had caused damage assessed (even more implausibly) at £100. As well as removing a precisely itemised and spectacular haul of 200 pike, 1,000 roach, 1,000 perch and 5,000 eels, they had destroyed a fish weir worth £20 – an allegation which Selot did not, in principle, deny. He countered, however, by asserting that Jenney had trespassed on *his* property, and that he had every right to protect his stretch of the Yare from poachers.[87]

Meanwhile, the dispute over Heylesdon's manor dragged on. In November 1459, Jenney proffered even larger bonds of £100 to abide by the recommendations of six new mediators, John Heydon and his own brother, William (the future judge), acting on his part, while none other than the prior of Horsham St Faith was to speak for the hospital. Once again, negotiations foundered. Two years later, in April 1461, the priors of Norwich and Woodbridge and two other arbitrators were called in to attempt another settlement. Since compromise still proved elusive, they turned to two umpires, whose status and authority made it possible to impose a solution. The terms of the award promulgated by Bishop Lyhart and John Mowbray, the young earl of Surrey (who inherited his father's dukedom of Norfolk during the proceedings), suggest that resistance had hitherto come principally from Selot, whose claims to the property were now upheld in their entirety. Since Surrey was only eighteen when the ruling was made, Lyhart may well have enjoyed an unusual degree of freedom to press the hospital's case. There is reason to suppose, too, that John Heydon, who had hitherto given Jenney his unequivocal support, was disinclined to proceed any further against an erstwhile friend, or risk losing the goodwill of Lyhart and his circle. His uncharacteristic readiness to compromise eventually led Selot to make generous provision for his obit, as well as Bishop Lyhart's, to be celebrated annually for eighty years with great splendour in the hospital church. The manor of Heylesdon, together with all its appurtenances in Cringleford, Hethersett, Colney and Eaton, was now assigned to the master and his successors, both parties being required to cease all disputes and actions then hanging between them.[88] Jenney's comprehensive defeat was, in fact, made worse by the umpires' attempts at appeasement. Whereas the common law left only winners and losers, arbitration sought to work through compromise, and usually offered compensation of some kind. The hospital was therefore instructed to pay him £13, which it slyly did by pardoning his contentious arrears of rent, rather than handing over hard cash. This must have been a bitter pill to swallow, but Jenney duly disposed of his title by a fine in the Court of Common Pleas to Selot and his trustees. Bishop Lyhart, John Smyth and the influential Norwich merchant, John Gilbert (one of Selot's oldest friends), performed this office, their involvement serving as an eloquent testimony to the range of 'good lordship' at the hospital's disposal.[89] An agreement of September 1461, whereby Selot undertook to pay the prior of Horsham St Faith's an annuity of 26*s* 8*d* from the hospital's estates in Cringleford, invites further speculation.[90] Had Jenney's suspicions about the master's abuse of hospitality and penchant for bribery been justified?

Selot was far too shrewd to place all his eggs in one, Lancastrian basket, especially during the turbulent 1450s. He had also cultivated the support of the de la Poles' rivals, the Mowbrays, and had employed the earl of Surrey's father, John, duke of Norfolk, as a feoffee of the estates in Hethel and East Carleton which he acquired in June 1455 and later used (along with Heylesdon's manor) to fund the above-mentioned obits. Roger Bigod, earl of Norfolk, had released property in this area to Walter Suffield for his original endowment, and successive holders of the earldom had retained interests there. But more than good neighbourliness was at stake. Coming within a matter of days of the Yorkist victory over the Court party at the battle of St Albans, when the duke had thrown in his lot with the rebel lords, Norfolk's involvement in this transaction suggests that Selot was a very astute operator indeed. He also enlisted the support of Bishop Lyhart and John Heydon (before the quarrel over Heylesdon's), their trusteeship offering a comprehensive insurance policy against most political eventualities.[91] Here, too, Selot had run into conflict with a prominent local landowner, Nicholas Appleyard, whom he successfully sued at common law before December 1456, forcing him to relinquish any further claims upon the property in question.[92] The Appleyards had long memories, however, and half a century later Nicholas's heir and namesake attempted to recover the estate. Once again, the family faced a doughty opponent: after at least three years' litigation in the royal courts, William Soper (master 1504–19) secured a remarkably one-sided arbitration award, which not only upheld his title, but actually extended the hospital's rights by allowing it to graze 120 sheep as well as cattle on the Hethel commons, and 'yerely dygge . . . for tile erthe and bryke erthe'.[93]

During the reign of Edward IV, Selot continued to exploit the good will and influence of friends whose authority in the region was reinforced by their status at Court. One such was Sir Henry Grey of Ketteringham, a prominent Yorkist who served as a justice of the peace and royal commissioner in East Anglia and was duly made a trustee of Heylesdon's manor as well as the manor of Mundham and other estates belonging to the hospital.[94] Acting on information received from Sir Henry during the 1470s, Doctor Selot had Christina Baker of Intwood 'publicly proclaimed excommunicate' and imprisoned for defamation. Despite her insistence that Selot had acted unjustly 'without legal form' neither he nor Bishop Goldwell would relent, and she was finally driven, in 1480, to appeal to the Pope himself. During the course of these proceedings, Christina was bound over in heavy securities at Westminster, each of her four mainpernors being obliged to offer pledges of £40 on her behalf. One of them was none other than John Jenney, whose bonds were confiscated by the Crown in November of that year and shared between Grey and another courtier.[95] The story behind the bare facts of this particular dispute remains hidden, but it is hardly fanciful to assume that Jenney was still nursing a sense of grievance and would have been more than happy to abet, if not actually maintain, anyone who attacked his old enemy.[96]

Not even Selot, secure in the support of his episcopal patrons, Lyhart and Goldwell, and possessed of a reticulum of powerful lay well-wishers, could always be so intransigent. This was especially the case when he came up against the rival claims of a powerful religious house, such as Sawtry Abbey. His efforts to extricate St Giles's from its obligation to pay an annual pension of 66*s* 8*d* (charged upon the temporalities of the parish church at Costessey) to the abbot, and to force him to settle arrears of rent due from a tenement in Holme Street, placed him at an evident disadvantage. Four lay arbitrators agreed, in 1470, that St Giles's would purchase the tenement and others nearby through an intermediary for the unusually large sum of £120, but that henceforward the abbot would relinquish his pension and all other rights in the parish church of Costessey. In this instance, the hospital made quite substantial concessions, especially as the tenements then needed repair and full payment was to be made immediately, under securities of £200.[97]

Settlements out of court, as well as litigation itself, could generate considerable expenses in the way of legal fees, the cost of searching for evidence and the inevitable sweeteners given to interested parties. It has been estimated that one-fifth of the entries in the cartulary of St Mark's hospital, Bristol, concern attempts by the house to defend itself against lay and ecclesiastical adversaries. After one bruising round of litigation in the court of Common Pleas, the master was obliged to alienate rents worth £8 a year in return for cash to pay off his debts.[98] An episcopal grant made to St Giles's in 1340 refers to the problems caused by certain 'sons of iniquity', whose malicious attempts to undermine the rights and titles of the hospital added greatly to its financial burdens.[99] Declining receipts from Repps and Bastwick in the early sixteenth century may have been due as much to resistance over the payment of tithes as to economic stagnation. Expenses sustained in suing the parishioners came to almost £11 between 1526 and 1528, consuming over two years' net profits, and requiring a subvention of cash which the receiver general could ill afford.[100] Yet almost every year he spent a few pounds on gifts to attorneys and other potentially useful individuals, such as the king's escheator and the bailiffs of powerful neighbours. In 1397, for example, the countess of Norfolk's surveyor received 6*s* 8*d* 'for his counsel', routine legal fees came to 23*s* 4*d*, and a substantial sum of almost £7 was set aside for expenses in London and payments made to the notary, Roger Ulf.[101] Proper record-keeping and care with regard to the storage and preservation of evidence could obviously help to reduce costs and ensure success in the courts, besides improving financial efficiency. We have already seen how much attention was given to such matters at St Giles's during the later Middle Ages. Indeed, as early as 1270, Hamon de Calthorpe had been acting as keeper of charters belonging to John de Vaux, which he then handed over safely in a chest to the latter's executors, along with a sum of 20 marks due to the deceased.[102]

St Giles's was served by a number of talented and conscientious priests, such as Richard Braunche and Robert Godfrey, who not only found employment as administrators and accountants, but effectively deputised for masters with other commitments in the diocese. Such an arrangement was actually written into the 1331 statutes of the hospital of St Mary Elsing in Cripplegate, London, whereas at St Giles's it appears to have evolved as the career pattern of the masters changed.[103] Braunche served as sacristan of St Helen's church between at least 1465 and the early 1480s, by which time he was also steward of the hospital and collector of its rents in Norwich. A man of obvious ability, he went on to become master of the college of the Blessed Virgin at Mettingham. His promotion is understandable, since, like his patrons, Selot and Smyth, he forged useful contacts with prominent landowners in the region, numbering the Hobarts, Boleyns and Heydons among his acquaintance.[104] His successor as rent collector and steward, Robert Godfrey, was a veritable renaissance man: besides accounting as receiver general of hospital revenues in the 1480s, he was also engaged as organist and is twice described as a 'bachiller in law'. Selot had head-hunted him in 1477 with the formal promise of an additional 13*s* 4*d* a year, payable while he remained a member of the community. It was upon him that responsibility for managing the hospital fell on John Smyth's death in 1489. He presided over the election of Oliver Dynham and headed the discontented chapter at the time of Bishop Goldwell's visitation three years later. As we have already seen, he spent the rest of his life at St Giles's, providing invaluable continuity over the best part of four decades. His desire for perpetual commemoration there with 'obyte with *placebo*, *dirige* and masse of requiem be note' was clearly more than a matter of conventional piety.[105]

Appointments of this calibre appear to have been links in the great chain of patronage, forged by the late medieval masters, who needed trustworthy assistants. As well as improved career prospects, of the sort enjoyed by Braunche, immediate rewards were also forthcoming. On the death or resignation of Hugh Acton, in September 1454, Peter Goos, a newly appointed hospital chaplain, took over as receiver general, almost certainly on the personal recommendation of Doctor Selot. He had the latter to thank for his preferment to the living at Costessey, where he was allowed to farm the vicarage, with its rents, tithes and demesnes, for life, free of charge, in lieu of a stipend. Goos, in return, appeared with Sir Henry Grey as a trustee of the hospital's acquisitions in Cringleford and Carleton, while Selot and the two attorneys who had allegedly been bribed with a fish supper in 1457 were parties to conveyances involving his kinsman, Henry Goos. It was surely no coincidence that one John Goos became keeper of the granaries at Costessey in 1458, at which point a priest named Walter Goos served the living. During this period Peter also acted from time to time as parochial chaplain at Bastwick, where his kinsmen, James and Robert, were frequently employed to oversee harvests and other agricultural works.[106] Here was a close community which protected its members and their families.

There was, however, no real substitute for friends in high places. Hospitals, in common with other landowners, had to fight for survival in a ruthless world; they could not afford to stand aloof from the scramble for 'good lordship'. Finances may often have been strained, but a house like St Giles's had clearly more to offer its well-wishers than hard cash. Setting aside its awesome powers as a spiritual intermediary between God and repentant sinners, there were other more immediately useful bargaining counters at its disposal. As we have already seen, the offer of subsidised accommodation or even free private quarters in the hospital precincts could be used to reward loyal supporters and attract influential protectors. Robert Ippeswell, a graduate in canon law and Official to the archdeacon of Norwich, occupied lodgings near the gates for over twenty years, presumably on the recommendation of Doctor Selot, to whom he was very close. During the 1470s, he rented one of the hospital's properties at Horstead, and was a party to the above-mentioned release made by the abbot of Sawtry. 'Master Salatt and Ypswell' were together branded as creatures of the de la Poles by Margaret Paston, in 1465, when both were deemed to have perverted the course of justice on their behalf. Ippeswell died under a far blacker cloud, however, having been accused of malversation and theft while he was master of the Carnary Chapel in the cathedral precinct – charges which the Pastons would have gleefully endorsed.[107] Their anger was also directed against Nicholas Ovy, namesake, and probably son, of Selot's attorney in the 1450s, who was retained jointly by the duke of Suffolk and the hospital from about 1475 onwards. Besides acting as the house's auditor for a period of ten years, Ovy was involved in several major property transactions along with Doctor Selot, John Smyth, John Jullys and other senior staff. Like Ippeswell, whom he knew intimately, he was one of the hospital's tenants, renting various holdings in the city, while his kinsman, John Ovy, rector of Uggeshall and parish chaplain of Blythburgh, spent at least fifty-eight weeks as a boarder in the precinct between 1486 and 1489. A man of great ability and not a little ruthlessness, Nicholas became recorder of Norwich, a position which clearly increased his value as both friend and employee.[108]

Legal advisors to the bishops of Norwich, such as the canonist, Doctor John Scarlet, who frequently stayed at St Giles's over the years 1498–1501, also made fluent advocates.[109] Shortly afterwards, the young son of Henry VII's attorney general and chief counsellor, Sir James Hobart, was given free board and lodging in return for his father's 'good counsel past and to come'.[110] This proved a shrewd investment: as executor to Bishop Goldwell, Hobart was then helping to expedite the foundation of a large and valuable chantry at St Giles's, while also perhaps ensuring that a substantial part of the residue of the late bishop's estate found its way into the hospital's coffers. We should remember that Master Jullys's great rebuilding programme was just getting under way, and that Hobart, as a local man and former recorder of Norwich, may well have encouraged him to improve the facilities. Working alongside his co-executors, Nicholas Goldwell, William Soper and John Jullys, on the complex property transactions involved in setting up an endowment theoretically worth about £38 a year, he had ample opportunity to forge strong personal links with successive masters.[111] In the event, however, Hobart's support at Westminster turned out to be even more worthwhile.

Always watchful where the enforcement and observance of the Statute of Mortmain was concerned, officers of the Crown rarely missed an opportunity to prosecute offenders.[112] In 1409, for example, Roger Pratt had mounted an ultimately successful defence against charges laid in the court of King's Bench at Westminster that the hospital had illicitly acquired the advowson of the church of Mundham St Peter and other property in the area '*en ffraude d'estatut*'.[113] When, between 1505 and 1507, William Soper, as master, had to defend himself in the court of the Royal Exchequer against two further allegations of concealment, Sir James's presence on the bench secured another rare victory for the accused. The first case concerned the lands in Hethel and Carleton previously acquired by John Selot, which Henry VII's officials, acting with their customary vigilance, had seized on the ground that the necessary royal licence had never been obtained. In 1462 Selot had, however, prudently secured a general pardon (still preserved in the hospital archives), which the court grudgingly accepted. Soper was also said to have appropriated for his own use the *leprosarium* of St Mary Magdalen in Sprowston, a misunderstanding which had arisen from the fact that two of his predecessors (Nicholas Goldwell and John Jullys) had been made wardens by episcopal appointment. Here, too, his explanation satisfied the bench.[114] Soper was accorded a royal pardon of his own on 19 July 1508, but clearly had to pay heavily for it. Hobart's political star had been on the wane since a confrontation over *praemunire* legislation in 1506, and his sudden resignation of the attorney generalship in the following year deprived St Giles's of a powerful ally at Court. Although the master had cleared himself of any breach of statute law, he was bound over in securities totalling £400 'to be true in his allegiance for life' and obliged under further pledges of £100 to pay £50 to King Henry.[115]

Such experiences help to explain why the more assertive of St Giles's twenty-seven masters set out deliberately and unashamedly to win support wherever they could find it. Did they not have a sacred duty to protect the hospital and conserve its resources? John Smyth may have received a rather better press from the Pastons than Doctor Selot, but he was not universally admired. If John Paston I regarded him as 'oure old freende', William Worcester had good reason to be more sceptical, dismissing him as 'non holsom counceller'. Besides criticising his demeanour in the ecclesiastical courts, Worcester bitterly resented the loss of a personal corrody at St Benet's abbey, which the monks had rescinded and awarded to Smyth instead. The days of monastic raiding parties on the hospitals' Broadland estates were clearly over: it made better sense to cultivate such a well-connected neighbour.[116] The Austin Friars of Norwich certainly regretted their decision to adopt a more confrontational approach. Claiming that Smyth and the brethren of St Giles's had reneged on an agreement to pay a priest to sing at Hildebrand's hospital 'for all Cristen soules', their prior attempted to recover the money with damages in the local courts. Such, however, was the 'favour and gret asistens to the seid master . . . shewid and had, as well by the . . . shrevis [sheriffs] as othir' that the friars soon found themselves in the dock.[117] Smyth, like so many of the late medieval masters, not only enjoyed the favour of his bishop, but also of a significant proportion of Norwich's ruling elite.

THE HOSPITAL AND THE CITY

Maintaining, as they did, a standard of living barely distinguishable from that of the affluent merchant class, and frequently consorting with the rulers of Norwich by virtue of their other official duties, most of the late medieval masters of St Giles's were drawn into the political and social life of the city. Whatever hard feelings may have arisen over the hospital's situation in an exempt liberty outside the jurisdiction of the corporation or its too intimate association with the de la Poles and their retainers, personal relations between individual citizens and senior clergy appear to have been cordial. These were the men who together comprised only a small proportion of Norwich's taxpayers (just 6 per cent in 1525) but had accumulated almost two-thirds of its wealth and property.[118] As potential benefactors they were clearly to be cultivated; and most of the masters seem to have relished the opportunity to do so. Hamon de Calthorpe's appointment as executor of St Giles's leading lay patron, William Dunwich, in 1272, serves as the first of many examples of the friendship, trust and mutual backscratching which united hospital clergy and prosperous laymen. Indeed, Hamon received personal legacies of plate and jewellery, as well as bequests for the hospital, from Dunwich and his wife.[119]

At least nine of the seventeen masters who served between 1399 and 1546 belonged to the guild of St George, which had been founded in 1385 as a religious and charitable fraternity, but rapidly became the most politically important organisation in the city.[120] Accorded a royal charter of incorporation in 1417, it was restructured on hierarchical lines after the disturbances of the 1440s to give members of the aldermanic bench complete control over its affairs. Although craftsmen and others of the middling sort were still admitted to its ranks, real authority rested in comparatively few hands. Noblemen (including the first duke of Suffolk), local gentry and senior ecclesiastics were happy to associate themselves with such a prestigious body.[121] At guild feasts and assemblies successive masters of the hospital rubbed shoulders with the rich and powerful, becoming the executors, trustees, attorneys and personal friends of men whose solemn exequies would eventually be performed in the hospital church, and whose wills would, hopefully, contain additional legacies for the priests, choristers, almsmen and nurses. It will be recalled from Chapter III that work on the home farm at the Lathes, just outside Norwich, ground to a halt in May 1429, so that Robert Spenser, then master and a member of the guild, could borrow a horse to ride in the mayor's procession. His predecessor, Roger Pratt, also mingled busily among the great and the good, eventually becoming one of their number himself.

Much of Pratt's authority derived from a long-standing connection with William Setman, alderman, MP and one of the most active philanthropists in early fifteenth-century Norwich. Setman knew the hospital well, having been a feoffee of the estates in Cringleford which John Derlyngton intended to use for the support of his chantry there. His fiduciary duties were shared with the shire knight, William Rees of Tharston, a former sheriff, justice of the peace and escheator of Norfolk.[122] Both men had, indeed, helped to acquire the necessary royal letters patent approving the endowment, in 1410, and may even have contributed towards the £60 fee demanded by the Crown for its licence.[123] Their ties with the master were extremely close. Rees made his will almost immediately afterwards, leaving generous doles to the patients and sisters of St Giles's and a personal gift of £10 to Pratt, whose labours as an executor brought him into prolonged contact with the courtier, Sir Simon Felbrigg, and other Norfolk notables, thus further extending his network of potential well-wishers.[124] As Setman's principal trustee for the best part of thirty years, he was also kept busy implementing a series of substantial endowments upon the college of St Mary in the Fields and the Austin Friars.[125] After such a long association, the alderman naturally trusted him to execute his will of 1429, a handsome bequest of £13 6*s* 8*d* for repairs to the hospital and legacies to the inmates serving as his reward. Once again, Pratt's responsibilities were onerous, involving the distribution of at least £86 among the poor of Norwich and the surrounding countryside as well as all the other charitable works with which his friend hoped to secure a place in paradise.[126]

In their anxiety to discharge their duties, Pratt and one of his co-executors appear to have shown less concern for the spiritual health of a third colleague, reputedly seizing over £62 'by grete force and manas [menaces]' from his effects shortly after he died, even though all his accounts had been settled. Pratt demonstrably possessed the steely lack of sentiment characteristic of a successful bureaucrat. While executing the will of another prominent Norwich merchant, John Asgar, in July 1437, he was accused by the latter's widow of evicting her from the matrimonial home and reducing her to beggary. Her claim to have been caused 'suche distresse and heuyness that hit is like to be cause of her dethe and uttir destruccion withoute she be remedyed', was, however, dismissed by the Court of Chancery for lack of proof.[127] In this context it is worth noting the outcome of a confrontation between Pratt and another member of the guild of St George, which took place about a year earlier. When Pratt flounced off in an unchristian fit of pique after being called 'the falsest that myght goo up on herthe', and ostentatiously withdrew his 'helpely handes of good and of fortheryng to the seid fraternite', the guildsmen were so alarmed that they promptly expelled his traducer.[128] His good lordship clearly meant a great deal.

John Selot also forged close relationships with his associates in the guild of St George. Chief among them was the sometime mayor of Norwich, John Gilbert, whose confidence in him was perhaps even greater than William Setman's had been in his predecessor. Shortly before his death, in 1466, Gilbert named Doctor Selot as the first of his five executors, assigning him and his colleague, John Heydon (to whom he was by then fully reconciled), far larger bequests than the others, and naturally remembering the hospital in his will. Charged with raising over £460 from Gilbert's estate to support his offspring, as well as implementing pious bequests 'lyche as it is seyn moste pleasyng to God and profite to my soule', the executors were also responsible for 'puttyng and gidyng' seven young children and selecting husbands for three of them. Selot was still preoccupied with the administration of this estate ten years later, and, like Roger Pratt before him, he became embroiled in litigation because of his duties.[129] He sued the mercer, Thomas Cambridge, in Chancery for refusing to surrender the deeds of one of Gilbert's properties, naming the hospital's attorney, Nicholas Ovy, as his security.[130]

Disputes of this kind were far too common in mercantile circles to disturb Selot's easy relations with the ruling elite. A formal composition, made in 1472 between him and the rulers of Norwich for the provision of a priest to minister to the prisoners in the Guildhall, certainly suggests that both he and the hospital commanded their trust. In return for a cash payment of £200 from the estates of two deceased aldermen, Ralph Segryme and Richard Brown, Selot and the brethren of St Giles's contracted to find a chaplain to celebrate mass daily in the chapel of St Barbara for 'the relief and comfort' of the prisoners incarcerated nearby. The chaplain was also to intercede for the good estate of the mayor, the commonalty of Norwich, the deceased and their families and of a third alderman named John Wilby, who had endowed and equipped the chapel. It is significant that, although the priest in question was to hold no other benefice with cure, provision was specifically made for the master to appoint a hospital chaplain should there be a shortage of acceptable candidates.[131] Can any wider conclusions be drawn from this welcome bequest? That the hospital was increasingly seen as a foundation run by, and for, a clerical and mercantile elite seems inescapable. A comparison between the wills of some sixty-six Norwich aldermen made over the years 1490 to 1532 and those of a less select group of 364 citizens from the same period reveals that the former were far more likely to leave money to St Giles's. Although these findings remain impressionistic, it looks as if over a quarter of the aldermen remembered the hospital, while fewer than one-tenth of the citizenry as a whole did so.[132]

Like many other influential figures, the masters of St Giles's were in demand as mediators, whose role was to settle quarrels out of court as amicably, cheaply and quickly as possible. Parties to arbitration commonly engaged the services of powerful friends or patrons (as John Selot did in his dispute with John Jenney), who could defend their interests, while at the same time demanding sufficient respect to make an award binding.[133] The procedure adopted on such occasions owed a great deal to that employed in the ecclesiastical courts, where so many of the hospital's senior clergy served as notaries or judges. Few of the twenty-seven masters can have faced a challenge as difficult as that presented to John Derlyngton, who was called upon settle a quarrel between his imperious patron, Bishop Despenser, and the dean of the college of St Mary in the Fields. That the latter was happy to accept his ruling, despite his close relationship with the bishop, speaks volumes for his impartiality, as does Despenser's outright rejection of it.[134] In theory, if not always in practice, the Church advocated compromise, or at least a cessation of hostilities, which is what Doctor Selot achieved when he rode out to Hellesdon, in 1465, to end an armed confrontation between the duke of Suffolk's men and the Pastons. On this occasion, the latter accepted his efforts at peacekeeping, and may for once have been glad that he carried so much weight with the duke. It is, therefore, hardly surprising to find John Smyth, his successor, urging them to seek an amicable settlement at a later stage in their dispute.[135]

Success was not, however, guaranteed. John Hecker's efforts to achieve reconciliation in the parish of Cringleford after the vicar had been defamed by one of his flock were resented by some of the parishioners because he so clearly favoured the priest. The appointment of William Sekyngton, bachelor of laws and former master of St Giles's, as one of the three arbitrators chosen to restore order to the city of Norwich in 1443 after the outbreak of rioting known as Gladman's Insurrection reflects his high standing among certain members of the urban elite. But his previous connection with Sir Thomas Tuddenham rendered him equally suspect in the eyes of the rival faction. He and his colleagues, Sir John Clifton and Walter Aslak, were briefly held captive by some of the rebels, who nursed serious reservations as to their impartiality.[136] Even so, although his efforts proved abortive, the simple fact of Sekyngton's involvement as a mediator in a civic dispute of this magnitude illustrates clearly enough the influence and prestige enjoyed by the fifteenth-century masters of St Giles's. The expertise gained by some of their number in mercantile affairs is also noteworthy. In May 1466, for example, the ubiquitous John Selot joined with five laymen (two of whom were aldermen) in adjudicating between the Norwich worsted weaver, Reginald Harneys, and a merchant from Bruges. Their dispute hinged upon the terms of a bond in £100 concerning the delivery of cloth, and required a good deal of specialist knowledge about international trade.[137]

Although a few of the late medieval masters were as rich and well-connected as their friends in the city, their wealth certainly did not derive from the hospital's coffers. On the contrary, some must have been prepared to underwrite expenses from the outset, and none can have expected to profit financially from this particular appointment. On paper, at least, the mastership of St Giles's did not appear an especially rewarding prospect. The annual stipend of £4, supplemented by a single set of robes and the occasional pair of boots, compared unfavourably with that enjoyed by priests or cantarists in wealthy urban parishes, where an income of twice this amount was not unusual.[138] Free board and lodging counted for a good deal, though, and we know that during the later Middle Ages the master's private quarters were comfortably appointed with plate and hangings. This should remind us that status was not simply determined in crude monetary terms. That the master possessed awesome reserves of spiritual authority has already been established; at a secular level, too, his influence was wide ranging. The power to negotiate the leases of over fifty properties in Norwich alone, to hire craftsmen (often for ambitious building projects involving a substantial capital outlay), to engage domestic staff, to choose bedesmen and corrodians and to contract for the provisioning of a sizeable community further increased his influence in the region. Although, when compared to the Benedictine monastery and the friaries of Norwich, the hospital of St Giles commanded relatively modest resources, it still constituted a notable economic and social presence.

CHAPTER VI

PAUPERS AND PROVISIONS

Furst, men schuld wilfully fede pore hungry men and thursty.
For in that they fede Iesu Crist, as hym self sayth in the gospel,
And also Iesu Crist gyfys body and sowle, lyf and catel to vs for this ende,
And fedis vs wyth his flesch and his blod in sacrament of the awter,
And gaf hys precious herte blod on the cros
To bryng vs owt of mischef of synnys and paynys . . .

Be gret resoun owe we to vysite seke men,
Sethyn Crist for oure nede deyd on the cros
To bryng vs out of seknesse and synne and kepes vs out of bodily seknesse:
For we schuld help other seke men, and be this help deserue the blyss of heuyn.

[First, men should feed the hungry and thirsty poor of their own free will, since by so doing they feed Jesus Christ, as he says in the Gospel [Matthew 25: 35–40]. And also Jesus Christ gives his body and soul, his life and his possessions, to us for this end; and he feeds us with his flesh and his blood in the sacrament of the altar; and he gave his precious heart's blood on the Cross to deliver us from the perils of sin and suffering . . . .

It is all the more important that we visit the sick, since Christ died for our sakes on the Cross to save us from sickness and sin, and keep us safe from earthly desire: so we should help those who are ill, and through this help grow worthy of the joys of heaven.]

The Lay Folks' Mass Book

The striking lack of documentary evidence for the presence of either physicians or surgeons in English hospitals before the sixteenth century has perplexed some historians, who have tried, with predictable lack of success, to make the most of a handful of tenuous connections.[1] The numerous and detailed accounts for St Giles's are silent about the provision of medical help in the infirmary, and say little of dealings between the staff and Norwich's growing community of barber-surgeons, leeches and apothecaries. We know that two physicians, who were styled *Magister* but had evidently not attended university, dwelt in Holme Street during the fifteenth century, and that the chaplains engaged a barber who may have bled them periodically as well as shaving them and cutting their hair.[2] Some of the graduate masters probably familiarised themselves with medical theory at Oxford or

Cambridge, although it is highly unlikely that they, or any of the royal physicians who secured the wardenships of other English medieval hospitals, actually tended the poor. The situation was very different in the larger hospitals of France and Italy, where expert treatment was regularly available, often at the hands of senior practitioners. These institutions were far wealthier as well as bigger than their English counterparts, and were, moreover, situated in major urban centres, such as Paris and Florence, where physicians and surgeons had organised themselves with great efficiency into colleges and guilds. Since they were geared to the treatment of acute cases, and anticipated a regular turnover of patients, sometimes numbering several thousand a year, hospitals of this kind provided newly qualified or trainee practitioners with valuable experience.[3] Civic, as opposed to ecclesiastical, authorities encouraged this trend, adopting a strictly utilitarian approach to the needs of the poor. In the 1430s the rulers of Lyon criticised local physicians for abandoning hospital patients to 'ignorant brothers, superstitious monks, empirics [and] self-proclaimed sorcerers'. Care of the soul evidently took second place where the creation of a healthy workforce was concerned.[4] Acute cases made special demands upon any establishment: even comparatively modest Catalan hospitals, such as Santa Creu in Barcelona and En Clapers in Valencia, retained lay specialists to treat the sick and wounded.[5] As we shall see, several English houses, by contrast, refused to accept potentially disruptive or demanding patients, preferring the elderly, the disabled and chronic cases whose requirements could be met by basic nursing care. So too did a sizeable number of small continental hospitals. The cost of professional services was clearly a significant consideration for institutions beset by financial problems, and it is important to remember that only a small proportion of the population could, in any event, ever afford the fees of a leading surgeon or university-trained physician. For the poor, in particular, healing often came at the hands of unlettered women in the home or local community.[6] As yet lacking the type of collegiate or institutional structures which incorporated work in hospitals and among the needy, English medieval practitioners were left to perform works of charity on an individual rather than a collective basis. Some may have been assiduous on this score, but it is unwise to speculate.

A comparison with the infirmary of Norwich cathedral priory, which lay barely a few hundred yards away from St Giles's hospital, shows what type of treatment more privileged members of society – whether lay or religious – received when they fell ill. The infirmary was a large building with its own chapel and spacious hall, constructed along the same lines as an open-ward hospital.[7] Yet notwithstanding the emphasis placed by the monks on spiritual medicine, the very best physical care was expected, if not always delivered. Complaints about the poor provision afforded to sick monks in various East Anglian houses refer repeatedly to the absence of trained medical and surgical personnel, which was seen as a serious failing. Indeed, the Customary drawn up in 1379 for the guidance of the Norwich Benedictines stipulated that a fully qualified (that is graduate) physician should be provided by the infirmarer whenever necessary. He appears to have followed this precept until the 1490s, when standards began to decline.[8] A total of thirty-eight infirmarers' rolls for the period 1312 to 1530 survive in the archive of the Dean and Chapter. Although they are less informative than the remarkably detailed set available for Westminster abbey in this period, they present a similar picture of what, by contemporary standards, constituted regular, highly priced and expert attention.[9] In accordance with the fundamental principles of medical theory, great emphasis was placed upon the prevention of disease through the management of bodily humours. All the monks were regularly phlebotomised in a special chamber, set apart to avoid pollution, having their own servant to tend them during the two or three days' rest which customarily followed this prophylactic measure.[10] When unwell, they were attended by physicians or surgeons, who were either retained by contract or called in as circumstances required. In 1347–8, for example, the *medicus*, Master Geoffrey de Suffield, drew his usual annuity of 20*s* for treating sick brethren, and other colleagues were paid on an *ad hoc* basis for specific services. No fewer than twenty-three named monks (about half the community) then received medication at a cost of about £3.[11]

In addition to the provision of hospitality for visiting practitioners, the accounts record a regular outlay on glass phials used to inspect the monks' urine. Uroscopy was the principal diagnostic tool of the medieval physician, and one member of the Norwich monastic community who studied at Oxford in the fifteenth century actually wrote a short treatise on the subject.[12] A fee for the examination of urine was paid by the infirmarer to *medici* such as Master Mark (who also supplied clysters) and Master Conrad, a Cambridge graduate who lodged in the cathedral precinct during the 1470s.[13] Unlike the choir monks, senior office-holders and their staff received private treatment funded out of their own departmental budgets. In cases of protracted or serious illness care did not come cheaply. The precentor spent 29*s* 10*d* on medication for one monk alone in 1356–7. Tended at a cost of 25*s* 6*d* in 1427–8, Thomas Herward lived on in indifferent health for many years, unlike William Stondhall, who died in 1454–5 after running up a bill of 16*s* 8*d* during his last months.[14] A significant proportion of these expenses went on drugs as well as professional fees. Whereas the Westminster abbey monks employed the services of local apothecaries, the Norwich infirmarer appears to have prepared most of his own *materia medica*, which required manual skill as well as expert knowledge. Costly foreign imports, such as frankincense, dragon's blood, senna, cassia, liquorice, sugar (a vital ingredient in electuaries), mace and turbit, were processed on the premises, along with herbs grown in the infirmarer's garden. That he was well prepared for this task is evident from the supply of an alembic and other equipment for distillation, as well as enough glasses, boxes and storage jars to equip an apothecary's shop.[15] Although they called upon specialist help when diagnosing their charges, some of the infirmarers must have been well versed in classical medical theory. The library at Norwich cathedral was one of the finest in England, housing well over a thousand volumes by the Dissolution. Almost all these books were then destroyed, but we know that they included works by Galen, Avicenna and Aristotle, as well as various texts on diet, the regimen of health and medical astrology.[16]

Care at this level was clearly beyond the means of a moderately sized hospital, such as St Giles's, whose *raison d'etre* was, first and foremost, the provision of spiritual medicine for patrons and benefactors. It does not, however, necessarily follow that the physical well-being of the inmates counted for little. On the contrary, T.S. Miller's sweeping assertion that Western medieval hospitals in general showed 'little careful thought for the comfort, cleanliness or, ironically, health of the patients', seriously underestimates the importance accorded to diet and environment by founders and episcopal visitors alike.[17] Neglect, indifference and deprivation were to be found in many pre-Dissolution houses, but others demonstrated a genuine concern for the bodies, as well as the souls, of almsmen and patients.

CARING FOR THE POOR

Walter Suffield's generous provision of thirty beds or more, with mattresses, linen and coverlets, was enshrined in his two foundation charters and augmented in his will. Ironically, we know almost as much about the history of these beds as we do about their occupants, English medieval hospital patients being notoriously hard to document. Since, like the poor in general, they depended to a significant degree upon spontaneous, day-to-day acts of charity, which did not necessarily find their way into administrative records or even wills, they remain an often intangible presence. The loss of much of the ancillary evidence used in the compilation of accounts renders them even more invisible. Day books, noting the consumption of food by staff, visitors and patients in remarkable detail, were kept in many English hospitals.[18] Those for St Anthony's, London, contain invaluable information about the care of children and almsmen, as well as general standards of living, in this affluent institution during the late fifteenth century.[19] The destruction of similar journals presented at the annual audit by the steward of St Giles's makes it impossible to tell how many people were being fed at any given time, or to determine the quality of their diet. Assertions made to Henry VIII's commissioners in 1535 that the hospital earmarked no less than £45 a year for the support of poor choristers, nurses, bedesmen and wayfarers, together with the provision of daily meals for the indigent, almost certainly exaggerated the scale of its charitable work, while underestimating the outlay on resident priests and boarders.[20] It is, however, apparent that the general paucity of references to the sick poor in the surviving accounts cannot be equated with neglect. Nor do the modest sums spent upon them in comparison with expenditure on the clerical establishment imply too radical a shift away from the founder's original purpose. Although there can be little doubt that almsgiving and the care of the destitute soon lagged far behind the commemoration of the Christian departed in its scale of priorities, the hospital never entirely abandoned its practical responsibilities to Christ's representatives on earth.

The latter had, after all, a crucial part to play as intercessors for the souls of their benefactors. One such was William Dunwich, St Giles's most celebrated lay patron. In his will of December 1272, he bequeathed sums totalling £40 for the support of five sick paupers 'in all their necessities for ever, which poor persons shall lie . . . in five beds so that when any one of them is restored to health or enters the way of all flesh another infirm person shall rapidly be substituted in his place and honestly cared for'.[21] His legacy accorded with Walter Suffield's obvious intention that, as well as catering for elderly priests, the disabled and the terminally sick, the hospital should provide facilities for short-stay patients 'beset by illness'. These last would have comprised men (but almost certainly not women) suffering from hunger and exhaustion, poor and sick pilgrims travelling between East Anglia's many healing shrines, and the victims of acute diseases, such as gastric infections, scabies, pneumonia and ague. They were to be received with kindness, nursed in an appropriate manner, and once fully recovered sent on their way free of charge along with all their possessions.[22] Nothing is known about the procedures adopted at St Giles's for screening and admitting patients, although in hospitals throughout Europe nursing sisters as well as the master or his deputy played a significant part at the reception stage.[23] The sacristan may well have been charged with responsibility for the sick, as was the case at St John's hospital, Oxford, where his duties in the church and infirmary merged seamlessly. It was he who heard the patients' confessions on arrival.[24]

The medical condition of some patients, and by inference a lack of selectivity with regard to admissions, exercised members of Bishop Suffield's family, who had strong views about the way the hospital should be managed. In June 1309, after what appears to have been protracted litigation on this score, the master secured a release of property in Calthorpe and Erpingham from Walter de Calthorpe in return for a formal agreement that the hospital would fully support two paupers and a chaplain to be nominated by the donor and his heirs in perpetuity. De Calthorpe's insistence that the brethren should receive additional nominees until they had atoned for 'past lapses' suggests that a long-standing arrangement over the deployment of patronage had been repeatedly breached.[25] As Patricia Cullum has shown in her study of St Leonard's hospital, York, the endowment of private beds was popular with benefactors who sought personal commemoration but lacked the means to found a hospital. Like de Calthorpe, many of them expected to exercise rights of presentation, which they regarded in the same light as any other hereditary privilege.[26] Although hospitals welcomed the opportunity to extend their resources in this way, they were often obliged to accommodate patients whose circumstances seemed far from desperate. Patrons also tended to interfere. De Calthorpe's grant was, indeed, conditional upon a further undertaking that the number of patients and priests would not henceforth exceed limits first established by 'the blessed Lord Walter'. Initial plans for acquiring more than the original thirty beds 'as funds allowed' may no longer have seemed feasible when finances were under such strain, although the insidious expansion of the clerical establishment was perhaps a more immediate bone of contention. His additional requirement that anybody suffering from 'an intolerable disease' should henceforward be refused admittance, and that patients who currently gave cause for alarm should be transferred at once to 'another place' brought St Giles's into line with many similar institutions. Yet it imposed restrictions which the founder had not seen fit to make. Whereas many hospitals, such as those dedicated to St John the Baptist at Bridgwater, Oxford and Cambridge, excluded a variety of persons ranging from the wounded and ulcerated to 'lewd pregnant women', St Giles's appears to have been less selective in all but the matter of gender.[27] The undesirables mentioned by de Calthorpe perhaps included epileptics and the insane, but are more likely to have been lepers, whose removal to the civic *leprosaria* or the Magdalen hospital at Sprowston could easily have been effected. It seems unlikely that a man as meticulous as Suffield would have omitted to ban any category of person whom he viewed as potentially dangerous or disruptive, although in this instance he may have assumed that lepers would automatically be sent elsewhere. It is, on the other hand, worth noting that mixed hospitals, accommodating lepers in separate lodgings not far from other patients, were by no means unusual, and that Norwich possessed no *leprosarium* on its eastern approaches.[28]

That St Giles's was still performing an important role as a refuge for the destitute, hungry and aged in the 1340s is evident from the wording of Bishop Beck's licence for the appropriation of Mundham St Peter.[29] Did the masters continue to honour these weighty obligations after the upheavals of the Black Death and the hospital's transformation into a college for secular priests? In his will of 1357, Richard Clere of Ormesby, a prominent Norfolk landowner, left a generous bequest of £13 6*s* 8*d* to the master, 40*d* to each of the resident chaplains, the two 'brothers' and four sisters, and 2*s* 'to each bed lying in the [hospital] church'.[30] The sick paupers were, presumably, to join in prayers for his salvation, being in every sense a captive congregation, bound morally by the ties of obligation and physically by those of illness. Such passivity was attractive to patrons, as William Dunwich had already demonstrated when endowing his chantry at St Giles's in about 1271. The priest who celebrated mass there daily was to turn and exhort 'those recumbent in bed in the said hospital and other bystanders' to intercede for his salvation, an act of Christian charity they could hardly refuse.[31] As was the case in so many other open-ward infirmaries of this period, the close proximity of beds to the great and side altars is understood, and with it the clear visibility of the Host during the Mass. The therapeutic qualities of the Eucharist, described in Chapter IV, made it essential that the divine office should regularly be celebrated before the patients. Although Suffield's revised foundation statutes suspended services in the chapel whenever a woman resided in the precinct, he made sure that 'one mass only *for the sake of the sick near the altar* should be said for them alone' during such periods.[32] Herein lay one of the reasons for excluding the insane from hospitals; theologians such as Thomas Aquinas argued that 'the possessed' and others lacking reason should not even *look upon*, let alone receive, the sacrament, lest they pollute it with their gaze.[33]

The construction of the chancel and rebuilding of the nave in the 1380s either proceeded in tandem with the erection of an new infirmary hall or constituted the first stage of a carefully planned sequence designed to spread the cost and minimise disruption for parishioners and patients.[34] John Ely, who was buried in the new choir in 1383, left 2*s* to be divided between 'the poor lying in the said hospital', so it looks as if some beds remained available while work was in progress. Derlyngton's bell-tower was almost certainly added after the west end was more or less finished, which would suggest a completion date of about 1396 [see Plate 31]. With four bays, a great west window and north and south aisles 20 m in length, the hall alone represented a major undertaking. It occupied approximately one-third of the new building, and was as wide as the nave, to which it gave access until the 1570s [see Map III].

Expenditure on a new two-storey infirmary at St Mary Spital, Bishopsgate, in about 1280, was clearly necessitated by the expansion of the hospital chapel into the transepts which had previously served as men's and women's wards. The sixty or so beds it provided could not, however, satisfy the growing demand for relief in times of famine and overpopulation, and in the second quarter of the fourteenth century an extension was added with room for another fifty. Each bed and its surrounds occupied a space of about

2 × 2.5 m, with a wide central aisle where priests and nurses could move freely.[35] On this basis, the west end of St Giles's hospital could have comfortably accommodated about sixteen beds on the ground floor, two fitting neatly into each bay in the north and south aisles.[36] The positioning of a small window with miniature perpendicular tracery high up at the end of the south aisle, giving a clear view into the nave, suggests, however, that the infirmary hall actually had two storeys from the outset (like that at St Mary's), and thus twice the capacity [see Plate 36]. Only the central aisle opened directly, via a great archway, into the nave; the south and north aisles, where all the beds would have been placed, were separated from it by solid stone walls. Windows (then in both walls) would have allowed some of the patients on the upper storey to see the side altars in the nave, although the rood screen would have obscured their view of the chancel. As planned and constructed in the late fourteenth century, the new infirmary hall easily met the requirements of the foundation statutes by providing space for at least thirty beds and some sixty or so patients. It probably housed at least one altar, too, where mass could be said for their immediate benefit. But did this spacious and lofty infirmary hall fulfil its original purpose for long?

Occasional references in the hospital's late fifteenth-century accounts to a *domus infirmaria, domus Dei* or *domus pauperum* are ambiguous. Was this 'house of the poor' another name for the western 'infirmary' end of the hospital church, or a detached and far less impressive lodging elsewhere in the outer courtyard? The second alternative seems far more likely, not least because the *domus Dei* was thatched whereas the church was by then expensively roofed with tile and lead.[37] It is significant that the great west window is invariably described as belonging to the hospital church rather than the *domus Dei*. Indeed, when Bishop Goldwell arrived '*ad portam occidentalem ecclesiae*' to hold his visitation of 1492 the doors below this window were thrown open to receive him, so he could process down the entire length of the building to the accompaniment of the organs and the choir.[38] Would such a procession (of which there must have been many) have made its way through an open ward? Goldwell may have wished to bless the sick as the founder had expected his successors to do whenever they visited the hospital, but some of them, at least, lay out of sight by then in another part of the precinct. Unlike the church, the *domus pauperum* came in for comparatively few running repairs. In 1469–70 a reeder and his assistant worked for two days with their servants on the roof, and in the following year one John Tyler spent almost a week completing the job.[39] John Jullys's major rebuilding schemes did not extend to the comfort of the sick poor, but his successor felt obliged to effect some improvements to their lodgings. Between 1506 and 1508 the roof of 'Goddeshous', which had apparently been neglected for some time, was finally overhauled and work was done on the guttering.[40] Further repairs were needed by 1512–13, lack of proper maintenance having perhaps compounded the problem. Then a reeder and his servant were hired for twenty days, and over 16*s* was spent on thatch and seven waggons of clay for use on 'Goddeshous and other dwellings'. That the sick poor, or at least a few almsmen, continued to occupy the *domus Dei* is evident from the master's readiness to spend the comparatively large sum of 69*s* on a completely new roof four years later.[41]

Although the fabric of their lodgings may initially have left a good deal to be desired, the removal of some, if not all, of the long-stay patients to separate quarters cannot simply be dismissed as evidence of the marginalisation of a few inconvenient paupers. This move reflects a trend towards greater privacy common in many older open-ward hospitals, where infirmary halls were either being partitioned (as at St Mary's, Canterbury, and St Mary's, Strood) or restructured altogether to create individual lodgings (as at St John's, Lichfield, and St Nicholas's, Salisbury).[42] Some institutions, such as St Mary's, Bishopsgate, and St Thomas's, Southwark, which continued to receive the sick poor and travellers in large numbers, retained their open wards but also acquired homes for resident almsmen.[43] The newer almshouses then springing up across the country in large numbers almost invariably offered their inmates private quarters from the outset, encouraging them to read, meditate and pray for the salvation of their patrons.[44] As diet and standards of living improved during the late fourteenth century, a comparatively fitter population with a longer life expectancy began to make very different demands upon institutionalised charity. An inspecting dignitary, such as Archbishop Wickwane, could no longer insist upon the removal of 'secret and suspect hiding places or cells' (*secreta et suspecta diverticula sive cellule*), as he had done in 1279 at St Giles's hospital, Beverley.[45]

Between 1479 and 1503 the receiver general of St Giles's recorded modest payments to named 'paupers lying in bed', who shared an allowance of up to 18*s* a year to pay for herring and extra bread. Usually two or three in number, they were not the only long-stay patients, for we know that more mobile, anonymous inmates took their meals in the hall. The names of thirteen bedridden individuals are recorded during this period: two stayed for approximately six years, one for four years, one for three, two for two years and the rest for periods ranging from eleven months to six weeks. Some, at least, appear to have had close connections with St Giles's. The William Hogepound who abruptly left his post as hospital brewer at the end of May 1500 moved immediately into the almshouse where he spent the next four months, if not longer. References in the accounts to his servant, one Hugh Hogepound, confirm that the brethren tended to recruit staff from local families, and were prepared to care for them in adversity.[46] From 1505 onwards, the hospital elected to support one 'bedesman', who received 17*s* 4*d* a year (4*d* a week) for food, over and above a daily allocation of bread and ale. There was understandably some competition for this allowance. John Langton (1505–11) lost his place to John Sheppard, but recovered it again in 1516. The next almsman, Nicholas Porter (1521–3), received his dole '*vice et loco fratris*', which suggests that he may have been one of the frail and elderly clerics whom the founder had been so anxious to protect. The last in the line, Edmund Mountford, was from 1525 onwards supported by the master and brethren out of their own pockets, presumably because of straitened financial circumstances.[47]

If these men took up residence in 'Godeshous', who occupied the infirmary? The ground floor, which from the 1440s possessed an inner door leading to the refectory and thence to the kitchens, may have remained an open space for the reception and accommodation of a few deserving cases in search of overnight shelter. Each of these men was entitled to one halfpenny's worth of food, presumably upon arrival in the evening.[48] Daily meals were perhaps also served there to non-resident dependents as well as to the hospital's workmen and menial servants. The poor scholars possibly ate alongside them, and some may have slept in cubicles above.[49] Whereas two doors gave direct access to the infirmary from the outer courtyard, the refectory opened on to the cloister alone. Such a clear demarcation between the brethren and the laity, between private and public, would have maintained the spatial boundaries so important in a religious community, while also preserving the necessary distinctions of class and wealth dear to men like John Selot [see Map III].[50] In accordance with the trends noted above, the upper storey of the new infirmary was quite probably partitioned into chambers from the outset. These would have become available for general use as the number of patients declined. Yet whatever changes may have been made, the poor still remained a constant, if less conspicuous, presence in the outer precinct throughout the fifteenth century and beyond.

According to Henry VI's mortmain licence of 1451, the hospital was still feeding thirteen paupers each day, just as Suffield had required 200 years earlier. They were presumably drawn from the local community and thus selected on the basis of merit as well as need. St Giles's then also housed an unspecified number of infirm chaplains and provided refuge to 'other poor people, as and when they arrive, *converging on the hospital* in search of a bed for the night'. Seven impoverished scholars, now described as choristers, were given lodging as well as food, but the number of nurses had been reduced to two, perhaps because only eight 'debilitated paupers' remained in their immediate care.[51] The nature and quality of the facilities available to these men and successive generations of indigents before them are hard to determine. Piecemeal scraps of evidence, combined with our knowledge of life in other English hospitals of a similar size, suggest that conditions were spartan, but by no means inadequate.

Royal letters patent of 1411 approving the endowment of Archdeacon Derlyngton's chantry record a grant of fuel worth 20*s* a year by the prior of Horsham St Faith, 'to the use and profit of the poor and infirm'.[52] Stray references of this kind reveal the extent to which even relatively affluent houses, such as St Giles's, relied upon the goodwill of friends and neighbours. Gifts of fuel, so vital for the heating of draughty infirmary halls, helped to augment the hospital's own supplies and were a recognised act of Christian charity. One of the principal tasks of nurses at the Savoy hospital in London was to light fires in the morning and evening to warm the wards.[53] Paupers receiving doles of food at St Giles's were permitted to eat by an open hearth in winter: this, too, would have required significant quantities of kindling. The cartularies of St Bartholomew's hospital, London, and St Thomas's, Southwark, record similar endowments of property and rents made especially for the benefit of the sick. Supplementary doles, pittances, clothes, lamps and linen for the patients, as well as the occasional luxury of white bread and additional meals for distribution to the poor at the gates, came as perpetual alms from pious donors.[54] Grants to St Giles's tended to be offered simply as free alms, and rarely specified what services, if any, were to be provided for the welfare of the patients. The latter would, however, have benefited from arrangements made in the 1260s and 1270s for the provision of lights in the hospital church, most notably for the upkeep of a lamp burning at night by the Cross.[55]

A striking feature of St Bartholomew's, and undoubtedly of many other urban hospitals, is the frequency with which local tradespeople donated supplies on a purely *ad hoc* basis, some grudgingly, others 'with maruellus deuocion . . . that studied to fulfill the plenytude of the lawe that is charite'.[56] It is now impossible to tell how far the brewers and bakers of Holme Street contributed towards the work of their hospital. Substantial gifts, such as a consignment of wheat received from the alderman, William Hayward, in 1505–6, and the two 'great cod fish' donated by another benefactor two years later, are sometimes recorded in the accounts.[57] But evidence of outside assistance otherwise derives almost entirely from wills, which at best present only a small part of the overall picture.[58] We have already seen that, although testamentary bequests to St Giles's from the laity of Norwich in general declined somewhat after 1440, support from the clergy and members of the mercantile elite remained constant. These men and women were anxious to avail themselves of the spiritual services offered on an increasingly impressive scale by the hospital, and reserved their principal largesse for its priests and choristers. Yet most set aside at least a few pence for the sick poor and their nurses too. Although they appear relatively modest, legacies such as the 6*d* left in 1464 by Thomas Spynk, a chaplain at St Stephen's in Norwich, to 'each person lying in St Giles's hospital' represented a week's allowance in many of the country's almshouses, and would have enabled the recipient to purchase significant quantities of food and drink.[59] In this respect, at least, the paupers who were still lucky enough to secure a bed had good reason to welcome the hospital's transformation into a college for secular clergy.

Many testators and well-wishers provided specific comforts, often in the form of linen or warm coverlets. In 1448–9 a master carpenter was paid 20*d* (approximately five days' wages) for making and repairing the beds of the poor, but the hospital generally relied on external funding for their upkeep.[60] In 1465 Richard Hosst set aside the substantial sum of 10*s* for further repairs; and in 1501 the alderman, Richard Ferrour, left money to St Giles's and St Paul's to furnish each hospital with twelve sets of large counterpanes for 'the pouer beddes'.[61] Linen was a popular gift, within the means of less affluent benefactors such as the widowed Isabella Keeson, who presented two pairs of sheets to 'Goddeshous' in 1505–6. One year later a practical legacy from Robert Bosse, who was buried in the chapter house, comprised two more pairs of new sheets, three old ones, a pair of linen cloths and a leather cushion, all intended for 'the beds of the poor in Goddeshous'. The receiver general's accounts for the early sixteenth century contain several further references to the 'Goddeshousebeddes', which seem to have been well appointed, largely through the generosity of local people.[62] Lack of proper beds or bedding for the sick was a recurrent complaint voiced by the members of religious communities in East Anglia during this period. The almsmen of St Giles's may, in fact, have been better cared for than many of the region's monks and canons.[63]

Did some potential benefactors harbour reservations about the way their money might be used? As early as 1382, one Norwich testator had insisted that a sum of 15*s* left by him to the hospitals of St Giles and St Paul should be reserved for the poor rather than the rich (*non divitibus*) dwelling there.[64] Less affluent citizens with limited resources may have preferred to spend their money on parochial relief which could be administered according to their precise wishes and would reach a specific target. Since St Giles's still opened its doors to poor travellers, they may also have felt uneasy about the possibility of encouraging sturdy beggars and other undesirables. It cannot, however, be assumed that the hospital accepted all wayfarers indiscriminately. At the Savoy, in London, priority was first given to the sick and moribund (other than lepers), then to the halt, blind and decrepit, thirdly to the truly destitute and last of all to poor but otherwise able-bodied men looking for accommodation.[65] This hospital had 100 beds, but St Giles's operated on a far more modest scale, with facilities for only six wayfarers 'staying by night' in the 1530s.[66]

The will of Richard Hawze, who died in the hospital during the previous decade, provides some insight into the life and status of the men who sought refuge there. They were by no means all humble paupers, although some appear to have been terminally sick. Every one of Hawze's bequests (which came to the not inconsiderable sum of 27*s* 10*d*) went to the hospital or its staff, two separate gifts of 3*s* 4*d* being left to the receiver general, Robert Treswell, and the one remaining sister, Dame Elizabeth Ordyng. The latter received an additional reward of 20*d* 'for kepyng me', while her anonymous servant, who had been engaged in 1526 to replace Dame Alice Bothumsyll, was given 2*d*.[67] Another otherwise undocumented domestic servant or nurse called Beatrice Sharpe received 4*d*. Treswell and Dame Elizabeth were together named as executors, charged with responsibility for compiling an inventory of the deceased's effects and trusted by him to dispose of any residue 'with laude and prayse to almyghty God' for the good of his soul.[68] Elizabeth's two assistants may have been drawn from the substantial pool of surplus female labour then to be found in most English towns as a consequence of economic recession and the restrictive practices of the male craft guilds.[69] Such women were happy to accept menial work in hospitals, almshouses and monasteries in return for basic board or other payment in kind, and were often held to be harder working and more reliable than the professed sisters who were by then entering hospitals as pensioners rather than nurses.[70] Although the laundress employed by the brethren was the only female servant with a permanent place on the pay roll, the receiver general occasionally sanctioned modest rewards to women. A certain 'pauper' named Agnes was, for example, given 16*d* in 1509–10 for helping one of the sisters.[71] Sir Thomas More believed that, in providing work for vagrants or 'loyterers' of both sexes, religious houses offered the most useful and socially acceptable assistance to the able-bodied.[72] As early as 1396 the receiver general's expenditure on household servants included an allocation of 71*s* 1*d* 'to various poor in bread, fish and meat', presumably in return for their labour.[73] Such charity extended to those who had known better days, for Dame Elizabeth was herself an almswoman of sorts, albeit one whose role was not too different from that first envisaged by the founder.

NURSES AND CORRODIANS

In common with other thirteenth-century foundation statutes, Walter Suffield's ordinances for the government of St Giles's hospital are reticent about the nursing activities to be undertaken by the four sisters. As a canon lawyer, he was more concerned to establish precise rules with regard to their dress, comportment and segregation, and thus to avoid the manifold problems of laxity and incontinence likely to beset a mixed community. His insistence that the sisters should be 'of good life and honest conversation approved over many years, being fifty years old or a little less' was, as we have seen, entirely in keeping with contemporary medical and theological ideas about the dangers posed by menstruating women.[74] It also echoed St Paul's warning to Timothy on the subject of flighty young widows of uncertain vocation (First Epistle 5: 9–13), and was clearly designed to protect priests and patients from the snares of lust. A more positive, and not incompatible, view of the older female carer emphasised her experience, reliability and breadth of knowledge, which meant that she could safely be left, as Suffield had wished, to 'take good care of the infirm and other sick' without further instructions.[75] At the Hôtel Dieu, Paris, for example, postulants could expect thirty or forty years of hard labour before being entrusted with senior positions on the wards [see Plate 14]. Beyond urging his nurses to 'change the sheets and other bed clothes as often as necessary', and to 'serve the poor humbly in necessary things as far as they are able' the bishop wisely allowed them a free hand.[76]

Such concern for the state of the patients' linen shows an awareness of the practicalities of hospital life implicit rather than explicit in most English statutes of this period, and is perhaps further evidence of the involvement of the physician, Richard of Wendover, in drawing up those for St Giles's. It also reflects the ubiquitous influence of the Augustinian rule, which placed great emphasis upon the need for physical as well as spiritual cleanliness.[77] Yet little was set down on parchment. Nurses might occasionally be required to wash their patients and supervise their visits to the latrines (St Leonard's, York, and St Laurence's, Canterbury), or remain on duty at night (St James's, Northallerton), but few practical, as opposed to moral, guidelines were established for their benefit.[78] Not until the foundation of the Savoy hospital, in the early sixteenth century, were detailed hygienic regulations along the Italian model incorporated into such documents, although the task of washing soiled sheets and clothing had long been acknowledged as one of the nurse's most onerous duties. At the Hôtel Dieu, the nine sisters and six postulants employed in the laundries dealt with upwards of 900 sheets a week in all weathers throughout the later Middle Ages [see Plate 4]. The burden at St Giles's was far lighter, but there were fewer staff to share it.[79]

The medieval *regimen sanitatis* (regimen of health), which was followed with varying degrees of sophistication and commitment at all but the lowest levels of English society, regarded a clean and pleasant environment, nourishing food, warmth, security and adequate rest as prerequisites for recovery from sickness.[80] Most hospitals of any size attempted to implement these recommendations so far as funds allowed. Practice may often have fallen short of theory, but the basic tenets of nursing care differed little from those recommended by late twentieth-century health professionals.[81] If, on balance, the medieval sister confined her attentions to the body, taking an inferior place below the physician of souls, it is still important to remember that physical and spiritual treatment proceeded hand in hand. To distinguish between the two medicines, as historians from a more secular age often tend to do, would have seemed not only futile but perverse. Nurses played a notable part in the quest for inner cleanliness, too, by encouraging their charges to confess, repent and 'live joyfully in the Lord', these being the first steps on the road to recuperation.[82] Hospital statutes throughout Europe extolled the virtues of a caring and cheerful disposition and its therapeutic benefits for the patient, while also stressing the nurse's obligation to urge resignation in the face of suffering. Regulations drawn up in 1238 for the hospital of Notre Dame de Tournai insisted

> that the sick should be treated kindly, for in dealing harshly with them the whole purpose [of care] is defeated . . . Sisters are required to tend the sick very gently and considerately, to console them in their adversity and to exhort them to recognise in everything the chastisement of the Lord [see Plate 37].[83]

It is, therefore, noteworthy that when Bishop Suffield came to revise his statutes he inserted the word '*benigne*' into the rules dealing with admissions and also urged the need for humility. Not all the sisters had apparently taken their responsibilities to heart.[84]

Notwithstanding his strictures about the age of the four nurses, Suffield clearly expected to recruit active, healthy women, capable of heavy manual labour. When they were not engaged in tending the sick poor, their time was to be spent on other pious and charitable works. The founder's insistence that services in the chapel should be suspended if any other women lodged in the precinct may not have been specifically directed at female corrodians (private boarders), but clearly excluded them. So too did an unambiguous ruling in the revised statutes that all brothers and sisters were to be admitted freely without charge or the formal approval of the bishop.[85] Suffield's own dependents were a different matter. He set a clear precedent in his will of 1256 by awarding one livery of appropriate food and clothing at St Giles's for life to his salter, Gilbert, and a corrody of board and lodging to a chaplain named Robert, who was already a resident.[86] There is no direct evidence to suggest that any of his successors used the hospital as a retirement home for their domestic staff or retainers. It seems almost certain that, like Walter de Calthorpe, they expected a say in the allocation of beds for the sick poor, and that they sometimes appropriated such places for their own servants. Even so, all the information which survives about corrodians at St Giles's concerns people who either bought their accommodation outright or made some financial contribution, rather than being nominated by an episcopal patron.

As we have already seen, the sale of corrodies offered such a tempting solution to worsening economic problems that it seemed legitimate to ignore the founder's wishes. One way round the prohibition on female residents, adopted by the Norwich merchant, Robert de Bungay, when he made his will in 1376, was to offer the brethren a substantial rental income if they agreed to find his widow 'a decent chamber in Holme Street' where she could end her days under the watchful eyes of the brethren, but safely outside the walls.[87] In practice, however, the simple expedient of receiving female pensioners into the sisterhood made it possible to accommodate at least one or two corrodians in the precinct without contravening the letter, if not the spirit, of the founder's wishes. In 1309, the same date as the above-mentioned agreement with Walter de Calthorpe, the widowed Mary de Attleburgh pledged her estates in Seething to the hospital in return for a corrody for life as a hospital sister.[88] But would she and her kind be ready or able to tend sick paupers? The disagreeable nature of this task was a common *topos* in the homiletic literature of the period. Many pious women actively sought to humble themselves in the service of Christ's poor, but others were less enthusiastic. Sisters at St Katherine's hospital, London, and St Leonard's, York, expressed an alarming predilection for gaudy and unsuitable clothing, which not only constituted a breach of canon law, but proved impracticable when nursing the sick.[89]

Despite the frequent complaints made in visitation reports, the sale of corrodies, which secured a lifetime's board, lodging and sometimes clothing for the recipient, as well as of more circumscribed liveries of food and robes, became increasingly common in English hospitals. Along with the equally insidious practice of earmarking resources for the support of elderly retainers or relatives of the patron, excessive 'privatisation' threatened to undermine discipline, deprive the poor of assistance and diminish spiritual life. Commissioners sent to investigate abuses at the hospital of the Holy Innocents, Beverley, in 1316, reported with dismay that the new inmates, who had paid handsomely for their places, felt no obligation whatsoever to spend their days in church with the poor brethren, and categorically refused to pray for the salvation of the founders.[90] Not even souls in purgatory could escape the malign effects of the early fourteenth-century economic crisis. Ironically, given that the purpose of this exercise was to make money, 'indiscreet sales and grantings of liveries and corrodies' on a scale apparent at such houses as St Leonard's, York, St Saviour's, Bury St Edmunds, and St Thomas's, Southwark, could aggravate rather than ameliorate financial problems.[91] Since the purchase price of a full corrody was usually calculated by estimating the institutional cost of ten years' support, the potential longevity of the recipient became a matter of pressing concern. Charges of greed, short-term opportunism and exploitation abounded. Against the immediate benefits of cash in hand had to be set the problems posed by unwanted boarders who disobligingly refused to die. Should the corrodian survive for more than a decade, he or she became a charge on the hospital, which was legally bound to honour its commitments. In such circumstances, as the author of *Dives and Pauper* remarked, 'charite is exylyd out of the congregacion, for whan the monye is payyd the religious that seldyn the lyuersonys [liveries] desyryn the deth of the byere'.[92]

Yet, notwithstanding the trenchant and often justified criticisms voiced by reformers, corrodies could extend the charitable remit of a hospital, enabling it to assist some of the victims of life-cycle poverty encountered in Chapter I. Elderly widows no longer capable of work, or young women unable to find employment in a shrinking labour market, could not expect to remain long above the poverty line without help.[93] They gladly exchanged whatever possessions or property they might have in return for the promise of shelter. Those capable of nursing the sick, washing linen, serving in the kitchens or (as at St Paul's, Norwich) teaching the young to read, could make an appropriate contribution to the community until they, too, needed care.[94] Although this meant that some female pensioners added to the general burden, it at least provided a valuable safety-net for individuals who otherwise faced an uncertain future. One such was Agnes, widow of Simon Gillot, a 'good and faithful servant' of the abbot of Bury St Edmunds, who was permitted in 1444 to occupy her late husband's corrody at St Saviour's hospital. Being seriously ill and incapable of supporting her young children without begging, she qualified for support on grounds of need as much as connection.[95] Unless they were completely moribund, women in her position had none the less to make some contribution towards their support. Even the blind, frail and elderly were expected to engage in manual work, if only carding, knitting or spinning. The Norwich Census of the Poor, compiled in 1570, reveals that women well into their seventies remained active in the labour market, being thus able to supplement the alms they received.[96] In 1479, one of the sisters at St Giles's bought two stones of wool from the hospital's Cringleford flock, presumably for spinning in the precinct.[97]

Few of St Giles's corrodians enjoyed complete financial independence. The purchase of three places for sums totalling £90 in the 1330s seems exceptional to that decade, and, in any event, involved only men. As we have seen in Chapter III, these transactions took place at a time when the hospital was desperately raising money for the acquisition of property. Indeed, it even *borrowed* sums totalling £4 from the sisters in order to increase its holdings. The only hint of subsequent dealings on this scale appears in an account for 1375, when a sister named Amice received £4 from the receiver general 'for her corrody'. If her pension was for life, she would probably have paid about £40 for admission into the sisterhood, and would thus almost certainly have been excused any nursing duties. Significantly, the task of buying additional herrings for the poor fell that year to Sister Isabella, who was not a corrodian.[98] During the fifteenth and sixteenth centuries neither St Paul's hospital nor St Giles's asked more than a few pounds for admission. Although the statutes of St Paul's categorically forbade the sale of places, by 1492 the resident (or 'full') sisters were charged a standard fee of £6 13*s* 4*d* upon entry. Relatively speaking this represented a substantial payment, equivalent to the annual salary of a successful master craftsman, but spread over a decade it came to just 3*d* a week. Since the hospital was committed to pay the thirteen sisters weekly doles of 8*d* we may assume that all but the bedridden earned the rest by caring for patients and undertaking other tasks.[99]

Both the charge for admission to the sisterhood and the weekly doles (between 4*d* and 6*d*) were significantly lower at St Giles's. On the entry of Alice Bothumsyll as a sister in about 1517 her kinsman, Stephen Bothumsyll, paid the master 66*s* 8*d* in instalments spread over four or five years. This seems to have been the customary rate for entry, as Dame Elizabeth Ordyng, who joined the hospital at about the same time, was then paying off a similar sum, described in the accounts as 'alms'. The master, John Hecker, personally settled the balance of her debt in 1523–4, since she evidently found it hard to raise the money. Yet Alice, on the other hand, appears to have been a woman of some substance: when she left the hospital in March 1526 to live at Watton it cost 3*s* 4*d* to transport her and her possessions by cart. The founder's requirement that all goods should be held in common had long been abandoned, as, in this instance, had the idea of profession for life. Since she was, however, immediately replaced by a domestic servant, it seems that Dame Alice had hitherto discharged all her nursing duties in person until age or incapacity made this impossible.[100] After its refoundation, in 1547, the hospital engaged 'poor matrons', whose need was, presumably, even greater. Yet although the professional services of surgeons and barbers were then made available to the inmates, female healers continued to command respect. During the second half of the sixteenth century at least fourteen separate payments were made to women such as 'Mother Balles', who possessed specialist skills, notably with regard to the treatment of leg ulcers.[101]

Ordinances drawn up in 1241 for the hospital of St John the Baptist, Nottingham, had stipulated that the brethren were to keep well away from the sisters' quarters 'unless seized with illness', when they might presumably seek admission for treatment.[102] However great their nursing skills may have been, the sisters at St Giles's did not tend any of the hospital chaplains when they were sick, respecting right up to the Dissolution Suffield's insistence that close physical proximity between the sexes should be avoided at all times.[103] Before his death, in 1521, John Veryes was cared for by a respectably married 'nese' named Alice Soppe, to whom he bequeathed by far his largest legacy (40*s*), along with a gown for her husband. During his twenty years at St Giles's Veryes had none the less grown attached to Dame Alice and Dame Elizabeth. At 3*s* 4*d* each, their legacies were as generous as one promised by him to the master of the choristers. Dame Alice, a particular favourite, stood to inherit Veryes's few personal possessions as well.[104] Thomas Preese and William Steele, both of whom evidently succumbed to an outbreak of plague or some other epidemic in May 1529, were together tended by the wife of one Richard Broke. The two chaplains drew up almost identical wills on the same day, each leaving their nurse 'for her good attendauns that she hath given to me often tymys in my siknes' their featherbeds, pillows and linen. Neither seems to have been very affluent, but, like Veryes, they remembered the hospital sisters, along with Nicholas the bedesman.[105]

What else do we know of these women? Because of the decision to pay sisters a cash dole in lieu of certain meals, the full names of six of their number are recorded between 1502 and 1527.[106] Emma Cauwold and Alice Wells spent longest in the hospital, their respective terms of fifteen and fourteen years making them as much part of the community as any of the chaplains. But none of the sisters served for less than six years, which suggests a strong element of continuity. That some, if not all, still regarded their calling as a vocation is evident from the presence of a 'novice' named Joanna [*recte* Alice] Kyng, in 1502–3. She presumably took her vows of poverty, chastity and obedience, as the founder had required, before becoming a fully fledged sister in 1505–6. Just like nuns from local families, individual sisters inspired affection and were mentioned personally by Norwich testators.[107] In her very modest will of 1381 Isabel de Brook, who lived near the hospital, set aside a shilling to be shared by three named sisters of St Giles's. The latter were respectfully entitled '*dominae*', this being a courtesy title generally accorded to female religious and later adopted in the hospital accounts.[108] Bartholomew Peacock, vicar of Surlingham, an old friend of St Giles's who requested burial in the hospital church two years later, left the same sum (one shilling) to each of the sisters as he did to the chaplains, which suggests a parity of esteem.[109] It was they, after all, who assumed by far the greatest responsibility for the care of the poor, and thus for executing the Seven Comfortable Works vicariously on behalf of patrons and benefactors. The merchant, Richard Brown, likewise ranked the sisters and brothers together in his will of 1461, although his token bequest of 8*d* to each pales into insignificance beside the £200 he left 'after the discrecioun of myne executours' for distribution among the *resident* poor of the city over a period of ten years.[110]

Legacies made an appreciable difference to the sisterhood as well as the almsmen, and are often revealing. A bequest of 20*s* left by the philanthropist, William Setman, in 1429, to Matilda Upgate contrasts sharply with the 2*s* he set aside for the other nurses, and presupposes either long acquaintance or particular need. William Fualeyn (d. 1523), the hospital's rent collector, who must have regarded the sisters as part of an extended family, left exactly as much to each of them as he did to his own godchildren.[111] Ties of kinship were real as well as metaphorical, drawing many of the house's tradesmen, priests, choristers and master craftsmen into a close and mutually supportive network. The carpenter, Edmund Cauwold, played a notable part in building the cloisters between 1447 and 1451, and was paid no less than £9 by the receiver general in 1467–8 for his work on a new watermill at Cringleford.[112] Forty years later Dame Emma Cauwold, one of the sisters, was accorded the unusual honour of burial in the hospital church, the cost of her funeral, which came to 3*s* 4*d*, being met out of the alms chest. Her relationship to Edmund remains a matter of conjecture, but the hospital's current millwright, Thomas Cauwold, who had apparently inherited the family business, boarded for four weeks in the precinct during her last illness.[113] In 1520, around the time of Alice Bothumsyll's admission, one of the menial servants, allocated a 1*d* dole on the day of Bishop Goldwell's obit, bore the same unusual surname, which suggests another family connection.

Well before this date the sisters frequently appeared in accounts and wills alike alongside 'the poor' as objects of charity. This may in part have been a matter of administrative convenience, since they would have run errands on behalf of the almsmen and taken charge of their effects. But the Norwich testator who left 1*d* in 1468 'to iche poor man and woman in the seid hospitall levyng on almes' made no such distinction. Just three years later the alderman, John Chittock, allocated 6*s* 8*d* to be shared equally between the sisters and the paupers.[114] Both Margaret Paston (1482) and the Norwich lawyer, Henry Ferman (1503), bequeathed 2*d* to 'eche bedesman and suster' at St Giles's; Agnes Thorpe (1503) left them each 6*d*; and the alderman, Thomas Aldryche (1529), also remembered 'the poor folk of the said hospital, as well men as women'.[115] Just as the sick poor of St Giles's and the patients at St Paul's hospital were often ranked together by testators, so the sisters of both institutions tended to attract similar bequests. Sir Thomas Erpingham's legacy, made in 1428, of £6 13*s* 4*d* to the 'sustres and poure folk' of St Giles's and an equivalent sum to those at St Paul's was unusually generous, but not otherwise remarkable. In 1507, for instance, Henry Hilton left 4*d* to each of the women, along with 2*d* to every 'pore creature' at the two hospitals.[116]

Once the brethren, conducts and choristers who celebrated perpetual obits at St Giles's had been paid, any surplus revenues were usually distributed among the servants, bedesmen and sisters. When making arrangements for the funding of his anniversary from rents in St Vedast's parish, in 1512, Robert Godfrey stipulated that doles should be paid annually on that day to everyone living in the hospital, not just the priests.[117] In practice resources may often have proved insufficient, but we know that between 1520 and 1528 endowments for the commemoration of Bishop Goldwell (23 January), John Jullys (23 July) and John Smyth (early summer) each produced as much as 30*s* a year for general distribution. The master took the lion's share of up to 6*s* 8*d* a time, but this still left 1*s* for every brother and sister, while the boy choristers could rely on at least 4*d*. The hospital itself observed Maundy Thursday, the feasts of the Annunciation (25 March) and of St Giles (1 September), Easter Sunday, the founder's anniversary (19 May) and Christmas by giving doles of a few pence or additional pittances of fish or meat to its poor residents. Since, as a general rule, their diet was adequate but monotonous, these festive occasions must have been eagerly awaited. At the hospital of St Giles, Beverley, the sick paupers who normally lived on bread and pottage were promised eggs, beef, pork, mutton and ale at Christmas, along with fresh straw for their bedding. Michaelmas was marked by a feast of goose and cheese. Life at St Giles's was somewhat less austere, but the year was still punctuated by culinary as well as liturgical highlights.[118]

The quality and quantity of daily fare in late medieval hospitals concerned episcopal visitors, who were keenly aware of the importance of diet, 'the first instrument of medicine', to staff as well as patients. In 1387 William of Wykeham criticised the weak ale (*insipidus potus*) and inedible bread given to the sick poor at St Thomas's, Southwark, and insisted upon a more nourishing and appropriate diet. Incompetence or corruption, as well as genuine hardship, meant that servants, nurses and lesser brethren might also be obliged to subsist on inadequate, sometimes contaminated rations. The sisters at St Bartholomew's hospital, London, complained in 1316 about their impoverished diet, which may, in turn, account for the low standards of nursing then encountered by Bishop Segrave.[119] Protests of this kind were not, however, unique to hospitals, being voiced by the members of religious communities throughout England. Food and drink were, quite literally, a topic of consuming interest to men and women with time on their hands, and not all fault-finding can be taken too seriously. Bishop Suffield had recognised that the brethren would be tempted to linger over meals, chattering among themselves and thus forgetting their sacred duty.[120] Gossip soon deteriorated into backbiting. 'Brawling, noise and murmuring at table' disrupted the daily round at St Leonard's hospital, York, as also did late suppers after compline, which the master forbade in 1294 as a cause of indiscipline. The diet at St Leonard's was more than sufficient, with ample provision of bread, ale, mutton, beef, pork, cheese and fish costing over £444 a year (over half net receipts) in the 1370s.[121] But in many houses supplies intended as alms for the sick poor were diverted to relatives, servants or even dogs, while in others embezzlement and inefficiency occasioned widespread abuses.[122] Much depended upon the probity and competence of the officials responsible for overseeing the delivery, storage, preparation and distribution of large quantities of consumables. The task of provisioning a charitable institution of even modest size, such as St Giles's, should not be underestimated.

PROVISIONING THE HOSPITAL

The assumption that medieval English hospitals helped only a narrow elite of deserving cases and barely impinged upon the lives of the wider community takes little account of the range of services offered, initially at least, by the more affluent foundations. Towards the close of the Middle Ages many of them made rigorous economies, cutting back what may hitherto have been quite liberal disbursements. In 1338, for example, the hospital of St Leonard at Skirbeck, Lincolnshire, supported twenty sick and debilitated paupers in the infirmary and fed twice that number in the hall each day. At just over £51, the cost of food and drink for the entire establishment accounted for more than two-thirds of the annual budget, which probably explains why the number of inmates was subsequently reduced and other eleemosynary activities were abandoned altogether.[123] Yet, even during periods of recession and antagonism towards the vagrant poor, the ritualised distribution of food and drink remained the most potent and emotive of the Seven Comfortable Works.[124] Hunger was still a harsh fact of medieval life, its alleviation demonstrably recalling Christ's sacrifice in the Mass, which was celebrated several times a day in hospital chapels and churches throughout the country. Donors could, moreover, expect – and exact – immediate recompense by way of intercessionary prayers from the recipients of their bounty. When arranging for the prior of the Carthusians at Hull to give a substantial allowance of food each day to two paupers, the duchess of Suffolk left nothing to chance. The ceremony was to take place before two 'stone images' of herself and the late duke, each bearing a jug and dish as symbols of their munificence.[125]

At St Giles's the distribution of food to non-residents took three different forms. First came the daily provision of meals worth one penny each to thirteen designated paupers, whose numbers were to be doubled whenever the bishop paid a visit. Given the proximity of the episcopal palace, and the intimate relations between the masters and their patrons, such events must have been frequent. Secondly, by the fifteenth century the seven poor scholars whom Suffield had undertaken to feed during the school term were being supported throughout the year as choristers, at a cost of 8*d* a week in food and drink alone.[126] A third, traditional demand on resources comprised large scale (and thus far less selective) annual doles of food and drink to 100 paupers on the founder's anniversary and to 180 paupers on the feast of the Annunciation (25 March). Each person was then entitled to a halfpenny loaf and a *ferculum* or 'mess' of wheat, together with eggs or cheese to the same value. In addition, bread was available to all comers every Saturday during the lean period before the harvest.[127] From time to time, the brethren also agreed to dispense food, cash or clothing on behalf of affluent lay or ecclesiastical testators. In his will of 1497, for example, Bishop Goldwell instructed them to pay weekly doles of 4*d* to his twenty bedesmen, ensuring that paupers who had already received alms at their hands should be ineligible for further help.[128]

Since regular meals had also to be provided for staff, almsmen, travellers, workmen and boarders, the demands upon senior administrators and household servants were considerable. How well did they respond? Accounts kept by the steward and receiver general contain a great deal of evidence about the nature and cost of food purchases and deliveries of estate produce to the precinct between 1315 and 1527. A comprehensive analysis of expenditure on provisions can be undertaken for years of relatively full archival coverage, most notably during the first half of the fourteenth century and the period 1465–1527 [Tables A and B below]. We also have a good idea of the provenance of comestibles bought during this period. Because of the preponderance of fast days in the ecclesiastical calendar, fish supplies were of great importance to the hospital, and the receiver general himself made regular trips to Cley, Wiveton, Winterton, Cromer, Lowestoft and Yarmouth to negotiate prices on the quays.[129] The part played by the fishmonger, William Hecker of Cley, in provisioning the hospital during the late fifteenth century has already been noted, as has his bequest of salt to the value of £20. Such generosity is understandable. Not only did one of his close relatives become master of St Giles's; between 1483 and 1486 alone his dealings with the hospital were worth as much as the legacy.[130] Substantial profits were certainly to be made by supplying the region's many religious houses with cod, eels, mackerel and herring.

Valuable as it is, however, the surviving evidence remains tantalisingly incomplete. Because transactions are invariably recorded in bulk, a study of individual diets, along the lines undertaken with telling effect by Barbara Harvey in her work on the Westminster abbey Benedictines, is out of the question.[131] Even at their fullest, the accounts provide only a partial guide to the standard of living enjoyed by the staff of St Giles's and say little about that of the almsmen and paupers. During the sixteenth century, for example, the number of home-reared pigs, cattle and sheep slaughtered from stock in any one year was usually noted by the receiver general on the dorse of his final account as a precaution against fraud [Table D]. These entries provide useful evidence of a trend away from beef consumption towards mutton and pork, which is hardly surprising in view of the hospital's investment in its Cringleford flock and *domus porcorum*. But the receiver rarely bothered to monitor consignments of game, poultry, dairy produce, honey and eggs from the estates or precinct, since these could always be checked against the steward's journals and the local accounts.

Before the retreat from direct management in the fifteenth century, such contributions made an appreciable difference to the variety and quality of hospital fare. In 1329–30, for example, the rector of Calthorpe dispatched 24 geese, 8 capons, 20 hens, 36 pullets, 60 large cheeses, 7 casks of butter and 2,200 eggs to the hospital kitchen, in addition to the more valuable pigs and cattle which would have been recorded by the receiver.[132] Eggs, a staple of the diet in many hospitals, were also laid by the hens, ducks and geese in the precinct, while milk came from the dairy cows which grazed in the meadows during summer. Nor is any mention made of the fruit, herbs and vegetables supplied from the hospital's home farm, gardens and orchards. Pears were usually bought for the celebrations on St Giles's day, but apples lay freely to hand and were stored each year in the *domus pomorum*.[133] John Russell's *Boke of Nurture*, which provides a fascinating insight into the diversity of the upper-class diet in the later Middle Ages, suggests that these would have been served roasted or stewed in syrup as a digestive after a heavy meal.[134] At St Anthony's hospital, London, where garden space was limited, 'erbys' were bought for daily consumption by the entire community.[135] Against the warnings about fresh fruit, salads and green vegetables found in the *regimen sanitatis* and other popular advice literature, must be set the archaeological evidence from houses such as St Mary's, Bishopsgate, where a wide variety of fruit was eaten.[136] 'Plomes, dameseyns, grapes and chery, suche in sesons of the yere are served to make men mery', ran a popular refrain; just as is the case today, medieval men and women did not invariably follow the advice of their physicians.[137]

The proportion of fresh fish caught locally and in the hospital's own ponds, as compared with the salt or smoked fish bought in large quantities from merchants on the Norfolk coast (celebrated for deep-sea as well as a herring fisheries), likewise remains open to conjecture. Sir Thomas Browne wrote lyrically in the seventeenth century of the abundant supplies of pike, tench, bream, roach, lamprey, perch and dace teeming in the rivers and broads between Norwich and the sea, where many of the hospital's estates lay.[138] Excavations on the medieval waterfront, just west of St Giles's, have unearthed the remains of most of these fish, along with those of whiting, trout, rudd, chub, thornback ray, flounder and bass, as well as more common staples of the residents' diet.[139] We know roughly how many barrels of salt or smoked herring, eels, sprats, cod, mackerel and ling (a type of preserved cod) were bought from year to year, but have no means of estimating the total amount of fish eaten by a community which theoretically followed the same dietary regulations as the Augustinians. As we have seen in Chapter II, the hospital's ponds were regularly stocked with pike and roach, some of which must have found their way to the master's table. So, presumably, did the regular purchases of salmon and turbot, which in 1511–12 cost no less than 33*s* 4*d* and would have been considered inappropriate fare for the poor.[140]

Status is just as likely to have determined the quality and diversity of a person's diet at St Giles's hospital as it did in the households of the county gentry and members of the mercantile elite.[141] At St Anthony's, London, a hospital which spent lavishly on food, clear distinctions were maintained between the almsmen, patients and children ('the hospital') and members of the clerical establishment ('the hall'), who gourmandised on an impressive scale. During a fairly typical week, in July 1495, for example, the entire community shared dishes of pottage, mutton, beef, veal and eggs, but whereas 'the hospital' received supplementary portions of haddock and salt fish, 'the hall' also dined on pork, rabbit, duck, chicken, turbot, carp and superior cuts of mutton. On feast days the discrepancy was even more apparent.[142] Senior clergy at St Giles's are unlikely to have lived so high on the hog, but they did observe similar conventions. It was understood that menial servants and the poor would consume maslin bread from mixed grains (in this case barley, rye and wheat), while the brethren and their guests ate finely milled wheaten loaves, which were lower in fibre. Pottage, made from pulses, oats and barley, perhaps augmented with vegetables and bacon from the precinct, was a dish for the lower orders, who usually received a salted or smoked herring rather than a cut of meat for their main meal. At its best, their diet was far richer in vitamins A, D and B, and generally healthier than that of the senior brethren, whose high consumption of fat and protein carried a number of potential risks.[143] Herrings and eels were plentiful, cheap and easy to store in large barrels, which were regularly inspected and repaired by the hospital's cooper. Worth no less than 7*s* apiece in the early sixteenth century, the barrels were themselves an investment, the cost testifying both to their size and durability on repeated journeys to and from the coast.[144] Along with salt cod, another dietary staple, herring, mackerel and eels would also have been consumed by the brethren on fast days, although they were otherwise regarded with disdain by anyone in a position to pick and choose.

Some purchases were clearly reserved for the master, his guests and senior clergy. Their helpings would have been larger, too, on the assumption that any leftovers could be shared among the poor.[145] From 1319 onwards, if not before, sugar, dates, plums, raisins, currants, figs, almonds, ginger, saffron, rice, agaric, aniseed, cinnamon, cassia, cloves, mace, pepper, cumin and other spices used in the more affluent households of later medieval England were purchased each year by the steward. Some came from London, where they were evidently bought wholesale, cutting out the middleman.[146] Contrary to popular belief, spices were rarely used to camouflage the taste of rotting or badly cured meat. Supplies of beef, pork and mutton at St Giles's were often fresh, and, as in other affluent households, condiments served to enhance rather than mask flavour. They were also held to possess valuable medicinal qualities, helping to assist the digestive process and balance the humours. Such luxuries were not available to the poor, whose palates were, in any event, considered cruder and less sophisticated. Dishes such as pike in a ginger and cinnamon sauce would have been confined to the master's table.[147] The food of the paupers and servants is more likely to have been flavoured with mustard, garlic, leeks, onions and vinegar, which cost little, if anything, but were more nutritious.[148]

Wine was offered on special occasions, and, as we have seen in Chapter II, beer made an appearance in the refectory during the early sixteenth century. But neither was intended for general consumption, ale being the house's principal beverage, drunk by everyone irrespective of rank. The purchase in 1505–6 of half a gallon of sweet wine, a gallon of claret and two of white wine, was largely intended to mark St Giles's day. Wine was also offered to important visitors, such as the prior of Rumburgh, who enjoyed a glass or two and a meal of fresh rabbit costing 10*d* while discussing legal business with Doctor Selot in 1465–6. Sixty pairs of rabbits came as rent in kind from the warren at Cringleford during the early sixteenth century, when cony (a rich source of vitamin A) was still regarded as superior fare.[149] The evidence given in Tables A and B thus constitutes no more than a very basic guide to expenditure on food and drink, while none the less underscoring the importance accorded to hospitality at all social levels. In this regard the brethren of St Giles's conformed to the same pattern as many lay landowners, for whom the conspicuous consumption and distribution of food served an important political as well as philanthropic purpose. Help given by the sheriff of Norfolk, in a lawsuit fought in 1435–6, was rewarded by the gift of six fat capons and a dozen pullets for 'aid and favour'. It will be recalled that Selot stood accused in 1459 of bribing the prior of Horsham's attorneys with a lavish supper of fish and wine.[150] Bishop Nykke's visitation report of 1514 does not survive, but the circumstances of his inspection suggest that it ought to have been favourable. Fortified by four gallons of claret, a gallon of malmsey and a large quantity of the best ale, entertained by the city waits and feasted by a hired cook whose fee alone came to 4*s*, the bishop and his entourage would have been churlish indeed to find fault with their hosts.[151]

Emphasis upon monetary transactions alone, as we have seen, presents only part of the picture. During the period covered by Table A, almost all the hospital's grain supplies, including barley for malting, came directly from its estates at minimal cost to the receiver general. A glance at Table B shows how expensive grain purchases could be in the years after direct management had been largely abandoned. Conversely, whereas meat tended to be bought specifically for the larder (either on the hoof or as dressed carcasses) during the fourteenth century, stock purchases during the 1500s rarely distinguish between animals intended for breeding, resale after fattening or butchering. This is because animal husbandry, a promising solution to worsening economic problems, was now largely managed by the receiver general. Between 1500 and 1507, for example, he may have spent as much as £70 on building up the hospital's herds and flocks, although comparatively few beasts were earmarked for immediate consumption by the brethren. Table A thus includes the cost of meat purchases, while Table B does not. We are, however, able to tell roughly how many animals were slaughtered from stock between 1502 and 1527 [Table D], and can thus establish a *minimum* level of meat consumption.

A final and major caveat concerns the steward's annual outlay on provisions acquired in the markets of Norwich. This appears as a short entry under the sub-heading 'diets' in the late medieval accounts and in Tables A and B. Without the evidence contained in his day books, we know nothing more about these transactions beyond the fact that they contributed sums of up to £40 a year to the city's economy and thus further strengthened the hospital's links with the local community. Most purchases were probably made for the brethren and boarders rather than the house's various dependents, but this, too, remains uncertain. What did the steward buy? Almost certainly shellfish, which were eaten in large quantities by the religious communities and citizens of Norwich. Oysters, cockles, mussels and whelks (from the north Norfolk coast) added variety as well as valuable minerals and vitamins to the diet.[152] Ready-prepared meat and poultry and some fish would have supplemented the receiver general's purchases; and it may often have been necessary to lay in extra supplies of bread and ale. An annual expenditure of £36 on 'diets' (as in 1320–1 and 1335–6) would have provided twenty-four meals worth 1*d* every day throughout the year. Since the steward was well placed to make substantial economies of scale, the number may, in fact, have been far higher. Any estimate of the hospital's ability to fulfil its various obligations must clearly take his disbursements into account. Fuel supplies bought specifically for the bakery and kitchen present fewer problems. Rarely rising much above £2 a year they have been included, along with salt, condiments and other miscellaneous items in the category of 'other expenses'. These last were generally quite modest, but major purchases, such as the 181 barrels of verjuice acquired for cooking in 1500–1 at a cost of just under £17, could add appreciably to an otherwise fairly predictable outlay.[153]

Table A: Expenditure on Provisions at St Giles's Hospital 1318–75[154]

Year	Diets	Fish	Meat	Other	Total	Percentage of all current expenses
1318–19	33	14	1	8	56	52.3
1319–20	32	20	5	3	60	54.5
1320–1	36	15	15	7	73	60.3
1321–2	37	21	16	8	82	47.9 (62.1)[155]
1326–7	25	16	4	10	52	56.5
1327–8	35	20	9	2	66	52.8
1335–6	36	14	9	22	81	40.2 (49.0)[156]
1372–3	38	16	19	14	87	53.3
1374–5	25	26	20	9	80	45.7

[Figures have been rounded up or down to the nearest pound sterling]

Allowing for the unusually high outgoings sustained in 1321–2 and 1335–6 because of property transactions, the hospital seems to have spent an average of about 53 per cent (or £70) of its total current expenditure on dietary provision during this period. Like many other houses of religion, it thus conformed to a pattern found among the gentry and lesser nobility of medieval England.[157] The striking rise to 60 per cent and more in the early 1320s was clearly due to the effects of protracted famine and the other problems discussed in Chapter III. By the early sixteenth century the annual amount spent on food and its preparation averaged around 56 per cent of total expenses, or £64 a year. Marked seasonal fluctuations were caused largely by the state of the grain market, which now had a major impact upon the receiver general's budget. In well over a third (ten) of the years analysed in Table B grain purchases constituted the largest single item of expenditure. Inflationary prices in part explain the remarkable figures for 1519–20, which was the first year of John Hecker's mastership, and thus perhaps also a time of increased hospitality. Corn then reputedly cost more than it had for almost a century, with disastrous consequences for the urban poor. Following the lead of the civic authorities (or perhaps even setting them an example), the hospital distributed more than 2,000 additional maslin loaves a year during the period between 1519 and 1522 [Table C].[158] Since the brethren had raised considerable sums by selling their surplus grain in the fourteenth century, it is apparent that the diminished sums available for food purchases between 1465 and 1527 were, in fact, being stretched far further to pay for substantial quantities of barley, wheat, oats and rye. Even during the mastership of John Jullys, when the hospital briefly returned to direct management on some of its estates because of the growing demand for grain, its spending power and attendant capacity for poor relief were still significantly reduced.

Table B: Expenditure on Provisions at St Giles's Hospital 1465–1527[159]

Year	Diets	Fish	Meat	Other	Total	Percentage of all current expenses
1465–6	28	8	9	6	51	42.8
1483–4	30	17	17	7	71	59.6
1486–7	35	12	11	11	69	63.8
1488–9	31	12	9	7	59	60.2
1499–1500	37	29	7	5	78	70.2
1500–1	25	39	9	20	93	61.5
1502–3	28	33	8	12	81	45.7
1505–6	23	11	8	8	50	47.1
1506–7	23	11	9	7	50	48.5
1507–8	25	20	9	6	60	46.1
1509–10	24	18	9	7	58	54.2
1510–11	23	16	7	6	52	53.0
1511–12	23	13	10	5	51	52.5
1512–13	21	30	13	4	68	59.6
1513–14	26	38	14	4	82	66.1
1514–15	28	30	10	7	75	60.9

continued opposite

Year	Diets	Fish	Meat	Other	Total	Percentage of all current expenses
1515–16	28	23	9	3	63	48.4
1516–17	18	22	9	3	52	46.4
1519–20	41	42	10	10	103	76.8
1521–2	30	31	14	6	81	64.8
1522–3	34	13	7	12	66	54.5
1523–4	26	15	5	7	53	58.5
1524–5	27	31	9	2	69	56.5
1525–6	30	32	6	4	72	61.0
1526–7	26	20	7	6	59	49.1

[Figures have been rounded up or down to the nearest pound sterling]

Despite the manifold financial problems which they faced during the early sixteenth century, the brethren of St Giles's did their best to ensure that at least some of the founder's wishes with regard to the support of the local poor were upheld. This meant that regular supplies of bread and ale, the basic constituents of medieval poor relief, had to be maintained. Home-production is not necessarily a guarantee of quality, but the fact that barley was malted, ale brewed, corn ground and bread baked on the premises at least ensured freshness and promised (even if it did not deliver) proper supervision. East Anglian visitation reports of this period contain a litany of protests about substandard food and indifference towards the deserving poor in houses across the region, but none were voiced at St Giles's.[160] It is, once again, important to stress that the calculations presented in Table C take no account of the steward's annual outlay on 'diets', and thus represent a *bare minimum* of quantities consumed. They are based on grain supply statistics for late medieval London, where one quarter of wheat was expected to produce about 476 pounds of bread (a rate of 59.5 pounds avoirdupois per bushel). One quarter of maslin, which is coarser, did not go quite so far (about 461 pounds of bread a quarter, at a rate of 57.6 pounds avoirdupois per bushel).[161] The standard loaf weighed around 2 pounds, and, generating slightly over 2,000 calories, was considered just enough to keep body and soul together. Dependents of St Giles's probably had to share their daily bread. In 1510–11, for example, an average of just nineteen maslin loaves a day could have been baked from the grain set aside for menial servants and paupers. Unless the steward bought in additional supplies of bread, this suggests that half or quarter portions were generally distributed. Since cooked food was also served, such an arrangement does not seem ungenerous. The statutes of St James's hospital, Northallerton, ruled that thirty paupers were to be fed daily on half a wheat loaf and a mess of pottage, and at St Giles's a dish of fish, eggs, cheese or pottage provided additional sustenance.[162] Save for their emphasis on a meat rather than a fish diet, regulations established in 1839 by the Trustees of the Great Hospital for the care of inmates differed little from these arrangements. Each resident was then allocated 13 ounces of wheat bread and two pints ofbeer a day, along with butter, cheese and a helping of boiled mutton or beef. 'Pease soup' (pottage), a reminder of the medieval past, still featured on the weekly menu.[163]

During the Middle Ages meals were usually accompanied by ale, an important source of energy and nourishment. Depending on the strength of the brew, a quarter of malt was expected to produce on average between 50 and 96 gallons, although a lighter ale of 109 gallons to the quarter was consumed in later medieval London.[164] The brethren probably reserved the strongest ale and beer for their own use, and the weakest for the poor. In 1505–6, for example, the receiver general spent 27*s* on buying the best ale (*cervisa optima*) for one of the chaplains and a lay chorister, whose voices had to kept sweet. Perhaps they disliked the new-fangled taste for beer, and wished to revert to old habits. The figures in Table C assume an average of about 80 gallons of ale per quarter of malt, which may be an underestimate. On this reckoning, in 1510–11 the hospital brewery would have produced an average of approximately 24 gallons of ale and beer a day. The almsmen and non-resident dependents were probably given a quart or two as their daily allocation. Even if, as seems likely, the brethren and their guests consumed less than the basic gallon a day enjoyed by the Westminster abbey monks, additional supplies would have been needed for other requirements, such as cooking.[165] The steward probably did business with the alewives of Holme Street, many of whom were presented by local jurors for persistent breaches of the assize. One of the most notorious offenders in the 1440s was Emmotta Bettyns, wife of the hospital's former rent collector. For over thirty years she and her husband rented the hostelry near Bishop's Bridge from St Giles's, and were thus ideally situated to make good any shortfall in the brewery.[166]

Table C: Consumption of Ale and Bread at St Giles's Hospital 1465–1527[167]

Year	Malt (gallons of ale)		Wheat (pounds of bread)		Maslin (pounds of bread)	
1465–6	133	(10,640)	46	(21,896)	28.5	(13,138)
1471–2	167	(13,360)	52	(24,752)	35	(16,135)
1499–1500	114	(9,120)	28.5	(13,566)	18.5	(8,528)
1500–1	154	(12,320)	43	(20,468)	40	(18,440)
1502–3	122	(9,760)	60	(28,560)	31	(14,291)
1505–6	105	(8,400)	27	(12,852)	22.5	(10,372)
1506–7	85.5	(6,840)	31.5	(14,994)	23	(10,603)
1507–8	83	(6,640)	27	(12,852)	25	(11,525)
1509–10	89	(7,120)	28	(13,328)	23.5	(10,833)
1510–11	108	(8,640)	28.5	(13,566)	31	(14,291)
1511–12	100	(8,000)	30.5	(14,518)	26	(11,986)
1512–13	91.5	(7,320)	29.5	(14,042)	26.5	(12,216)
1513–14	103	(8,240)	30	(14,280)	27.5	(12,677)
1514–15	100	(8,000)	26.5	(12,614)	26.5	(12,216)

continued opposite

Year	Malt (gallons of ale)		Wheat (pounds of bread)		Maslin (pounds of bread)	
1515–16	87.5	(7,000)	27	(12,852)	26.5	(12,216)
1516–17	85	(6,800)	19.5	(9,282)	29	(13,369)
1519–20	85	(6,800)	32	(15,232)	34	(15,674)
1521–2	82	(6,560)	18.5	(8,806)	36.5	(16,826)
1522–3	66	(5,280)	25	(11,900)	20.5	(9,450)
1523–4	57	(4,560)	18.5	(8,806)	31	(14,291)
1524–5	90	(7,200)	20	(9,520)	30.5	(14,060)
1525–6	78.5	(6,280)	33	(15,708)	11	(5,071)
1526–7	42	(3,360)	19	(9,044)	18	(8,298)

[Figures outside the brackets are in quarters]

Because of changes in accounting practice it is impossible to present such a detailed analysis of bread and ale production before 1465, although we know that far larger consignments of malt, barley and wheat were delivered to the precinct when the hospital still managed its own demesnes and collected its tithes. In 1318–19 alone, 260 quarters of malt (a potential 20,800 gallons of ale, an average of 57 gallons a day) and 232 quarters of rye, wheat and barley (up to 110,432 pounds of bread, an average of 151 loaves a day) reached the precinct granaries. There is, unfortunately, no way of telling how much of this grain went to the indigent, how much to the brethren and how much was dispatched for sale in local markets, where famine conditions guaranteed high prices. That poor relief was offered on a far larger scale for at least the first half of the fourteenth century, seems, however, beyond question and is only to be expected given the dramatic fluctuations in demand. It is worth noting in this context that the almoner of Norwich cathedral was then in a position to distribute an average of between 240 and 274 loaves a day to the poor, but that the average had fallen to a mere 78 by the early 1400s.[168]

Whether lay or religious, the fifteenth-century English were heroic carnivores. As standards of living among the population as a whole began to rise, increased consumption of beef became a regular feature of life among the upper echelons of the peasant and artisan classes, while the gentry showed a greater predilection for mutton. Regular and conspicuous meat eating none the less remained a mark of status, which at St Giles's would have been conferred upon the brethren, senior clergy boarding in the precinct and distinguished visitors. The salt ling and cod served frequently in the refectory provided them with an additional source of protein. These were sizeable fish, each capable of feeding at least six people.[169] In some years stockfish, a generic name for any type of large salted fish, were also bought on the Norfolk coast. Table D, which is derived from the receiver general's accounts, constitutes a guide to *minimum* quantities of such foodstuffs consumed at St Giles's during the early sixteenth century, over and above an average of around five large barrels of herring and indeterminate quantities of eels (running to several thousands) purchased annually. In 1513–14, for example, approximately 1,410 substantial portions of salt cod (an average of four per day) could have been served, irrespective of whatever the steward may have bought. A bare minimum of five bullocks, ten pigs and fifteen sheep were then butchered on the premises for a core establishment comprising the master, nine chaplains (some of whom would have been absent from time to time on official business), conducts and choristers, eight choir boys and five resident servants. Fifteen boarders (*perhendinarii*) lodged for periods of between six days and forty-six weeks, some being conducts and others part-time choristers. There are few signs of the sustained over-indulgence practised by the Westminster abbey Benedictines, but enough evidence has survived to suggest that life at St Giles's was comfortable for the staff and more than bearable for the small, increasingly select band of almsmen and paupers who continued to enjoy Walter Suffield's bounty.

Table D: Consumption of Fish and Meat from Stock, 1502–3[170]

Year	Cattle	Pigs	Sheep	Cod	Stockfish
1502–3	28	4	115	268	–
1505–6	11	16	86	304	44
1506–7	9	11	77	222	7
1507–8	10	12	68	273	–
1509–10	4	12	29	221	–
1510–11	3	14	40	200	–
1511–12	9	20	47	290	–
1512–13	6	17	24	190	–
1513–14	5	10	15	235	–
1514–15	2	13	3	239	–
1515–16	3	14	–	237	–
1516–17	20	35	–	200	–
1519–20	15	2	–	250	86
1521–2	19	11	–	280	63
1522–3	5	9	2	370	100
1523–4	2	21	30	156	60
1524–5	3	20	16	300	60
1525–6	1	15	15	141	–
1526–7	1	33	7	217	–

DOMESTIC SERVANTS AND OTHER LAY EMPLOYEES

In an attempt to safeguard the peace and sanctity of their creations, the founders of hospitals following a religious or quasi-religious rule were anxious to keep the secular world at bay. Recognising that a community dedicated to the service of the poor and the performance of the *opus Dei* would require a great deal of practical support, they were nevertheless reluctant to admit a potentially unruly labour force. One solution, adopted at

St Giles's hospital, Beverley, in 1279, was to offer places to able-bodied paupers seeking employment, as well as to the sick, promising them a generous allocation of food in return for work.[171] A more common response was to follow the Cistercian practice of recruiting lay brothers, or *conversi*, bound by vows of chastity, poverty and obedience, who could be entrusted with daily administrative and menial tasks, while also sharing in the religious life of the institution when time allowed.[172] The Augustinian Order, which made such a notable contribution to the running of medieval hospitals, welcomed *conversi*, on the clear understanding that they would 'labour for the profit of the Church in things corporeal'. The bread of idleness was not for them.[173] Regulations drawn up in 1244 by Archbishop Gray for St James's hospital, Northallerton, allowed a modest secular presence in the precinct. The cook and another servant who doubled as brewer and baker, along with their two boys, were not bound by a common rule. But the porter, butler, larderer (who also looked after the gardens), granger and steward had to be clerks or lay brothers, a necessary measure in the case of the steward, who was responsible for the infirmary and the care of relics.[174] At St Giles's, Kepier, which served as a model for these ordinances, six lay brothers discharged all domestic and administrative duties. Such an exclusive arrangement appealed to Walter Suffield, who felt that four lay brothers would between them be sufficient 'to attend diligently and faithfully to the business' of his own hospital, both at home and on errands outside. They were to dress in white tunics and grey scapulars, share a common lodging and obey the master in every respect.[175]

As the clerical establishment expanded, the lay brothers gradually disappeared from the precinct. In 1322 the bishop of Norwich ordered that one of the *conversi* who had recently died should be replaced by a suitable priest, 'able to celebrate daily for the souls of the founder and benefactors of the hospital'. Manual and routine administrative tasks were now assigned to domestic servants.[176] As we have seen in Chapter II, St Giles's already employed a number of hired hands by the early fourteenth century. The cook, butler and baker (who served as brewer until the appointment of a specialist for a few years in the 1500s), along with their boys, were, however, the only staff ever to receive a fixed stipend and annual livery of cloth. Others, such as the laundress, swineherd and granger, were paid token sums, which could be supplemented with comestibles. In marked contrast to the heavy expenditure on provisions, the wages of domestic servants thus accounted for only a fraction of the receiver general's budget. Payment in kind, comprising full board and accommodation, if required, was still worth having, along with the less tangible benefits of working for men such as Archdeacons Derlyngton and Selot. Indeed, until the years following the first outbreak of plague, when the hospital's senior domestic staff were first able to demand a modest annual salary, everyone was reimbursed in this rather *ad hoc* fashion. By the 1370s, the baker, steward and cook could expect a robe and 13*s* 4*d* a year, which had risen to 20*s* by the end of the century. Delays in payment were by no means unusual, although the three men and their boys continued to be fed and housed at the hospital's expense and were well placed to make up their wages in other ways.[177]

By 1465–6, when the steward had assumed responsibility for managing and paying the lay workforce, the total wage bill came to just over £8, while liveries costing between 4*s* and 5*s* each, according to status, along with other items of clothing, accounted for less than

£5. These outgoings constituted barely 10 per cent of overall expenditure, and together cost slightly less than the stipends of the master and his four or five chaplains. The butler, who seems by then to have been the senior lay employee, received 26*s* 8*d* a year, the baker 23*s* 4*d*, and the cook 20*s* as before. The master's servant earned 16*s*, while the two boys who assisted the baker and cook took home 13*s* 4*d* and 8*s* respectively. Smaller sums were paid to other specialists, such as a barber, a mole-catcher, a millwright and the man who polished the pewter. Stipends fluctuated slightly over the following decades. For a brief period during the mastership of John Jullys a clerk of the kitchen, William Ferriby, held office at 26*s* 8*d* a year.[178] Hospitality on the scale envisaged by this entrepreneurial master demanded sweeping changes in the domestic establishment, but, like the appointment of a beer-brewer, his improvements proved relatively short-lived. This last innovation meant that the baker had temporarily to take a cut in salary to 16*s*, although on resuming charge of the brewery, in about 1509, he was able to secure a significant pay rise. Economies during the 1520s may reflect the house's financial difficulties: Stephen Green, the butler, agreed to work for nothing in 1524–5, and his successor accepted just 10*s* a year. By this point, however, the butler had become a figure of some consequence in the household, whose other duties brought ample remuneration.

The career of William Fualeyn, who held this post almost continuously between about 1497 and 1516, provides an illuminating insight into the lives and connections of the laymen who helped to run St Giles's, and of the close community which surrounded the hospital. During this period he also served two terms as rent collector in Norwich, being thus responsible for repairs and building works in the precinct during the late 1490s and again from 1505 to 1515. Such a position brought with it many opportunities for self-advancement, not least being the chance to rent a prime Holme Street property, with stable and garden, from the hospital for his own use. Fualeyn was a neighbour of Richard Frevylle, master of the choristers, and godfather of the young Edmund Frevylle, who later became a chaplain at St Giles's. His wife Margaret, a spinster, purchased sheepskins and wool from the Cringleford flock, while his kinsman, John Fualeyn, found frequent employment as a master mason and stone cutter in and around the hospital. John was, for instance, hired for a month in 1512–13 to repair the walls in the great garden and kitchen, having by then himself leased a Holme Street tenement where there was plenty of space for stone-working.[179] William's will of 1523 reveals the warmth of his attachment to an institution which he had served loyally for almost two decades. He asked to be buried beside his wife in the hospital church, and left almost all his modest bequests to the chaplains, nurses and choristers. Even the porter, who is not mentioned in any of the surviving accounts, received a legacy. Fualeyn had good reason to be grateful. Shortly before his retirement, in 1515–16, the receiver general had sanctioned an expenditure of over £4 on major repairs to his tenement, including the construction of two new houses on the site. Yet the rent of 12*s* a year remained unchanged until he died. Significantly, his deathbed will was drawn up and witnessed in the presence of two of the hospital chaplains, which suggests that the house provided spiritual as well as physical care for its former employees.[180] Lest Fualeyn's experience be considered unrepresentative, we might turn to one of his predecessors as rent collector, the above-mentioned John Bettyns, whose elaborate bequests for posthumous commemoration at St Giles's have already been noted in Chapter IV. Bettyns's sideline as an innkeeper made him a far wealthier and more influential figure, although he owed his initial success to Robert Spenser, during whose mastership he had secured his long and profitable lease of the hospital's Holme Street hostelry. That he was chosen to execute Spenser's will reflects the intimacy of their relationship; he, in turn, appointed two hospital chaplains as his executors, and his new 'master', Doctor Selot, to supervise them.[181]

A community such as St Giles's naturally tended to employ a workforce drawn from among its own tenants. However noisy and polluted life on the margins may have been, it at least guaranteed the constant availability of smiths, limeburners, masons and other artisans whose skills helped to keep the hospital and its properties in a state of good repair. Accounts compiled by Bettyns, Fualeyn and the other late medieval rent collectors show that the master craftsmen engaged on major building projects in and around the precinct often rented houses, workshops and yards nearby. When preparing large quantities of stone for the chancel at Hardley, in 1458–9, Robert Everard (who was later to design the new nave and spire of Norwich cathedral), hired a workshop opposite St Giles's from his other employers, the monks, but most of the hospital's masons including his kinsman, John Everard, preferred to rent direct from the master.[182] During the 1430s the freemasons, Richard Walpole, John Brythmere and John Ecclys, and the roofer, Robert Stuggy, lived in Holme Street, being not only close to the hospital but also the river, by which their materials were transported.[183] Henry Tebbe, a reeder who leased holdings near the precinct between 1487 and 1513, supplied large quantities of thatch as well as labour. In 1505–6 alone he and his men were paid over £5 by the brethren for work on their Norwich properties. His neighbours during this period included Robert Semyll, a carpenter, Thomas Runtyng, a general builder, and at least three jobbing labourers, all of whom found regular employment at St Giles's. Semyll's departure from Holme Street did not mark the end of his association with the hospital: his skills as a carpenter were so highly valued that the master paid another tenant to supply him with free board and lodging whenever his services were required.[184]

The brethren's activities as employers and consumers, along with their daily distribution of alms to thirteen local paupers and other charitable work undertaken in times of hardship, strengthened their links with the men and women of Holme Street. These, in turn, broadened the connections forged at a higher social level by successive masters with members of the civic elite, and must have influenced the debate over the hospital's future which overshadowed the years before its formal surrender to the Crown and eventual refoundation in 1547. That the rich and elaborately decorated hospital church also served the local parish intensified this sense of community and wove St Giles's more closely into the fabric of civic life and worship. The fifteenth-century transition from open-ward infirmary to select and efficiently managed almshouse provided another important argument in its favour. Unlike countless other late medieval hospitals it still demonstrably catered for the deserving poor, promising its employees and their dependents a degree of security in their old age. But survival was by no means a foregone conclusion. The hospital and its patrons had to travel a difficult and potentially dangerous road as religious reform became a matter of high politics, subject to the vagaries of a capricious monarch.

CHAPTER VII

THE DISSOLUTION

> His life had hitherto been so quiet, so free from strife; his little early troubles had required nothing but passive fortitude; his subsequent prosperity had never forced upon him any active cares – had never brought him into disagreeable contact with anyone. He felt that he would give almost anything – much more than he knew he ought to do – to relieve himself from the storm which he feared was coming. It was so hard that the pleasant waters of his little stream should be disturbed and muddied by rough hands; that his quiet paths should be made a battlefield; that the unobtrusive corner of the world which had been allotted to him, as though by Providence, should be invaded and desecrated, and all within made miserable and unsound.
>
> Anthony Trollope, *The Warden*

The first half of the sixteenth century witnessed a number of sweeping changes in the provision, organisation and funding of institutional relief for the indigent poor. Throughout Europe, it became increasingly obvious that existing structures were inadequate to meet the demands of a rising population beset by a cyclical round of epidemics and food shortages, as well as the pressures of mounting inflation. A common ethic of Christian humanism meant that protestant and catholic thinkers alike shared an interest in programmes for the alleviation of poverty and the introduction of medical services, although doctrinal differences may have had a more profound effect on shaping national and regional responses than revisionist historians, writing in the 1960s and 1970s, have allowed. Projected reforms hinged, with varying degrees of success, upon the introduction of measures designed to centralise and improve the distribution of welfare, while placing the urban poor themselves under far stricter surveillance. Steps were taken to identify and enumerate deserving cases, to introduce special taxes, rates and other levies which could be administered by the secular authorities and to bring hospitals more firmly under the control of city corporations and guilds.[1] Often in response to specific crises, such as plague, famine and the pox, the rulers of Nüremberg, Hamburg, Strasbourg, Regensburg, Mons, Ypres and Venice provided models in the 1520s which were rapidly adopted elsewhere. Other European cities, from Toledo to Danzig and Stockholm to Lyon, were likewise driven by force of circumstance and religious zeal to seek alternatives to the well-intentioned but often uncoordinated efforts of individual benefactors and institutions.[2]

It has recently been argued that, whereas the economic and social problems of sixteenth-century urban society were broadly similar throughout Europe, protestant states, such as

England, effectively reversed their scale of values, prioritising the physical and moral welfare of the living, suffering pauper rather than the salvation of his or her patron.[3] Ministers of Henry VIII and Edward VI certainly regarded themselves as architects of a godly commonwealth, constructed on earth for the health of the body politic. But did they really face the daunting task of 'rebuilding a system of social welfare from scratch'?[4] Such a view arises from the presumption that the monastic almonries and hospitals which fell victim to religious change in the 1530s and 1540s had previously carried a heavy burden of almsgiving not easily borne on other shoulders. Medieval men and women had already expressed reservations on this score. Indeed, the failure of hospitals to discharge their charitable obligations had generated controversy long before the Reformation. During the late fourteenth century, the Dominican preacher and Cambridge scholar, John Bromyard, deplored the current situation:

> Scarcely is there another land in which so few places of hospitality or 'God's Houses' can be found for the reception of the poor . . . and even in those few, when a few enter with not a little pleading and sometimes payment too, those in charge devour all they have.[5]

Bromyard preached from a secure position within the ecclesiastical establishment, being one of the most prominent of John Wycliffe's many opponents. Attacks from outside were even more outspoken and aggressive. From 1395 onwards, if not earlier, lollard-inspired proposals for the disendowment of the Church and the redistribution of its temporal goods suggested ways in which hospital provision might be improved, either by closing down institutions which no longer helped the poor or else increasing the number of almshouses devoted solely to this task. A proposal that 100 such places could be endowed with confiscated ecclesiastical property was considered in the Parliament of 1410.[6] Although it proved too radical by far, the bill seems to have attracted strong support in what was an unusually outspoken Lower House. It probably inspired a Commons petition for the reform of hospitals under royal and episcopal jurisdiction, which was submitted to Henry V in the spring of 1414.

The misappropriation of funds initially donated for the benefit of the sick poor was of particular concern to MPs. 'And now as things stand', they complained:

> the majority of hospitals in your said realm are fallen into decay, and their goods and profits diverted and put to other use, as much by clergy as by layfolk. Whereby many men and women have died in great misery for want of help, livelihood and succour, to the displeasure of God and peril of the souls of those who spoil and spend what belongs to the poor.[7]

Henry V not only approved the bill, but also insisted that delegates to the Council of Constance should address the specific question of financial irregularities in hospitals when they came to consider 'the reformation of the Universal Church'. Yet, one year later, the Commons were driven to protest that nothing had been done to implement their proposals, and to suggest that the terms of reference of the commissioners who were supposed to be investigating abuses should be widened.[8] Henry's absence in France probably accounts for the lukewarm response to this second bill, which marked the end of a short-lived initiative for change.[9]

In the last resort, however, the gentlemen and merchants who sat in the Lower House were themselves much to blame for the diversion of hospital funds into chantries and elaborate liturgical practices. Rather than continuing to agitate for reform, several adopted the more pragmatic approach of founding almshouses and *maisons Dieu*, which could be managed according to their specific instructions. Well over half of the charitable institutions known to have been planned (if not actually put into commission) in medieval England and almost all those endowed after the mid-fourteenth century fell into this category.[10] The great majority constituted a decisive response to pressing social and moral issues on the part of laymen and women confident of their own judgement and administrative skills. A number of late fourteenth- and early fifteenth-century MPs, among whom Thomas Holme (York), Richard Whittington (London), Roger Thornton (Newcastle-upon-Tyne) and John Plumtree (Nottingham) are the most notable, went to considerable lengths to ensure that their foundations remained under secular control.[11] It was also at this time that the more affluent guilds of London and York, often at the prompting of individual benefactors, such as the influential London merchant, John Churchman (d. 1413), began providing subsidised accommodation for reputable elderly or disabled brethren who could no longer support themselves.[12] By the close of the fifteenth century, however, the Tailors' almshouses, which had cost Churchman and his executors over £100 to build, had been largely superseded by more adaptable and localised schemes for poor relief centred upon the city parish. Here, well before the Tudor poor law began to take shape, private almsgiving could be directed with a greater degree of 'godly rigour' towards approved and accepted members of the local community.[13]

In Norwich, a city celebrated for the number, size and relative wealth of its parish churches, the merchant elite evidently preferred this alternative from an early date. Even allowing for the fact that the five extra mural leper houses were used to accommodate the sick poor during the fifteenth century, the striking dearth of almshouse provision (all the more remarkable in comparison with far smaller towns, such as Kingston-upon-Hull) would otherwise be hard to explain.[14] Considerable reserves of capital and expertise were required to set up a *maison Dieu*, and it has been convincingly argued that the majority of smaller foundations were never intended to last for very long. They offered an *ad hoc*, pragmatic solution to the problem of caring for elderly neighbours, servants or poor relatives, and (like most chantries) had a finite existence.[15] Transience was certainly the order of the day in Norwich, where none of the handful of refuges briefly noted in the records survived for more than a few years at the very longest. Three appear fleetingly to the west of the city in the late thirteenth and early fourteenth centuries, when poor immigrants were colonising the open spaces around Coslany during a period of intense overcrowding [see Map I]. A fourth endowment, planned in this area by a local priest named Richard de Breccles, was clearly envisaged on a more permanent scale, although his estate was so encumbered with debt that the scheme had to be abandoned. The brothers John and Walter Danyell, who made provision in their joint will of 1418 for almshouses 'of new construction and ordinance' near St Stephen's gate to the south, clearly did not want for money, but the project likewise foundered after their deaths. Passing references in antiquarian collections to two other hospices (which are not documented in any extant medieval sources) are unreliable, and still leave a total of only six short-lived foundations, and a seventh which never opened its doors at all.[16]

York, by contrast, could boast between twelve and eighteen late medieval *maisons Dieu*, as well as five other hospitals run under the auspices of civic guilds and fraternities. At least two of Bristol's eleven almshouses had likewise been founded by the city's craftsmen and merchants.[17] Although several of Norwich's eighteen guilds were clearly too poor to contemplate such a step, others certainly possessed the necessary resources, yet never chose to provide shelter for their less fortunate brethren. On the other hand, the city housed at least four informal communities of religious women, one of which 'dwelling in Westwyk' may have continued the work of an earlier almshouse. The sisters probably helped to care for the sick and disadvantaged of their local parishes, a task commonly undertaken by women at all but the meanest level of society.[18] The chance survival of accounts from the household of Katherine, the relict of Walter de Norwich, sometime treasurer of England, suggests that the contribution made by wives and widows of her social class must often have been considerable. She left her Suffolk manor of Mettingham in January 1377 to spend several weeks at the family residence in Norwich. Throughout the entire period, thirteen paupers received a dole each day of herring and bread, specially baked from her own grain. Additional food was made available on Good Friday and on the anniversary of her husband's death. She was thus providing about the same number of daily meals for non-resident dependents as St Giles's hospital, albeit from a far smaller budget. In the following century, Isabella, Lady Morely, who also lived in the city, bought cloth and fuel as alms for her poor neighbours.[19] Documentary evidence of this kind is rare, and hints at the existence of a loosely but effectively organised welfare network, firmly and exclusively based in the local community.

The provision of hospitality, the distribution of food, drink and clothing, and the support of the sick were Comfortable Works enjoined upon all Christians during their lifetimes as well as through testamentary bequests. The residents of Norwich had every incentive to concentrate their charitable efforts on the parish, which was a focus of loyalty and pride, as well as of personal piety. The structure of the city, with its forty-six parish churches, many of which had been spectacularly rebuilt, extended or embellished during the two centuries before the Reformation, helped to foster these sentiments.[20] With an average population of well below 300 souls during the fifteenth century, the Norwich parish was, moreover, a manageable, close-knit unit for the effective administration of relief whenever it might be required. But it could also prove hostile and intolerant. Margery Kempe's admonition to her priest that far greater spiritual merit was to be earned by giving to friends and neighbours, whose moral rectitude could easily be established, accorded ill with Christ's teaching about generosity to strangers, but none the less struck a common chord. 'It was mor almes to helpun him that thei knewyn wel for wel dysposyd folke and her owyn neybowrys', she urged, 'than other strawngerys whech thei knew not.'[21]

The wills of Norwich's leading citizens, frequently witnessed and executed by the masters of St Giles's hospital, reflect a similar conviction that charity should begin at home.

Roger Pratt's friend, William Setman, was, for example, anxious to help 'the lame, the blind and the severely disabled *residing continually in Norwich*', while Walter Danyell left considerable sums of money to be distributed by his executors among the sick poor *living in his parish* and the *most deserving and crippled residents* of the city.[22] Measures of this kind, which depended upon the generosity of individual donors, may have provided an adequate safety net for the 'shamefaced', reputable and housebound poor of Norwich during periods of economic and social stability, but did little to help vagrants, beggars or other potentially disruptive outsiders.[23] Nor is there much evidence of compassion for the predicament of the casual labourer, who managed to keep his or her head just above water during periods of employment but faced a grim struggle for survival when jobs were scarce. Institutional relief for members of this vulnerable group was at best sporadic, their requirements barely understood.[24] Doles of money, food and clothing, shelter and basic medical care had traditionally been offered to the needy by the older hospital foundations and monastic almonries of medieval England. Yet, even in those houses which contrived to perform some of their original functions, the will, the energy and the funds to tackle what once again threatened to become a pressing social problem remained wanting. As we have seen, St Giles's continued to admit a small number of poor travellers until the Dissolution, but most of its diminishing charitable resources were directed into the upkeep of an almshouse and the distribution of parochial doles.

W.K. Jordan's comprehensive pronouncements about 'the calamitous decay of medieval charitable institutions' and the 'long and inexorable process of the deterioration of monasticism' have been widely questioned, not least because of his uncritical use and interpretation of financial evidence.[25] Nor did he allow for regional or local variations. Approving comments made by Sir Thomas More about the great crowds of 'poore folke' who received alms at the gates of Westminster abbey, and the duke of Norfolk's less compassionate view of the 'sturdy beggars' maintained by several Yorkshire monasteries suggest that some houses discharged an important eleemosynary role right up to the Dissolution.[26] So too do the widespread (but often politically motivated) contemporary protests concerning the desperate situation of the homeless poor after Henry VIII's commissioners began their work.[27] Yet against the the favourable report of one fifteenth-century London citizen regarding the valuable contribution made by a number of the city's oldest, quasi-monastic hospitals must be set Henry VII's celebrated assertion that 'there be fewe or noon commune Hospitallis within this our Reame, and . . . for lack of theim infinite nombre of power nedie people miserably daily die, no man putting hande of helpe or remedie'.[28] Claims advanced in 1652 by the antiquary, Jeremiah Stevens, that 'we had 110 great hospitals (as appeareth upon record) demolished at one clappe in the tempest of King Henry Eight in his rage, by the losse of wich our poore att this daye do suffer extremly in all partes . . .' betray a nostalgic longing for a mythical, prelapsarian past.[29] The reality was often very different.

Few historians who have examined specific institutions in depth would now deny that the majority of English religious houses encountered serious financial problems during the later Middle Ages and were consequently obliged to reduce or even abandon charitable relief. The blatant 'indifference and neglectfulness', 'mismanagement and outright theft' and 'grave abuses' which Jordan blamed for this decline seem, however, to have been far less ubiquitous than he supposed.[30] The gravest allegations which could be levelled against the monks of Norwich cathedral priory (and of many other houses) in the early 1530s were small-mindedness, conservatism and lack of vocation. The chronic and irreversible fall in revenues which beset their community made reductions in the almoner's budget inescapable.[31] Between 1378 and 1533 the average amount of grain milled each year for distribution among the poor fell from 132 quarters to a mere 24 which would have provided no more than about sixteen loaves a day. Spectacular funeral doles, such as the £21 assigned *in usus pauperum* on the death of Prior Henry de Lakenham in 1310, were few and far between in the fourteenth century and unknown thereafter. On the eve of the Dissolution twelve bedesmen were being supported in the monastery at an annual cost of almost £17, while an additional £10 was spent each year on doles of bread, herring, drink and money for general distribution in memory of the founder on Maundy Thursday. Neither of these provisions (which represent the two extremes of highly selective and almost totally indiscriminate almsgiving) offered anything in the way of regular help to the labouring or vagrant poor, whose numbers were beginning to rise and who still slipped through the fragile welfare net. Indeed, even if the modest handouts of cash and bread distributed by the almoner are taken into account, the priory's outlay on almsgiving represented only around 3 per cent of annual expenditure as recorded in the accounts of 1534. The prioress of Carrow spent even less: a mere 1 per cent of her disposable income went on alms at this time.[32] These figures reflect a general trend apparent in most early sixteenth-century English monasteries, which had rarely, in any event, ever followed the recommendation that one-tenth of disposable income should go to the poor.[33]

Allowing for the fact that unrecorded gifts of food and clothing may have been regularly made by the almoner, it is hard to reconcile this evidence with the claim that the poor of Norwich could rely upon 'the beneficence of one of the most generous houses in late medieval England'.[34] As already noted in Chapter VI, the monastic hospital of St Paul had, from the late fourteenth century, catered almost exclusively for about a score of respectable almswomen. It depended for survival upon a small and fast declining landed income, supplemented by alms from private benefactors, whose legacies and donations helped to feed and clothe the poorer sisters and the few remaining patients. So parlous was their financial situation that, by the 1480s, their stipends were over two months in arrears, and the master was obliged to charge for admission.[35] Nor had the monks been able to maintain the old leper hospital at Sprowston, which by the 1530s had become little more than a wayside chapel, all surplus profits passing directly into the hands of an absentee pluralist.[36] Hildebrand's hospital in Conisford, which had originally offered lodgings to poor pilgrims and the homeless entering Norwich from the south east, had long since ceased to cater for more than a handful of deserving cases. In 1429, the above-mentioned William Setman had offered a substantial endowment on the understanding that the original statutes would be properly observed, which suggests that here, too, the founder's wishes had been forgotten. In this instance, dissatisfaction may have been compounded by disputes over patronage, but, as usual, the sick poor were the losers. By the end of the century revenues were counted in shillings rather than pounds, leaving the occasional inmates entirely dependent upon the charity of local parishioners.[37]

The situation at St Giles's was very different. However pressing its financial difficulties may have been, it had hitherto always been able to rely upon a groundswell of support from members of the ruling elite. Perhaps because the hospital occupied such a prominent place in the city, directly under the eye of its powerful episcopal and lay patrons, high disciplinary and administrative standards seem to have been constantly maintained. The breath of scandal did not disturb the serenity of Doctor Selot's cloisters. Visitations held by Bishop Nykke in the 1520s and 1530s present a picture of genteel decline, as the annual deficit between income and expenditure rose steadily and arrears of unpaid rent climbed inexorably towards the £200 mark. Yet although, in 1526, the hospital could support only half the full complement of chaplains (assisted by three conducts and two boarders), John Hecker, the master, had punctiliously discharged all his responsibilities. Proper records were efficiently kept and most of the brethren expressed complete satisfaction with their lot. So they well might, despite the fact that Hecker or one of his predecessors stood charged with further losses of £50, which made it harder to balance the budget. Little else gave cause for concern. His kinsman, William Hecker, seized the opportunity to deny rumours about an illicit liaison with the wife of one 'Ropkyn de Holmestrete'. These had presumably been spread by another of the chaplains, with whom he was said to bicker constantly in the choir. Such peccadilloes were small beer when compared with the catalogue of mayhem and vice which reputedly gave the 'bawdy hospital' of St Thomas, Southwark, its unsavoury reputation.[38] His almost immediate departure suggests, even so, that family connections were no protection when the house's good name was at stake.

Six years later one of the vacancies among the chaplains had been filled, but the hospital then lacked a precentor, who played a vital role in the conduct of the liturgy. Further evidence of worsening economic problems and an attendant loss of morale may be found in the brothers' anxiety about the state of the fabric. The late Master Hecker had apparently been slow to distribute money left by his predecessor, John Smyth, for the celebration of his obit, although he had completed the more important task of squaring his accounts. Being, as we have seen, a local man who had spent most of his life at St Giles's, Hecker lacked the resources to underwrite expenditure for long periods as some of his predecessors had done. But the only other reservations expressed at this time concerned the employment of married servants, which one chaplain, mindful of the founder's strict rulings on celibacy, deemed unacceptable.[39] Compared with other East Anglian houses, such as Butley priory, where there was neither a sacrist nor a precentor, where the servants were insolent and the community riven by discord, where the presbytery and the chapter house lay in ruins and the monks evidently lacked food, fuel and medical care, and where overspending ran at almost £50 a year, St Giles's appeared a haven of tranquillity.[40] Depositions taken at the hospital of St Mary in the Newarke, Leicester, in 1525, reveal another community at odds with itself, allegations of corruption, negligence and mismanagement being banded about with little thought for the consequences. 'You have so departed from the founder's words and meaning that certain statutes . . . appear to be almost abrogated by disuse or by ill-keeping of the same', admonished Bishop Longland. His injunctions were damning:

> We have found also that your founder's pious will has been sorely wounded as regards the admission of the hundred poor folk and ten women; that persons rich and not poor, strong and not weak, healthy and able to work, have been received by means of money . . . contrary to the statute . . . We have found, moreover, that certain of the canons and ministers of the college . . . have haunted the taverns in the town of Leicester even until they were drunk, and, from their overmuch kindness with women in the town . . . have incurred infamy; that they have made privy conspiracies, leagues, brawls and quarrels, and sometimes even have come to blows; that the serving women, moreover, abide continually in the canons' houses, and other women have often had access to their houses . . . to the great scandal of the said college.[41]

Evidence such as this gave ammunition to reformers, who welcomed Henry VIII's decision, in 1534, to declare himself supreme head of the English Church. All regular clergy and members of institutions such as St Giles's, which were seen as potential centres of resistance, had to take a comprehensive oath, renouncing 'the bishop of Rome', swearing obedience to the King as Christ's lieutenant on earth and accepting the issue of Henry's Queen, Anne Boleyn, as heirs to the throne of England.[42] The imposition of new ecclesiastical taxes, payable directly to the Crown, was, however, hampered by lack of reliable information. When approving the necessary legislation, Parliament expressed concern that alms given to the poor 'by reason of any foundacyon or ordynaunce' should be exempt from taxation.[43] Even so, King Henry's great survey of ecclesiastical property, the *Valor Ecclesiasticus*, extended to all the more substantial hospitals run by the Church, and in its final form assessed over a hundred such institutions. Since a substantial proportion had effectively abandoned their charitable work, and many were sorely decayed, such an exercise seemed partially justified. But St Giles's was not among those which had forgotten their original purpose.

The destruction of all annual accounts and day books compiled for the hospital between 1527 and 1548 makes it impossible to ascertain the accuracy of claims that around £45 was earmarked in 1535 for charitable purposes. Although it evidently satisfied King Henry's commissioners, the return then submitted by the brethren seems to have been considerably inflated. At an estimated £173, anticipated net annual income certainly exceeded any sums raised since the fourteenth century, and did not allow for arrears.[44] It was clearly important to reassure the government of St Giles's continuing viability. The rulers of Norwich would have been far easier to convince, for the hospital still made a more significant contribution towards poor relief than any of the city's other charitable institutions, and devoted a far greater proportion of its revenues to almsgiving than the cathedral monks. Perhaps anticipating the rocky road which lay ahead, the brethren were clearly anxious that their work should be recognised, and they did, indeed, escape the first round of dissolutions which followed hard on the completion of the *Valor Ecclesiasticus*. Nicholas Orme has already suggested that hospitals were the accidental victims of a government which had set its long-term sights on the great monastic foundations. Those which survived the parliamentary statute of 1536, authorising the dismemberment of all houses worth less than £200 a year, certainly could not rest secure. That the government would stop short of wholesale dissolution, and thus forgo far richer pickings, seemed unlikely, especially as persuasive doctrinal arguments could now be marshalled to justify the confiscation by a protestant state of *all* ecclesiastical property dedicated to the service of the dead rather than the living. As Cardinal William Allen was later to argue in his spirited defence of the doctrine of purgatory, the *raison d'être* of every charitable foundation in England was thus undermined:

> All the noble monuments, not onely in oure commonwelthe, but through Christes churche, do beare sufficient testimonie of our first faithe herin. This doctrine (as the whole worlde knoweth) founded all Bisshoprikes, buylded al Churchies, raysed al Oratories, instituted al Collegies, indued all Schooles, maintened all hospitalles, set forwarde al woorkes of charitye and religion, of what sorte so euer they bee. Take a way the praiers and practise for the deade, ether al these monuments must fall, or elles they must stand agaynste the first founders will and meaninge. Looke in the statutes of all noble foundacions, and of all charitable woorkes, euer sithe the first daie of oure happy calling to Christes faithe, whether they doo not expressely testifie, that theire worke of almose and deuotion was for this one especiall respect, to be payde and songe for, as they call it, after theire deathes . . .[45]

More seriously in the long term, laymen and women soon began to recognise the economic advantages to be gained by abandoning these beliefs, and with them any obligation to maintain the chantries and chapels which tied up so much ancestral wealth.[46] For the next decade St Giles's faced an uncertain future.

A PERIOD OF TRANSITION

The character and religious sympathies of the master assumed particular importance at this difficult time. Throughout the region, a volatile brew of political and religious factionalism simmered constantly near boiling point. If the doctrine of purgatory were firmly and finally to be rejected, where would this leave institutions such as St Giles's whose very existence was predicated upon the power of intercessionary prayer and good works to purchase salvation? And if dissolution were avoided, what might be done to return them more fully to their original purpose as refuges for the sick and aged poor? Sensitivity to the requirements of the civic authorities and a pragmatic acceptance of the need for compromise were prerequisites for survival. The brutal world of Tudor *realpolitik* cast a shadow over the hospital, where, for the first time in 300 years, national affairs determined how and by whom it would be run. The resignation of Thomas Cappe, late in 1535, coincided with his replacement as Official of the archdeacon of Norwich and the surrender of his prebend at the college of St Mary in the Fields.[47] Cappe was no longer a young man, but his sudden retirement from active life in the diocese probably owed more to the decline and death of his patron, the formidable Bishop Nykke, than it did to old age. As one of the most determined and reactionary members of the English episcopate, Nykke had struggled hard to restrain the tide of evangelism in East Anglia, only to suffer humiliation and disgrace at the hands of Thomas Cromwell.[48] Four charges of wrongful excommunication and other abuses of authority levelled against Cappe in the local consistory court during the space of one single year (1525–6) suggest that he shared the bishop's arch-conservatism, which was as uncongenial to the rulers of Norwich as it was to Cromwell's party at Westminster.[49] Although he lived on in the city, as vicar of St Stephen's, until after December 1545, no further preferment came his way.[50]

The next master, Thomas Simmondes, who also succeeded to Cappe's prebend at St Mary's, is said by Blomefield to have been one of the bishop's private chaplains.[51] Perhaps for this reason he was destined to be no more than a caretaker, serving for only a few months until a more acceptable candidate could be found. Robert Codde, who was appointed by the Crown in March 1536, while the temporalities of the see of Norwich were still in royal hands, seems, on the face of things, an even less promising choice, at least so far as the reformers were concerned.[52] He had been prior of the Augustinian house at Bromehill before joining the order's more socially prestigious community at Pentney, also in Norfolk. During his fifteen or so years as prior, the canons there had enjoyed a 'very honest name' as 'goode religious persones', and had brought nothing but credit upon their order. Attempts to undermine Codde's reputation in the 1530s through allegations of sexual impropriety (with none other than the prioress of Marham) carried little conviction. Following a series of laudatory visitation reports came a glowing testimony from Cromwell's own commissioners, who urged that the priory should be left undisturbed because it had been so efficiently managed. Codde, they noted, 'relieves those quarters wondrously where he dwells, and it would be a pity not to spare a house that feeds so many indigent poor, which is in a good state, maintains a good service and does so many charitable deeds'.[53] Their recommendations were ignored. Although the canons of Pentney asked King Henry for permission 'to continue and remain in religion', Codde himself bowed to the inevitable, pocketed his pension and underwent a dramatic conversion. By February 1537 he was involved with the King's visitor, Sir Richard Southwell, in the demolition of the shrine of the Holy Rood at Bromholm. Besides acting as his confidential messenger to Cromwell, he took personal responsibility for delivering one of the most famous relics in East Anglia to the iconoclasts at Westminster.[54] An element of calculation may have prompted this remarkable *volte face*, which went far beyond the trimming tactics of most former religious. Perhaps he remained, like Southwell, a conservative at heart and hoped to moderate the impact of reform. His will of August 1546, with its invocation of the Blessed Virgin and request for a priest to 'singe for my sowle', suggests that the triumph of the old guard during Henry VIII's last days was not entirely unpleasing to him.[55] He was certainly well qualified, and even better placed, to protect St Giles's. Not only did some of the most influential figures at Court favour his appointment to the mastership; his arrival at the hospital must have been even more welcome to the rulers of Norwich, through whose ranks his own younger brother, Thomas, was rapidly beginning to rise.

Having served in the early 1530s as a constable and councillor for Wymer ward and an officer in the guild of St George, Thomas Codde became an alderman in 1538. He remained a prominent figure in the civic hierarchy and an active participant in the affairs of the guild until just before his death, thirty years later, by which time he had discharged one term as sheriff and two as mayor of England's second city.[56] Like many previous masters, Robert Codde also belonged to the guild, where he mixed amicably with his brother's friends and associates.[57] They, rather than any episcopal patron, were now giving serious thought to the hospital's future role in civic schemes for poor relief and education. These ideas emerged gradually, not least because members of the ruling elite, anchored firmly in the culture of the parish, were as yet unaccustomed to thinking collectively in terms of broad-based institutionalised schemes for public welfare. The unsettled political and religious climate also made long-term planning impossible. As the reform movement, spearheaded by Cromwell and Archbishop Cranmer, lost momentum in the late 1530s, the prospect of further doctrinal change began to recede. By the summer of 1538, it looked as if the celebration of private masses might remain a permanent feature of English religious life. While not actually accepting that the sacrifice of the Mass benefited the dead, the Six Articles passed by Parliament in the following June adopted an otherwise traditional stance in keeping with King Henry's own views.[58] But was St Giles's really out of the wood? Driven by greed, the piecemeal dismemberment of the established Church had already acquired a momentum of its own and the juggernaut could not be stopped.

One by one, under a variety of very different circumstances, institutions which had avoided dissolution in 1536 surrendered to the Crown. On 2 May 1538 the monastic cathedral of Holy Trinity, Norwich, was the first in England to be refounded as a secular college. The former Benedictine, William Rugge, proved as compliant a bishop as his predecessor, Nykke, had been obdurate, and thus acquiesced readily in all King Henry's demands.[59] Although it was bought at great expense, the new charter allowed almost complete continuity from religious community to secular chapter. By acting quickly and making the best of unenviable circumstances, the monks were able to negotiate far more favourable provisions than any of the other reconstituted cathedral chapters, which subsequently took shape between 1540 and 1542.[60] Theirs was not a common experience. Intense pressure at both a local and a national level was brought to bear upon smaller communities, such as the Norwich Dominicans, who occupied a prime site on the banks of the River Wensum, north of the castle and the guildhall [see Map II]. Rumours that the friary might be suppressed led the civic authorities to send two aldermen to the duke of Norfolk's seat at Kenninghall, in August 1538, 'to haue hys grace's will and pleasure iff the cominaltie shall make sute to the Kynge's grace to haue the graunte off blak ffreres house'. As later proved to be the case when the corporation moved to acquire St Giles's hospital, intensive political lobbying was essential from the outset. The duke, a protector and patron of the house, whose conservative faction had by then regained the initiative at Court, evidently lent his support. But the campaign dragged on, necessitating 'gret labour, diligence, sute and means', as well as considerable expenditure over the next two years.[61] Augustine Steward, the alderman most closely involved in these negotiations, exerted his influence as MP for Norwich to push matters along, carefully cultivating Thomas Cromwell on the way for additional insurance [see Plate 38].[62] Finally, on 1 June 1540, a mere ten days before the latter's dramatic and unexpected fall from power, royal letters patent were issued confirming the sale of Blackfriars to the city for £81, although Henry VIII later demanded an additional payment of £152 to cover the value of the lead on the convent roof.[63]

The corporation intended to put the friary to immediate practical use through the construction of a 'fayer and large halle' for common assemblies. Its riverside location made it an ideal storage place for the supplies of grain bought 'for the ease of the poore inhabytans of the cyte' in large quantities during the famine years of the 1540s.[64] Plans to employ some of the buildings as a commercial centre were also mooted, but the need for facilities to house a 'perpetual free-scole . . . for the good erudicion and education of yought in lerning and vertue' seemed especially urgent. Despite the dilapidated state of the buildings, which ate even further into the city's revenues, boys from what had previously been the episcopal school were taught there for a few years in the early 1540s until better facilities could be found.[65] This early exercise in civic lobbying at Westminster provided the corporation with valuable experience when it came to the far longer and costlier negotiations over the fate of St Giles's hospital. The attendant debates about the use of Blackfriars also served to focus the minds of the aldermen and councillors on the dual issues of education and poor relief, which, from the time of Walter Suffield, had been so closely connected. Indeed, as we have seen, almost 300 years after its foundation the hospital was still maintaining seven grammar school boys in accordance with the bishop's wishes.[66]

Rendered temporarily homeless by the fires of 1507, the scholars had, however, long since vacated their premises on the riverbank to the west of the hospital precinct. Having taken possession of the site at about this time, the master and brethren leased first one half of the ruined school house and then the other to their neighbour, Sir Philip Calthorpe, whose Norwich residence abutted on the school yard. The damage may have been so extensive as to preclude the cost of rebuilding. By 1516 the boys appear to have received their tuition along with pupils from the almonry school in the cathedral, a convenient arrangement from the hospital's standpoint, but one which must have irritated the more zealous evangelicals among the ruling elite, as well as others who had been caught up in the city's long-standing dispute with the monks over their exempt liberties.[67] There was, however, no immediate prospect of a return to the Holme Street site, all of which lay in Calthorpe's hands by 1524. In June 1536, when the hospital's future already hung in the balance, Sir Philip's widow seized the opportunity to secure from Robert Codde a further lease of 'all [the] yerd or clos called the scolehous yerd, with the hous therin standyng', for a definitive period of ninety-nine years.[68]

The purchase of Blackfriars, in part necessitated by the search for more suitable accommodation for the schoolboys, was completed at a time of mounting uncertainty so far as St Giles's was concerned. At some point between 1538 and 1540, Robert Codde and his three remaining chaplains made a formal surrender of the hospital to King Henry, responding with understandable alacrity the moment they received written instructions from Thomas Cromwell.[69] During this period (which saw the fall of the last surviving monasteries) many of the larger urban hospitals, including St Leonard's, York, St Mark's, Bristol, and the London houses of St Mary's, Bishopsgate, and St Thomas Acon, also passed into royal hands.[70] Senior staff could be bought off with fat pensions, and compliant placemen jobbed in to attest the necessary documents, smoothing the way for confiscation and dismemberment.[71] Cases of intimidation by crown agents and courtiers anxious for a share of the spoils must also have been common. Bearing in mind Codde's own links with reformers at Court and in the city, the possibility of bribery or coercion in this instance seems less likely. Although it is by no means certain that he and his friends on the corporation had already formulated a coherent strategy so far as schemes for the use of ecclesiastical property were concerned, the possibility of turning St Giles's into a poor house and free school to be maintained under civic management, along with the Blackfriars, must already have attracted interest. But would the Crown agree?

The absence of anything approaching a clear-cut government policy with regard to either the acquisition or ultimate fate of hospitals like St Giles's reflects the short-term expediency characteristic of the Dissolution as a whole. Asset stripping and opportunism flourished. A petition addressed to King Henry by the mayor of London, Sir Richard Gresham, in 1537–8, 'for the ayde and comforte of the poore, sykke, blynde, aged and impotent persones, beyng not hable to helpe theymselffs nor havyng any place certeyn wheryn they may be lodged cherysshed and refresshed tyll they be cured and holpen' presented an eloquent case for the transfer of three hospitals and a monastery into the city's hands. In phrases reminiscent of continental programmes for civic improvement discussed at the start of the next chapter, the mayor warned of the health hazard posed by 'myserable people lyeng in the streete, offendyng every clene person passyng by the way with theyre fylthye and nasty savors'; he stressed the important role to be played by a salaried medical and surgical staff in putting the poor to work; and, predictably, promised firm action against 'sturdy beggars'.[72] Yet all to no avail. Royal favourites such as Sir Richard Long and Sir Richard Rich, who secured two of the hospitals in question for redevelopment, had a prior claim upon the King's bounty.[73]

The rapacity of Henry's courtiers notwithstanding, an *ad hoc*, uncoordinated approach to the question of hospitals could hardly be avoided. It was impossible to categorise institutions which differed so widely in terms of status, resources and function. Since, moreover, as reformers constantly complained, many hospitals had long ceased to perform any significant eleemosynary role, there seemed little to distinguish them from other houses of religion and no good reason to arrest the 'creeping process' of piecemeal dissolution and dismemberment.[74] On the other hand, the need for an alternative system to replace institutions which, like St Giles's, *had* shown continuing concern for the welfare and education of the poor, in schools, almshouses, infirmaries and soup kitchens, was already apparent far beyond London. Many positive opportunities had arisen for creating a new, more efficient and integrated system of relief. While agreeing, retrospectively, to legalise the surrender of ecclesiastical property, including hospitals, into royal hands, the Parliament of 1539 recommended that a wide-ranging programme of social reconstruction be undertaken in conjunction with royal plans for the creation of an unspecified number of new bishoprics. The preamble to the ensuing Act, drafted by King Henry himself, has been seen as a cynical attempt to reassure the House of Commons with empty promises of reform:

> To th'entent that from hensforthe . . . God's worde myght the better be setforth, childern brought upp in lerning, clerkes norished in the universyties, olde servauntes decayed to have lyvynges, almeshouses for poore folke to be systeyned in, reders of Grece, Ebrewe and Laten to have good stipend, daylie almes to be ministred . . .[75]

Irrespective of his motives, most of Henry's proposals remained a pious hope. Even on paper, schemes mooted over the next three years for the support of almsmen and free grammar schools in as many as fifteen or twenty newly constituted cathedral chapters did little more than tinker with a growing social problem. After further cuts and revisions, the measures which finally earned royal approval would have offered permanent places to only 124 almsmen throughout the entire country, and did nothing to help the truly destitute.[76]

It soon became apparent that local rather than national initiatives would determine whatever provision, if any, England's new cathedrals might make for the sick poor. Being an earlier refoundation, Norwich cathedral was not allocated a quota of royal almsmen in the early 1540s, although it appears to have supported about half a dozen.[77] In addition, however, the chapter continued to maintain the old monastic hospital of St Paul, which escaped dissolution to serve as a temporary refuge for a handful of 'pore straungers, vagrantes [and] syck and impotent persons'. It was acquired by the city in 1565 and duly converted into one of England's earliest Bridewells, or workhouses, for the correction of 'idle and lusty beggars'.[78] Closer in function to the role originally planned for it by Bishop Everard than it had been for almost two centuries, the hospital was run during this interim period by one of the former sisters, Dame Agnes Lyon, and attracted considerable support from the citizens of Norwich. At least seventeen Norwich wills proved between 1550 and 1571 contain bequests to the 'armesse-house' or 'poore-house' of St Paul, with its 'pore mennys beddys' and their sick, paralytic occupants.[79] In monetary terms some of these legacies were extremely generous, yet the hospital was never more than a stopgap. Almost invariably dependent upon subventions from the cathedral priory, it had faced a steady and irreversible decline in net annual income from £72 in 1363 to approximately one-third of this sum in the early 1530s.[80] No formal proposals were made by either the chapter or the corporation to increase the endowment or otherwise set it on a more stable financial footing, probably because St Giles's presented a better alternative. Not only were its revenues far greater and its buildings ripe for conversion; the house could, with careful planning, be brought under the direct and undivided rule of the civic elite.

It is important to remember at this point that the corporation already exercised authority over the five leper houses strategically situated at gates to the south, west and north of the city [see Map I]. That at least some of these small and poorly endowed institutions still received lepers in the later fifteenth century is clear from a variety of sources, including injunctions of 1473 concerning the sale of food to their inmates in the open market.[81] The gradual decline of leprosy meant, however, that places became available for men and women suffering from other diseases or disabilities, such as the pox, which inspired even greater revulsion.[82] Wills of the period *c.* 1450 to 1532 refer indiscriminately to the 'lazars', 'lepyrs' and 'sykemen' of these institutions, as well as to children, which suggests that poor pregnant women and orphans may occasionally have been housed there too.[83] Although lepers and other individuals with disfiguring diseases were generally permitted to solicit alms in the immediate vicinity of their dwellings, they would often appoint healthy proctors or 'foregoers' to beg further afield on their behalf. As late as 1529, the brothers and sisters of the hospital of SS Mary and Clement, which lay outside St Augustine's gates, chose one Thomas Parys to be their 'true and authorised proctor' to raise funds throughout

England on behalf of the 'infirm and lepers' in their house. Like most *leprosaria*, this hospital was almost totally dependent upon public charity and thus open to exploitation by its new proctor, who was required to submit four accounts every year and take immediate legal action against all impostors.[84]

The civic authorities were no less anxious to eliminate abuses. They had, from the outset, done their best to implement national poor law enactments of 1531 and 1536, which sought to distinguish between idle and impotent paupers through the licensing of beggars and the introduction of measures for the provision of relief by local communities. From their point of view, it was necessary to ensure that hospital places and licenses to beg in Norwich went only to the most deserving and reputable cases. For this reason the freedom of the masters or keepers of the five leper houses to grant permits under their own seals had to be carefully regulated, in accordance with the corporation's strict policy on mendicancy. Nor were other shortcomings tolerated. In August 1541 the mayor's court learned how 'oon Creyforth', master of the leper house at St Giles's gates, employed six proctors, charging each 8*s* 6*d* a year for their licences. It was alleged that 'he usith to gett pour lame and diseased personz, promysyng them to fynd [support] them, and, when he hath them, then he compellith them to begge for a lyuyng or elles they shall haue nothing . . .'.[85] Matters were far worse at the 'sykehouse' near St Stephen's gates, where only one of the seven proctors, who were paid 20*s* a year to beg by the master, appeared incapable of work. The others included 'a talle man and clene and not diseased, abill to bere the kinge's standerd', and an adolescent of about sixteen. A similar state of affairs also came to light at the Westwick sickhouse.[86] As a result, two of the masters were immediately bound over under heavy securities to behave better in future, and all five were instructed to surrender to the court every licence they had previously issued, along with the seals used for authentication.

By the early 1540s, then, the city was anxious to reform its *leprosaria* by integrating them more fully into a general system for charitable relief. This, in turn, meant maximising the number of places available for the sick poor and preventing further abuses by those in authority.[87] It is now impossible to tell how many patients these extra mural hospitals could accommodate at any one time, but the corporation is unlikely to have seen them as a viable alternative to a more centralised and larger institution for the elderly and impotent. Rather, they offered convenient places for the reception and segregation of 'the incurable, the infectious and the scandalous', who posed too great a moral or physical threat to be accepted as the inmates of a conventional poor house.[88] Patients of this kind were hardly more welcome in the new-style urban hospitals than they had been in their medieval precursors, largely because they were difficult to nurse, disconcerting to other patients and unlikely to recover. But the civic authorities had still to find a home for aged, chronically sick and decrepit paupers. The argument in favour of purchasing or otherwise negotiating a lease of St Giles's was thus overwhelming, as also was the need to move quickly before it was diverted to some other use.

Whereas some of the hospitals which surrendered voluntarily to the Crown during the years before 1545 disappeared almost at once, others were left to soldier on, albeit under threat of imminent closure. St Leonard's, York, lasted for about two years after the King's agents took over, in 1539, the initial intention apparently being to replace the Augustinian canons and keep the infirmary open. But nothing came of these plans. By 1541 the number of 'blind, lame, bedridden and very old bodies' had already fallen from sixty to forty-four, since it seemed inadvisable to admit new ones.[89] The prospects for St Giles's appear to have been rather more hopeful. For a start, the house retained complete control of its estates after Codde dispatched the formal deed of surrender to Cromwell in London. Along with the chaplains, he was party, as master, to a number of conveyances made between 1538 and 1544 with local landowners and citizens of Norwich, including his own brother.[90] Alderman Thomas Codde's lease for twenty-one years of all the hospital's property at Gildencroft and the Lathes, along with over 53 acres of farmland just outside the city, was made in October 1544 on unusually favourable terms. In marked contrast to their customary policy, the brethren of St Giles's undertook to erect 'at their owne propre costes and charges' a barn large enough to store 'all suche corne and grasse as shall growe in and upon the premysses' and to maintain all the other buildings as well.[91]

Perhaps Codde was anxious to exploit his connection with the house before it was too late, as he also took on the farm of hospital property in Wroxham during this period. He was not alone in turning uncertainty about the future to his own advantage: other notable local figures, such as Augustine Steward, Alexander Mather, Robert Rugge and William Rogers (each of whom was destined to play a significant part in the hospital's later history), followed his example.[92] Throughout England laymen and clergy alike hoped to salvage something from the coming wreckage. In about 1542, for instance, the master of St John's hospital, Nottingham, had replaced lead roofing worth almost £10 with cheaper, inferior slate, pocketing the profits.[93] This state of affairs grew worse as private patrons attempted to recover property which had once belonged to their ancestors and speculators moved in for the kill. Notwithstanding their close links with the rulers of Norwich, Robert Codde and the two chaplains who continued to serve at St Giles's experienced their share of 'dewlyshe and detestable crwelte' at the hands of one Robert Wace, whom they accused of using 'unlawfull and crafty practyse to lete and hynder the celebracion of . . . devyne servyce and deades of chartye' through vexatious litigation. Their claims to have been too old and ill to appear in court when summoned, and to have been subjected to wrongful imprisonment as a result were almost certainly exaggerated, but, like the Norwich Dominicans, their fear of intimidation was almost certainly justified.[94]

Many hospitals and chantries which had not jumped the gun by handing over their possessions to the Crown were now falling prey to predatory individuals or public bodies with a vested interest in their material assets. Alarmed at the threat to a valuable and hitherto neglected resource, the government introduced retrospective legislation in 1545 annulling all such confiscations, and seizing into its own hands any remaining 'chauntryes, colleges, hospitalles and other places' liable to pay first fruits and tithes to the King. The first Chantry Act laid great stress upon Henry's desire for reform, 'to th'entent that almes to the poore people and other good, vertuouse and charitable deedes mought be made and done', but it still had a rough passage through Parliament.[95] Henry himself appeared in the Lords to address his subjects on the corrosive effects of avarice upon the body politic; but his own desperate need for money remained transparent.[96] The royal commissioners who set out early in 1546 to survey the institutions in question expressed no particular interest in the charitable relief they still performed, nor, significantly, did the new legislative programme address any doctrinal issues concerning the value of intercessionary prayer. Crude material gain was the overwhelming motive

As J.J. Scarisbrick has argued, local communities were not only thus obliged to take the initiative in order to win back or retain their schools and hospitals; they often had to fight hard and pay handsomely into the bargain.[97] The tortuous processes involved can rarely be described at length, but the survival of minute books and accounts recording the deliberations and expenses of the rulers of Norwich at this time makes it possible to document in uniquely vivid detail their struggle to acquire St Giles's. This began in earnest during the aftermath of a serious outbreak of plague, during which the mortality rate appears to have more than trebled. As usual, the poor bore the brunt of the epidemic. Food shortages were so acute that in September 1544 the authorities took the then still unusual step of spending £86 on 300 combs of grain for resale at subsidised rates to 'the poore inhabytans of the cyte'. An influx of famished vagrants from the surrounding countryside prompted the predictable reaction against outsiders, whose presence not only seemed to threaten economic and social order, but also to breed conditions ('much people in a small room living uncleanly and sluttishly') likely to generate the poisonous miasmas of disease.[98] Six months later, the mayor's court ordered each alderman and his constables to ascertain 'what pore pepill goo aboute and begge in ther warde and how long thei haue duellid in the citie and whose tenauntes thei be'.[99] Along with the problem of clearing unwholesome and potentially dangerous paupers off the streets, went the need to provide accommodation for elderly and disabled residents whose relatives (if they survived) could no longer support them. Under such circumstances, the lack of adequate hospital provision and the fear that what little remained might soon be lost must have caused widespread anxiety. Shades of the medieval belief in almsdeeds as a means of assuaging divine wrath also lingered on. The ointment of charity would surely relieve the sores of the body politic, placating God and improving the spiritual health of the nation. So Christian humanists taught, and so many Norwich aldermen undoubtedly believed.[100]

The arrival of King Henry's commissioners early in 1546, and the very real possibility that the site and buildings of St Giles's hospital might be sold for speculative development, galvanised the authorities into action. Technically speaking, since the hospital had already surrendered to the Crown, it lay outside the remit of the Chantry Act. But would it survive intact for much longer? On 13 February 1546, William Rogers, a former mayor and MP for Norwich, submitted a motion to the mayor's court that the civic authorities should make formal suit to King Henry for control of St Giles's, 'expressing what releff pore people have daily there'.[101] Despite his uncompromising rejection of any belief in the efficacy of good works as a means to salvation, Rogers was a noted philanthropist with a commitment to schemes for the regeneration of civic trade and industry. His voice carried considerable authority, not least because he was a popular figure in the mercantile community.[102] About six weeks later, on 24 March, 'a certen peticon', drawn up by the city's legal counsel 'was redde openly and distynctly' to the court, it being agreed that one copy should be sent forthwith to the King while another remained in the safekeeping of the chamberlain.[103]

16. The south-west corner of the cloisters at St Giles's would have found little favour with late medieval critics of the established church, who complained bitterly about the waste of resources spent on 'heye chyrchis'. On the west side of the cloister stands the refectory (built in the 1450s), and on the south the new infirmary, completed at the close of the fourteenth century, when the great bell tower, just visible over the roof, was added through the patronage of Archdeacon Derlyngton. The clerestory ran along the full length of the nave as well as the infirmary, giving the whole building a pleasing symmetry and sense of spatial cohesion. (Photograph Royal Commission on Historical Monuments)

17. The seal of St Giles's hospital, used to authenticate official documents, depicts an incident from one of the most famous legends concerning the patron saint. Having given away all his goods to the poor, Giles lived for many years as a hermit and was fed each day on the milk of a hind. One day the saint was accidentally shot when the animal fled from a hunting party, and an abbey was built for him in recompense by his assailants. The inscription reads 'the seal of the master and brothers of St Giles's of Norwich', and the mitre surmounting a cross at the base advertises the house's strong episcopal connections. (BL, Department of Manuscripts, D.C.F. xxxix)

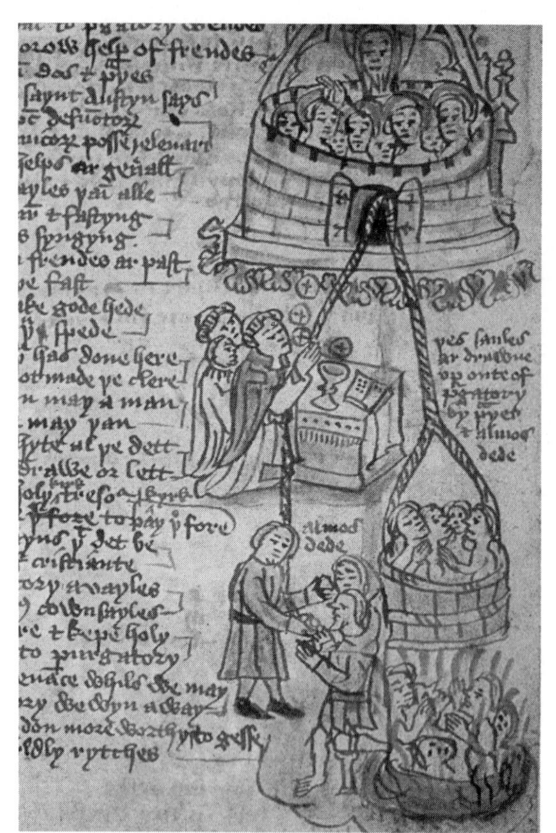

18. Masses, prayers and almsgiving help, quite literally, to winch tormented souls out of purgatory, where they are being cleansed of sin by fire, upwards towards the celestial city. A hospital such as St Giles's, which combined the performance of the Seven Comfortable Works with an increasingly elaborate provision of suffrages for the dead, was thus especially well placed to attract the patronage of men and women whose fear of sudden death, without the benefits of confession and absolution, was heightened by repeated plague epidemics. (BL, Department of Manuscripts, Add. Ms 37,049, fo 22v)

19. The 'dongon', later known as the Cow Tower, stood at the north-eastern extremity of the hospital precinct, on a bend in the River Wensum, and is said once to have belonged to the prior of Norwich. The brethren of St Giles's disposed of it, along with a narrow stretch of the river bank, to the city in about 1378, thus ridding themselves of any financial responsibility for the upkeep of a crucial link in the city's defences. It cost the corporation over £84 to repair in the 1390s, but was manifestly no deterrent to Kett's rebels, who crossed the river near this point with comparative ease in 1549, despite the battery of guns in the hospital meadow. (Photograph Richard Tilbrook)

20. Travelling down Holme Street from Bishop's Bridge towards the cathedral, the early nineteenth-century visitor would have been struck, like his medieval predecessor, by the hospital's impressive walls, gatehouse and porch. Security was a major issue in the Middle Ages, for spiritual as well as practical reasons, since it was vital to preserve the sanctity of a building dedicated to spiritual healing. The proximity of St Helen's church, which until its demolition in about 1270 stood just across the road from the hospital inside the walled precinct of the cathedral, explains why friction occurred over parochial rights. Henceforward the parishioners of St Helen's worshipped in the nave of the hospital church, to which the porch to the right of this picture gave immediate access. (Trustees of the Great Hospital)

21. Still used for grazing in the early nineteenth century, as this watercolour shows, the hospital meadows continued to support livestock long after the Middle Ages. Then many of the beasts would have been slaughtered on the premises for immediate consumption. This view from the north bank of the River Wensum shows the Cow Tower, and, on the far right, the 'creek' which led due south towards the bakery and other service quarters from at least 1300. The hospital maintained an elaborate drainage system, essential on such a marshy site, prone to flooding. The proximity of the cathedral, with its tall spire, is striking. (Trustees of the Great Hospital, with permission from Ms Brigid Land)

22. The refectory or hall at St Giles's was completed in the mid-fifteenth century, the windows on the left of the picture, which overlook the cloister (east), being glazed in 1457. The windows to the right gave a view of the outer courtyard of the hospital (west), although visitors were obliged to enter via the cloisters, the master's quarters (north) or the infirmary (south), which lay on the other side of the wall here facing the viewer. The small doorway on the right of the post-Dissolution fireplace marks what was once a larger entrance to the infirmary through which food from the hall and kitchens (north) could be served to travellers, non-resident almsmen and others of lowly status. This spacious building, with its imposing king-posts and tie beams, provided an appropriate setting for masters such as John Selot (1455–79) to entertain the influential guests from city and diocese upon whose support they depended. (Photograph Royal Commission on Historical Monuments)

23. Bricked up after the Dissolution, the entrance to the hospital's late medieval chapter house on the east side of the cloister once provided an impressive testimony to the combined power of spiritual and temporal patronage. The carving in the centre probably depicted St Giles in his abbatial robes, while the arms of John Molet, prior of the Norwich Benedictines (1453–71) appear on the left and of Bishop Walter Lyhart (1446–72) on the right. The two men almost certainly contributed towards the cost of building the cloisters, Lyhart, in particular, being an influential fugure at the Court of Henry VI and an intimate of John Selot, the hospital's most authoritative medieval master [see also Plates 30 and 32]. (Photograph Royal Commission on Historical Monuments)

24. The half-ruined medieval tower is all that remains of the free chapel at Bastwick, which was appropriated to St Giles's, along with the nearby rectory of St Peter's, Repps, in 1261. Although it was potentially the richest of the hospital's many holdings in rural Norfolk, this Broadland estate suffered badly from flooding as well as the other manifold economic problems experienced by landowners in the region from the early fourteenth century onwards. As a result revenues slumped, and by the 1520s the hospital was engaged in a bitter and expensive legal battle with parishioners over the payment of tithes. (Photograph Carole Rawcliffe)

25. Part of the original endowment settled upon St Giles's by Bishop Walter Suffield, the appropriated living of St Mary's South Walsham also lay on the rich alluvial soils of Broadland, and should have made a notable contribution to the hospital's granaries as well as its coffers. But profits fell here, too, financial difficulties being aggravated by the hostility of the neighbouring Benedictines at St Benet's abbey. Another problem lay in the cost to the hospital of maintaining its parish churches, which, as this picture shows, required a substantial capital outlay and proved a constant drain on resources. (Photograph Carole Rawcliffe)

26. The south front of St Giles's hospital seen from what, before 1270, would have been the approximate site of St Helen's church in the cathedral precinct. From east to west are: the medieval chancel (constructed in the 1380s and walled off as a ward for poor women in c. 1570); Bishop Goldwell's late fifteenth-century chantry chapel in the south transept of the medieval nave (which was largely rebuilt at the same time as the chancel, and from c. 1547 onwards served as a parish church); the porch, which was surmounted in the Middle Ages by another chantry chapel; the late fourteenth-century infirmary, which lost an aisle in Kett's rebellion and later became a separate ward for poor men; and Archdeacon Derlyngton's bell•tower, completed in 1397, at the end of this ambitious architectural programme. The three chimneys were added in the late sixteenth century, when fireplaces were constructed in the men's and women's wards. (Photograph Royal Commission on Historical Monuments)

27. The chancel of St Giles's was executed in a decorated perpendicular style then comparatively new to the region. The architect may well have been the royal mason, John Wodhirst, who had previously worked at Westminster abbey. The project certainly marked an investment in artistic patronage at the highest level, its initial impact being now hard to imagine after the iconoclasm and structural changes of the mid-sixteenth century. The window furthest to the west, shaded by trees, had been made narrower than the others to permit the insertion of stairs leading to the top of the rood screen. It was here that a stone partition was inserted in c. 1570 completely to separate the chancel from what had been the medieval nave and now became the hospital church. The chancel was also divided horizontally into two storeys at this time to create more room for the paupers. But for the damage caused by Kett's rebellion, however, it (or a new building on the same site) would have housed the grammar school which figured so prominently in the 1547 statutes of the refounded hospital. (Photograph Royal Commission on Historical Monuments)

28. After some debate, the rulers of Norwich opted in May 1549 to retain the ceiling of the chancel, having removed the stained glass, choir stalls, organs, vestments, plate and service books. Some sense of the splendour of the original building thus remains, and of the fine acoustic, so necessary for the elaborate liturgical ceremonies which late medieval patrons demanded. By the close of the fifteenth century, the hospital possessed at least two organs and impressive musical resources, one of the choir masters having trained at St George's chapel, Windsor. (Photograph Royal Commission on Historical Monuments)

29. Decorated initials embellish the chant for St Stephen's day (26 December) in the hospital's fourteenth-century processional. In accordance with the Salisbury Use, the rubric below instructs the priest to cense the altar dedicated to the Apostles and then the image of St John the Evangelist. There is no evidence to suggest that St Giles's had such an altar or image, although it housed a profusion of side altars dedicated to, among others, Saints Nicholas, Anne, Katherine, Helen and Mary the Virgin. (BL, Department of Manuscripts, Add. Ms 57,534, fo 13v)

30. Lest they be in any doubt as to the identity of their benefactors, the staff, patients and parishioners of medieval hospitals and almshouses (such as Ewelme, in Oxfordshire) were surrounded by visual reminders. At St Giles's the restructured nave of the hospital church was divided into three bays by clustered columns, on which the heraldic trappings of wealthy patrons were displayed. Prominent among these were the arms of Bishop Goldwell, to whom the hospital owed so much [see Plate 15]. The nave also contained side altars, whose images, frontals and plate would have provided further colour, as would the decorated wall hangings and stained glass. (Photograph Richard Tilbrook)

31. Thanks to the generosity of Archdeacon John Derlyngton, a former master (1372–6), the hospital was able to construct its massive bell tower at the close of the fourteenth century. Costing almost £100, it proclaimed the political as well as the spiritual authority of the hospital, and underscores the important role played by St Giles's in the struggle to impose and foster religious orthodoxy. Four large bells were tolled during the funerals and memorial services of benefactors, despatching their souls on a speedy journey through purgatory. On the left of the tower stood the infirmary, its great west window, originally in the perpendicular style with stained glass, having been restructured with mullions during the late sixteenth century. (Photograph Royal Commission on Historical Monuments)

32. Surprisingly, in view of their close proximity, relations between the staff of St Giles's and their powerful neighbours, the Norwich Benedictines, remained fairly amicable for most of the later Middle Ages. Once the dispute over parochial jurisdictions had been settled, in 1270, only minor disagreements caused irritation. Successive priors retained an interest in the affairs of the hospital, some, such as John Molet, whose arms were displayed in both nave and chapter house [see Plate 23], being recognised as important patrons, alongside the bishops of Norwich. (Photograph Royal Commission on Historical Monuments)

33 and 34. Several of the late medieval masters of St Giles's contributed handsomely towards the upkeep and improvement of the fabric. John Hecker (1519–32) commissioned a finely carved set of bench ends for the nave, one of which, now lost, showed him kneeling in prayer. The initials 'HEC' beneath St Margaret and her adversary (left), the dragon, recall his generosity. Since the parishioners of Holme Street worshipped in the nave, the appearance of St Margaret, patron saint of women in childbirth, was especially fitting. Her cult flourished among the East Anglian laity, and she also appears on one of the bosses in Goldwell's chantry [see Plate 15]. Hecker's other bench ends included depictions of the symbols of the four Evangelists. The angel of St Matthew (right), bearing the scroll containing his gospel, is especially striking for the elegance and immediacy of its execution. Benches not only helped to enforce discipline among the congregation, but made it easier for listeners to concentrate on sermons and increasingly complex liturgical ceremonies with long musical interludes. The nave at St Giles's may have had pews from the late fourteenth century; the chancel certainly possessed elaborate choir stalls, which were dismantled at the reformation. (Photographs Carole Rawcliffe)

35. St Giles's was not the only episcopal foundation in medieval Norwich to provide a lavish setting for the commemoration of the Christian departed. The Carnary Chapel, founded as a chantry in 1316 by Bishop Salmon, lay a few yards to the west of the cathedral, and may well have provided the inspiration for the rebuilding of St Giles's at the end of the century, as it, too, had been designed by a royal architect. Appropriately, under the circumstances, it became the home of the new post-Dissolution grammar school, which would almost certainly have been situated in the hospital precinct had the infirmary not been partially destroyed in 1549. (Photograph Carole Rawcliffe)

36. That the late medieval infirmary had two storeys from the outset is apparent from the position of this window half way up the east-facing wall of its south aisle, allowing a clear view of the nave and a glimpse of the chancel beyond. A similar window, in the wall of the north aisle, was removed when the central aisle, which had hitherto opened directly into the nave, was closed off after the Dissolution. Once the damage inflicted by Kett's rebels on the south side of the infirmary had been made good, by 1585, the two storeys were occupied by male paupers. (Photograph Royal Commission on Historical Monuments)

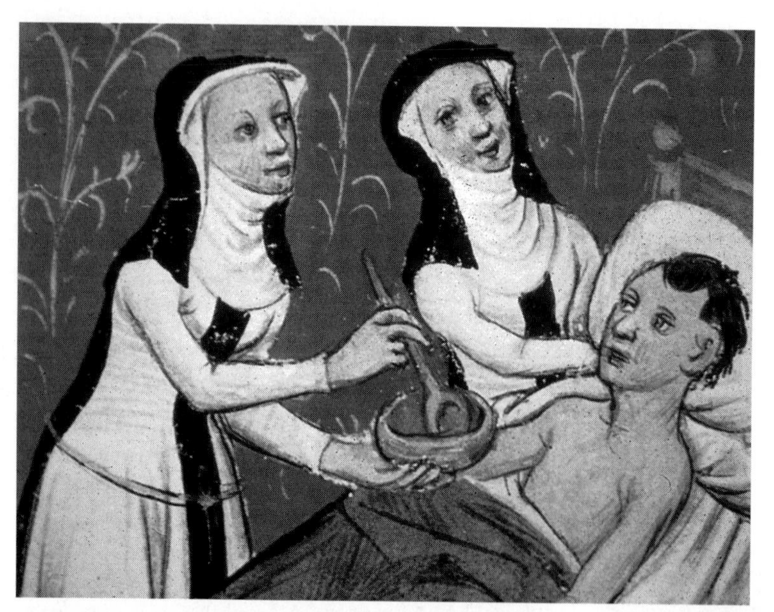

37. Notwithstanding the emphasis on their spiritual health, patients at St Giles's enjoyed a relatively high standard of physical care and a nourishing, if basic, diet. As in so many other medieval European hospitals, emphasis was placed on cleanliness and treating the sick poor with compassion. Kindliness and a cheerful disposition were deemed essential qualities in a nurse, along with sexual continence, to be maintained through strict segregation. As a further precaution at St Giles's, Bishop Suffield insisted that the four sisters should be not much younger than fifty. (Archives of the Hospital of Notre Dame, Tournai, foundation charter of 1238)

38. Augustine Steward (d. 1570) was one of the most influential figures of mid-sixteenth century Norwich, his authority on the aldermanic bench and in Parliament being greatly strengthened by connections at the Court of Henry VIII. He helped to mastermind the acquisition of both Blackfriars and St Giles's hospital after their confiscation by the Crown, and proved a notable benefactor of the hospital during its difficult early years as a poor house. A keen advocate of schemes for the moral and practical improvement of the city, he put into practice the humanist agenda for civic renewal then fashionable in royal circles. (Norfolk Museums Service, Castle Museum, Norwich)

39. Peter Rede (d. 1568) was related by marriage to Augustine Steward, being himself the son of Edward Rede, who served three times as mayor of Norwich and also represented the city in Parliament during the Reformation period. Although he never sought high civic office, Peter had a no less eventful a career, during which he saw action at the siege of Tunis, and was knighted by the Emperor Charles V. Like so many parvenu *gentlemen on the make, Rede was anxious to exploit the opportunities for self-enrichment created by the volatile political situation, and leased hospital properties on highly advantageous terms. (Norfolk Museums Service, Castle Museum, Norwich)*

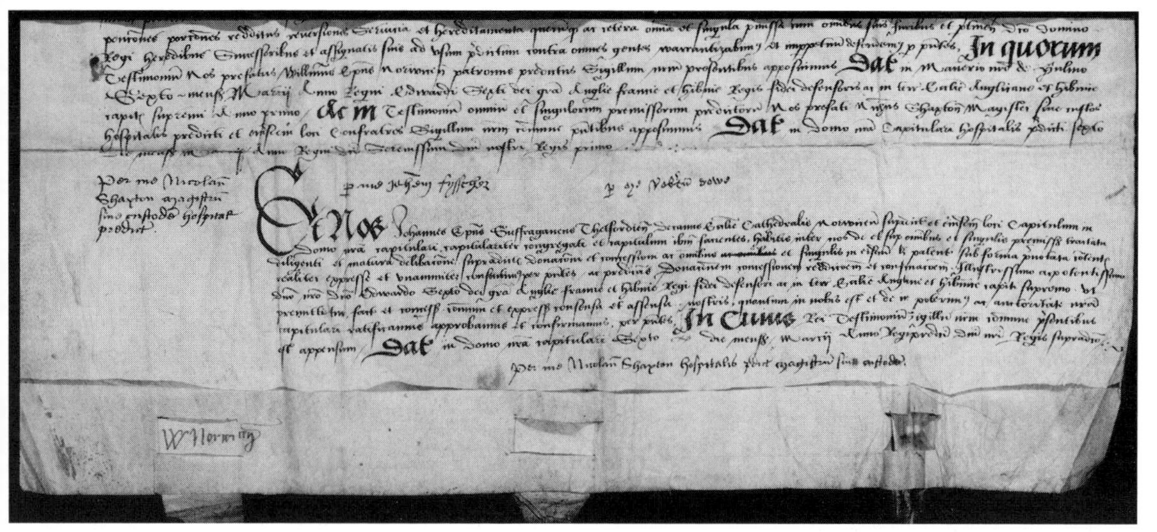

40. The formal deed of surrender, dated 6 March 1547, signed and sealed in the chapter house of St Giles's hospital by the new master, Nicholas Shaxton, formerly Bishop of Salisbury, and the two remaining brothers, John Fysher and Robert Dowe. Fysher, who later assumed office as master, was retained at this time as the hospital's sole priest (a dramatic reduction in numbers from the fifteenth century), while Dowe acted as its visitor at the guildhall prison. Both men gave dedicated service to the hospital, Fysher being especially committed to the new protestant agenda. (PRO, E322/178)

41. The high quality workmanship still apparent in the medieval fabric of St Giles's should remind us that the larger English hospitals were centres of artistic excellence and significant employers of leading craftsmen. This boss from Bishop Goldwell's chantry chapel [see Plate 15] merits comparison with others executed at roughly the same time for the nave and cloisters of Norwich cathedral; the hospital clearly drew upon the same pool of master masons. It depicts the Ascension, being part of a cycle illustrating incidents from the life of Christ. His feet are still visible as He ascends through the intricately carved fan vaulting of heaven, leaving his disciples in a state of consternation below. (Photograph Carole Rawcliffe)

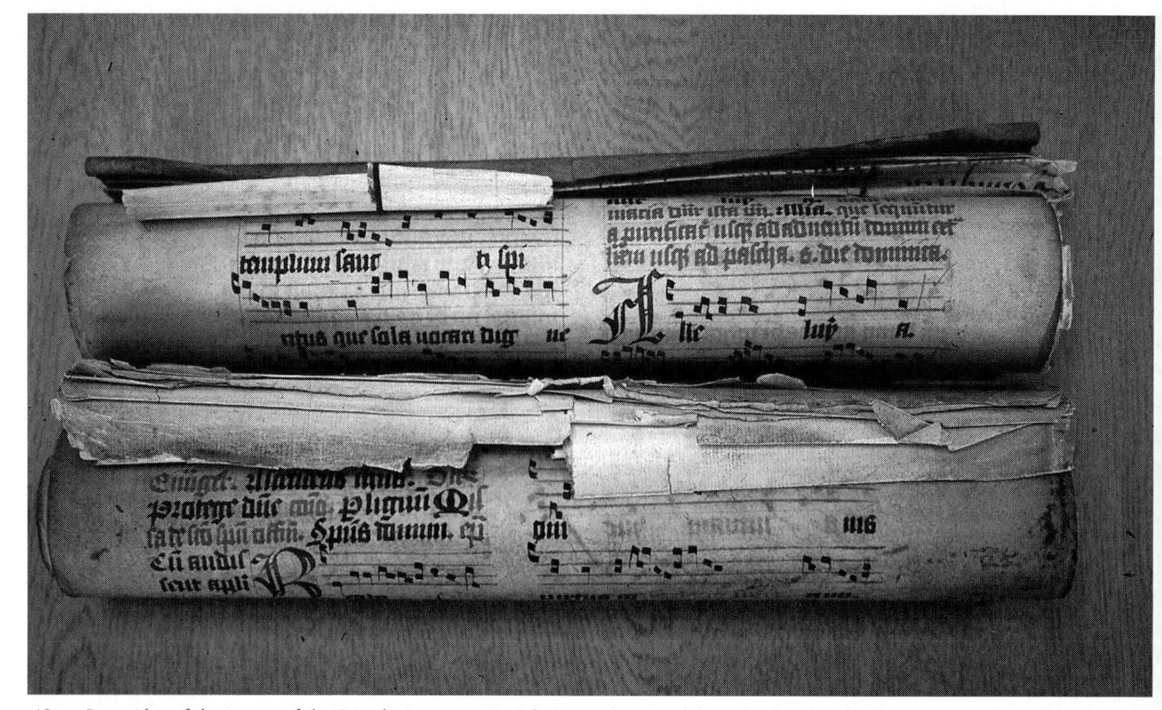

42. *Some idea of the impact of the Dissolution upon St Giles's may be gained from the fact that the first accounts prepared by the new keepers (in English rather than Latin to assist comprehension on the part of a lay readership) were wrapped in pages torn from medieval service books. Paper accounts for 1548–9 and 1550–1 are, for instance, bound in parchment leaves ripped from one of the hospital's fifteenth-century missals, recording the sequences for four votive masses, including one of the Blessed Virgin. (NRO, NCR, 24A, GH accounts, box 1548–56)*

43. *As Bishop Suffield had decreed in his foundation statutes, services at St Giles's routinely followed the Salisbury Use. On this page from the hospital missal appears notation for chants accompanying the Mass of the offices of the Cross (left) and of the Holy Ghost (right).*

44. The arrival at God's House of the master surgeon, John Porter, who was retained in 1547 at a substantial fee, marked one of many new departures in the post-Dissolution history of St Giles's. Following the recommendations of sixteenth-century reformers, the corporation of Norwich recognised that medical provision was essential if the sick poor were to remain productive members of society. Great emphasis was, however, still placed upon the moral worth of the patient and the benefits of exposure, through regular sermons, to the word of God. (Title page from Paracelsus, Opus Chirurgicum, *1565)*

45. A nineteenth-century sketch of the lower floor of what had once been the medieval infirmary, but which for the previous 250 years, at least, had provided permanent lodgings for a number of male paupers. Each inmate was assigned a private cubicle and obliged to wear a uniform. Care was still provided by nurses and discipline remained strict. During the years following the Dissolution the godly magistrates of Norwich were affronted by the rowdy and sometimes drunken behaviour of the poor in God's House, who preferred the alehouse to the preaching yard. (Trustees of the Great Hospital, Norwich)

46. The upper floor of what, before the Dissolution, had been the infirmary hall. The wall and chimney breast facing the viewer were erected in the late sixteenth century; previously the entire central archway of the east end had opened into the nave of the hospital church, as had the west end of the chancel. It was thus possible to see from one end of the main hospital building to the other. A lattice screen may well have provided a degree of privacy for the occupants, some of whom probably lived in partitioned cells, which were then becoming popular in the old style open-ward English hospitals. The infirmary was almost certainly divided into two storeys from the outset [see Plate 36], the floor of the upper ward being slightly lower than it now is. (Photograph Royal Commission on Historical Monuments)

Not a moment was lost. Over the weeks following Lady Day (25 March), the aldermen marshalled the considerable expertise at their disposal in order to safeguard their hospital once and for all. An entry in the Chamberlains' Account Book for the year ending 29 September 1546 shows how much effort was initially involved:

> Payd to yong Master [Richard] Catlyn the yonger ffor his paynes and counsell taken with the comyssioners sittyng upon the Acte ffor Colleges and Chauntryes, and drawyng a petycon to the Kynge's maiestie ffor the hospitall: xvjs. To Mr [John] Corbet ffor his labour, counsell and paynes in the seid sute and ffor drawyng a certifficat ffor the master of the hospitall: viijs. To Mr Catlynge's clerk ffor twyes writing the peticon wherof ones after Mr [John] Gosnold had corrected it: iijs vjd. To Mr Corbette's clerk ffor new writyng the certifficat after his master had drawn it: ijs. To Richard Framyngham ffor writing of ij copies of the peticon and ij copies of the certiffiecetes: ijs. Item: to Mr Gosnalle's clerk ffor a copy of the precepte and an other of the articles sent to the chirchewardens [of St Helen's]: ijs. To Mr [John] Godsalve's clerk ffor writing of the peticon in parchemyn and delyverd to Mr [Thomas] Cod: ijs. To Richard Framyngham ffor writing of certen copies as of the peticon, certifficate, value of the landes, instruccons and a letter to Sir Nicholas Hare, knight, which Mr Cod bere with hym to London ffor the same sute: xijd. To Mr Codde, alderman, ffor his costes and paynes rydyng to London in mid-Lent weke to make sute in the same: xxvjs viijd. And to hym the xiij daye of Auguste ffor his costes, laboure and paynes beyng at London in Ester terme xviij dayes and in Mighelmes terme x dayes at ijs the daye: liiijs. And in rewarde ffor his paynes vjs aboute the same sute. And to Thomas Mersham, alderman, ffor his costes in Auguste to London ffor the same mater and ffor certen rewardes that he gaff ther ffor the fforthryng of the sute theryn, as it appereth by a bill sygned with Mr Meyr's [the mayor's] hande: xlviijs vd. And paid to hym more ffor hys costes to London and ffrom thense to the Courte ffor the seid sute in the latter ende of Septembre, as appereth by a like bill signed as is afforeseid: lvijs vjd. *Summa*: xj li ixs jd [£11 9*s* 1*d*][104]

This was clearly a sustained exercise in political lobbying, which capitalised upon experience already gained in the suit for Blackfriars, as well as in the epic and recently successful campaign against the cathedral chapter for control over its exempt jurisdictions. A glance at the names of its counsel and spokesmen suggests that the corporation had good reason to expect a successful outcome, while nevertheless exploiting every means at its disposal. Although he was still relatively young, the lawyer, Richard Catlyn, had served as Member for Norwich in the previous Parliament, and was destined to rise to the top of his profession.[105] His colleague, John Corbet, another lawyer and former MP, was then sitting on the county bench, while also acting as steward of the court of the sheriff of Norwich.[106] As a new appointment to the court of aldermen, Thomas Marsham was sufficiently youthful and energetic to undertake some of the arduous business in London, armed with the skills he had acquired in the early 1540s as sheriff and auditor of Norwich.[107] But by far the heaviest burden fell upon Thomas Codde. Not surprisingly, given his close relationship with the master of St Giles's and his knowledge of its finances, he assumed personal responsibility for most of the detailed negotiations in London. After at least two preliminary visits, he was authorised by the mayor and aldermen on 12 May 1546 to 'attende upon the Kynge's maiestie and his highnes counsell . . . to ffolowe the sute begon for the hospitall'.[108]

As the payments listed above and other records kept by the mayor's court reveal, Codde and his fellow petitioners could rely on the goodwill of influential contacts at Westminster, who were assiduously cultivated. Without such vital support it was almost impossible to gain access to the King, or to proceed through the daunting network of bureaucracy erected by the officials of the Court of Augmentations, which managed the property and effects confiscated from dissolved religious houses. John Gosnold, solicitor of this court and *custos rotulorum* for Suffolk,[109] appears to have provided useful information through his clerk. The involvement of John Godsalve in the drafting of the original petition to King Henry must have been even more encouraging, since he was one of the royal commissioners appointed to survey chantries in Norfolk under the terms of the recent Act. More to the point, he was also the lessee of hospital property in Thorpe, near Norwich, so he had a more personal interest in the affairs of the house. Although his first return as MP for Norwich, in 1539, had been forced upon the city by Thomas Cromwell, he was chosen again, in a free election, four years later, possibly because of his powerful connections in London legal circles and his surprisingly close links with Cromwell's old enemy, the duke of Norfolk.[110] These he shared with the then master of the Court of Requests, Sir Nicholas Hare, a Suffolk lawyer, whom Codde first consulted in person early in 1546, when the corporation was planning its strategy. At the start of his career, in the 1530s, Hare had not only worked alongside John Corbet as counsel to the city of Norwich at Westminster, but had also held a series of legal appointments (including that of recorder) in Norwich itself.[111] Master Robert Codde's old friend, Sir Richard Southwell, was an intimate of Corbet's and, like him, another of Norfolk's clients. Although, as second general surveyor of the King's estates, he wielded considerable authority in his own right, his association with the leader of the then dominant conservative faction at Court made him an even more valuable ally. Some measure of the support he is likely to have given at this time to plans for the institutional relief of poverty in the city may be gained from his will of 1561, in which he left £120 to the poor of Norwich. The money was to be spent in annual instalments of £10, the first of which was to buy beds for the paupers in the newly acquired hospital.[112]

At some point before the early summer of 1546, King Henry had considered selling St Giles's hospital to Sir William Woodhouse, whose readiness to accommodate the mayor and aldermen seems surprising in light of the businesslike and unsentimental way in which he had enriched himself with the spoils of local monastic houses. A Norfolk gentleman by birth, Woodhouse played a prominent part in county politics, and had already achieved national celebrity as a naval commander. Using the influence which his successes at sea bestowed, he had built up a substantial estate by purchasing and leasing land from dissolved religious houses, including the two priories of Hickling and Ingham, Heringby college and the Yarmouth Blackfriars. He was, however, seriously ill at this time, and therefore perhaps more receptive than usual to the needs of the sick poor.[113] On 5 June, Thomas Codde appeared before the civic authorities to report, in buoyant mood, that he had

> made sute to Master Chaunceler of the [Court of] Augmentacon [Sir Edward North], Sir Richard Southwell, Sir Nicholas Hare and Sir William Wodehouse, knyght, ffor the opteyneng of the sute to the Kynge's maiestie ffor the hospitall . . . And that he hath obteyned ther goode willes; and that the said Sir William Wodehouse, who hath the preferment of the same of the Kinge's maiestie, iff it be sold, will make no sute therffor, nor hynder the seid citie if the Kynge's maiestie's pleasure be mynded to, and ffor, the said citie, savyng to hym his preferement iff it shall so stande with the Kynge's maiestie's plesure . . .[114]

Not everything went according to plan, for the health of the master of St Giles's soon became a cause for concern. Something of the emotional stress and physical exhaustion experienced by men such as Robert Codde as they fought to protect the institutions in their care is evident from records concerning the surrender of St Thomas's hospital, York. Frankly acknowledging the toll upon his health of the 'importune suttes, trobles and vexacions that he susteyned for the defence of the right of the said hospitall', the master, William Pinder, pronounced himself too 'sikely and aged' to continue the fight. His solution was to enlist the support of the mayor and corporation, who took over the management of the house in 1552, just as the rulers of Norwich had done at St Giles's.[115] Codde also appears to have buckled under the strain. He made his will on 9 August 1546, naming his influential younger brother as an executor, and died at some point over the next five or six weeks. It was, no doubt, because of Thomas Codde's impending bereavement that the mayor was authorised at the beginning of September to choose another suitable person to 'attende upon the sute begon for the hospitall' in London.[116] Arrangements concerning St Giles's had clearly not yet been finalised; and, despite Thomas's optimistic report to his colleagues, the royal assent was by no means a foregone conclusion. It is interesting to note that Robert Codde left 20*s* for the hospital priests to purchase black gowns and 6*s* 8*d* to 'syster Elyanor', one of the nurses who was evidently still in residence. His generous bequests to the poor of Norwich, which included supplies of wood for five years 'in the colde wynter', doles to 'bethred people' and the provision of a lifetime's support for a woman named Elizabeth Woodyard, did not, however, extend to the hospital, whose future had yet to be determined.[117] When Thomas drew up his own testament, twelve years later, he made good this omission by leaving rents and property in Norwich 'towardes the releif of the poore people within the said hospitall'. Elaborate arrangements for the celebration of an annual obit with *dirige* and requiem mass for the salvation of his late brother's soul confirm the impression that neither Thomas nor Robert had fully identified with the evangelical cause, a view shared by one local artisan, who, in 1549, reviled the mayor-elect for being 'a popish knave'. Queen Elizabeth's accession put paid to any plans he and his co-religionists may have harboured for a return to traditional medieval practices at St Giles's.[118]

News of Robert Codde's death, meanwhile, spread quickly around the region. And, although the hospital's fate remained undecided, at least one candidate stepped forward for the vacant post of master. By 20 September, the former bishop of Salisbury, disappointed by his failure to secure a living in Bury St Edmunds, had notified the King's council in London of his readiness to accept in its place 'the mastership of a poor hospital in Norwich'.[119] Having but recently escaped a martyr's fate on the bonfires at Smithfield, he had to take whatever crumbs of royal charity might be thrown in his direction. In certain respects he was admirably qualified for the appointment, being the first master of St Giles's actively to have espoused the new 'humanist' agenda for social and educational reform. How far his enthusiasm for change had survived the experience of persecution and public humiliation is, however, open to debate. Just as the life and aspirations of Walter Suffield help us to understand the reform movement which inspired him to found St Giles's, so the vicissitudes of Nicholas Shaxton's career provide a graphic illustration of the doctrinal rifts which marked its last days as a house of religion.

NICHOLAS SHAXTON, THE LAST MASTER

Like many other Norfolk men in search of a university education, Shaxton studied at Gonville Hall, Cambridge, which had, by the early 1530s, attracted notoriety as a hotbed of evangelical thought. 'I here of no clerke that hath come ought lately of that collage', remarked the arch-conservative Bishop Nykke, 'but sauerith of the friynge panne, though he speke neuer so holely'.[120] Shaxton had taken his first degree in 1507, at the same time as Sir William Buttes, another Gonville scholar who did much to foster the cause of religious reform during his years as physician to Henry VIII. His background remains obscure. He may, perhaps, have been the son or nephew of a Norwich *rentier* and stone mason, which would account for some of the disparaging remarks about his lack of breeding made by detractors.[121] Although his appointment as vicar of Mattishall, in 1516, consolidated his links with Norfolk, Shaxton continued to live in Cambridge throughout this period, mixing with a group of dedicated evangelicals headed by Hugh Latimer, Thomas Cranmer (the future archbishop of Canterbury) and Thomas Bilney, a radical preacher with an enthusiastic following throughout the region.[122] Shaxton's friendship with Buttes, the long-standing association between his college and the family of Anne Boleyn and his own virulent antipathy to the Pope, 'that man of Rome', ensured his selection on a panel of Oxford and Cambridge divines which met in 1530 to consider the 'great matter' of Henry VIII's divorce from Queen Katherine.[123] As might be expected, he was also an enthusiastic advocate of the translation and dissemination of protestant texts among the laity. Attempts on his part to circulate 'heretical' books in the diocese of Norwich, coupled with outspoken pronouncements on such contentious issues as clerical celibacy and the existence of purgatory, brought down upon him the wrath of Bishop Nykke. Since an episcopal licence was necessary before he could preach in the diocese, Shaxton soon became the object of intense and unwelcome scrutiny. At least two senior ecclesiastics, one of whom was Robert Codde, spoke out in his defence, but he was briefly imprisoned at Hoxne in June 1531, before being forced to make a public abjuration of all his 'Lutheran' heresies.[124] He had a narrow escape. One month later, Thomas Bilney was burnt by the bishop, having previously expressed exactly the same heretical opinions. His death unleashed a wave of iconoclasm across East Anglia, and prompted the citizens of Norwich, whose mayor had himself run the risk of martyrdom, to consider an appeal to Parliament. Whatever personal regrets Nykke may have harboured over the affair arose from his error in eliminating the lesser of the two dangerous heresiarchs. 'Christ's mother!', he is said to have exclaimed, 'I have burnt Abel and let Cain go free!'[125]

Despite his public recantation, Shaxton's credibility as a proselytising evangelical remained unscathed. King Henry's marriage early in 1533 to Anne Boleyn, a Christian humanist with a keen interest in social as well as religious issues, greatly strengthened the hand of the reforming group at Court. It was to her that the protestant exile, Simon Fish, sent his controversial tract, *A Supplicacyon for the Beggers*, on its publication in 1528, confident that she would press his case and defend his arguments before its dedicatee, the King:

> But whate remedy to releue vs your poore, sike, lame and sore bedemen? To make many hospitals for the relief of the poore people? Nay truely. The more the worse; for euer the fatte of the hole foundacion hangeth on the prestes berdes. Dyuers of your noble predecessours, kinges of this realme, haue gyuen londes to monasteries to giue a certein somme of money yerely to the poore people, wherof, for the aunciente of the tyme, they giue neuer one peny . . .[126]

Anne's interest in the question of religious reform was practical as well as academic. It was probably because of her personal involvement in schemes for the alleviation of poverty that William Marshall made her the dedicatee of his 1535 translation of the comprehensive proposals for charitable relief previously adopted at Ypres and widely admired in humanist circles.[127] Reports of Anne's munificence towards the poor were widely circulated as protestant propaganda in the reign of her daughter, Elizabeth. Her chaplain and biographer, William Latymer (d. 1583), records the exhortatory addresses she delivered to members of her household. These drew heavily upon the ideas of evangelical reformers like Fish, while reiterating far older concerns of the kind voiced a century earlier by Margery Kempe. It was, for example, necessary for her almoners to pay

> especiall regarde in the choise of suche poore peopell as shalbe founde moste nedye; not vagrante and lasie beggers, whoo in every place besides are releved abundantly, but poore nedie and impotente house holders over charged with children, not havinge any substance, comforte or relyve other wyse.[128]

Shaxton himself must often have acted upon these instructions, since he was employed for two years after Anne's marriage in just such a position.[129] To him would also have fallen the task of distributing Maundy money among 'symple poor women' and perhaps of delivering the sheets and clothing which, Latymer assures us, were stitched personally by her ladies-in-waiting out of the canvas and flannel she bought for them.[130]

The Queen's enthusiasm for change went far beyond her household. This became the centre of a network of patronage, skilfully managed with the help of Shaxton's 'old acquainted friend', Archbishop Cranmer, and Anne's principal ally in matters of religion, the seemingly indomitable Thomas Cromwell.[131] Preferment, including a prebend at

St Stephen's, Westminster, and the post of treasurer of Salisbury cathedral, soon came Shaxton's way, as did the opportunity to preach before the King. Both he and Latimer, who was similarly honoured, were rapidly elevated to the episcopate, becoming, respectively, bishops of Salisbury and Worcester.[132] Blinded by reforming zeal, neither of them possessed either the political skills or circumspection to steer a safe course in choppy waters. Shaxton's friends and patrons found him a sore trial. Not even the execution for treason, in 1536, of Queen Anne served to undermine his convictions or dent his confidence.[133] Faced with hectoring, admonitory letters which threatened and complained by turns, the King's vicegerent veered from the defensive to the exasperated. 'Let rasshe iugement rule men of lesse witte and discretion', Cromwell advised, adding that 'wilfulnes becomith all men better then a bisshop, whych shold alwayes teach vs to lacke gladly our own will.'[134] Yet Shaxton remained obdurate. His confrontational behaviour in the diocese of Salisbury placed Cromwell in the uncharacteristic role of mediator, struggling to reassure the conservatives and restrain the radicals, whose extremism threatened to undermine his careful work towards reform.[135] Shaxton's diocesan injunctions of 1538, for example, constituted a frontal assault on traditional religious practices, antagonised the leading citizens of Salisbury and poisoned relations with the cathedral chapter. His attack on the 'ydolatrie of vaine thinges: namely stinking bootes, mucke combes, ragged rochettes, rotten girdles, pyld purses, great bullock horns, lockes of heer, filthy ragges and gobbetts of wodde, under the name of parcells of the Holy Cross' was not destined to win friends in a city noted for its lucrative pilgrim trade.[136] By the spring of 1539 his vendetta against the abbot of Reading, his constant feuding with the chapter at Salisbury, his rapidly deteriorating relations with the mayor and commonalty there and, most dangerous of all, his failure to obey the King's wishes in matters of patronage had each tested Cromwell's patience to the limit.[137]

'I would wish that I were no bishop, but obscure in some corner, to sing to myself and my muses . . . I lived with much more ease before I was bishop', he had once protested when his patron showed especial irritation.[138] The passage of the Six Articles in the Parliament of 1539 brought retirement closer than Shaxton had expected. Unfortunately for him, however, it was not accompanied by obscurity. With considerable bravery, the 'lewd fool', as one conservative dismissed him, spoke out against the Articles, which provided, in unambiguous terms, a strictly traditional definition of such contentious doctrinal issues as clerical celibacy and transubstantiation (the denial of which became a capital offence).[139] He and Latimer were the only evangelical bishops to resign their sees, quite possibly under pressure from the Crown. Rumours that Shaxton would face the death penalty unless he recanted his 'past errors' were rife during the summer, which he spent under arrest, in the custody of the bishop of Bath.[140] In November 1539 he wrote plaintively to Cromwell from the episcopal residence at Chew, begging him to intervene with the King to obtain his release and the grant of a royal pension. Ever the consummate politician, his patron had ridden out the storm and was able to oblige. It looks very much as if the generous annuities of £66 13*s* 4*d* assigned to both Shaxton and Latimer as early as the previous August had been secured through his good graces.[141] Any hopes the disgraced bishops may have had of returning to favour were, however, dashed by Cromwell's own fall and execution in the following year. Reports current in 1541 that they had been prohibited from preaching in either London, Oxford, Cambridge or their former dioceses suggest that the rehabilitation process had still a long way to go.[142] Yet, despite the government's constant hounding of radical clergy, they otherwise remained at liberty to mount the pulpit.

Not long afterwards, Shaxton's old protector, Archbishop Cranmer, managed to find him a congenial and apparently safe living at Hadleigh. This small Suffolk town was already celebrated as a 'university of the learned', where evangelism flourished. Thomas Bilney had been rector there, and Shaxton served alongside his evangelically minded successors.[143] Perhaps under the influence of Rowland Taylor, who arrived in 1544, he took the extreme step of getting married and the potentially fatal one of rejecting transubstantiation. He may have come to believe that his activities were no longer of interest to the conservatives at Court, but they were in search of bait with which to catch bigger fish in the royal household.[144] The death of Sir William Buttes, in 1545, marked the beginning of a campaign of persecution designed to extirpate evangelism once and for all. On 15 May 1546, John Kirby, a Suffolk radical, was apprehended for 'yvel opinion concerning the most Blessed Sacrament', removed to Ipswich and burnt, while Shaxton went under arrest to London.[145] One month later, he and four others were arraigned for heresy at the Guildhall and condemned to the stake. Considerable pressure was brought to bear upon them to convert 'from their heresie of the Sacrament of the alter unto the true belief'. Faced with the prospect of an agonising death, Shaxton recanted for the second time in his career. Unlike his fellow prisoner, Anne Askew, he was not physically tortured, although the refined and prolonged torment of his public humiliation broke him as effectively as the rack.

Having abjured his heresies on 19 June (the day after sentence was passed), Shaxton was reputedly sent to persuade Anne Askew to do likewise. Her reproaches became the stuff of protestant legend, which, inevitably, presented him in a wretched light. Early in July Shaxton addressed an abject letter of recantation to King Henry. 'I mooste humblie evyn from the botome of myne harte thanke your excellent majestie that ye have hadde this godlie care for my soull health,' he wrote

> that by youre mooste gracyous meanes I am broughte and reduced from that dampnable errour that I was in. And surelye hadde not this youre pytie and compassion been I woolde obstynatelye have dyed in the same, and so from the temporall fyer shulde have goon to the everlastyng fyer of hell.[146]

His claim to have fallen 'myserablye nowe in myne olde age evyn within this yere . . . into that mooste detestable and mooste abhomynable heresye of them that bee callid Sacramentaries' explains why he was despatched to Hadleigh to preach down the heretical doctrines he had so recently espoused. But first he was forced to deliver a penitential sermon at Smithfield, on 16 July, while Anne and her three companions went to the stake before a huge crowd of onlookers. A few days later, on 1 August, he preached the Sunday sermon at St Paul's Cross, describing his recent conversion 'with weepinge eies, exhorting the people to beware by him, and to abolish such hereticall bookes of English, which was the occasion of his fall'.[147]

Claiming that he had betrayed their cause to save his own skin, Shaxton's former friends now rubbed salt into the wound.[148] Since he had been obliged, like Cranmer before him, to repudiate his wife as well as his beliefs, he incurred an additional battery of personal abuse as a hypocritical timeserver. The didactic verses on the dangers of sexual incontinence which he allegedly composed for her guidance at this time make it hard to sympathise wholeheartedly with his predicament. They do him little credit as a poet and even less as a husband, but were a godsend to the evangelicals. His former friend, the polemicist Robert Crowley, printed the poem, with a scathing commentary, in the preface of an even more vituperative attack on Shaxton which appeared two years later. It was easy enough to mock the once zealous protestant for forsaking 'the chaste matrimonie of Christe, and [embracing] that idolatrouse whoredome of . . . Rome'.[149] Rowland Taylor, who later went to the stake as a heretic at a time when Shaxton was personally responsible for persecuting evangelicals, felt so bitter that he even scribbled abuse about the traitor 'Tonshax' in the margins of his Latin Bible.[150] Shaxton was therefore as anxious to leave Hadleigh as the godly residents were to see him go. Although he kept livestock and other goods there until his death ten years later, he remained an absentee. His wife and a child now tarred with the brush of illegitimacy were a painful embarrassment to be put firmly behind him, if never forgotten.[151] The ingeniously named Thomas Drastab (bastard spelt backwards) who boarded in the house of a friend was almost certainly his son. In his will of 1556, a document notable for the complete absence of any personal religious sentiments, Shaxton left the residue of a substantial estate to Thomas Alabaster of Hadleigh 'to the behooff and profytt' of the boy when he eventually came of age. In the event of young Thomas's early death, the bequest was to be distributed as alms among the town's poor: an appropriate legacy on the part of one who had served at Court as a royal almoner and had subsequently put his experiences to practical use in Norwich's new hospital.[152]

CHAPTER VIII

GODDES HOWSE

> I will have . . . Hospitalls of all kindes for children, orphans, old folkes, sickmen, madmen, souldiers, pesthouses, etc. not built *precario* or by gowty benefactors, who, when by fraud and rapine they have extorted all their lives, oppressed whole Provinces, societies, etc. give something to pious uses, build a satisfactory Almes-house, Schoole, or bridge, etc. at their last end, or before perhaps, which is no otherwise then to steale a Goose, and sticke downe a feather, rob a thousand to releeve ten: And those Hospitalls so built and maintained, not by Collections, benevolences, donaries, for a set number (as in ours) just so many and no more, at such a rate, but for all those who stand in need, be they more or lesse . . .
>
> Robert Burton, *The Anatomy of Melancholy*

The idea that cleanliness and godliness or, conversely, dirt and sin, were intimately connected tends to be associated with the rise of Puritanism in late sixteenth and seventeenth-century England.[1] Yet parallels between physical and moral hygiene had long been drawn. Edmund Rich, Bishop Suffield's friend and mentor, was, for example, famed for the sweet odour of sanctity emanating from 'the lovely flowers' of his virtue. Dirt, squalor and noisome smells were, on the other hand, common attributes of the devil: the stench of evil reeked from hell to heaven, and sin was frequently described as a foul miasma, contaminating everyone who inhaled its poison. It is thus not surprising that Rich, like many other saintly bishops, attempted to sweep away 'the filth of avarice and impurity' from his household.[2] In keeping with a long tradition which stigmatised lepers and Jews as carriers of disease, malodorous vagrants, ruffians, beggars and other social outcasts were branded from the late 1340s onwards as disseminators of bubonic plague (known to contemporaries as the *morbus pauperum* or disease of the poor). Indeed, in Italy they sometimes had to wear the same kind of identifying costume or badge, which marked them out as a potential source of infection. During epidemics in York 'the poore and impotent folke' were ordered to remain at home 'and not goe beggyng abrode', a hygienic precaution accompanied by steps for the removal of vagrants. From Norwich to Siena, streets were simultaneously cleansed of ordure and undesirables, as measures for moral and physical sanitation proceeded hand in hand.[3]

Medical metaphors could be pursued even further. During periods of popular discontent, self-induced poverty and vagrancy were described as malignant growths on the body politic, rotting its limbs and calling for radical surgery.[4] At the time of the Pilgrimage of Grace, in 1536, Henry VIII forsook his self-appointed role as England's 'good physician' to present himself as a surgeon, ready and able to amputate its corrupt members.[5] In what was little short of a *post-mortem*, composed during the aftermath of Kett's Rebellion, in 1549, one commentator observed:

> When we see a great number of flies in a yeare, we naturallie iudge it like to be a great plague, and hauing so great a swarming of loitering vagabonds, readie to beg and brall at euerie mans doore, which declare a greater infection, can we not looke for greeuouser and perillouser danger than the plague is? Who can therefore otherwise deeme, but this one deadlie hurt, wherewith the commonwelth of our nation is wounded, beside all other is so pestilent, that there can be no more hurtfull thing in a well gouerned estate . . . Wherefore order must be kept in the commonwealth like health in the bodie, and all the drift of policie looketh to this end . . . Desperate sicknesse in physicke must haue desperate remedies, for meane medicines will neuer helpe great griefes.[6]

Ironically, the damage caused by Kett's followers to the fabric of the medieval buildings proved the immediate catalyst needed to generate adequate funding for Norwich's recently acquired hospital. The generosity of its new patrons reflects an understandable fear that without adequate help even the respectable poor might be driven to extremes. Anxiety on this score lingered on, fuelled by a growing concern about vagrancy, and explains why pioneering measures for charitable relief were adopted with such alacrity in Norwich during the 1570s.[7] Attempts by a group of catholic sympathisers to mobilise armed support in the city after the collapse of a more serious rebellion in the north had then proved abortive. Queen Elizabeth's government was, even so, alive to the constant threat posed by 'a great multitude of people of mean and base sort', and determined that they should be kept in a state of 'quietness and obedience'. Sharp words from William Cecil on the subject of itinerant beggars may have prompted the corporation of Norwich to embark on a far more comprehensive and comparatively more humane policy than he in fact envisaged. Heavy flooding and the attendant demand for 'relyfe of bread, drynke and herryng to be given to the pore on the further side of the water [Wensum]' must have provided an additional, and more immediate, incentive.[8] Having marshalled their evidence by instigating a major census of the resident poor, the aldermen adopted an integrated scheme for 'mayntayninge the indigente and nedie' and putting the young to work. Once again, much was made of the dangerous consequences of indiscriminate almsgiving to diseased vagrants, whose unclothed bodies 'eaton with vermyne and corrupte diseases' suggested a life of vice, offensive to God and lethal to the commonwealth.[9]

At the best of times, poverty aroused misgivings, tinged with contempt. Depositions taken in the Norwich consistory court during the early sixteenth century reveal a tendency to regard penniless testators as 'corrupt', 'of ill repute', open to bribery and intimidation, half-witted or unreliable.[10] A conviction that the sick poor, however worthy, should be isolated from public view and kept at a safe distance from healthy men and women also gained currency during this period. As Brian Pullan remarks in his study of wealth and poverty in renaissance Venice, the thin 'veneer of holiness' sentimentally applied to Christ's poor soon melted away when fear of the miasmas of disease took hold in crowded urban conditions.[11] While recognising, as medieval writers had done before him, that 'membres of Cryste's mistycall body ioyned by faythe and charyte ought wyllyngly and mercyfully to offre helpe to suche as haue nede', William Marshall argued in 1535 that sick beggars 'infectynge the ayre' placed all citizens at risk.[12] His translation of the influential Ypres scheme for poor relief, noted in the previous chapter, came at a time when the pox, then endemic across Europe, was seen not only as a further threat to health but also to public order and morality. The provision of 'common hospytalles' alongside schemes for parochial relief would, he hoped, remove a conspicuous and unpleasant source of danger from the streets:

> At gates also and churche porches the dysfygured syghtes of these vysured [deformed] pore men ar nat now sene all roughe and scouruy and ronnynge with matter, bothe vgely to loke on and euyll smellynge to the nose, and ouer that to some tender stomakes lothsome . . . The comen welth hath nowe lesse hurte and lesse corruptyon that so many sore folkes be gone the helth of the cytie is nowe more safe. The contagyouse folkes are by theymselfe, whose infection often times priuely crepynge as a canker hathe caused moche deth in the people . . .[13]

That men and women hitherto unable to support themselves might once again become productive members of society added further force to his recommendations regarding the provision of free medical treatment in such institutions. The most novel aspect of proposals for new poor law legislation submitted to the English government in 1535, and quite possibly drafted by Marshall himself, was that paupers should receive such treatment out of the public purse. His programme, which aimed to get the indigent back to work through subsidised employment, proved too controversial for the MPs and peers then assembled at Westminster, although not, eventually, for the rulers of Norwich. In its final form, the short-lived Act of 1536 merely required local authorities to 'socour, fynde and kepe' their impotent poor by means of voluntary alms raised through the medium of the parish, while strictly forbidding the distribution of 'common and open doolis' by private individuals.[14]

But where were these 'pore, impotent, lame, feble, syke and disseased people' to be lodged? Thomas More's vision in *Utopia* (1516) of a city served by four extra mural hospitals, capable of accommodating and treating the sick from all walks of life, was certainly not inspired by anything then available in England.[15] Like Henry VII, who deplored the absence of adequate institutional provision, More was clearly influenced by developments in Italy, which also made him an enthusiastic advocate of compulsory sanitary measures, including the removal of beggars from city streets during epidemics.[16] The most popular model, extolled and emulated throughout Europe, was the Florentine hospital of Santa Maria Nuova. The latter was described by the English protestant, William Thomas, in 1545, in terms almost identical to those used by More in his paean to the virtues of civic humanism.[17] Its statutes had already been consulted by King Henry and his advisers when they began planning the Savoy, the first English hospital specifically to retain the services of paid medical staff for the benefit of the sick poor.[18] Cleanliness had always been a high priority in the larger English medieval hospitals, but, as we have seen in Chapter VI, the means of achieving it were never spelt out. Nurses at Henry's new foundation were, however, left in no doubt about their responsibilities in this quarter, since everything, from the deployment of delousing ovens and baths to the replacement of all soiled or used linen, was minutely regulated in ordinances drawn up in the 1520s. The sisters had, among many other tasks, 'not only to purify the dormitory and cleanse it of all putrefaction, faeces, filth, corrupt matter and any other impurity, dirt and cobwebs, but also of anything whatsoever that smells bad and savours strongly, or may generate an evil or unhealthy stench'.[19]

The adoption in England of stricter measures for social control and public health, often based on continental models, owed a good deal to the skilful propaganda of humanists such as Thomas More. Reform became a matter of civic pride, a commodity which the rulers of Norwich, with their enthusiasm for the trappings of Italianate culture, possessed in abundance. Such schemes were also an immediate, practical response to taxing social and economic problems. In order to cope with recurrent epidemics, food shortages, dramatic shifts in population, galloping inflation and periods of serious dearth, most sixteenth-century cities of any size rapidly developed the complex administrative infrastructures necessary to run centralised agencies for the poor. Successive outbreaks of plague, sweating sickness, the pox and other infectious diseases in England likewise prompted attempts, from 1512 onwards, to improve the education of medical practitioners along continental lines, and, as noted in the previous chapter, made civic authorities, such as those of Norwich, increasingly receptive to the idea of institutionalised relief.[20]

Unlike most of the leading towns and cities of mid-sixteenth-century England, however, Norwich did not experience any significant rise in population before the influx of Dutch and Walloon immigrants in the 1570s. This was partly because of a protracted slump in the international textile trade, which began in the 1520s and gradually spread to other vulnerable groups. In May 1549, just a few weeks before the outbreak of Kett's rebellion, the common council complained about the 'foreigners and beggars' flocking into Norwich as masons, carpenters and other skilled artisans left the city to find work elsewhere. Years of economic stagnation, interspersed with food shortages and unusually high mortality rates, gave rise to an unstable labour market, and meant that local workmen often faced long periods of enforced idleness.[21] By this stage, the rulers of Norwich appear to have grown more sympathetic towards the victims of cyclical unemployment, or at least to have recognised that a blanket refusal of aid to the labouring poor and their many dependents would cause more social problems than it solved. Although they were at pains to uphold the poor law enactments of the 1530s with regard to the licensing and control of beggars, some of the more affluent citizens did not, for instance, abandon the practice of distributing alms from their own doors.[22]

In this respect, at least, they adopted a more realistic approach than the government, which tended to distinguish only between the idle and the impotent poor, concentrating upon the extirpation of vagrancy at the expense of those who genuinely wanted to work.[23] The dismemberment during the late 1540s of Norwich's numerous religious guilds and fraternities deprived some unemployed artisans of regular support, and many others of spontaneous gifts of food and clothing. Although the total amount of assistance involved appears never to have been very great, the sudden cessation of even quite modest doles could have serious consequences during such difficult times.[24] Following royal injunctions of 1547 reiterating the demand that all parish churches should possess an alms chest, the wardens of at least fourteen Norwich churches made generous provision for 'the comforte and relyff of the poore folkys in the paryssh' out of money raised by selling off plate and other doctrinally suspect items. Since returns for only twenty city churches have survived, it looks as if leading members of the community took these responsibilities to heart, some parishes voting sums of up to £20 for welfare purposes.[25] Nevertheless, long before the Census of the Poor brought home in graphic detail the scale of the problem in their midst, members of the civic elite clearly recognised that *ad hoc* relief of this kind, however effectively managed, was simply not enough.

These same individuals were now anxious to make more permanent provision for the reputable aged and sick poor by acquiring and enlarging the medieval hospital of St Giles. That medical help was also to be available there suggests a readiness to put into practice the new and still comparatively radical ideas of Marshall and his circle. Progress was, however, dogged by delays and uncertainty about finances and organisation. The rulers of Norwich had, as we have seen, few examples to follow and were constantly feeling their way towards innovative solutions for unprecedented problems. That theirs was the first English provincial city to introduce compulsory levies for the poor has long been recognised by historians, yet the real purpose of these novel impositions, which were paid directly into the hospital's coffers, rather than into schemes for parochial relief, has hitherto gone unremarked. It would be hard to find more telling evidence of the corporation's commitment to the idea of integrated welfare, especially as the new foundation was to house a school as well as wards for the godly poor. According to the Spanish humanist, Juan Luis Vives, who had frequented Henry VIII's Court during the 1520s, one of the principal tasks of the renaissance hospital was to encourage learning and equip the young for work with a decent education. It was thus a means of drawing moral 'foulness' away from the rest of the body politic before infection set in.[26]

THE POOR HOUSE TAKES SHAPE

Negotiations over the fate of St Giles's had dragged on for the best part of eleven months, when, on 22 December 1546, the mayor of Norwich was able to announce significant progress. He informed the Assembly that 'his highnes plesur' now hinged upon the performance of 'certen couenauntes' or formal undertakings by the city, whereupon those present 'graunted to be contributors and helpers to the same euery man after his abilitie [to pay]'.[27] No significant sums of money (beyond routine legal and administrative costs) changed hands at this time, but King Henry clearly expected the citizens to underwrite the cost of their reconstituted and reformed hospital. He, in turn, agreed that once all St Giles's estates and possessions had been 'assured and taken' into royal ownership they would be handed over to the city, to hold in perpetuity at an annual rent of £9 payable to the Court of Augmentations, but otherwise free of any obligation to render either first fruits or tithes.[28] The people of Norwich were also promised a licence permitting them to acquire additional land to the value of £200 a year, with which to support the new 'howse of the poore in Holmestreet' or 'Goddes Howse', as it was henceforth to be known.

As merchants and tradesmen with a wealth of shared commercial experience, the aldermen who helped finalise these arrangements were well aware of the need to make adequate long-term provision for an establishment which, on the one hand, would be far bigger and costlier than its predecessor, but, on the other, would no longer be able to exploit the rich vein of clerical and episcopal patronage available throughout the Middle Ages. Although the first Chantry Act had demonstrably lacked either a sense of urgency or a coherent theological programme, the doctrine of purgatory had already been sufficiently undermined to threaten a serious decline in bequests from pious donors.[29] The rulers of Norwich expected that civic pride and Christian compassion would eventually make good this collective loss of confidence in the efficacy of good works. But they were as anxious as Walter Suffield had been 300 years earlier to set the hospital upon a sound financial and administrative footing from the very beginning. The composition between King and corporation was thus remarkably thorough, concerning not only the 'releife of poore people', but also the cure of St Helen's parish church and the endowment of a grammar school. The original text, carefully drafted by Thomas Codde and his associates over the summer of 1546, does not survive, although it formed the basis of a definitive agreement reached at the start of Edward VI's reign in the following year, and can thus be reconstituted in some detail.[30]

One of the most striking and predictable features of the new hospital was to be the dismantling of the old collegiate structure, and with it the almost complete abandonment of elaborate ritual and liturgy. The contrast with late medieval practice could hardly have been greater, the gradual decline of the pre-Dissolution establishment of choristers and cantarists having made such a change relatively painless. Henceforward a single, 'sufficiently learned' priest was to serve the paupers as well as the parishioners at a fee of £6 13*s* 4*d* a year. Probably because the funds to support a visiting chaplain at the Guildhall had been donated to St Giles's by two aldermen, the rulers of Norwich accepted that the hospital should still discharge this responsibility. A slightly lower stipend was therefore assigned to a second priest responsible for celebrating mass and hearing the confessions of prisoners, as well as accompanying 'suche as shall goo to execucion' on their way to the scaffold. Although the hospital's dedication to St Giles had been swept away, along with its obligations to commemorate the dead, the civic authorities had no quarrel with the two remaining chaplains, John Fysher and Robert Dowe, whom they permitted to occupy these posts.[31] No other clergymen or choristers appeared on the payroll. Economies in this quarter were, however, more than offset by plans to find the boys of the old episcopal and almonry schools a permanent home. As part of their 'couenant' with King Henry, the mayor and corporation promised 'to erecte within the seid citie one ffree scole wheryn youthe shalbe enstructed and taught without any charge to ther ffrendes, and to prouyde a scole maister and an usher [under master] meete and sufficient ffor ther lernung in the latyn tonge, discrecon and other vertuous qualities'.[32] As Paul Griffiths reminds us, 'pedagogy was seen by contemporaries as a vital aspect of reform, and a means to steer young people away from the centuries of darkness and ignorance'.[33] The hospital was to be a place for the disciplining and correction of youth: a carrot, as it were, compared to the stick wielded with greater force at the Bridewell.

Since the salaries of the two schoolmasters (respectively £10 and £6 13*s* 4*d* a year) were to constitute a permanent charge upon the hospital budget, and, like the priests, the pair of them were to reside permanently in the precinct, it seems reasonable to assume that at this point the corporation intended to move the scholars there as well. Their temporary quarters at Blackfriars had clearly proved unsuitable; and the acquisition of St Giles's offered a unique opportunity to combine two goals of the godly commonwealth, namely the care of the deserving poor and the Christian education of the young. As a distinguished scholar, who had spent most of his life in academic circles at Cambridge (where he elected to end his days), Nicholas Shaxton may well have found this aspect of his new post especially attractive. His views almost certainly coincided with those of another royal almoner, Richard Cox, who complained in the late 1540s of 'the great lack in this realm of schools, preachers, houses and livings for [the] impotent, orphans, widows, poor and miserable', warning presciently that 'the realm will come into foul ignorance and barbarousness when the reward of learning is gone'. Cox, in turn, was echoing Sir Thomas Elyot's spirited defence of pedagogy in *The Boke Named the Gouernor*, of which Shaxton possessed a copy.[34] His library also included Erasmus's *Enchiridion*, a work celebrated among humanists because of its insistence that Christians should not only share their resources among the poor but also 'teach the ignorant'.[35]

Cox's jeremiad notwithstanding, throughout the country, in towns and cities as far apart as Bristol and Newcastle, members of the merchant class were founding and maintaining schools which, as often as not, were run under the auspices of local guilds or corporations. The rulers of Yarmouth set out, in 1551, to convert the medieval hospital of St Mary Magdalen into a school with private quarters for a 'learned man' capable of teaching Latin grammar to local boys.[36] A loan, 'for the settyng foreward of the grammer skole' was advanced to the master, who was permitted to take 'tymber of the haven [harbour] for reparacion of the seid skole howse'.[37] In London, the Mercers' Company raised enough money to buy the hospital of St Thomas Acon from the Crown, on the understanding that it would continue to support the old school, with free places for twenty-five pupils.[38] The aldermen of Norwich hoped to do even better by remodelling the city's largest hospital while at the same time encouraging the spread of 'polite learning': a central plank in the campaign to transform potential vagrants into productive and obedient citizens. According to the laboured but godly sentiments of one local schoolmaster, the health and cohesion of the body politic was as dependent upon education as it was on poor relief:

> Provide for the poore that Impoteunte bee
> As Charryte maye moue yow theire nede when ye see.
> For who so the hungrie and thirstie shall feede
> God will rewarde him even folde for his deede.
> Cause yoothe to be trayned and seasoned in Tyme,
> In vertew and Labour from synnes vice and cryme,
> But when men be careles and soffer you the stylle,
> The Cyttie ys plaged in wrecke of such eavelle.[39]

Throughout Europe, the teaching of Christian doctrine and morality to the young ('instructing children in the way of God') ranked as a superior work of mercy. In Venice, for example, educational schemes based upon the hospital of the Incurabili were promoted as 'a form of spiritual benevolence', even more meritorious than the care of the syphilitic patients.[40] As had been the case in the Middle Ages, such activities also served to arrest the spread of heretical or subversive opinions, and were thus attractive on both sides of the doctrinal divide.

Power to appoint, supervise and, if necessary, remove the occupants of the four posts described above was to lie with the mayor and aldermen, who were required to fill all vacancies promptly, according to a clearly defined bureaucratic procedure. A porter or steward, rent collector, butler and cook were to receive wages ranging from 60*s* to 26*s* 8*d* a year, supplemented with clothing, food and drink. They, too, were to be civic appointees, answerable to the corporation, and devoted to the efficient management of an institution whose principal concern was henceforward to be the care of the poor. In this respect, at least, the new statutes marked a return to first principles. Whereas Bishop Suffield had planned to provide thirty beds or more, as the resources of the house permitted, the corporation now undertook to make permanently available at its own cost 'suffitient and conuenient lodginge, meate, drinke, bedding, wood and all other things necessary' for forty paupers

> to be resident, lyinge, abidinge and found from tyme to tyme . . . the same ffourty poore persons euery of them to be all waies remouable from day to day, weeke to weeke, month to month and tyme to tyme. And other to be taken and receiued into their roomes and places at and by the discretion of such person and persons as shalbe named and elected from tyme to tyme by the maior . . . with the assent of the most part of the said aldermen . . . to omit, receiue, take and remoue in to and from the said howse of the poore or Goddes Howse the said fforty poure persons.[41]

The hospital was thus intended to be more than a simple almshouse. Provision for a potentially rapid turnover of at least some patients suggests that, where possible, the poor were to be made fit for work and then discharged into the community. In theory, a rigorous selection procedure was to be enforced by the keeper and overseers, who were themselves answerable to, and removable by, the civic authorities. Difficult or disruptive inmates might soon find themselves back on the streets; as had been the case throughout the medieval period, the threat of expulsion constituted a powerful means of imposing order. Nor were valuable resources to be spent on those who were seriously or terminally ill. From the outset, it appears that dangerous, moribund, incurable or infectious cases would be accommodated elsewhere.[42] Not long after the refoundation of God's House, the keepers of four of the five extra mural 'spytelhouses' discussed in the previous chapter were summoned to appear in person before the mayor's court:

> and, upon reuelacon made by the mayer, *et cetera*, howe many lazers [lepers] wer at the said gates, it was orderd and agreed that thei and euery of them shalbe bounden with suerties that they nor any of them shall nat recyue, suffer ner mayn teyn in ther

houses, nor any of them, any person or persons but such as shalbe admytted by the mayer, *et cetera*. And also kepe goode and honest rule . . .[43]

Concern lest the keepers might resort to their former practice of admitting sturdy beggars was combined with a desire to leave places free for those who seemed past hope. That referrals would be made by persons in authority was formally enshrined in an agreement reached in the 1570s between the corporation and the new keeper of the hospital of SS Mary and Clement. The latter was to care for all the 'diseased persons' recommended to him by the mayor and the bishop of Norwich, a sure sign of moves towards a more focused and coordinated strategy.[44] If evidence from London and other urban centres across Europe is any guide, many of these unfortunates would have been suffering from the *morbus Gallicus*, or French pox, a disease of epidemic proportions in sixteenth-century England.[45] The records of God's House reveal that some were men and women who could no longer be allowed to remain with the other residents. A female patient spent eight months at the former *leprosarium* outside St Giles's gates at the hospital's expense in 1560–1; and a second inmate was despatched to the 'lazar hows' near Fyebridge about ten years later.[46]

Basic medical care had still to be provided for the elderly, lame and impotent deemed suitable for admission to God's House. As in 1249, the task of making beds and tending the sick was assigned to four women, whose annual allowance of 33*s* 4*d* each was initially supposed to include the cost of food and apparel. The sisters of St Giles's had previously been assigned rather less, although the new rate was far from generous. At slightly over 7*d* a week, it was 3*d* lower than the stipend drawn before the onset of galloping inflation by sisters at the Savoy, and was exactly half the wage which Henry VIII had considered paying the nurses in his projected London almshouse. The latter were, moreover, each to receive cloth worth 20*s* a year for their clothing. No such discrepancy obtained where the master, Nicholas Shaxton, was concerned. His annuity of £20, confirmed in April 1547, followed the King's own recommended salary scale, and did not, moreover, include the free board and private quarters set aside for him at the hospital.[47] It was apparently understood that he would exercise a close supervisory role, but the authority of the corporation in matters of finance and administration remained absolute. Its members and their successors were, quite simply, to be 'masters, rulers and gouernors of the said late hospitall ordeyned nowe for the poore . . . and of the people ther'.[48] In this respect, at least, the new foundation bore a striking resemblance to the restructured Hôpital General in Geneva, which was managed by four or five *procureurs* drawn from the city's mercantile elite. The *hospitaller*, or keeper, whose terms of employment were similar to Shaxton's, remained answerable to this small but extremely powerful lay body, as notable for its business acumen as it was for its influence in civic affairs.[49]

Although they had yet to secure King Henry's final approval, these plans were already common knowledge by late December 1546. John Whetacre, who had taught the choristers at St Giles's as a young man, was well aware that they involved proposals for setting up a grammar school, having perhaps been approached for an expert opinion. In his will of 2 January 1547, he bequeathed a reversionary interest in land worth £20 a year 'to the fre scole which shalbe at Sent Gyles the hospitall in Norwich . . . to be erected by the kinge's maiestye's graunt'.[50] Ironically, he outlived King Henry, whose death, a mere twenty-two days later, occurred just as negotiations were about to be concluded. Most of the essential documentation had been completed, but it was still necessary to revise the contract with the city to take account of Edward VI's youth, the authority of Protector Somerset and the role of the late King's executors, who had been charged with the implementation of any grants or gifts promised by him but not fulfilled in his lifetime. Fortunately for the corporation, Sir Richard Southwell had been appointed to assist the executors, and was thus able to expedite matters.[51] On 5 March 1547, just one week before Southwell took a seat on the privy council, Nicholas Shaxton was formally inducted as master of St Giles's by the bishop of Norwich; and on the following day, in the chapter house of the hospital, he and the two remaining brothers signed a deed of surrender relinquishing all the house's possessions to the Crown [see Plate 40].[52]

Since Robert Codde and his fellow chaplains had already made a similar release in the late 1530s, this undertaking appears superfluous, but Shaxton's assent was viewed as a necessary precursor to the drafting on 8 March of an indenture tripartite between the King, the executors and the city, setting out all the arrangements discussed above. To make the agreement legally binding, each of the three parties had to ensure that their copy had been sealed by the other two. On 13 April, after the common seal of the city had been ceremonially appended to the parts belonging to the King and the executors, Thomas Marsham was despatched to London to effect the necessary exchange and deliver a valor of the hospital's estates to the clerks in Chancery.[53] This was more than an empty formality, for the King had promised that by 24 June royal letters patent would be issued under the Great Seal confirming the change of ownership, and Marsham's familiarity with the Byzantine procedures of the Westminster bureaucracy made him an ideal messenger. So much so, that the letters were issued with unusual speed on 7 May, depositions being taken three days later in Norwich by none other than John Corbet. He had been commissioned by the government to 'receyue the knowlege of the seid mayer, sheriffes and comminaltie' with regard to the contents of the various sealed indentures, which were then to be enrolled in Chancery.[54] Even at this final stage, the informal network of contacts between Norwich and Westminster proved remarkably useful.

As itemised in the King's letters patent, the rents, tenements and other properties granted to the city for the upkeep of God's House were identical to those listed in the *Valor Ecclesiasticus*. The anticipated net income of £152 a year was about £21 lower than that given in the return of 1535, however, and was thus a rather more realistic estimate of what the corporation might initially have hoped to collect. If the hospital was, moreover, to secure royal approval for further acquisitions it could not risk appearing too affluent.[55] By dint of careful management and the negotiation of new leases, the civic authorities contrived to increase the *potential* value of the pre-Dissolution estates to almost £200 net in 1548–9, which was a remarkable achievement, even allowing for the effects of rampant inflation.[56] Yet, despite the financial acumen of its new administrators, the old endowment was clearly insufficient. On the basis of calculations recorded on the hospital's own copy of the agreement with Edward VI and his father's executors, no less than £160 would have been needed to support the forty paupers at a fixed *per capita* rate of £4 a year. In all, projected annual outgoings came to £224, which included wages, but made no allowance for feeding and clothing staff, for maintaining the fabric of the hospital, for transport, rents due to other landowners or the cost of casual labour, or for running the estates. Nor did this figure leave any reserves to cover incidental items, such as building projects on the various manors.[57] In addition, the city had to meet the not inconsiderable cost of its suit for the ownership of St Giles's, which still constituted a drain on resources as late as 1548.[58] The far heavier charge of converting the medieval hospital, with its redundant chancel and priests' quarters, into a home for forty paupers and the new grammar school also threatened to upset the budget. The rulers of Norwich would, sooner rather than later, have to dig deep into their pockets, not simply to cover these initial one-off expenses, but also to increase the rent roll through long-term investment in property. Their initial response was, however, to move cautiously, first seeking to exploit the existing resources more effectively.

Accounts for the first year of the new hospital's existence have been lost, but the city records provide some insight into the immediate steps taken for managing its affairs. The appointment of a receiver or supervisor, who was also to farm part of the precinct 'ffor the profite of the citie', generated some controversy. Thomas Codde seemed the obvious choice, but the manner of his selection caused resentment, evidently because it smacked of cronyism and preferential dealing on the part of a narrow elite. Although (or perhaps because) he commanded the support of such influential figures as Augustine Steward and William Rogers, Codde felt moved to appear before the mayor's court on 27 July 1547 and offer the farm competitively to the highest bidder. After a free and frank exchange involving 'many communicacions', it was finally agreed that he might retain the receivership 'as one most mete ffor the same', but the coterie of aldermen which had hitherto taken charge of hospital business was clearly chastened by the experience.[59] Henceforward Codde and his associates were to be fully accountable to their fellow citizens. Yet, despite this outspoken expression of disapproval, a firm bedrock of trust and confidence clearly remained. On 26 October a supervisory committee of four aldermen was appointed with the unanimous approval of the Assembly to oversee God's House. Augustine Steward was promptly replaced because he had to attend Parliament, but William Rogers and Richard Catlyn (who had also played a significant part in the negotiations of 1546) continued to serve.[60] One of their first tasks was to take formal seisin of property in Burlingham 'and other townes . . . goven to the maier . . . to the sustentacion of the pore ffolkes of the hospitall' by local philanthropists.[61]

A number of eminent citizens, including John Corbet, Thomas Marsham, Richard Catlyn and Peter Rede [see Plate 39], either negotiated new leases of hospital property at this time or had their old ones confirmed. In light of their previous experience, the authorities were at pains to demonstrate that neither social position nor a long-standing connection with the poor house would bestow an unfair advantage. The elaborate precautions now in place suggest that insider dealing, or its sixteenth-century equivalent, may hitherto have occurred.[62] Marsham's petition for the farm of a 'void ground' in St Andrew's parish was, for instance, subject to the careful scrutiny of a subcommittee of two aldermen and four councillors assigned by the entire Assembly to survey and evaluate the property. The group was headed by Thomas Codde, who himself remained under close supervision.[63] On 11 May of that year the mayor, the mayor elect, the chamberlain and nine others were delegated to 'haue the vewe and ouersight of the reparacions of Master Cod don at the hospitall', which confirms that his position was no empty sinecure. It should be noted, too, that by the summer of 1549 rents from the city had doubled in value as compared with the 1535 figure, in part because Codde himself was paying the not insubstantial sum of £7 a year for the farm of the hospital precinct.[64] As we have seen in Chapter II, this would have brought him extensive pasture and meadowland, as well as valuable reserves of timber and roofing material.

ADVANCES AND REVERSALS

Codde's only surviving account as supervisor (or receiver general) covers the year ending 24 June 1549, and shows how much progress had been made in setting up the new poor house. Compiled in English rather than Latin, so that members of the Assembly would have no problems with the audit, his lengthy statement lists receipts of £204 (*recte* £200) from property and franchises, supplemented by a further £75 in 'foreign' or outside subventions of various kinds. These included one payment of £20 from the city chamberlain, who had clearly donated a similar sum the year before, and another raised by Thomas Sotherton for 'certen goodes and utensylles solde out of the hospitall to dyuers persons'. That the hospital church had already been stripped of its books, vestments, plate and furnishings is evident from the account itself, which is bound in one of the illuminated folios torn from a medieval missal [see Plates 42 and 43]. When Mary Tudor ascended the throne in 1553 and reintroduced 'roman' ritual, the surveyor was obliged to purchase a number of books and liturgical objects, including a processional, to replace what had been sold, lost or destroyed.[65] A further £20 came from the sale of lead from the parish church at Hardley and bells from the chapel at Bastwick, and thus helped to offset a repair bill of over £42 sustained by Codde during the process of rebuilding. *Ad hoc* contributions of this kind were desperately needed to make up a shortfall of almost £100 between landed income and expenditure. Despite his efforts to balance the books with the help of external funding, Codde's disbursements of £295 left him over £15 in the red, a figure roughly equivalent to the annual rents payable by the hospital to the Court of Augmentations, the dean and chapter of Norwich cathedral and other local landowners. Any lingering suspicions among his political opponents that the surveyorship might be milked for profit were by now clearly discredited. It is unlikely that Codde ever recovered all the short-term loans he advanced during this period.

The largest single item of expenditure sustained over the financial year 1548–9 was the cost of 'dyettes' for the forty 'poore folkes, men and women' already in residence. The total outlay of £80 was exactly half that envisaged in 1547, but the additional cost of fuel (£15 6*s* 7*d*), clothing (77*s* 11*d*) and burying the dead (9*s* 8*d*) meant that, on average, each pauper cost about 49*s* a year. As so often proved to be the case, savings made at the expense of the poor were consumed by inflated administrative expenses. At just over £103, the wages, 'dyettes' and liveries of hospital staff and the retainers paid to experts, such as the lawyer, John Corbet, and the auditor, John Pykerell, together constituted the greatest aggregate charge on the budget. Where possible, the authorities tried to follow the rates established in the indenture of 1547, but there were some variations. Nicholas Shaxton negotiated an additional 66*s* 8*d* a year, while two of the four nurses and the usher of the school received far less than their salaried entitlement, perhaps because they had not served for very long. On the other hand, each of the nurses and all of the other wage-earners were now allowed between 31*s* and 60*s* a year for food, which considerably improved their conditions of service. Additional fees, not recorded in King Edward's agreement, had also to be paid. Modest annuities totalling £6 6*s* 8*d* were assigned to parish priests at Seething, Mundham and Calthorpe, whose livings still lay in the hospital's gift. An even larger sum of £6 16*s* 8*d* was set aside for a practitioner of physical rather than spiritual medicine, the surgeon, John Porter.

The appearance on the payroll of one of the city's leading medical men, retained 'to gyue his dyligence to the poore peopull within the hospitall' at a salary slightly higher than that of the resident chaplain, John Fysher, reveals the extent to which priorities had shifted from spiritual to physical health [see Plate 44]. A few years earlier, the polemicist, Henry Brinklow, had advocated just such a measure, through the setting up in every English town of a hospital for the support of paupers, 'such as be not able to labor, syck, sore, blynd and lame':

> euery one of them to haue wherwith to lyue, and to haue pore whole women to mynystre vnto them . . . Let phisicyans and surgeons be found in euery such town or cyte, where such houses be, to loke vpon the pore in that towne and in all other ioyning vnto it; and thei to lyue vpon thier stipend only, without taking any peny of there pore, vpon payne of losing both his earys and his stypend also.[66]

The rulers of Norwich were pragmatic rather than sentimental. An experienced surgeon would be able to assess the needs and eligibility of prospective patients, determining who might be past hope, 'to the great lette and hinderaunce of the curing and helping of many other', while also identifying worthwhile cases likely to benefit from medical attention.[67] Since neither age nor physical decrepitude were, in themselves, deemed sufficient to prevent the labouring classes from earning a living, and thus escaping the snares of idleness, investment in a surgeon who could patch up anyone still capable of work must have seemed a profitable investment. As the Milanese humanist, Leon Battista Alberti, had remarked in the previous century, 'there is no-one so handicapped as to be incapable of making some form of contribution to society: even a blind man may be usefully employed in rope making'.[68] Since, as we have already seen, Norwich women in their seventies and eighties were still expected to spin, the services of such a practitioner might be said to pay for themselves.[69]

The recruitment of a prominent surgeon, as accustomed to the cut and thrust of the market place as he was to that of the operating table, was not without difficulties. Porter had already served twice as master of the Norwich guild of barbers and barber-surgeons, and perhaps for this reason found either the level of remuneration or the conditions of employment in the hospital unacceptable. He may have attempted to charge the inmates for treatment, or have used the hospital as a convenient place for seeing his own patients.[70] On 5 January 1549, the mayor's court learnt that he had been given two months' notice 'to leaue the same withoute that there be had somme other agrement'. A compromise was apparently reached, although by June Porter himself had taken umbrage. Turning a deaf ear to pleas from the civic authorities, he 'utterly refused' to renew his contract.[71] He was replaced by the surgeon, Thomas Reynolds, and the barber, William Belton, who between them received just £4 a year, and attended the poor conscientiously for some time.[72]

As had been agreed in 1547, the salaries of the master and usher of the city's grammar school became an immediate charge upon the hospital's budget, although the prospect of moving their pupils from Blackfriars to the precinct gradually began to recede. This was not because of any lack of commitment on the part of the authorities, initially at least. Now the chancel was no longer needed for elaborate liturgical ceremonies, the space could be put to other uses, and the old, pre-1383 layout reintroduced. It is hard to tell how badly in need of repair the fabric and furnishings may have been by this date, since years of neglect and uncertainty, as well as occasional iconoclasm, had undoubtedly taken their toll. At about this time, the mayor and aldermen of York found 'moche decay' at St Anthony's hospital, which they pronounced 'lyke to fall doune shortly except moche cost of reparacons be made'. Their decision to sell off the lead and tile to raise money for the building of a poor house and 'common scole' on the site thus seemed amply justified on practical as well as doctrinal grounds.[73] St Giles's was far from ruinous, but the prospect of restoring the church to its former glory was just as remote.

On 15 March 1549, the Assembly met to debate plans 'concerning the quere [chancel] of the late hospitall, whiche is thoughte mete and conuenyente to be usid for the gramer schole, and that the leade thereuppon mighte be taken of and amployid to some other use and so couerid with reede or tyle'. An alternative scheme for demolishing the chancel altogether and selling the fabric to help pay off some of the hospital's mounting debts also had many advocates. The mayor, five aldermen, the two sheriffs and eight councillors were accordingly despatched 'to the spitall' that very afternoon to see if any other buildings could be commandeered for the pupils instead.[74] The outcome of their visit is not recorded, but on 1 May the Assembly agreed that the entire chancel should be 'taken downe and solde to th'use of the citie'.[75] Ten days later two new surveyors of 'the landes and possessions of the late hospitall' were appointed for the ensuing year, one nominated by the aldermen and the other by the common councillors, while two aldermen and two councillors assumed the task of appraising whatever contents might still be offered for sale.[76] The six, carefully selected to avoid charges of factionalism, evidently preferred less drastic measures, for on 31 May the Assembly changed its mind again. The lead, paving stones, stalls and canopies were now to be sold as agreed, but the panelled ceiling, windows, ironwork, metal fittings and roof would remain.[77] The process of conversion from chancel into grammar school, which would have left the old infirmary to the west of the nave and some of the lodgings around the cloister available for the poor, may well have begun by the early summer of 1549. If so, little progress can have been made before the cataclysmic upheavals of July and August brought redevelopment to a halt.

The arrival on St Leonard's hill, just across the river from the hospital, of an army of insurgents several thousand strong marked the beginning of one of the most celebrated events in the history of Norwich, and, indeed, of the entire region. Now recognised as part of a widespread, and almost certainly coordinated, series of popular protests, or 'stirs', the uprising known as Kett's Rebellion was mounted in support of a coherent programme of social, agrarian and economic change.[78] As had been the case in 1381, its leaders were men of some substance, who spoke on behalf of the smallholder or tenant farmer, but they also addressed wider social issues. The fine rhetoric of reformers such as Protector Somerset and his friends had not been matched by their deeds. Despite the government's concern that its final, frontal assault on the doctrine of purgatory should not result in a diminution of almsgiving, it set a poor example. Covetousness and avarice had become 'the new idolatry' to be attacked by protestant polemicists and commonwealth men, such as Shaxton's erstwhile friend, Robert Crowley, with all the vituperation they had previously directed against the Church of Rome.[79] If anything, the situation of the poor and disadvantaged had grown worse, as their needs were pushed aside in the 'gadarene rush' for spoils generated by the second Chantry Act of December 1547. Crowley's satirical verses on the subject of a merchant who returns home from the Levant to find a 'lordely house' built on the site of his local hospital and the poor driven out 'to lye and dye in corners' expressed the keen sense of disillusionment felt by many like-minded radicals. Faced with the prospect of a wretched, impoverished old age, he argued, the young would more readily risk their lives in acts of open rebellion.[80]

The dismantling of the disciplinary structures of the Roman Church, and the relative freedom accorded to the promptings of individual conscience in protestant England encouraged a distrust of authority which went far beyond the questioning of religious dogma. Acutely sensitive to the possibility that controversy might spill over into physical violence, the rulers of Norwich tried hard to exercise a restraining influence.[81] They encountered a difficult task, compounded by a succession of worsening economic and social problems. Individual acts of charity no longer sufficed to allay the prospect of disorder, yet the alternatives offered no sure hope of success. In London, a meteoric rise in food prices had prompted the introduction, in October 1547, of the City's first compulsory poor rate.[82] It was at this time that the mayor and aldermen, like those of Norwich, began the difficult and costly business of restructuring hospital provision, an undertaking made all the harder by the influx of paupers into the capital.[83] The money thus raised was earmarked for the 'sustentacyon, maynteynyng and fyndyng' of 'poore sicke and indigent persones' in the newly refounded and chronically underfunded hospital of St Bartholomew.[84] But it was demonstrably insufficient. Similar problems, albeit on a far less dramatic scale, were apparent throughout East Anglia. As the royal commissioners appointed to survey the remaining chantries and religious houses reported shortly afterwards, Bury St Edmunds had suffered badly in the aftermath of dissolution, being left without any school in a radius of twenty miles 'for the vertuous educacyon and bringing upp of yowth, nor eny hospytall or other lyke foundacion for the cumforte or relieffe of the pouer, of whiche theare is an excedinge greate nombre . . .'.[85]

Ambitious lawyers, such as John Corbet, who ruthlessly exploited holdings acquired through the dismemberment of ecclesiastical property, aroused particular animosity. Corbet had built up a sizeable estate just outside Norwich, to which, in June 1548, he added the former leper house of St Mary Magdalen, its 144 acres of land and extensive grazing rights.[86] The sale of the hospital and its attached chapel to a parvenu landowner may itself have provoked considerable indignation, although it is clear from the *Valor Ecclesiasticus* that patients were no longer housed there. The loss of the chapel caused far less outrage than its conversion to a pigeon loft or dovecote, since the birds devastated the crops of neighbouring tenant farmers. As the rebels hastened towards their camp they ripped up enclosures and destroyed part of the old *leprosarium*, which now so clearly symbolised the failure of the new commonwealth.[87] Their relations with the rulers of Norwich were more ambivalent. A highly coloured account of the ensuing 'commoycion' written by Nicholas Sotherton, who belonged to one of the most influential families in the city, attempted to play down the early participation of his friends and kinsmen in the stirs. Yet the mayor, none other than Thomas Codde, and his senior colleagues were frequent visitors to the rebel camp, where they took an active – if cautious – part in deliberations. Only after Kett's rejection of royal letters of pardon, on 21 July, did they put the city on a defensive footing, while Codde himself assumed a role halfway between hostage and reluctant collaborator. By then, however, battle lines had been drawn. Although Sotherton sought to exculpate the civic elite by portraying Kett's supporters in the worst possible light, he did not exaggerate the effect of the 'campyng tyme' upon the hospital. The diversion of food supplies to the rebels probably deprived the inmates of regular provisions from the outset, but once the gates had been closed the threat became more immediate. On 21 July, 'the ordenaunce of the cyttie was placed alongst the ryuer with good guard of men in the hospitall myddowes, for that it was weakest place; and, as they of the cyttie shott at them, [the rebels] did the lyke into the cyttie all the nyght.'[88] Resistance proved futile and Kett's men were easily able to ford the Wensum and breach the defences of Bishopgate [see Plate 3]. Coming and going along Holme Street during the next few days, they evidently left the paupers and their keepers in peace, although the elderly patients can hardly have been unaffected by such a disturbance. Nicholas Shaxton remained in residence at the hospital, where he contrived to maintain a semblance of order. Between 21 June and 1 August he spent just over £10 on the 'dyettes of xl poore folkes with officers and kepers', together with the latter's fees and wages, which suggests that it was possible to follow a relatively normal routine.[89]

The somewhat belated arrival on 30 July of the marquess of Northampton at the head of a relief force led to renewed fighting. After a rash but initially successful move against the insurgents, Northampton was taken by surprise two days later as they once again crossed the river at Bishopgate, 'the rebels in great rage entring the citie by the hospitall'. The opposing forces clashed just a few hundred yards further west, outside the bishop's palace, where 'there insued a bloudie conflict betwixt them, which continued long with great fiercenesse and eger reuenge on both parts'.[90] The young Lord Sheffield was killed in a skirmish 'about the hospital corner by founding of his horse in a dyke', and the marquess panicked. He and his followers fled in total disarray, 'euerie man making the best shift he could to saue himselfe'.[91] Furious at what they saw as an act of betrayal by members of the civic elite, Kett's men exacted immediate reprisals. Sotherton's description of the triumphant army as a gang of ill-disciplined and rapacious savages ranks as propaganda rather than accurate reportage, although his account of the devastation along Bishopgate can be fully corroborated. 'The rebellis had set the whole howses in the streete callid Holmstreete afyer on both sydes', he noted, 'with a greett part of the hospitall, howses of office that longid to the poore in that howse, and allsoe the cyttie gates called Bishop gates, with the leade therof molten.'[92]

This was a period of real crisis for the hospital, as all forms of organisation collapsed. Shaxton seems to have fled Norwich with the marquess, leaving his priest to cope alone in the ruins without any supplies or the funds to buy them. In the apparent absence of the master, the task of feeding the forty paupers was shouldered by John Fysher, who valiantly kept the wolf from the door by begging. 'Almes of goode peopull by him collected' between 1 and 22 August comprised two barrels of beer, six gallons of ale, six bushels of grain, thirty-four loaves, three cheeses and a modest amount of salted fish. Donations of about 56*s* also helped to tide the hospital over until the royal council at Westminster was able to reassert its authority.[93] A second and much larger expeditionary force left London in mid-August under the command of the earl of Warwick, who had clearly learned from his predecessor's mistakes. On his arrival the rebels were driven from the city, causing further damage at Bishopgate and killing a number of its defenders. A few returned on 'Black Sunday', 25 August, to set fire to the waterfront area in Conisford, where the hospital also owned property.[94] Sobered by this harrowing experience, the rulers of Norwich were left to survey the smoking rubble and reconsider their plans for God's House.

The annual accounts submitted in June 1550 by Thomas King, a minor civic official who acted as rent collector for the new receiver, alderman Thomas Necton, paint a gloomy picture of widespread devastation in and around the precinct. Codde's departure from office, almost certainly as a result of the traumatic events of the previous summer, had heightened the sense of dislocation, although he continued to take an active interest in the hospital's affairs. No tithes or offerings could be collected by John Fysher for the upkeep of St Helen's church because 'the hooll strete whiche belong to the same is brente by the rebelles in the commocyion tyme'.[95] The hospital's losses comprised nine tenements, two messuages and three houses in Holme Street, and a tenement in Conisford, all of which had been totally destroyed. At least the sites were still attractive to redevelopers, such as the consortium of four investors fronted by Thomas Codde, who secured by far the lion's share of the newly vacant land.[96] The precinct, which Codde had leased for £7 a year, was, however, temporarily left 'destitute of a fermour by reason of the commocyon and brynnyng' until Necton took over in March 1550. Here, too, a number of houses and outbuildings had been torched by Kett's men. But by far the greatest long-term damage was sustained along the south side of the old infirmary. The aisle nearest to the street was destroyed and only partially rebuilt and releaded much later, in 1585, giving the west end of the building, beyond the medieval nave, the asymmetrical appearance it still has today [see Plate 26]. Part of the chancel may also have been burnt, as repairs were then also effected to 'certain decayed placys on the southyle over the womens beddes'.[97] When restoration work began on the ceiling in the 1950s the architect found that 'a part of its east end had at one time been damaged by fire' and the surrounding 'begrimed untouched portion' clumsily repainted.[98]

Notwithstanding these reversals, receipts from the hospital's property in Norwich (£33) and its country estates (£162) over the year ending June 1550 were only £5 down on the previous year. This was partly because of the generosity of Edmund Wood, who had died in office as mayor in autumn 1548, leaving a number of charitable bequests for civic improvement. Among them were legacies of £20 for the education of poor children in the city, of £100 for removing 'the filthe of the streates after the manner and custume of London' and of £40 to provide subsidised grain for the poor in times of famine. As well as setting aside £20 to be spent over the next five years on 'healing poore diseased personnes', he assigned a number of tenements in Norwich for the support of God's House.[99] The property in question lay in St Saviour's parish to the north of the Wensum and earned the hospital almost £7 in the following year. The gift was opportune, but served merely to make good some of the losses caused by Kett's men; it did not increase the rent roll as Wood had intended. The prospect of solvency was now even more remote than it had been in 1548, and seemed in the aftermath of the rebellion to be fast retreating. In reality, the hospital was in no position to survive unaided, and could not afford to repair, let alone convert, what remained of the medieval buildings. The corporation could no longer postpone the reckoning; an immediate and substantial injection of capital was clearly needed if the enterprise was not to founder. Kett's Rebellion proved to be the catalyst for renewed action. Fear among the wealthier householders of Norwich that the local poor, many of whom had supported the insurgents, might once again rise up to devastating effect provided fertile soil for the nascent programme of charitable relief.

The mayor and aldermen had previously encountered some resistance to the idea of parish rates and other compulsory levies for the benefit of the poor. At least two attempts had been made in 1548 to list the names of potential contributors with an eye to eliciting far larger and more regular donations along the lines recently assayed in London. In May 1549, on the very eve of Kett's rebellion, the authorities had been given sweeping powers to assess what each male resident could afford, if necessary imprisoning anyone who refused to pay.[100] The response was now more positive. By the end of June 1550, no less than £283 had been paid into the hospital's coffers from outside sources, bringing net receipts up to a promising £479. The sale of paving stones and other parts of the chancel finally went ahead after understandable delays and fetched £25. The commissioners appointed to oversee the auction shrewdly decided to cut their losses by offering bricks, tiles and assorted materials salvaged from the precinct on the open market as well, and were thus able to raise a further £13. But these relatively modest contributions merely served to pay off personal loans made by the two aldermen, Thomas Codde and Thomas Morley, leaving larger debts of £84 'whiche the sayd howse dyd owe to the comminalte of the cite syns the first tym it was apteynd' still unsettled. To meet this substantial charge, the Assembly decided, on 29 November 1549, to levy a special tax or 'aeyde of the poore' throughout the city on terms to be agreed by the mayor and aldermen.[101] In all, just over £80 was collected at this time and used by Thomas Codde to satisfy some of the creditors who, like himself, had helped to bear the immediate cost of securing St Giles's from the Crown and setting the new foundation on its feet.[102]

Further subventions followed. In the current climate of iconoclasm and evangelical reform the corporation found it relatively easy to dismantle three of the city's poorer churches, selling off the fabric and contents to raise more money for the hospital.[103] The parish church of St Clement, Conisford, which may have been partially destroyed by Kett's men, was designated a free chapel by the corporation. It could thus be dissolved under the terms of the second Chantry Act and converted to secular use after such saleable items as the lead, bells and stonework of the north aisle had been removed. To the purchase price of £27 paid by Leonard Sotherton for the site was added a further £6 for 'marbyll stones and other pavements', all the profits being earmarked for God's House.[104] So too was a sum of £62 raised by Thomas Marsham from the fabric of St Crouch's church, Pottergate, and another of £49 from All Saints' church near the Magdalen Gate, both areas having also sustained heavy damage during the recent uprising. These two churches had been acquired from the dean and chapter and were promptly demolished, in the latter instance to the great dismay of the parishioners, who were forced to surrender their plate as well. Two silver chalices had been removed to safety by the churchwardens, but despite their obvious reluctance to part with treasures from their catholic past every remaining asset was commandeered to discharge the hospital's debts.[105] Although Marsham retained £40 in his own hands as a reserve, and the dean and chapter demanded a payment of £27 to buy out their interest, the situation had begun to look far healthier. Indeed, Thomas King's technical deficit of £8 at the close of his long and complex account for 1549–50 gives an erroneous impression of overspending, since about £33 had already been set aside for structural repairs 'within the seyte of the seid poore house'. As a precaution in the event of further disorder, provisions worth as much again had, moreover, been laid in for use over the next financial year. The auditor and four surveyors who approved and signed this document had good reason to feel more optimistic, even though the hospital had not yet fought its way to complete recovery.

THE SCHOLARS AND THE POOR

It was now generally accepted that God's House would require a sizeable injection of capital every year for the foreseeable future. The experimental 'aeyde' of November 1549 seemed well worth repeating, not least because it spread the financial burden more equitably. In 1550–1 the churchwardens of seventeen city parishes raised a second, more substantial 'benevolence' of £170 'towardes the releif, ayde and conforth of the poore peopull' in the hospital and, more specifically, to help augment the existing endowment.[106] Although, in contrast to 1549, contributions appear to have been voluntary, similar procedures obtained. Collections on this scale had not previously been assayed in provincial England and mark another step towards the implementation of a coherent policy for poor relief in Norwich. They certainly merit favourable comparison with efforts made in London between 1547 and 1552 to get the near-bankrupt hospital of St Bartholomew back into commission.[107] Here the medieval estates, which Henry VIII had restored to the citizens on the condition that they would provide additional property to the same value, had failed to produce more than a fraction of estimated income. Disputes, slander and 'priue backebityng' had also dogged the enterprise, prompting the civic authorities to publish a detailed account of the measures taken for governing the house. They claimed that some 800 patients had been cured of 'pocques, fystules, fithie blaynes and sores' during its first five years, while a further ninety-two had 'forsaken this life . . . whiche elles might haue died and stoncke in the iyes and noses of the Citie'. It is impossible to verify these figures, but there can be no doubt that the cost of 'beddyng and shifte for so many sore and diseased, and the excessyue prices of all thynges at this day' proved a heavy financial burden for the Londoners concerned.[108]

Notwithstanding the obvious differences of size and function, similar problems occurred at God's House, Norwich. As late as November 1551, Thomas Codde, Thomas Necton and his receiver, Thomas King, were between them still owed at least £56, which they had provided out of their own coffers to support the hospital inmates. This was partly because escalating food prices made it impossible to keep within the strict budget set by the corporation. Necton claimed to have lost over £5 through inflation ('by reasoun of the falle of money') during the time it had taken to settle his account, and to have spent a further £10 because of 'the derthe and skarcenes of gryene and victuelles'.[109] He did not exaggerate. In the aftermath of Kett's rebellion the city assigned over £200 for the purchase of wheat and rye 'to voyde a greate dearthe which is thought to be and ensewe hereafter'. Fear at the prospect of further disorder loosened the purse-strings of the wealthy citizens, who once again subsidised the sale of grain at 'reasonable pryces to the poore' throughout the early summer of 1550.[110] Perhaps for this reason the rulers of Norwich were spared the charges of incompetence, malversation of revenues and indifference to the fate of the needy which dogged the aldermen concerned with St Bartholomew's. Nor did they have to cope with such a large, and constantly growing regiment of sick paupers. But the problem of finding a home for the free school was no nearer a solution, especially as the men and women living in God's House could no longer use the half-devastated infirmary and had, presumably, taken up residence in the chancel. The possibility of accommodating the scholars in the precinct now seemed remote, and alternative lodgings had to be found nearby. Having shared with the medieval hospital of St Giles an obligation to commemorate the dead, it seemed appropriate that Bishop Salmon's chantry should now be used to help God's House educate the living. The chapel, with its charnel house below, had been seized by the Crown in 1548, and sold, in July of that year, to the ubiquitous Richard Catlyn. Its next owner, Robert Jermy, agreed to release his title to God's House for a cash payment of £67, which was allocated out of civic funds at a meeting of the Assembly in September 1550.[111] Over the next few years considerable sums were expended by the mayor and aldermen in converting 'the charnel' into a school, where the names and arms of benefactors from Edward VI downwards were prominently displayed.[112] The hospital precinct thus remained the preserve of the poor, whose standards of living and behaviour had already become a matter of some concern to the corporation.

Like so many other events in his turbulent career, the departure of Nicholas Shaxton in October 1550 did not pass without controversy. That his priest, John Fysher, was in many ways better suited to the daily round of supervising elderly and often difficult patients had probably become apparent long before the crisis of August 1549. Perhaps Shaxton was invited to resign. He may, on the other hand, have felt that he had served out his time in the wilderness and could now go back to Cambridge in the hope of better things. In this he was not disappointed: the accession of Queen Mary four years later brought him preferment as suffragan bishop of Ely, and the welcome opportunity to revenge himself upon those who had so cruelly mocked his return to the catholic fold. Two evangelicals were, indeed, condemned by him to death at the stake and he sat in judgement upon another. Yet in one respect his departure proved a heavy blow for the hospital, which was contractually obliged to redeem his pension at a cost of £80. Over half the 'benevolence' raised by the people of Norwich that year left the city in his coffers, while £25 of the rest went to pay off new loans advanced by Thomas Codde.[113]

Nor, as John Fysher made plain to the corporation at this time, were the hospital's difficulties solely financial. During Shaxton's mastership 'dyuers abusys' of a disciplinary nature had evidently gone unchecked, with the result that the inmates (engagingly described by the Victorian antiquaries, William Hudson and J.C. Tingey, as 'a very rough assembly') had grown rebellious and quarrelsome.[114] Protesting that only 'godly peple' should live in God's House, Fysher suggested twelve basic rules, to be read to each patient upon arrival, and again every three months, 'for the more *erudycyon* to them seluys and *quyett* in the howss'. His proposals provide a vivid – if not unbiased – picture of life in the new institution, and confirm that the majority of residents were comparatively mobile. The requirement that each of them should attend church for four hours every day (rising before six in summer) followed the practice of many medieval almshouses, although the obligation to intercede on behalf of departed benefactors had now given way to the need for self-improvement through private prayer and study of the scriptures. As well as receiving communion every three months, those who could walk were expected to attend sermons at the cathedral. Here Fysher admitted defeat, complaining that many inmates 'able to goo al the cyte ouer, and sume of them the cuntry also' would not cross the road to the preaching yard. His will of 1556 reveals an evangelical enthusiasm for a well-turned sermon, and suggests that this particular dereliction rankled more than the rest.[115] When, in the 1570s, arrangements were made by the mayor for the keeper and his wife to maintain and educate twelve poor children at the hospital so they might be apprenticed to reputable trades, the couple received orders 'uppon the holidaies to bringe them to sermounes, that they may learne to encreast in vertue, and be apt to serve with such good citizens as maie take them . . .'[116] It is uncertain when the pulpit, which now stands at the centre of the east end of St Helen's church, was first placed in this dominant position, but the word, as opposed to the macerated body, of God clearly assumed priority in the new hospital at an early stage.

Some residents had taken to wandering off and returning 'dronkyn hoome at euen with talys inowe', a habit which led Fysher to insist, as Walter Suffield had done before him, that they should never leave the precincts alone, or without permission.[117] Drunkenness, a particular bane of the godly commonwealth, elicited a harsh response. The Norwich-born physician, John Caius, blamed heavy alcohol consumption by the proletariat in ale-houses for the spread of sweating sickness at this time, while attempts to control the unruly poor of York focused upon the same threat to moral and physical health.[118] A sin in itself, inebriation so often proved the first step on the slippery slope to perdition. More immediately, it made the inmates truculent and prone to fisticuffs. Almost half of Fysher's proposed reforms were intended to prevent the fights and raucous squabbles which appear to have been a regular feature of life in the hospital both by day and by night. Since the deaf, who presumably shouted the loudest, were notable offenders in this respect, Fysher suggested that public and very visible punishments should be inflicted 'that the syht of ther eye myht reforme them to a dew ordyr'. To this end he proposed putting miscreants in the stocks, while also depriving those who brawled at meal times of their food. The antithesis of that 'quietness and obedience' so desirable in the model patient, as also in the model subject, noise was widely regarded as a sign of disorder, incontinence and defiance.[119] It clearly merited firm and very visible chastisement. But some patterns of behaviour were irredeemable and timeless: 'Wan I haue a beryall', Fysher protested, 'the men wylle nat help to bere them to ther grauys but make excusys and lat the women do ytt.'[120]

Another problem, which had exercised the founders of hospitals for centuries, was the understandable reluctance shown by inmates with possessions of their own to share them with others. Nor, as death approached, were they any readier to name the institution as sole, or even chief, beneficiary of whatever dispositions they might be able to make. Given the financial constraints within which God's House had initially to operate, the fate of even a few clothes, blankets or utensils was a matter of pressing concern. Fysher's remarks on this score suggest that some of his charges were far from destitute, and this fact alone may explain why petty theft preoccupied him so much. Indeed, with the passage of time, life at God's House became relatively comfortable, as Sir Richard Southwell's bequest of 1561 for the purchase of additional beds reveals. Sheets, mattresses and counterpanes to the value of £20 had already been provided by William Rogers, the alderman who had first proposed that St Giles's should be acquired by the city. He, too, was worried about pilfering, although his insistence that all linen should be marked, itemised and examined regularly by his executors suggests that he mistrusted the staff as well as the patients.[121]

As had previously been the case, the task of washing bedding and clothes fell to the four nurses. Some 'apparell' was provided for the paupers at a cost of about 78*s* in 1548–9, but laundry facilities remained minimal until enough money could be found to equip a separate wash-house. Although the civic authorities placed great stress upon the need to keep the poor cleanly and decently covered, standards of hygiene had initially to be maintained on a shoestring. In July 1549 the mayor's court rejected a request for 'a coper ketill with a gret tob . . . to wasshe the pore men's clothes theryn', presumably because of the cost. The nurses had thus to make do with 'two broken tubbes to boke and wasshe with', until in 1553 the keeper was allowed to spend £7 on this relatively expensive item.[122] It was then that the guild of St George, quite probably at the prompting of Thomas Codde, agreed to provide enough woollen cloth each year to make gowns for thirteen of the forty paupers 'releaved by the late hospitall nowe called Godes Howse in Holmestrete'. Each gown was to sport a 'conysaunce' or badge, which presumably incorporated the red cross of St George and served to identify the wearer as a client, or even past member, of Norwich's most powerful fraternity. For the previous five years the surveyors of the guild had presented a gown, a dinner and a modest dole to twelve poor men on St George's day, on the clear understanding that 'if any of them be admitted into the hospitall, then and ffrom thens furth the almes of the seide Company immediatly . . . to cease'. Now their generosity extended further, as, almost certainly, did their ability to influence the selection procedure, perhaps to the extent of reserving places for the respectable, 'shamefaced' poor.[123]

A second legacy from William Rogers and another from his widow made £30 available over the next six years for the provision of 'hoses, shirtes, shooes and other thinges necessary' for the paupers, who continued to rely upon private donations for all but their basic requirements.[124] As we have already seen in the case of the medieval almsmen, frugality did not necessarily imply indifference: at least when the authorities could expect so much practical support from outside. Where possible, they hoped that residents would be treated compassionately, however trying their behaviour. From time to time during these early years, specific items of clothing were bought for individual inmates, such as John Call, who received a new pair of shoes. On another occasion no less than 10*s* was spent in redeeming a feather bed pledged by one of the paupers as a security against a loan. The construction of a chimney in the medieval chancel shortly after Kett's rebellion suggests that the importance of keeping elderly men and women warm in such a cold and draughty building was fully recognised. At over £20 a year, expenditure on fuel was generous enough to provide open fires throughout the winter.

Food purchases are not itemised in the accounts for this period, although the standard diet is unlikely to have changed much since the early sixteenth century. Numerous barrels were bought for storing the home-brewed ale and beer which still constituted a staple source of nutrients. The acquisition of a milch cow 'for the releif of the poore' in 1550–1 provided milk for butter and cheese, while the installation of a new horse mill and oven ensured that corn could be ground for baking in the kitchens.[125] By 1566, the date of the first surviving contract made with a resident keeper, it was understood that the poor would be 'fedd with no courser bread then whole wheat bread without either rye or barlye to be putt and myxed therwith', a perceived improvement which would have significantly reduced levels of fibre, but must have been welcomed by elderly men and women with poor dentition. The keeper and his nurses were likewise bound 'well and gently [to] use and intreate the seid xl pore people and euery of them at all tymes, without eny correcion or beatyng of them or eny of them'. In theory, at least, care was by then taken to ensure that ample supplies of fuel would always be stored in the hospital; that a reserve of £26 would be kept there for the purchase of food in emergencies; and that places would be filled as soon as inmates died or moved on. The corporation insisted upon full accountability: not only were all admissions, deaths and departures to be entered in a ledger, but the possessions left by inmates and other testators, 'either of beddyng, sheetis, shirtes and smockes lynnen and woollen or monye', were to be listed promptly in full.[126]

As had been the case during the Middle Ages, the need for proper record-keeping was taken seriously. In 1561 'Master Mayour' exchanged 'stowte wordes' with the warden and his wife because of their failure to keep a 'note and boke' of 'souche gyftes and benyvolence of lynen and wollen and other gyfts'.[127] Vigilance on this score, which would have pleased John Fysher, was a necessary response to the steady stream of legacies now being made to the hospital by those men and women who had been instrumental in helping to secure it for the city. Few could afford the largesse of Augustine Steward, one of the wealthiest men in Elizabethan Norwich, whose gift of five tenements in St Swithun's parish, Westwick, was intended to accommodate poor widows 'of good name and fame' chosen on the hospital's recommendation.[128] Yet some, such as the house's first chaplain, Robert Dowe, are noteworthy because of their evident attachment to the inmates and their determination that the new foundation should survive a difficult birth. Dowe set aside almost all his modest estate for 'the relief and helpe of th'impotent and pore people' in 1552, at the end of an eventful career which had begun in the choir of St Giles's and ended among the paupers of God's House.[129] Unlike his former colleague, Robert Codde, he died secure in the knowledge that the hospital would endure.

ANOTHER UTOPIA?

Survival now effectively guaranteed, God's House and its governors embarked upon a steady process of expansion over the next half century. Net annual income rose from an average of £334 in the 1560s to over £420 in the 1580s, significant acquisitions being made after the Census of the Poor, in 1570, had once again alerted the ruling elite to the need for further investment. A gift of estates in and around the manor of Cringleford, one of the hospital's core medieval properties, came from Elizabeth I in 1571 from the confiscated holdings of the traitor, William Redmayne, underscoring the house's role as a bastion of the established secular order, just as it had once supported the authority of the Church.[130] In a programme remarkably similar to that already encountered in the early fourteenth century, loans were raised and gifts solicited in order to consolidate the hospital's territorial possessions and support a larger establishment. The number of resident paupers was duly augmented to fifty-four, which (along with the constant problem of inflation) accounts for the rise of almost £70 a year in outgoings sustained for their upkeep. Among these expenses, it is worth noting the annuity of £10 paid to Richard Durrant, who had initially been retained by the corporation for 'the releyfe of souch as shall fortune . . . to haue their legges, armes or the bones of other partes of ther lymes to be broken, and of souche as be poore and not able to pay for ther heling'.[131] At the same time, drastic changes were made to the surviving fabric, the most notable being the construction of stone partitions completely separating the parish church of St Helen from the old infirmary hall (to the west) and chancel (to the east) [see Plate 46]. The decision to house female paupers in the chancel was as a great an act of iconoclasm as any perpetrated at St Giles's since the Dissolution. The sacred space hitherto reserved for the priests, choristers and chaplains and the ritual of the Mass was to be occupied, and in some eyes profaned, for the next 400 years by a succession of elderly women, the insertion of a chimney on the site previously occupied by the high altar and the subdivision of the building into two storeys adding further insult to injury. The men were housed on the other side of the nave, in the infirmary.

Since all bonds for the purchase of paradise had been declared null and void, and the celestial treasury laid up by their ancestors pronounced bankrupt, we may conclude by asking what the rulers of Norwich hoped to achieve at God's House. Had the time, labour and money expended in converting a medieval hospital into a Tudor poor house produced the desired return? Fifty-four paupers, many of whom were clearly nominated by the guild of St George or individual aldermen, represented a mere drop in the ocean of human misery as it washed through the streets of early modern Norwich. In statistical terms, the new hospital could accommodate approximately one-third of 1 per cent of the city's population in the late 1570s, although the intention had never at any time been to create a centralised institution for the reception of large numbers of sick poor along continental lines. Hesitant attempts in London to reorganise the City's hospitals according to a Parisian or Florentine model were, indeed, doomed to failure, the diversion of financial support into more traditional schemes for parochial relief depriving these nascent institutions of the capital essential for proper development.[132] The rulers of Norwich were more pragmatic, aiming at an integrated system, which, where possible, would utilise the existing structure of the medieval parish for the distribution of aid, while providing limited care for the terminally sick, the infectious, the disabled and the elderly in specialist institutions. Additional help for the unemployed and other high-risk groups, such as women with children, came through the provision of subsidised or free housing for those in greatest need. By 1570 some 300 people were living in accommodation made available by the civic and ecclesiastical authorities, a significant number of these dwellings being located in the precinct of St Paul's hospital and in property which had previously belonged to St Giles's in the north of the city.[133] At least fifteen adults and seventeen children were, moreover, then lodging in the purlieus of God's House itself, their circumstances ranging from 'indeferent' to 'veri pore', and their presence testifying to a significant change in the nature and purpose of charitable effort from medieval times. If the fundamental rationale was now to put the poor to work, separating them from the contaminating influence of feckless vagrants and other outsiders, God's House (which also boasted a modest school for poor children) offered the obedient and compliant pauper a prospect of labour rewarded and a secure old age [see Plate 45]. It was as much a showcase for conspicuous altruism on the part of an elite frightened by civic unrest, as St Giles's had been a sturdy defence against the imagined fires of purgatory and miasmas of heresy. The efficacy of this new approach impressed Sir John Harrington, when he visited Norwich at the beginning of the next century. 'I should judge this city to be another Utopia', he observed. 'The people live so orderly, the streets kept so cleanly, the tradesmen, young and old, so industrious, the better sort so provident and withal so charitable, that it is rare to meet a beggar.'[134] He spoke without irony, having perhaps forgotten that Thomas More's imaginary island was notable for the elimination of any social undesirables likely to upset the calm and cleanliness of public life.[135]

APPENDIX I
THE STATUTES OF ST GILES'S HOSPITAL

Two manuscript copies of Bishop Suffield's second foundation charter (text B) survive. The first, which appears below in translation from the original Latin, is a near-contemporary copy of Pope Alexander IV's confirmation of 15 October 1257, and is preserved in the archives of the Dean and Chapter of Norwich cathedral (NRO, DCN 43/48). The second is a copy of the *inspeximus* of Alexander's letters issued in 1272 by Roger Skerning, bishop of Norwich, which is to be found among the legal material recorded by the civic authorities in their mid-fifteenth-century Book of Pleas. Entered under the heading 'Foundation of the Hospital of St Giles in Norwich', this is a corrupt text containing a number of minor errors and omissions (NRO, NCR, 17B, Book of Pleas, fos 48r–50r). It appears, along with a copy of William Dunwich's grant of land and rents in Holme Street to the hospital, between a rental of acquisitions made by the same authorities in 1377–78 (fo 47v) and evidence relating to purchases of property by the Norwich Carmelites (fo 50r).

Suffield's second, and evidently definitive, set of statutes drew heavily upon his first foundation charter, known to us in three thirteenth-century copies (NRO, NCR, 24B, nos 1 and 3; DCN 40/7, fos 76r–78v). In order to give a clear sense of the changes and improvements he wished to make, significant words and phrases which appear in the first charter (text A), but which were omitted from, or altered in, the second, are here italicised in square brackets. Suffield's additions to the first charter are denoted in bold print.

For ease of reference each article or ruling has been numbered, although neither the first nor the second charters use either enumeration or paragraphs, being set out in continuous prose. The numbers in round brackets denote the order in which each article appears in the first charter. The author is grateful to Miss M.M. Condon and Dr Robert Ball for their assistance in preparing this Appendix.

Alexander, the bishop, servant of the servants of God, to his beloved, the master and brethren of the hospital of St Giles, Norwich, greeting and apostolic benediction. When what is just and honest is sought from us, both the force of justice and the order of reason require that it should be put into effect through the solicitude of our office. Your petition shown to us explained that Walter, bishop of Norwich, of blessed memory, considering those rewards by which the king of eternal clemency repays zeal for mercy, founded on his own estate in the city of Norwich, from the goods which he had acquired by his own industry, in honour of the Holy and undivided Trinity, the glorious Virgin Mary, the blessed Anne, mother of that glorious Virgin, the blessed Giles and all the saints, the hospital in which you live the communal life, ordaining, among other things, that for all time there should be in the same hospital a master, who should diligently take care of the same, both in spirituals and temporals; and that four lay brethren should reside there continually to give faithful attention to the business of the hospital according to the disposition and order of the said master, both within the hospital and without, as is more fully contained in the letters of the same bishop made in this behalf. We therefore, harkening to your prayers, validating what was piously and prudently done by the same bishop, confirm it by apostolic authority, and strengthen it with the support of this present writing. Now we have caused the tenor of the said letters to be written down word for word, which is as follows:

Hail Mary, full of grace, the Lord is with thee, in the name of **the Holy and Undivided Trinity**, the Father, Son and Holy Ghost, Amen. We, Walter, **by the Mercy of God, bishop of Norwich** [A: '*although unworthy*'], omitting all **verbose** commentary and preface [A: '*of any kind*'], have decided to express **by these presents** the purpose and intent which we have long had in mind [A: '*for which we have laboured*'], and the desire which surpasses **and exceeds** every longing of our heart, ordaining, defining and enacting that the things contained in the present writing should be **inviolably** observed for all time.

1. (1) First, we have founded the hospital, which is called of the blessed Giles, in the city of Norwich in honour of the Holy **and Undivided** Trinity, the Glorious Virgin Mary, the blessed Anne, **mother of the Glorious Virgin**, the blessed Giles, and all the saints, on our estate and land which is of the fee of our church **of Norwich, acquired by our industry from the free tenants of the same**.
2. (2) Of which hospital one end extends to [A: '*the head abuts on*'] the street opposite the church of St Helen, beneath the wall of the court of the prior and convent of Norwich. And in width it stretches to the north as far as **the bank of** the great river flowing by [A: '*running through*'] the said city. And in length it stretches towards **the bridge called** bishop's bridge, as far as the ditch which lies between our fee and the fee of the **noble matron**, Lady Isabel de Cressy.
3. (3) **Moreover**, we will and have ordained that there be in this hospital in perpetuity a master to take **good** care of the same hospital, **both in temporals and in spirituals as we rehearse below, and this we enjoin upon him** for the remission of sins.
4. (17) There shall also be four lay brethren there to attend **diligently and faithfully** to the business of the hospital according to the disposition and ordinance of the master, both within the hospital and without.
5. (12, 13) There shall also be [A: '*in the house at least*'] three or four women [A: '*sisters*'] there, of good life and honest **conversation**, approved over many years, being fifty years old or a little less, to take **good** [A: '*charge and*'] care of all the infirm and other **sick** lying there. They shall change the sheets and other bed clothes as often as necessary, **and serve them humbly in necessary things as far as they are able**; and we **firmly** forbid that there shall be more women there, but everything should be done by the men, both in the brewhouse and in the other offices.

6. (4) The master shall **also** have with him four priests [A: '*chaplains*'] of **good fame and** honest conversation, **and well** instructed in the divine office, **also two clerks, to wit a deacon and a sub-deacon**, attending chiefly to divine service and worship, **besides those things which Our Lord Jesus Christ shall inspire**. Each of them shall specially observe this form:
7. (5) All shall rise [A: '*in the morning*'] at dawn when the great bell strikes, and leave the dormitory together [A: '*at the same time*'] and enter the church together, dressed in surplices and black, **round closed** copes. They shall sing [A: '*say*'] matins and the **other** hours with due chant and measured delivery, and immediately celebrate the mass of the day solemnly [A: '*with chant*']; **and the brethren and the sisters shall be there and hear divine service reverently**. And let none of them **presume to** leave the church or wander about the buildings or precinct before these things are finished, the master excepted, who may go out for necessary cause, and may give licence to the others to go out [A: '*with good cause*'] **for the utility of the house**.
8. **And in the offices of the Church we wish the use of the church of Sarum to be followed.**
9. (6) **We will and ordain also that** three masses should be celebrated in the hospital every day: one **the mass** of the day; the second of the Blessed Virgin **Mary**; and the third of the dead. Provided that one day each week there is a full service of St Giles, unless **it happens that it be hindered by the service of** [A: '*in time of*'] Lent or other [A: '*continuous*'] solemn feasts.
10. **After divine service is over the priests and clerks shall not wander about the city or other streets, but shall spend the day in reading, prayer, visiting the sick and other works of charity, unless by the order and licence of the master they should occupy themselves in other useful and honest business. We wish the same thing to be observed both by the brethren and the sisters. And in giving such licences, as in correction and other matters, the master shall be prudent and discreet.**
11. (12) **And** in this hospital there shall be thirty beds or more, according to its means, with mattresses and sheets and coverlets for the use of the infirm poor, so that when any poor man beset by illness comes thither he shall be **received kindly and** taken care of honestly [A: '*and appropriately*'] as befits his illness, until he is restored to health. **And when he is made well, everything he has brought with him shall be restored faithfully to him and he shall depart freely therewith**.
12. (14) **Moreover**, all the poor priests of the diocese of Norwich, who are broken with age or bedridden with [A: '*labour under*'] constant sickness so that they cannot celebrate divine service, if they have no other support [A: '*on which they are able to live*'] shall be received in the hospital to dwell there **as long as they live**, and shall be supported fittingly from the goods of the hospital [A: '*and have an honest place . . . and appropriate victuals*'] according to its means.
13. (11) **And** seven poor scholars of the schools of Norwich, apt to be taught **in grammar**, chosen **faithfully** by the faithful counsel of the schoolmaster on oath, shall

have every day of the year while the school is in session one meal in the aforesaid hospital. And, once they are properly taught in grammar, **seven** others shall be chosen to succeed them, according to the form stated above. And we wish this to be observed in perpetuity [A: '*in the said hospital*'].

14. (10) **Moreover**, there shall be fed in this hospital every day of the year in the same, to wit, in the house of the hospital, thirteen poor men who shall sit by the fire in front of the chimney [A: '*of the hospital in winter*'] **and similarly in the same place in the summer**, and they shall have [A: '*sufficient*'] good bread and drink and one dish of meat or fish, and sometimes of cheese and eggs [A: '*in appropriate quantity*'].
15. (15) **And in** this hospital **there** shall be an ark of the Lord (a poor box) from which poor people passing by shall receive alms **and free charitable assistance** every day, according to the means of the hospital. And from the feast of the Annunciation of the Blessed Mary (25 March) to the Assumption of the same glorious Virgin (15 August) there shall be **every Saturday** at a fixed time of day, the great bell being first rung, a distribution of bread to each of the poor persons then present, as much as may banish the hunger of the recipient for that time.
16. (16) **And, because** this hospital will be the house of God and [A: '*a church*'] of the bishops of Norwich, **we will and ordain that**, as often as the bishop of Norwich passes by the hospital and enters it and gives his blessing to the sick **and infirm** lying [A: '*and residing*'] in the hospital, he shall feed thirteen poor men there, for the health of his soul and the souls of all living and departed; and on the morrow a mass of the Holy Spirit shall be celebrated for him **and for all the dead**.
17. (7) **And** the master, priests [A: '*and his chaplains*'] **and brethren** shall eat in common in the same house of the same food and drink.
18. (8) And after dinner, all **returning thanks** together after the versicle [A: '*after grace*'], without drinking, at the tolling of the great bell, shall enter the church of the aforesaid hospital **of St Giles**, saying the psalm *Miserere mei Deus*. And when these things have been done **according to custom** [A:'*with devout obeisance*'], the master may return to the guests [A: '*taking with him whom he wishes*'], not for drinking [A: '*not for immoderate drinking or sitting about for long periods*'], but for recreation and seemliness [A: '*hospitality and honest recreation*']. **And when the master is absent, the senior priest shall supply his place in these matters**.
19. (19) In fasts, refreshments and food, the master, priests, brethren and sisters shall adopt and observe the custom of those who keep the rule of St Augustine, but they shall not wear their habit.
20. (20) The master and priests shall wear honest clothes **of their own choice, so long as they are** neither prohibited nor indecent [A: 'in seemly cloth not of a prohibited colour'], provided that in church [A: '*in divine service*'] they shall wear surplices and black, round copes **as noted above**.
21. (22) The brethren shall be dressed in white tunics and grey scapulars. The sisters shall be dressed in white tunics and grey mantles and **wear** black veils.
22. (7) And the master and priests shall come to rest and sleep under the same roof.
23. **The brethren shall also be together in a house by themselves**.

24. (24) The sisters shall eat and sleep **in one house together** by themselves, and no-one shall presume to enter their house except for necessary cause, having first sought and obtained permission from the master.
25. (8) After compline has been said, all shall go together **to the dormitory** [A: '*to lie down*'], unless the master or another by his special **command or** licence has to remain on account of the guests [A: '*for work*'], or for some other honest or necessary cause.
26. (23) The master of the aforesaid hospital, priests, brethren and sisters shall not eat or drink in the city **of Norwich outside their own house** except in religious houses. [A clause 34, and B clause 26 in Skerning's 1272 *inspeximus*: '*And we strictly forbid them to engage in trade or work for filthy lucre*'].
27. (22) The brethren and sisters shall vow continence. They shall have nothing of their own, but shall receive all their needs from the house by the hand and distribution of the master, and they shall also promise and observe obedience **to the master, as the priests do**.
28. **The master shall receive and admit the brethren and sisters freely, and not present them to the bishop**.
29. (18) And all those dwelling in the said hospital, that is to say the priests, brethren, sisters, clerks **and others** shall be **canonically** subject to the jurisdiction, **coercion** and, **canonically**, to the punishment of the master.
30. (18) **We will also that** the master shall hold a chapter meeting every Sunday, and on other occasions when required, and correct **and amend** all excesses and faults, and punish **and correct** delinquents according to the seriousness of the offence.
31. (28) The master of the hospital shall have no-one riding with him except one of the priests [A: '*chaplains*'], brethren or clerks of the same hospital, and the number of riders shall never exceed three [A: '*two or three*']. We will also that there be no squires or wanton boys in the said hospital.
32. (29) **Furthermore, we will that** no woman be received to sojourn or stay in the aforementioned hospital. And as often as this statute is broken [A: '*and anyone admitted*'] **we will and ordain that** the chapel **of the hospital** be suspended *ipso facto* from the divine office [A: '*worship*'] **as long as the woman remains there. But one mass only for the sake of the sick near the altar shall be said for them only**.
33. (21) The master **of the hospital** may hold and keep **an ecclesiastical benefice, even having cure of souls annexed, and other** possessions which he **canonically** held before he was made master. But that which he shall acquire after he becomes master shall be reserved to the use of the hospital. **And all those things shall be conserved in the lordship of the same hospital; and they shall remain in the possession of the said hospital in perpetuity**. And he shall promise that he will do, **effect** and conserve this, making a corporal oath **in confirmation**.
34. (30) The common seal of the house shall be under two keys, namely of the master and the senior brother **of the same. Nor shall anything be sealed with the same except in a meeting of the chapter, and in the presence of the brethren then in residence**.

35. (25, 26) And when **our beloved son in Christ**, Hamon de Calthorpe, now master **of the hospital**, resigns or dies [A: '*and on every subsequent vacancy*'], we will that this form be observed in perpetuity for the election of the master: **When the master is dead and his body has been buried, or when he has resigned**, the vacancy in the hospital shall be announced by two brethren to the prior **of the church** of Norwich. And the prior himself shall **immediately** summon the archdeacons of Norwich and Norfolk **by authority of this our ordinance** to meet **at Norwich** on a fixed day within three weeks, **to be reckoned from the death of the master or his resignation**, within the hospital **itself**, to consider **with one mind** [A: '*according to the will of God*'] the making of a new master. And these three, having first enquired **diligently** by the sworn testimony of the brethren of the same hospital [A: '*upon the suitability of the chaplains residing there*'], shall elect and appoint a fit and honest person to rule the said hospital from those priests, or from other priests from outside, as seems expedient to them according to God and their consciences, whom they shall present by their letters [A: '*patent*'] to the bishop **of Norwich within the space of eight days after the election is made**. And if the bishop **of Norwich** be then outside the realm **the person elected shall be presented** to the Official **of Norwich** who, **like the bishop**, shall admit him without any obstacle **or contradiction**. But if the said archdeacons do not come on the day appointed, we will that they be awaited for two days **following**; and if they do not come **during this time** the **said** prior [A: '*of Norwich without further delay*'], associating with himself the Official of the Consistory of Norwich and the dean of Norwich, shall proceed in the business for that turn as he should proceed with the **aforesaid** archdeacons. **And we will that the same form be observed if it happen that the said archdeaconries are then vacant**. But if one archdeaconry be vacant, **or if it happens that one archdeacon be then absent**, then the said prior shall proceed in the business with the (other) archdeacon present, associating with them the said Official of the consistory or dean [A: '*then the prior shall associate one of the above-named, whoever he chooses, with him*'], according to the form recited above. And we will that the same form be observed by the said archdeacons if the prior will not join with them, or if the priorate is then vacant. We will, moreover, that if the master of the hospital happen to resign or die while the priory of Norwich is vacant, the vacancy of the same hospital be announced to the said archdeacons forthwith, (and) that they should meet and come to elect a master under the form written. But if the prior and others named above have not agreed on a specific person, as aforesaid, within five weeks after the body of the master of the hospital is buried, **or after his resignation**, the bishop **of Norwich** shall provide a fit person for that turn.

36. (26, 27) This provision being [A: '*always*'] strictly observed: that whoever is to be appointed should be a priest and should swear continual residence [A: '*immediately after his admission*']. But if he has an ecclesiastical benefice he may spend time there, provided that he remain there no longer than eight days on any one occasion. Moreover, the said master shall swear at his appointment that, as far as he possibly can, he will **well and truly** keep **and manage** the hospital and everything that belongs to

it; also that he will not alienate its immoveable property, **and that he will faithfully expend the moveable property for the use of the house and Christ's poor within it**, according to our ordinance, **and cause it to be spent effectively**.

37. (25) And while the said hospital is vacant it shall be under the **guardianship and care of the** bishop **of Norwich** on these terms: that the bishop shall receive nothing at all of the goods of the hospital **in the vacancy**, but **immediately and without any difficulty** shall commit the custody **for the time** to one of the more discreet priests **of the said hospital**, who shall preserve everything **faithfully and without fraud** to the use of the poor and sick [A: '*to the work of the said hospital and to poor Christian people*'], **according to his oath, and who shall account faithfully to the master, who shall be appointed there, for all his receipts and expenses in the interim**.
38. **We will and command that these our statutes and others to be enacted by us in future for the correction, reformation, honesty and utility of the said hospital are to be strictly observed.**
39. (9) And we give this hospital **thus founded** with [A: '*the estate in which it is sited and*'] all its appurtenances to perpetual liberty. And everything within the bounds of the said hospital we **grant and** give to the said hospital, master and brethren [A: '*of the house*'] to the maintenance of them **and the poor** in free, pure and perpetual alms, without any service, exaction, suit of court or demands [A: '*or any other demands whatsoever*'], saving to ourself and our successors the right of patronage of the same hospital, and also **specially reserving** the correction and reformation in spirituals of all dwelling in the said hospital **to us and our successors**.
40. (33) And that this our provision and ordinance may not be hindered for want of things necessary in future, we grant the above-named possessions [A: 'goods and rents'], and also land in Hethel, with its appurtenances, to the aforesaid hospital, master and brethren for the maintenance of the poor **and sick**, and [A: '*grant, appropriate and*'] confirm to them by **the protection of** this present charter all the aforesaid things, **together with other goods which they possess at present, or will be able to acquire in future**.
41. (33) We also grant [A: '*appropriate*'] and confirm the churches of Calthorpe, Costessey, Cringleford, St Mary (South) Walsham, Hardley and Seething to their own use, saving to our **beloved in Christ** [A: '*dear sons*'], the prior and convent of Norwich, ten marks from the **goods of the** church of Seething when it is vacant, to be paid to them yearly at the two synods at Norwich by the hands of the master **of the hospital after they have obtained peaceful possession of the said church**. We grant also that they may lawfully enter and hold possession of the churches of St Mary (South) Walsham and of Seething when they are vacant by the authority of this our collation and confirmation, **without requiring any other consent or assent**.
42. (35) Moreover, we grant to them a perpetual and free chantry in the chapel **of the hospital**, which we have consecrated, along with their other oratories, together with the right of burial for the use of all who die **there**, and also of anyone else who wishes and chooses to be buried there, saving the rights of the parish churches.

43. (31, 32) **And** to all who observe this our ordinance, and who labour **by counsel and aid** that it may be kept, we impart the blessing of Almighty God **and of Our Lord Jesus Christ**. And we release them **mercifully** every year at the feast of St Giles from forty days of enjoined penance. But those who shall labour for the subversion of this our ordinance, or shall procure anything whereby the said ordinance may obtain less effect in future, **or who shall engineer anything against it maliciously** we bind them with the chain of excommunication by the authority of **Almighty God**, the Father, Son and Holy Spirit.
44. (36) And that all the above shall stand firm, stable and valid in perpetuity, our seal is affixed to the present writing, together with the seal of our chapter of Norwich, by whose **express** consent **and assent** we have granted, ordained and conferred all the above. Done in the chapter (house) at Norwich in the presence of **our beloved in Christ**, Simon, prior of Norwich, and his convent.

Therefore no man at all may make void this page of our confirmation, or through rash act contradict it. But, if anyone presume to attempt this, let him be aware that he will incur the wrath of Almighty God and of his apostles, Peter and Paul. Given at Viterbo, on the Ides of October in the third year of our Pontificate (15 October 1257).

APPENDIX II

MAJOR ACQUISITIONS OF PROPERTY BY ST GILES'S HOSPITAL, 1251–1512

Full documentation for all these accessions may be found in Chapter III.

1251: Appropriated livings of Calthorpe, Costessey, Cringleford, Hardley, Seething and South Walsham St Mary, with appurtenances; the manor of Erpingham.

1252: Land in Hethel and East Carleton.

1261: The appropriated living of Repps with the free chapel of Bastwick.

1272: By this date William Dunwich had settled on the hospital three messuages and rents worth £12 a year in Norwich, as well as meadowland near the precinct, which was then expanding fast along the north of Holme Street.

1280: By this date an arc of hospital properties to the north and east of Norwich comprised woods in Sprowston, the Lathes (outside St Augustine's gate) and meadows in Thorpe and at Carrow.

1284: Gildencroft in Coslany, Norwich.
During this decade the hospital also acquired land in Cantley, Catton, Horstead and Intwood, and more property in Cringleford, including a fishery and mill.

1318: Land in Earlham.

1321: Land in Reedham and unspecified 'land and marsh'.

1331: More land in Cringleford, Hardley, Hethel, Seething and Repps; fresh acquisitions in Limpenhow and Wickmere.
About this date a substantial estate in Rollesby (perhaps the manor itself) was purchased.

1334: More land in Cringleford, Seething and Repps; fresh acquisitions in Sisland and Thwaite; the appropriated livings of Mundham St Peter, with other property there, and of Thurlton.
Although the countess of Norfolk secured a royal licence to settle the advowson of South Walsham St Lawrence upon St Giles's her title was successfully challenged.

1381: More land in Calthorpe, Hardley, Loddon, Mundham, Repps and Sisland.

1385: By this date the hospital held over 50 acres of arable and marshland in Salhouse and Wroxham.

1410: The manor of Cringleford (Berford's).
Despite the award of a royal licence, the hospital's efforts to secure the appropriated living of Wickmere failed.

1450: The appropriated living of Mundham St Ethelbert and the manor of Mundham.

1455: More land (288 acres) and rents in Hethel and East Carleton (settled in trust on St Giles's in *c.* 1479 for 80 years in the hope of acquiring a permanent title in mortmain).

1461: The manor of Heylesdon's in Cringleford with appurtenances in Colney, Eaton and Hethersett (likewise settled in trust).

1465: The appropriated living of Coltishall (surrendered in 1522).

1489: More land (63 acres) in Coltishall and the manor of Rollesby (settled in trust on St Giles's in *c.* 1489 for 80 years in the hope of acquiring a permanent title in mortmain).

1498: The manor of 'Rokelles' in Trowse and other land to the south-east of Norwich.

1500: At about this time the hospital took possession of 'Skypwyth's in Conisford, Norwich.

1510: By this date the hospital had also acquired land in Horsford, Newton and Swannington, as well as two large areas of marshland in Fobbing (Essex). 'New' acquisitions in Salhouse and Wroxham may, however, have simply been confirmations of those made in 1385.

1512: Tenements in Conisford, Norwich.

APPENDIX III

MASTERS OF ST GILES'S HOSPITAL, 1249–1546

Hamon de Calthorpe: First master of St Giles's. Kinsman of Bishop Walter Suffield, who in 1256 made him an executor of his will and entrusted him with the performance of various pious works (Blomefield, *Norfolk*, iii, pp. 487–92). Beneficiary and executor of the will of William Dunwich, the hospital's chief lay patron, made in 1272 (NRO, NCR, 24B, no 7). Actively promoted the hospital's early expansion until his resignation soon after August 1274 (PRO, CP25(1) 157/81/1185, 82/1207, 158/84/1263, 88/1369, 98/1604, 1622, 159/100/1658; NRO, NCR, NPD, box 2, parish of St Augustine, nos 2, 5, 6; box 4, St Edward Conisford, nos 2, 5; box 5, St Helen, nos 27, 29, 33, 37, 38, 43; box 6, St Julian, no 3; box 7, St Peter Hungate, no 1; box 8, St Peter Mancroft, no 15; box 10, St Peter Parmentergate, nos 3, 4, SS Simon and Jude, nos 3, 6; NCR, 24B, no 48, *Liber Domus Dei*, fos 13v, 20r, 27v–28r, 43r–47r, 52v–54r, 56r–58r; 25A, no 217; 25B, nos 283, 291, 586, 594–6, 598, 605; 25C, nos 789, 795–6; 25D, nos 1236, 1240–1, 1263–6). His *alias*, de Belton, by which he is often known, suggested to Blomefield that he might have occupied this Suffolk living (*Norfolk*, iv, p. 398). He was certainly a pluralist, having been preferred to the two livings of Bacton and Colechurch by 1259, almost certainly on Bishop Suffield's recommendation (*CPL, 1198–1304*, p. 367).

Robert de Branford: Master by late 1274 (NRO, Phi 516; NCR, NPD, box 7, parish of St Peter Hungate, no 13). Active thereafter in the property market until about 1282 (BL, Add. Ch. 14,784; Toph. Cart. 56; NRO, Box 30E1, nos 12064, 12066; NCR, NPD, box 2, parish of St Augustine, no 8; box 4, St Edward Conisford, no 6; box 5, St Helen, nos 43, 47, St Gregory, no 4, St Matthew, nos 13, 16–18; box 10, SS Simon and Jude, nos 7–12; NCR 24B, no 48, *Liber Domus Dei*, fos 24r, 29v, 31v, 35r–35v, 38v–39r, 51r–51v, 54r–54v, 56r–56v, 58r–70v; 25A, no 232; 25B, nos 579, 590, 592–3, 597, 601–2, 613; 25C, nos 786, 794, 797). His unanimous election by the hospital brethren was unsuccessfully contested by Adam de Freston, archdeacon of Norfolk, in 1277 (NRO, Box 30E1, no 12067; Phi 516–18; NCR, 24B, no 8).

Godwin: The undated will of John Bonde of Norwich, an early patron of St Giles's, named 'Sir Godwin', the master, as an executor, along with a physician (*medicus*) called Richard. A note in a later hand on the dorse of this document records a date of 17 Edward I (1288), but this appears conjectural (NRO, NCR, NPD, box 7, parish of St Peter Hungate, no 17; Hudson and Tingey, *Records of the City of Norwich*, ii, pp. 358–9).

Martin de Brunstead: Master by 1285–6 (NRO, NCR, 24B, no 48, *Liber Domus Dei*, fos 33r–33v, 36r; NPD, box 4, parish of St Giles, no 1). Involved as such in property transactions concerning the hospital until at least 1290 (NPD, box 2, parish of St Augustine, nos 7, 9; box 5, St Helen, no 48, St Matthew, nos 19–21; box 10, SS Simon and Jude, no 12; 25C, nos 792, 798, 813; Box 30E1, nos 12059–60, 12070).

Thomas de Hemmersby *alias* **de Yarmouth**: Master by about 1290, and definitely by September 1291 (NRO, NCR, NPD, box 3, parish of St Crouch, no 1; 24B, no 48, *Liber Domus Dei*, fos 18v–19r; 25B, no 588). Involved in two major lawsuits in defence of hospital property in Norwich and Calthorpe (24B, nos 11, 15). As master, was a party to numerous conveyances in the city and county (NRO, Box 30E1, nos 12061–2, 12071, 12074; Phi 312; NCR, NPD, box 4, parish of St Edward Conisford, no 7; box 5, St Helen, no 45; 25B, no 580; BL, Add. Ch. 14,785). Accounted as receiver general in 1306, and perhaps throughout his mastership (NRO, NCR, 24A, GH accounts, 1306–1398). Probably died in 1312 rather than 1311, as Blomefield claimed, but there is no reason to doubt that he was buried in the hospital church under a brass memorial plate now lost (*Norfolk*, iv, p. 398).

Peter de Herlyngflete: Elected master 1 August 1312 and confirmed by Bishop Salmon in the following January (NRO, NCR, 24B, no 12). First appears in 1295 as a party to a conveyance of property in Holme Street, and was probably then a hospital chaplain (NPD, box 5, parish of St Matthew, no 10). While in office as master, purchased the advowson of the church of Mundham St Peter and other holdings for St Giles's, a party to these transactions being his kinsman, Stephen de Herlyngflete, rector of Lound, Suffolk. Stephen was involved with him in other items of hospital business as well (*CPR, 1330–1334*, pp. 123, 148, 518; NRO, Box 30E1, nos 12094–6; Phi 292–3, 525; NCR, 24B, nos 15, 48, *Liber Domus Dei*, fo 49v). Became embroiled, in 1323–4, in litigation on the hospital's behalf against the abbot of St Benet Holme (Box 30E1, no 12065) and also fought a case at the Thetford assizes in 1313 (NCR, 24B, no 15). Last mentioned as master in September 1344 (24B, no 50E).

Roger de Mettingham: Master by 16 February 1346 (NRO, NPD, box 6, parish of St Martin at Palace, no number). His 'first year' as a hospital chaplain was in *c.* 1330, when John de Mettingham was surveyor of the estates and senior priest. Not then paid, but by 1336 was drawing the standard fee of 20*s*, and helped to supervise harvest works. By 1339–40 Roger himself, then described as *dominus*, had become surveyor. Successfully defended the hospital, in 1347, against claims made by the vicar of Thwaite to tithes in Mundham (NRO, NCR, 24A, GH accounts, 1306–1398; 24B, no 21; 24C, Calthorpe accounts, 1315–1376; Box 30E1, no 12098); and reached an agreement with the vicar of Mundham over tithes in the following year (Box 30E1 no 12099). Died in office shortly before October 1372, when he must have been well over sixty (nos 12100, 12104; NCR, 25A, no 263; DN reg. III, book 6, fo 16v).

John Derlyngton: Collated as master 1 October 1372 on the death of his predecessor (NRO, DN reg. III, book 6, fo 16v). BCnL Oxford by 1363 and DCnL Cambridge by 1387. Originally from the north-west as his name suggests, Derlyngton was, until 1387, canon of Lanchester, Durham. Arrived in Norwich along with his patron, the forceful Bishop Despenser, who made him his vicar general (1371) and Official (1372), as well as securing for him preferment as a royal clerk. While master of St Giles's, occupied the Norfolk rectories of Hingham and Massingham, and went on to become a canon of the college of St Mary in the Fields and archdeacon of Norwich (*BRUC*, pp. 185–6). Acted as a deputy for the bishop while he was in Flanders in 1383, having power to remove, appoint and absolve officials of the cathedral church (NRO, DN reg. III, book 6, fos 89r–89v, 90v). Appointed by the Crown in 1401 to hear an appeal against a judgement in the Court of admiralty (*CPR, 1399–1401*, p. 535). His great influence was recognised by Despenser's kinsman, Lord Morley, who described him as one of the bishop's 'principal councillors'. Had the unenviable task of attempting, in 1405, to arbitrate in a quarrel between Despenser and the dean of St Mary's (Legge, *Anglo Norman Letters*, nos 75, 87). When Despenser died, in the following year, had custody of the spiritualities of the see, *sede vacante* (*BRUC*, pp. 185–6). Although his mastership was brief, he remained attached to St Giles's, and occupied a house in the precinct until his death. A leading benefactor of the hospital, he gave almost £80 for the building of the great bell-tower in 1396–7, and set aside his manor of Cringleford and the advowson of Wickmere, Norfolk, to endow a perpetual chantry. It was probably he as much as Despenser who planned and financed the construction of the new chancel, church and infirmary in the early 1380s (NRO, NCR, 24A, GH accounts, 1306–1398; 24B, nos 17, 59; *CPR, 1408–1413*, p. 187; PRO, C143/441/18). Died shortly before March 1410, and was also a benefactor of the abbey of St Benet Holme (Caley and Hunter, *Valor Ecclesiasticus*, iii, p. 366).

Roger de Erpingham: Collated as master 4 January 1376 (NRO, DN reg. III, book 6, fo 42r). Had been a hospital chaplain and administrator since at least 1362, when he incurred expenses on the manor of Costessey. By 1364, as *dominus* Roger, was collecting rents there, probably as receiver general of St Giles's. Little else is known of him beyond his involvement in routine property transactions (NRO, NCR, NPD, box 6, parish of St Martin Coslany, no 14; 18A, Chamberlains' Account Book, 1384–1448, fo 6v; 24C, GH Costessey accounts, 1338–1374).

John de Thornham: Collated as master 11 March 1395, being described as rector of Sparham, Norfolk, and the son of Robert de Thornham. Had previously been rector (from 1386 to 1393) of the Norwich parish church of SS Simon and Jude, and before that of Timworth, Suffolk (NRO, DN reg. III, book 6, fos 197v, 208r; Blomefield, *Norfolk*, iv, p. 354). Resigned as master in 1396, but remained involved in the hospital's affairs. A trustee in 1410 for the endowment of a chantry established there by his old patron, John Derlyngton, whom he had known since 1384. The latter had then stood bail on his behalf, obtaining his release after unspecified charges had been levelled against him at Westminster (*CPR, 1408–1413*, p. 187; *CCR, 1381–1385*, p. 566; PRO, C143/441/18). Sufficiently influential to secure a variety of papal licences for himself in 1399, he was an executor of Alexander Totington, bishop of Norwich (1406–13), and a party to the affairs of the prior of Horsham St Faith's near Norwich (*CPL 1396–1401*, pp. 215, 225, 228; *CPR, 1408–1413*, p. 187; *1422–1429*, p. 508; PRO, C143/441/17). Died before 23 April 1422, having left a bequest of 60*s* to the influential city guild of St George in the previous year (NRO, NCR, 8E-7, guild account for 9–10 Henry V).

Benedict Cobbe: Collated as master 17 March 1396, when he is described as coming from Terrington in Norfolk (NRO, DN reg. III, book 6, fo 208r). Almost certainly the *Dominus* Benedict who was surveyor and receiver general of the hospital from 1389–90 to at least 1398. His account for the year ending Michaelmas 1398 records payments of nearly £5 to the bishop of Norwich and his officials 'concerning the confirmation and installation of the master', which must relate to his own induction. Otherwise remains an obscure figure (NRO, NCR, 24A, GH accounts, 1306–1398; 24C, GH Costessey accounts, 1377–1399).

Roger Pratt: Collated as master 3 November 1399 at Westminster in the household (*hospitium*) of Robert Fonline, whom the VCH (*Norfolk, II*, p. 444) erroneously lists as one of the masters (NRO, DN reg. III, book 6, fo 251v). Successfully defended St Giles's against charges brought locally and at Westminster that the acquisition of Mundham St Peter in 1335, had breached the Statute of Mortmain (NRO, NCR, 24B, no 15). Notable for his connections with the mercantile elite of Norwich, Pratt was a prominent, and occasionally controversial, figure. From at least 1411 he was close to the rich and powerful alderman, William Setman, being a party to his endowment of the college of St Mary in the Fields and of the Austin Friars, and later his executor (*CPR, 1408–1413*, p. 268; *1413–1416*, p. 119; NRO, NCR, NPD, box 4, St Mary in the Fields, nos 6, 8; box 8, parish of St Peter Mancroft, nos 339, 346, 349, 351; Blomefield, *Norfolk*, iv, pp. 176–7; PRO, C143/442/18; Tanner, *Church in Late Medieval Norwich*, pp. 243–4). Involvement in the affairs of St Mary's brought him into contact with such notable figures as Sir Simon Felbrigg (Tanner, p. 213; *CPR, 1413–1416*, p. 139). Also associated, in his frequent capacity as a trustee, with Sir Henry Inglose and other members of county society (*CPR, 1422–1429*, p. 538; Lambeth Palace Library, reg. Arundel, II, fos 51r–51v). Participation in civic life had its drawbacks: in July 1437 Pratt was accused by the widow of John Asgar, whose will he was then executing, of reducing her to beggary (PRO, C1/9/277); and one of Setman's former associates claimed he had extorted goods by 'grete force and manas [menaces]' (C1/45/233). In 1436 a member of the Norwich guild of St George called him 'the falsest that myght goo up on herthe'. As a prominent guild member, Pratt had his adversary expelled and humiliated (Grace, *Gild of St George*, p. 39; NRO, NCR, 8E-7, guild accounts 8–9, 12–13 Henry VI). Also on friendly terms with the controversial alderman, Thomas Wetherby, and his even more notorious associate, John Heydon (NCR, 25A, GH Cringleford deeds, box IV, no 27). A man clearly worth cultivating: in July 1412, shortly after resigning the mastership of St Giles's, he was granted the life-tenancy of a dwelling house in the precinct and admitted to the hospital confraternity in return for his support (NCR, 24B, no 17). By then rector of Heigham, near Norwich, he retained the living for over twenty years. His financial acumen and command of patronage networks explain his re-election to the mastership in 1431.

Robert Spenser: Collated as master 22 June 1412 (NRO, DN reg. IV, book 7, fo 49r), one of his first acts being to provide accommodation for his predecessor. By then rector of Erpingham, Norfolk, he had until 1397 occupied the nearby living at Alby (*CPL, 1396–1404*, p. 49; *1404–1415*, p. 341; PRO, CP25(1) 169/184/128). Made his will in March 1430, leaving bequests to the church and poor of Erpingham and to staff and patients at the hospital. Also owned land in Shadingfield, Suffolk. By a codicil added in the following September, he sold his manor of Heylesdon's in Cringleford to St Giles's for £20 on the condition that his executors might freely remove all his effects from the hospital. The will was proved on 19 October following, with John Bettyns, one of the hospital's lay administrators, as an executor. Spenser was also involved in the affairs of the guild of St George, Norwich, which celebrated his obit. Also popular as a trustee (NRO, NCC, reg. Surflete, fos 60v–61r; NCR, 8E-7, guild accounts 8–9 Henry VI; 24B, no 18; PRO, CP25(1) 169/184/120, 185/37, 44).

William de Sekyngton: Installed as master at the bishop's palace, Norwich, 6 November 1430 (NRO, DN reg. V, book 9, fo 43r) but had effectively taken office by late October (NRO, NCR, 25A, GH Cringleford deeds, box IV, no 19). BCL and BCnL, probably Cambridge. Owed his preferment to William Alnwick, who made him his corrector or commissary general in August 1426, shortly after becoming bishop of Norwich. Also acted as inductor for all benefices under Alnwick's personal jurisdiction (NRO, DN reg. V, book 9, fo 18r; Hayes, 'William Alnwick', p. 116). Although Sekyngton did not remain long at St Giles's, he continued to enjoy the bishop's favour. Rector of Sutton, Norfolk, by November 1431, he was then permitted by papal licence to hold a second benefice. In August 1432 Alnwick further rewarded him with the rectory of St Mary in the Marsh, Norwich, and one year later he was made vicar of Lowestoft (DN reg. V, book 9, fos 59v, 116r; *CPL, 1427–1447*, p. 344). Accused at this time by John Brockley, alderman of Norwich, of complicity in a plot to disinherit him, but retained sufficient respect among at least one faction of the ruling elite to be made an arbitrator during the riots of 1443. Briefly imprisoned by the insurgents, he sustained no lasting harm (PRO, C1/12/165; KB9/84/1). Died a wealthy man in 1461. Endowed the Huntingdonshire church of St Margaret, Gidding, where his parents were buried, and established a bursary for the study of canon law or theology at Cambridge. Maintained his links with St Giles's, which lay near 'Butys Place', his home in the parish of St Clement, Norwich. Asked to be buried in the Bauchun chapel of Norwich cathedral, where he is reputedly depicted at prayer in one of the corbels (James, *Sculptured Bosses*, pp. ii–iii). Bequeathed money for requiem masses at the hospital, and named John Selot as supervisor and Simon Thornham as an executor (NRO, NCC, reg. Brosyard, fos 226r–27v).

Roger Pratt: Installed as master for the second time at the episcopal palace, Norwich, on 17 May 1431 (NRO, DN reg. V, book 9, fo 46v). Given Sekyngton's brief tenure of office and Pratt's knowledge of the hospital, it looks as if he may have been called in to deal with administrative or financial problems. Acted as receiver general of hospital revenues 1431–6, and helped Thomas Lucas to draw up his accounts as rent collector in Norwich (NRO, NCR, 24A, GH Norwich accounts, 1415–1460; 24C, Costessey accounts, 1422–1460). Relinquished office soon afterwards.

John Walpole: Collated as master on 28 November 1436, while rector of Shipdham, Norfolk (NRO, DN reg. V, book 9, fo 88v). Had recently exchanged his living at Swaffham, a few miles to the west, for this benefice (*CPR, 1436–1441*, p. 24). MA Oxford and fellow of Merton College to at least 1416 (*BRUO*, iii, pp. 1968–9). Admitted as a notary public in 1422 under the faculty of the prior of Thetford. In 1436 acted as a proctor for Sir Thomas Tuddenham in his notorious divorce case in the Norwich consistory court, some of the evidence being examined at his house in the parish of St Edmund, Fishergate, near St Giles's hospital (*CPL, 1417–1431*, p. 216; Virgoe, *East Anglian Society*, p. 123). Owed his promotion to the patronage of Bishop Alnwick, who made him rural dean of the diocese of Norwich, and, by 1429, dean of the cathedral priory manors then in episcopal hands. Alnwick exchanged the see of Norwich for that of Lincoln in 1436, and Walpole soon followed him as a trusted administrator, becoming rector of Gedney, Lincolnshire, and, in 1441, a canon of Lincoln cathedral. Died in 1445 (Hayes, 'William Alnwick', pp. 67, 71, 120; *BRUO*, iii, pp. 1968–9).

Hugh Acton: Collated as master 4 June 1437 (NRO, DN reg. V, book 10, fo 7v). Almost certainly a graduate, although his academic background remains unknown. Notary public by 1421; acted in November 1436 with John Walpole, his predecessor, as a proctor in the Tuddenham divorce case (Virgoe, *East Anglian Society*, p. 123). As a notary, he produced the documentation for the installation of both Roger Pratt (1431) and John Walpole (1436) as masters of St Giles's, and was also involved in the Norwich heresy trials of 1428–31 (DN, reg. V, book 9, fos 46v, 88v; Hayes, 'William Alnwick', p. 110). Accounted continuously as steward and receiver general of the hospital estates between Michaelmas 1438 and 1455. Acquired for St Giles's the manor of Mundham and advowson of St Ethelbert's there from Sir John Fastolf in 1450. May have been less active from 1453 onwards, as Peter Goos took over his more arduous duties (NRO, NCR, 24A, GH Norwich accounts, 1415–1460; 24C, Costessey accounts, 1422–1460; 24E, Hardley accounts, 1427–1460, mm. 11r–25r; Magdalen College, Oxford, Fastolf Additia, 2). [Jewson, *Great Hospital*, p. 48, states that **Simon Thornham** was master in 1451, although no supporting evidence has been found. On the contrary, a deposition by John Jenney, in the late 1450s, states that John Selot succeeded Hugh Acton, who died in office (NRO, NCR, 24D, GH unnumbered Cringleford miscellanea). Thornham's career certainly conforms to a pattern discernible among those of other late medieval masters (see *BRUC*, pp. 584–5; Davis, *Paston Letters*, ii, pp. 349, 545; NRO, NCC reg. Brosyard, fos 226r–27v; NCR, 8E-7, guild accounts 3–10 Edward IV)].

John Selot: Master by 1 June 1455 (NRO, Phi 621) and perhaps slightly before. His involvement, in November 1450, in the hospital's acquisition of Sir John Fastolf's Mundham estates suggests that he had by then established close personal links with the house (NRO, NCR, 25B, no 566; Magdalen College, Oxford, Fastolf Additia, 2). BcnL, BCL and DcnL Oxford by 1446 (*BRUO*, iii, p. 1667). Came from Twickenham, Middlesex, where he retained a modest estate throughout his life (PRO, C1/28/394). Admitted to Winchester College at the age of twelve, in 1428, and later, in 1470, presented a quantity of red worsted 'Norwich work' to make frontals for the chapel (T.F. Kirby, *Winchester Scholars* (London, 1888), p. 51; idem, *Annals of Winchester College* (London, 1892), p. 234). A picture of him, along with other early Wykehamists, is still preserved in the College (T.F. Kirby, 'On some Fifteenth-Century Drawings in Winchester College', *Archaeologia*, liii (part 1, 1892), opposite p. 233). A pluralist with livings as far apart as Lincolnshire and Cornwall, he began acquiring yet more benefices in Norfolk and Suffolk once his patron, Walter Lyhart, became Bishop of Norwich in 1446. Accompanied him on a diplomatic mission to Geneva in the following year, and was widely regarded as one of his most influential councillors. Preferred by Lyhart to a number of East Anglian rectories, as well as the mastership of the hospital of St Thomas, Beck, which he secured in 1454 (*BRUO*, iii, p. 1667; NRO, DN reg. VI, book 11, fo 74v). Farmer of the hospital of SS Mary and Nicholas, Massingham (Norfolk), from 1460 onwards (*CCR, 1461–1468*, p. 178). As master of St Giles's, became involved in a protracted dispute with the lawyer, John Jenney, over land in Cringleford, and was briefly imprisoned for bribery (above, pp. 147–50). Because he shared Lyhart's attachment to the unpopular de la Poles and their henchmen, he was considered biased as a judge in the ecclesiastical courts by the Paston family. They complained in the 1460s about the 'demenyng and parcialte' shown by Selot and Robert Ippeswell, his close friend and master of the Carnary Chapel (Davis, *Paston Letters*, i, pp. 320–2; ii, pp. 205, 349). Continued to serve Lyhart's successor, Bishop Goldwell, as chancellor, using his influence to help the hospital. Acquired land for St Giles's in Hethel and East Carleton after further litigation (NRO, Phi 621; Box 30E1, no 2111; NCR, 24B, nos 29, 61; 25D, nos 1249, 1259); strengthened its title to the manor and advowson of Mundham (25B, nos 544, 566), recovered land in Norwich and Costessey from the abbot of Sawtry (24B, nos 24, 62); and, in February 1465, purchased the rectory of Coltishall, Norfolk, for the support of future masters, being then himself installed as rector (Blomefield, *Norfolk*, vi, p. 309). A member of the guild of St George, Selot had many friends among the rulers of Norwich (NRO, NCR, 8E-7, guild accounts 3–15 Edward IV). Close to the wealthy alderman, John Gilbert, whose will he executed (NCR, 1C, rolls 19A, rot. 1, 19B, rot. 2, 19E, rots 2–3). Secured an endowment of £200 from two other leading citizens so that a hospital priest could serve prisoners in the Guildhall (NRO, NCC, reg. Jekkys, fos 47v–49r; NCR, 24B, no 25). Used the land he had recovered in Cringleford, Hethel, Carleton and Norwich to fund obits for himself, Lyhart and John Heydon. Died shortly after 25 March 1479; the obits were still being celebrated at St Giles's in 1535 (NCR, 24A, GH general accounts, 1465–1501, account for 1478–9; 25A, GH Cringleford deeds, box IV, nos 54, 56, 59, 60; Caley and Hunter, *Valor Ecclesiasticus*, iii, pp. 291–92).

John Smyth: Elected as master and as rector of Coltishall shortly before 6 September 1479, and installed soon after (NRO, DN reg. VII, book 12, fo 68v. *BRUC*, p. 534, is wrong in stating he was replaced in 1479: see NRO, NCR, 24B, no 26). BCL Cambridge. Between 1436 and 1457 occupied, at various times, the Norfolk rectories of Bawdeswell, Hackford, Caister, Yaxham and Reedham, together with the rectory of Fornham All Saints and the vicarages of Bramford and Honington, Suffolk. Promoted because of his administrative skills: by 1441 was vicar general to Bishop Brown, and during the 1460s served Walter Lyhart as chancellor. Ended his long and busy life as Official to Bishop Goldwell, who approved his election as master of St Giles's even though it had been 'ineptly' held by the brothers (*BRUC*, p. 534; *CPR, 1441–1446*, p. 45; *CPL, 1431–1447*, pp. 8, 517; Davis, *Paston Letters*, i, p. 356; NRO, DN reg. VII, book 12, fo 68v). Evidently well-liked by the hospital chaplains, he had retained lodgings in the precinct since 1455. A friend and associate of John Selot, he had been involved, from 1450 onwards, in conveyances of hospital property in Mundham and Cringleford. A zealous master, he accounted personally as receiver general of hospital revenues between 1478–81 (NRO, NCR, 24A, GH Norwich accounts, 1415–1460, 1465–1501, passim; general accounts, 1465–1501; 24B, nos 544, 566; 25A, GH Cringleford deeds, box IV, nos 43, 53, 54, 57, 59, 60; PRO, CP25(1) 170/192/3). Asked to be buried in the chancel, and left his manors of Colitishall and Rollesby to support a chantry and obits at the hospital. His deathbed will of June 1489 also contains generous bequests of cash, books and plate to beautify St Giles's (NRO, NCC, reg. Typpes, fos 17v–19v). Smyth's dealings with the Pastons are well documented: unlike his predecessor, he was esteemed by them as a source of sound practical advice. Sir John Fastolf's secretary, William Worcester, was less complimentary, having lost to him a corrody at the abbey of St Benet Holme, in 1468, and doubting his impartiality in the ecclesiastical courts (Davis, *Paston Letters*, i, pp. 266, 302–3, 356, 462, 448, 469, 511, 575–6, 574, 588; ii, pp. 232, 355, 365–6, 566, 568–9). Belonged to the guild of St George, Norwich, where he consorted with members of the ruling elite (NRO, NCR, 8E-7, guild accounts 3–19 Edward IV). The prior of the Austin friary, Norwich, complained that he exploited the 'favour and gret asistens' shown to him and the hospital by the sheriffs and other civic officials to unfair advantage (PRO, C1/64/31).

Oliver Dynham: Collated as master of St Giles's and rector of Coltishall 18 July 1489 (NRO, DN reg. VII, book 7, fo 138v; NCR, 24B, no 26). MA Oxford. Came from an old and distinguished Devon family. As a younger brother of John, Lord Dynham, treasurer of England under Henry VII, and brother-in-law of Fulk Bourgchier, Lord Fitzwarin, he could expect rapid preferment. Had just petitioned for the award of his BA when he obtained permission, in 1458, to trim his academic robes with fur (*Complete Peerage*, iv, pp. 369–82; v, pp. 509–10; *CCR, 1468–1476*, nos 936, 1454; *BRUO*, i, pp. 618–19). One year later, as a youth of nineteen, he secured a papal licence to hold two incompatible benefices with cure. Already rector of Poole in Dorset, Cheshunt in Hertfordshire, and Mildenhall, Suffolk, when, in 1463, the licence was increased to three (*CPL, 1455–1464*, pp. 570–1, 632; *1484–1492*, no 1075). A relentless pluralist, he acquired and exchanged a number of valuable canonries and rectories from Devon to Derbyshire, becoming a canon of St George's chapel Windsor by royal appointment and archdeacon of Norfolk in 1479, shortly after his elder brother had been ennobled by Edward IV. As a chaplain to the King and archdeacon of Surrey, he preferred to reside in Farnham, Surrey, where he asked to be buried in his will of April 1500 (*CPR, 1476–1485*, p. 222; PRO, PCC 9 Moone). These connections did not impress the brothers of St Giles's, who complained to Bishop Goldwell in 1492 that Dynham's absenteeism not only contravened the statutes but also encouraged unwelcome litigation, '*et aliis injuriis plus atis*' (Jessopp, *Visitations*, pp. 12–13).

Thomas Shenkwyn: Confirmed as both master of St Giles's and rector of Coltishall 8 July 1495 (NRO, DN reg. XXX, p. 51). BCL and DCL Cambridge. Began his administrative career in the 1480s, as Official of the archdeacon of Bedford, master of the hospital of St Leonard, Bedford (1485–93), and rector of Battlesden in Bedfordshire. Acquired and exchanged other benefices, including the rectories of Ashill, Norfolk, and Uffington, Lincolnshire. His appointment as master of the Norfolk hospital of St Thomas, Beck, in February 1490, marked the onset of rapid preferment in the diocese of Norwich, where he served between 1491 and 1495 as Official and chancellor to Bishop Goldwell. Was also Official of the archdeacon of Sudbury and rector of Markshall, Essex, from 1493 until his death in December 1497, being permitted by the Pope, in 1495, to hold three incompatible benefices with cure of souls at once (*BRUC*, p. 511; *CPL, 1471–1484*, p. 785; *1492–1498*, nos 473, 1438). Joined the Norwich guild of St George in April 1494, and was evidently resident in the city when he died. In his will, proved in December 1497, he asked to be buried in the chapel of the Blessed Virgin at St Giles's (Grace, *Gild of St George*, p. 85; NRO, NCR, 8E-7, guild account 9–10 Henry VII; PRO, PCC 15 Horne).

Nicholas Goldwell: Described by Blomefield and Tanner as rector of Coltishall, 1497, and thus as master (*Norfolk*, iv, p. 400; NRO, DN reg. XXX, p. 51). In office by January 1498, but clearly did not serve for much longer (NRO, NCR, 24D, GH Cringleford court rolls, 1485–1508, m. 6r). Brother of Bishop Goldwell, whom he followed to All Souls, Oxford. BCL Oxford and DCL Cambridge. Predictably, given his connections, held numerous canonries, rectories and archdeaconries throughout England, and especially in East Anglia. Also made master of the leper hospital of St Mary Magdalen, Sprowston, by his brother (*BRUO*, ii, p. 786; *BRUC*, pp. 262–3). In 1497–8 gave £20 to St Giles's as a gift and examined the accounts of the steward, Robert Godfrey, at the annual audit. Then designated archdeacon of Suffolk, rather than master of the hospital. Donated a further £20 two years later to repair fire damage, along with a quantity of salt as 'alms' for the household. During this period James, young son of Geoffrey Goldwell, was among the boarders (NRO, NCR, 24A, GH general accounts, 1465–1501, 1485–1509). Played a leading part in the endowment of his brother's chantry and annual obit at the hospital, being an executor of his will and trustee of the property earmarked for this purpose (24B nos 28, 66; BR61/2/19; PRO, PCC 35 Horne). Died in 1505. Buried at the college of St Mary in the Fields, Norwich, of which he had been dean, but left money to the hospital (PCC 40 Holgrave).

Robert Honywood: Collated as rector of Coltishall, and thus as master, 1498 (Blomefield, *Norfolk*, iv, p. 400; NRO, DN reg. XXX, p. 51). BCL and DCL, Oxford, where he spent several years as a fellow of All Souls, Bishop Goldwell's old college. Archdeacon of Norwich, 1497–1509 (*BRUO*, ii, p. 957), and immediate successor, in 1497, to Thomas Shenkwyn as master of St Thomas's hospital, Beck (*VCH Norfolk, II*, p. 439; PRO, C1/161/35). Chosen, along with John Jullys and Nicholas Goldwell, to execute the bishop's will of June 1497 (PRO, PCC 35 Horne). A trustee of property in and around Trowse, which was to support Goldwell's chantry in the hospital (NRO, BR61/2/19; NCR, 24B, no 66). Absent at the time of a visitation of St Giles's made, *sede vacante*, by the archbishop of Canterbury's Official, in April 1499. Finally resigned as master in March 1500, just over a year after Goldwell's death (Lambeth Palace Library, reg. Morton, II, fo 83r; NRO, NCR, 24B, no 27B). Enjoyed the favour of Bishop Nykke, serving as his vicar general in 1501, as rector of Blakeney, Norfolk, 1502–5, and dean of the collegiate church of St Mary in the Fields, Norwich (*BRUO*, ii, p. 957; NRO, DN reg. VIII, book 13, fo 14). Continued to lease accommodation from the hospital, although he failed to pay his rent (NRO, NCR, 24A, GH Norwich accounts, 1485–1509, 1510–1528, passim). Instrumental in setting up the annual obit for Goldwell at St Giles's and dispensing 'alms' to the hospital in his name (24A, GH general accounts, 1485–1508, account of the receiver general for 1505–6; 24B, no 28). Endowed masses for his patron's soul, both at St Mary's and at St George's chapel, Windsor (PRO, PCC 2 Bodfelde). Became a canon and prebendary of St George's by royal appointment in 1504, archdeacon of Taunton in 1509 and canon of Lichfield in 1512 (*CPR, 1494–1509*, p. 384; *BRUO*, ii, p. 957). Died in January 1523. His will of the previous December does not mention St Giles's hospital; he asked to be buried at Windsor, and left a substantial estate in Berkshire and Buckinghamshire (PRO, PCC 2 Bodfelde).

John Jullys: Collated as master of St Giles's and rector of Coltishall 10 and 11 March 1500 (NRO, NCR, 24B, nos 26, 27B). Rector of Blickling, Norfolk, by 1481, when he received papal permission to hold a second benefice (*CPL, 1475–1484*, p. 738). Became master of Hildebrond's hospital, Norwich, and rector of the city church of St Giles on the Hill in October 1497 through the patronage of Bishop Goldwell, who had recently named him and Robert Honywood as executors of his will and trustees of the estates he intended to settle upon St Giles's (Blomefield, *Norfolk*, iv, p. 7; NRO, DN reg. VII, book 12, fo 154r; BR61/2/19; PRO, PCC 35 Horne). In 1504 Bishop Nykke granted him the mastership of the hospital of St Mary Magdalen, Norwich, although, as William Soper later established, it was never appropriated to St Giles's (PRO, E368/280, rot 26r). Moved in distinguished circles, being close to Sir James Hobart, another of Goldwell's executors and attorney general to Henry VII, who befriended the hospital. Acted with Hobart in 1476–7 as a feoffee of property in Hunstanton and North Elmham (PRO, CP25(1) 170/193/53, 54). Also intimate with Sir William Boleyn, who made him and Edmund George, a clerk then living in the hospital, trustees of Hever castle and other estates in Kent (*CPR, 1500–1509*, no 179; NRO, NCR, 24A, GH general accounts, 1465–1501, account of the steward, 1500–1). Held land in trust for the lawyer, William Skipwith; and as supervisor of the will of the attorney, Henry Ferman, in 1503, was able to secure further patronage for St Giles's (PRO, CP25(1) 170/196/42; NRO, NCC, reg. Popy, fos 272v–74v). Jullys's appointment as master facilitated the implementation of Bishop Goldwell's plans to establish a chantry there (NRO, Box 30E1, nos 12112–13; NCR, 24B, no 66). It entrusted the hospital to a familiar and protective pair of hands. A William Jullys had been collector of its Norwich rents in 1423–4; and John assumed this post, along with the more prestigious office of steward, in 1472–3, being then a resident chaplain. Resigned his chaplaincy in 1476, but continued to rent a chamber and stable in the precinct between 1480 and 1497. This probably explains his remarkable generosity to a place which he regarded as his home: while master he instigated a comprehensive rebuilding programme, which cost him over £242 (NCR, 24A, GH Norwich accounts, 1415–1460, 1465–1501, 1485–1509, passim; general accounts, 1485–1508, passim). In May 1510, after his death, his brother, William Jullys of Norwich, was a party to the acquisition of estates in Salhouse by the hospital, in conjunction with Goldwell's surviving executors. By 1521 this property and land in Wroxham supported the cost of his obit (24A, Fobbing accounts, 1521–1528; 25B, no 701).

William Soper: Admitted as rector of Coltishall, and thus as master, 7 April 1504. MA Oxford by 1502, when he was already a canon of Wells cathedral and prebendary of Warminster, Wiltshire. Later became rector of the free chapel of Whitehall, Somerset, and deacon of Sedgebrook, Lincolnshire as well (*BRUO*, iii, p. 1729; PRO, PCC 8 Maynwaryng). An unashamed pluralist, in 1505 he obtained papal permission to combine the livings of Yeovilton, Somerset, and Bacton, Suffolk, without having to reside in either, or in any of his other benefices, while in Rome or studying at university (*CPL, 1503–1513*, no 420). A royal pardon issued to him as master of St Giles's, on 19 July 1508, describes him as living at Hoxne (almost certainly in Bishop Nykke's palace), although he was also then said to be domiciled in Norwich. Nykke had previously been archdeacon of Wells, which accounts for Soper's otherwise surprising move to East Anglia. He and five securities acting on his behalf were bound over by the King at this time in sums totalling £400, conditional upon the payment of £50 at Westminster within the year (*CCR, 1500–1509*, nos 892, 920; *CPR, 1494–1509*, p. 585). Such a heavy indemnity was probably demanded as a result of proceedings in the Exchequer Court, in 1507–8, arising from a misunderstanding over earlier episcopal grants of the mastership of St Mary's hospital, Sprowston, to Nicholas Goldwell and John Jullys (PRO, E368/280, rot. 26r). Thanks to the support of Sir James Hobart, Soper won his case, and also managed to defend the hospital against further charges of concealment concerning the land in Hethel and Carleton acquired by Selot (NRO, NCR, 24B, no 29). In 1511, through successful arbitration rather than litigation, he settled a long-running dispute over these estates (25D, no 1301). As master of St Thomas's hospital at Beck in Norfolk (where he succeeded Robert Honywood), he was involved in another protracted legal battle with a predatory landowner, whom he sued in the Court of Chancery (PRO, C1/161/35, 36, 163/54; STAC 2/18/118). His will, made in March 1519, almost certainly at St Giles's, reveals a sincere attachment to the hospital, where he was buried and to which he left generous bequests. A wealthy man, he owned estates in North Elmham (near Beck) and Bacton, as well as Yeovilton, which may have been his birthplace. Maintained contacts in London and left money for two chantry priests to celebrate for his soul at the Savoy Hospital. The will was proved in November 1520, and involved one of the hospital clerks in litigation over the detention of muniments (PRO, PCC 8 Maynwaryng; C1/583/52, 53).

John Hecker alias **Dalle**: Collated as rector of Coltishall and thus as master 1519 (Blomefield, *Norfolk*, iv, p. 400). During his tenure of office the rectory, which had been annexed to the mastership by papal bull of 1465, was recovered by the college of St Mary in the Fields, Norwich, with support from the Crown (ibid., vi, p. 309). Hecker had already spent over three decades as a hospital chaplain and senior administrator, having been admitted as one of the brethren in 1484–5. By Michaelmas 1497 he had become steward and surveyor of St Giles's, and was probably then receiver general as well. He combined all three posts from at least 1499 until 1502, and again from 1505 to March 1516 (Lambeth Palace Library, reg. Morton, II, fo 83r; NRO, NCR, 24A, GH general accounts, 1465–1501, 1485–1508, 1510–1525). Between 1498 and 1502 he also accounted as collector of rents in Norwich (GH Norwich accounts, 1485–1509). Other relatives shared these close connections. In 1497–8 one Nicholas Hecker, clerk, rented a chamber in the precinct; and a few years later a boy named William Hecker joined the paying boarders (general accounts, 1485–1509). In 1519, when John became master, William returned as one of the hospital chaplains, being made sacristan in 1524–5 (general accounts, 1510–1525). Accusations voiced in 1526 that the latter not only had illicit relations with a local woman, but also bickered in the choir, occasioned his almost immediate departure, family ties notwithstanding (Jessopp, *Visitations*, pp. 206–7). Another William Hecker, fishmonger of Cley on the Norfolk coast, had provisioned the hospital from 1483 onwards, and in 1509 bequeathed salt worth £20 to it as alms. His obit was celebrated there every April in return: quite possibly he was John's father (NRO, NCR, 24A, GH general accounts, 1485–1508). Hecker's financial expertise secured his appointment as Bishop Nykke's receiver before 1520, and in 1524–5 he examined the accounts of certain episcopal officials in his rooms at St Giles's. He shared Nykke's conservative principles: a harsh arbitration award pronounced by him in 1520 at the hospital in a case involving defamation of a priest provoked lay resistance (GH general accounts, 1510–25, account for 1524–5; PRO, PCC 8 Maynwaryng; Stone and Cozens-Hardy, *Norwich Consistory Court Depositions*, no 275). He also caused controversy in 1521 by excommunicating and removing the rector of Hedenham because he had, apparently, ignored a similar sentence pronounced against a local landowner who had failed to pay tithes to the hospital (NRO, NCR, 24B, nos 31–2). In 1526 a farmer from Bishop's Thorpe complained to Star Chamber about Hecker's use of violence to secure land for the hospital (PRO, STAC 2/35/3). Yet he fraternised amicably with the rulers of Norwich in the guild of St George, and in 1522 paid 40*s* to cover future contributions towards the annual feast (Grace, *Gild of St George*, p. 121). Furnished a set of elaborately carved bench ends in St Helen's church, being himself depicted at prayer on one now lost (Blomefield, *Norfolk*, iv, p. 379).

Thomas Cappe: Elected master 13 May 1532 (NRO, DN reg. IX, book 14, fo 20v). BA, DCnL Cambridge, where he twice audited the proctors' accounts; official of the archdeacon of Norwich, 1524–35; vicar of St Stephen's, Norwich, 1530–46; canon and prebendary of St Mary in the Fields, Norwich 1530–5 (*BRUC*, p. 123; Stone and Cozens-Hardy, *Norwich Consistory Court Depositions*, nos 324, 339, 366). While master, took on the lease of hospital property at Fobbing, Essex, and Sprowston (NRO, NCR, 20D, GH Lease Book 1530–1645, fos 1v–2v). Formally acknowledged the Act of Supremacy in August 1534, and was still in office when royal commissioners assessed the value of the hospital in 1535 (*LPFD*, vii (part 2), no 1121 (58); Caley and Hunter, *Valor Ecclesiasticus*, iii, pp. 291–2). Removed soon afterwards, perhaps for political reasons following the eclipse of his patron, the reactionary Bishop Nykke. Made his will in December 1545 and died two months later, leaving an estate in Norwich and bequests worth over £24. Had relatives in Heydon, Norfolk (NRO, NCC, reg. Puntyng, fos 169r–71r), which may have been his birthplace.

Thomas Simmondes: Master by 1535–6 (NRO, NCR, 20D, GH Lease Book, 1530–1645, fo 6v), but evidently little more than a stop-gap, pending the appointment of his successor. As domestic chaplain to Bishop Nykke, he too may have been regarded as a member of the 'old guard' (Blomefield, *Norfolk*, iv, p. 399). The loss of the hospital's accounts for the period makes it impossible to tell if he had been one of the brethren at some point, which seems likely.

Robert Codde: Appointed master by Henry VIII, *sede vacante*, 20 March 1536 (LPFD, xii (1), no 795 (33)). Owed his preferment to Robert Sherburne, the conservative bishop of Chichester, who wished to find him a secure living after the dissolution of the house of Augustinian canons at Pentney, Norfolk, where he had been a distinguished prior, noted for charity as well as efficiency (Jessopp, *Visitations*, p. 312). Allegations of sexual incontinence – with the abbess of Marham – may safely be ignored in the light of laudatory visitation reports and the praise accorded him by royal commissioners. Pragmatic in outlook, despite his inherent conservatism, being prepared to assist Thomas Cromwell in an iconoclastic programme of religious reform (*LPFD*, x, nos 364, 563; xii (1), no 512). Close links with the ruling elite of Norwich made him an ideal choice as master at this testing time. Belonged to the guild of St George (Grace, *Gild of St George*, p. 151), and was brother of Thomas Codde, who became an alderman of Norwich in 1538 and later rose to be mayor at the time of Kett's rebellion (Hawes, *Index to Norwich City Officers*, p. 40). Died, in September 1546, while negotiations were still in progress for the acquisition of St Giles's by the city. Thomas proved a notable protector to the hospital, and left property to it in 1558 for the benefit of the inmates and the commemoration of Robert's soul (NRO, NCC, reg. Hyll, fos 280r–82r; reg. Colman, fos 431r–37r).

NOTES

INTRODUCTION

1. For example, T.S. Miller, *The Birth of the Hospital in the Byzantine Empire* (Baltimore, 1985), p. 6, adopts a curiously anachronistic view for a medievalist, arguing that 'historians of medicine, physicians and hospital planners surely have good reason for paying little attention to medieval hospitals' because of their allegedly poor medical facilities.
2. J.R. Guy, 'Of the Writing of Hospital Histories there is No End', *Bulletin of the History of Medicine*, lix (1985), pp. 415–20.
3. See, for instance, K.M. Ludmerer, 'Writing the History of Hospitals', ibid., lvi (1982), pp. 106–9.
4. A useful review of recent European literature may be found in the introduction to J.W. Brodman, *Charity and Welfare: Hospitals and the Poor in Medieval Catalonia* (Philadelphia, 1998). The best survey of publications before the late 1980s appears in P. Horden, '"A Discipline of Relevance": The Historiography of the Later Medieval Hospital', *Social History of Medicine*, i (1988), pp. 359–74.
5. F.O. Touati, *Maladie et Société au Moyen Age* (Paris, 1998).
6. J. Andrews and others, *The History of Bethlem* (London, 1997).
7. L. Granshaw and R. Porter, *The Hospital in History* (London, 1989), particularly essays by Martha Carlin, Miri Rubin and John Henderson.
8. D. de Vos, *Hans Memling* (Bruges, 1994), pp. 138–45; R. Graham, 'The Order of St Antoine de Viennois', *Archaeological Journal*, lxxxiv (1927), p. 364.
9. PRO, E117/11/58, 12/29.
10. C. Thomas, B. Sloane and C. Phillpotts, *Excavations at the Priory and Hospital of St Mary Spital, London* (Museum of London Archaeology Service, Monograph 1, 1997).
11. R. Gilchrist, *Contemplation and Action: The Other Monasticism* (Leicester, 1995).
12. M. Rubin, *Charity and Community in Medieval Cambridge* (Cambridge, 1987). See also, eadem, 'Development and Change in English Hospitals, 1100–1500', in L. Granshaw and R. Porter, *The Hospital in History* (London, 1989), pp. 41–59; and 'Imagining Medieval Hospitals', in J. Barry and C. Jones, eds, *Medicine and Charity before the Welfare State* (London, 1991), pp. 14–25.
13. See, generally, M. Mollat, *The Poor in the Middle Ages* (New Haven, 1986), whose survey remains a classic text.
14. As, for instance, in his review of *The Creation of a Community* by D.G. Shaw, in *Urban History*, xxi (1994), pp. 289–91.
15. A.D. Brown, *Popular Piety in Late Medieval England: The Diocese of Salisbury 1250–1550* (Oxford, 1995), Chapter VIII. Cullum's articles on medieval Yorkshire are listed in the Bibliography at the end of this volume.
16. For background information about Norwich's other hospitals, see C. Rawcliffe, *The Hospitals of Medieval Norwich* (Studies in East Anglian History, ii, 1995).
17. F. Meeres, *Guide to the Records of Norwich Cathedral* (Norwich, 1998).
18. A gazetteer of English medieval hospitals and almshouses is included in D. Knowles and R.N. Hadcock, *Medieval Religious Houses, England and Wales* (London, second edn, 1971), but see N. Orme and M. Webster, *The English Hospital 1070–1570* (New Haven and London, 1995), pp. 10–11, for reservations about the accuracy of this list.
19. Horden, '"Discipline of Relevance"', p. 366.
20. Only a rudimentary and partial list of the archive has been made, giving a deceptive impression of its size: W. Hudson and J.C. Tingey, eds, *The Revised Catalogue of the Records of the City of Norwich* (Norwich, 1898), pp. 68–79.
21. John Kirkpatrick, *History of the Religious Orders and Communities, and of the Hospitals and Castle, of Norwich, Written about the Year 1725*, ed. D. Turner (Yarmouth, 1845), p. vi. This volume contains nothing on St Giles's, but a file of rough notes survives among his papers: NRO, NCR, 21F, box 11, file 69. Kirkpatrick was buried in the hospital church of St Helen, where his memorial still stands.
22. F. Blomefield, *An Essay towards a Topographical History of the County of Norfolk* (11 vols, 1805–10), iv, pp. 376–402.

23. These form the basis of Norman Tanner's valuable study, *The Church in Late Medieval Norwich* (Toronto, 1984).
24. See, for example, T.B. Pugh, 'The Magnates, Knights and Gentry', in S.B. Chrimes and others, *Fifteenth-Century England* (Manchester, 1972), p. 97, for comparative information about incomes.
25. J.F. Pound, ed., *The Norwich Census of the Poor, 1570* (NRS, xl, 1971).
26. Their respective publications are listed in the Bibliography. A number of Pelling's articles have been reproduced in *The Common Lot: Sickness, Medical Occupations and the Urban Poor in Early Modern England* (London, 1998).
27. Discussed at greater length in Chapters VII and VIII, below.

I. MEDICINE FOR THE SOUL

1. Appendix I, preamble.
2. As he said in his will. This document, sealed by witnesses, survives in NRO, NCR, 24B, no 2. A full but rather fanciful English abstract appears in Blomefield, *Norfolk*, iii, pp. 487–92.
3. Appendix I, preamble. See also NRO, N/MC 15/4.
4. Orme and Webster, *English Hospital*, p. 11, where the problem of precisely quantifying endowments is discussed.
5. Notwithstanding the Norman achievement in this regard, the statistics presented by E.J. Kealey, *Medieval Medicus* (Baltimore, 1981), pp. 82–106, err on the side of optimism, as do his claims regarding the scope of the earliest English hospitals.
6. Rawcliffe, *Hospitals of Medieval Norwich*, p. 27.
7. H.C. Darby, *The Domesday Geography of Eastern England* (Cambridge, 1971), pp. 111, 139–40; William de Malmesbury, *Gesta Rerum Anglorum*, ed. W. Stubbs (2 vols, RS, 1887–9), ii, p. 386.
8. Rawcliffe, *Hospitals of Medieval Norwich*, pp. 61–9, 142–3.
9. Ibid., pp. 65, 68, 142–4, 163–4.
10. H.A. Doubleday, ed., *VCH Norfolk, II* (London, 1901), pp. 455–7. St Mary's was still described as a hospital in the 1280s: NRO, NCR, 24B, no 48, *Liber Domus Dei*, fos 31v–32r.
11. B. Bolton, *Innocent III: Studies in Papal Authority and Pastoral Care* (Aldershot, 1995), Paper XI, p. 53.
12. See R.I. Moore, *The Formation of a Persecuting Society* (Oxford, 1987), for a classic account of the impact of papal reforms.
13. Doubleday, *VCH Norfolk, II*, pp. 428–31; NRO, NCR, 24B, no 2.
14. Bolton, *Innocent III*, Paper xviii, pp. 123–45, passim. See also R.I. Moore, 'Heresy as a Disease', in W. Lourdaux and V. Verhelst, eds, *The Concept of Heresy in the Middle Ages* (Louvain, 1976), pp. 1–11.
15. J. Le Goff, *Saint Louis* (Paris, 1996), Chapter X; M. Bouquet, ed., *Rerum Gallicarum et Francicarum Scriptores, XX* (Paris, 1840), pp. 90–100.
16. H. Johnstone, 'Poor Relief in the Royal Households of Thirteenth-Century England', *Speculum*, iv (1929), pp. 155–7.
17. *CPR, 1254–1256*, p. 222.
18. Rubin, *Charity and Community*, Chapter III, provides the best overview of changing attitudes to charity and the poor, set in a specific urban context. The practical application of Christ's teaching on poverty is examined by P.H. Cullum and P.J.P. Goldberg, 'Charitable Provision in Late Medieval York: "To the Praise of God and Use of the Poor"', *Northern History*, xxix (1993), pp. 24–39.
19. P. Quarré, *Les Primitifs Flamands, XIII, L'Hôtel Dieu de Beaune* (Brussels, 1973), p. 63 and passim.
20. J. Le Goff, *The Birth of Purgatory* (London, 1984), pp. 81–2, 147, 247–77, 283–5, 292–4.
21. Rawcliffe, *Hospitals of Medieval Norwich*, p. 2.
22. Norwich guild returns made in English in response to a government inquiry of 1388 may be found in T. Smith, L.T. Smith and L. Brentano, *English Gilds* (EETS, xl, 1890), pp. 14–44; those in Latin are PRO, C43/47/290–1, 293, 297, 299; C47/44/301, 303. Almost all make some provision for the burial of guild members.
23. Mollat, *Poor in the Middle Ages*, p. 145, observes that 'to die in a hospital was almost a privilege'.
24. C. Rawcliffe, 'Hospital Nurses and their Work', in R. Britnell, ed., *Daily Life in the Late Middle Ages* (Stroud, 1998), p. 50.
25. E.M. Goulburn and H. Symonds, eds, *The Life, Letters and Sermons of Bishop Herbert de Losinga* (2 vols, Oxford, 1878), i, p. 26.
26. Ibid., ii, pp. 424–7. His views were not original: see J.W. Alexander, 'Herbert of Norwich, 1091–1119', *Studies in Medieval and Renaissance History*, vi (1969), pp. 119–232.
27. P. Heath Barnum, ed., *Dives and Pauper* (EETS, cclxxv, 1976, and cclxxx, 1980), i (part 1), p. 63.
28. S. Wenzel, ed., *Fasciculus Morum: A Fourteenth-Century Preacher's Handbook* (Pennsylvania, 1989), p. 541.
29. Bartholomaeus Anglicus, *On the Properties of Things: John Trevisa's Translation of Bartholomaeus Anglicus' De*

Proprietatis Rerum, ed. M.C. Seymour (3 vols, Oxford, 1975–88), i, pp. 166, 168. These ideas were commonplace: see, for example, M.C. Pouchelle, *The Body and Surgery in the Middle Ages* (Oxford, 1990), pp. 109–20.

30. R. Palmer, 'The Church, Leprosy and Plague in Medieval and Early Modern Europe', *Studies in Church History*, xix (1982), pp. 86, 89.
31. N. Tanner, ed., *Decrees of the Ecumenical Councils* (2 vols, Georgetown, 1990), i, pp. 245–46. For a wider discussion of the perceived relationship between body and soul, see the collected writings of D.W. Amundsen, *Medicine, Society and Faith in the Ancient and Medieval Worlds* (Baltimore, 1996), notably Chapter VII.
32. Discussed at greater length in C. Rawcliffe, 'Medicine for the Soul: The Medieval English Hospital and the Quest for Spiritual Health', in R. Porter and J. Hinnells, eds, *Religion, Health and Suffering* (London, 1999), pp. 316–38.
33. T. Wright, ed., *The Historical Works of Giraldus Cambrensis* (London, reprint, 1968), p. 147.
34. M.W. Bloomfield, *The Seven Deadly Sins* (Michigan, 1952), pp. 176–7, 220–1. I am grateful to Ms Irina Metzler for permitting me to read her unpublished MA dissertation on 'Disability in the Middle Ages' (University of Reading, 1995), in which she develops these ideas.
35. The author's translation from François Villon, *Oeuvres*, ed. L. Thuasne (3 vols, Geneva, 1967), pp. 169–70. See also, D.A. Fein, *A Reading of Villon's Testament* (Alabama, 1984), pp. 22–3.
36. Bartholomaeus Anglicus, *Properties of Things*, i, p. 166; J.F. Hinnebusch, ed., *The Historia Occidentalis of Jacques de Vitry* (Fribourg, 1972), p. 148.
37. Rawcliffe, *Hospitals of Medieval Norwich*, Chapter II.
38. B. McRee, 'Charity and Gild Solidarity in Late Medieval England', *Journal of British Studies*, xxxii (1993), p. 204; Smith and others, *English Gilds*, pp. 14–44. The Carpenters (pp. 37–9) were especially strict in this respect. C. Dyer, *Standards of Living in the Later Middle Ages* (Cambridge, 1989), p. 237, provides earlier examples of selective almsgiving.
39. R.H. Frost, 'The Aldermen of Norwich, 1461–1509: A Study of a Civic Elite' (University of Cambridge, PhD thesis, 1996), pp. 104–5.
40. P. Slack, *Poverty and Policy in Tudor and Stuart England* (London, 1988), pp. 38–40, 72, 74.
41. M. Pelling, 'Illness among the Poor in an Early Modern English Town: The Norwich Census of 1570', *Continuity and Change*, iii (1988), pp. 278–9 (reproduced in eadem, *Common Lot*, Chapter III). These figures exclude Dutch and Walloon immigrants.
42. D. Pearsall, ed., *Piers Plowman by William Langland: An Edition of the C-Text* (York Medieval Texts, second series, 1978), Passus IX, lines 175–85. See M.K. McIntosh, 'Finding Language for Misconduct: Jurors in Fifteenth-Century Local Courts', in B.A. Hanawalt and D. Wallace, eds, *Bodies and Disciplines: Intersections of Literature and History in Fifteenth-Century England* (Minneapolis, 1996), pp. 107–8 and note 92, for a discussion of Langland's contribution to the very limited late medieval debate on the causes of poverty.
43. Thomas of Monmouth, *The Life and Miracles of Saint William of Norwich*, eds A. Jessopp and M.R. James (Cambridge, 1896), pp. 152–3.
44. Dyer, *Standards of Living*, Chapter VII, passim.
45. C. Richmond, 'Landlord and Tenant: The Paston Evidence', in J. Kermode, ed., *Enterprise and Individuals in Fifteenth Century England* (Stroud, 1991), p. 27.
46. R.M. Smith, 'Some Issues Concerning Families and their Property in Rural England 1250–1800', in idem, ed., *Land, Kinship and Life-Cycle* (Cambridge, 1984), pp. 68–85.
47. Pearsall, *Piers Plowman*, Passus IX, lines 70–97; E. Clark, 'Mothers at Risk of Poverty in the Medieval English Countryside', in J. Henderson and R. Wall, eds, *Poor Women and Children in the European Past* (London, 1994), pp. 139–59.
48. Pelling, 'Illness among the Poor', pp. 282–3.
49. J.D. Dawes and J.R. Magilton, *The Cemetery of St Helen-on-the-Walls, Aldwark* (York Archaeological Trust, 1980), pp. 51–9, 63, 84–109.
50. A. Stirland, 'The Human Bones', in B. Ayers, ed., *Excavations within the North-East Bailey of Norwich Castle*, 1979 (East Anglian Archaeology, xxviii, 1985), pp. 49–58; B. Ayers, *Digging Deeper: Recent Archaeology in Norwich* (Norfolk Museums Service, 1987), pp. 11–15. I am grateful to Ann Stirland and Jane Bown for permitting me to consult their unpublished report, *Criminals and Paupers: Excavations at the Site and Churchyard of St Margaret Fybridgegate, Norwich.*
51. M. Pelling, 'Appearance and Reality: Barber-Surgeons, the Body and Disease', in A.L. Beier and R. Finlay, eds, *London 1500–1700: The Making of the Metropolis* (London, 1986), pp. 89–92. See above, pp. 215–17.
52. M. Pelling, 'Apprenticeship, Health and Social Cohesion in Early Modern London', *History Workshop*, xxxvii (1994), pp. 49–50.

53. C. Rawcliffe, *Medicine and Society in Later Medieval England* (Stroud, 1995), Chapter III, passim; A. Stirland, 'Care in the Community', *International Journal of Osteology*, vii (1997), pp. 587–90.
54. L. Demaitre, *Doctor Bernard Gordon: Professor and Practitioner* (Toronto, 1980), p. 128.
55. Blomefield, *Norfolk*, iv, p. 377. See P.M. Stell, *Medical Practice in Medieval York* (University of York, Borthwick Paper, xc, 1996), pp. 16–23, for a discussion the medical response to such conditions.
56. Rawcliffe, *Hospitals of Medieval Norwich*, pp. 33–59, 122–5; see above, p. 163.
57. K. Manchester, 'Tuberculosis and Leprosy in Antiquity: An Interpretation', *Medical History*, xxviii (1984), pp. 162–73.
58. B. Gutman Rosencrantz, 'The Trouble with Bovine Tuberculosis', *Bulletin of the History of Medicine*, lix (1985), pp. 155–75; Stirland and Bown, *Criminals and Paupers*, Chapter II.
59. J.M. Bolton, '"The World Turned Upside Down": Plague as an Agent of Economic and Social Change', in W.M. Ormrod and P.G. Lindley, eds, *The Black Death in England* (Stamford, 1996), pp. 29–33.
60. *Calendar of Nottinghamshire Coroners' Inquests 1485–1558* (Thoroton Society, xxv, 1969), nos 233–4, 243–4, 247, 267.
61. R.C. Finucane, *Miracles and Pilgrims: Popular Beliefs in Medieval England* (New York, 1995), pp. 107–8; Thomas of Monmouth, *Life and Miracles of Saint William*, pp. 203–5.
62. W. Hudson, ed., *Leet Jurisdiction in the City of Norwich during the Thirteenth and Fourteenth Centuries* (Selden Society, v, 1892), pp. 8–10, 13, 16, 24, 47, 57, 60, 71; NRO, NCR, 16A, Norwich Assembly Proceedings, 1491–1553, fo 175v; Mayor's Court Book, 1510–1532, fos 11r, 48r, 168r, 169r, 193r, 207r.
63. NRO, DCN 79/5, Holme Street court leet, 23 Henry VI.
64. See Chapter II.
65. B. Tierney, 'The Decretists and the "Deserving Poor"', *Comparative Studies in Society and History*, i (1958–9), p. 366; T. Thomson and C. Ines, eds, *The Acts of the Parliament of Scotland* (12 vols, Edinburgh, 1844–75), ii, pp. 692, 729. See also *CIMisc., 1399–1422*, no 206.
66. N. Moore, ed., *The Book of the Foundation of St Bartholomew's Church in London* (EETS, clxiii, 1923), pp. 24–5.
67. B. Geremek, *The Margins of Society in Late Medieval Paris* (Cambridge, 1987), pp. 172–3; William Dugdale, *Monasticon Anglicanum*, eds J. Caley and others (6 vols, London, 1817–30), vi (part 2), pp. 704–7.
68. A. Luders and others, eds, *Statutes of the Realm* (11 vols, London, 1810–28), iii, 34 and 35 Hen. VIII, cap. viii.
69. Finucane, *Miracles and Pilgrims*, pp. 106–7.
70. B.F. Harvey, 'Introduction', in B.M.S. Campbell, ed., *Before the Black Death: Studies in the 'Crisis' of the Early Fourteenth Century* (Manchester, 1991), p. 20.
71. Appendix I, article 43; NRO, NCR, 24B, nos 4 and 9. Walpole issued a second indulgence in 1299: Harvard University, USA, Law School Library, Medieval Deed, no 180.
72. A. Gransden, ed., *The Chronicle of Bury St Edmunds, 1212–1301* (London, 1964), p. 123.
73. Rawcliffe, *Medicine and Society*, pp. 85–6; Bodleian Library, Oxford, Ms Ashmole 191, fos 46v–47v; W.H. Black, ed., *Catalogue of the Manuscripts Bequeathed unto the University of Oxford by Elias Ashmole* (Oxford, 1845), no 191.
74. Appendix I, article 15.
75. Gransden, *Chronicle of Bury St Edmunds*, p. 22. It has been suggested that monastic chroniclers exaggerated the effects of bad weather because they ate wheat bread. Barley, a staple of the peasant diet, was more resilient to damp: H.E. Hallam, 'The Climate of Eastern England, 1250–1350', *Agricultural History Review*, xxxi (1983), pp. 124–32.
76. See above, pp. 84–5, 181–2.
77. P.H. Cullum, 'Poverty and Charity in Early Fourteenth-Century England', in N. Rogers, ed., *England in the Fourteenth Century* (Stamford, 1993), pp. 147–48; *HMC Eighth Report, Part I* (London, 1881), pp. 352–3.
78. R.H. Hilton, 'Small Town Society in England before the Black Death', *Past and Present*, cv (1984), pp. 53–78.
79. E. Rutledge, 'Immigration and Population Growth in Early Fourteenth-Century Norwich: Evidence from the Tithing Roll', *Urban History Yearbook* (1988), p. 15.
80. B.M.S. Campbell, 'Population Pressure, Inheritance and the Land Market in a Fourteenth-Century Peasant Community', in R.M. Smith, ed., *Land, Kinship and Life-Cycle* (Cambridge, 1984), pp. 87–134.
81. J.R. Maddicott, *The English Peasantry and the Demands of the Crown 1294–1341* (Past and Present Supplement, i, 1975), pp. 18–21.
82. Rutledge, 'Immigration and Population Growth', pp. 25–7.
83. W. Hudson and J.C. Tingey, eds, *The Records of the City of Norwich* (2 vols, Norwich, 1906–10), i, pp. 189–90.
84. E. Rutledge, 'Landlords and Tenants: Housing and the Rented Property Market in Early Fourteenth-Century Norwich', *Urban History*, xxii (1995), pp. 12–14.
85. M. Atkin, 'Medieval Clay-Walled Building in Norwich', *Norfolk Archaeology*, xli (1991), pp. 171–85.

86. Blomefield, *Norfolk*, iv, p. 439; Ayers, *Digging Deeper*, p. 11.
87. M. Atkin, A. Carter and D.H. Evans, *Excavations in Norwich 1971–78, II* (East Anglian Archaeology, xxvi, 1985), pp. 77–8. See above, pp. 98, 201.
88. Rutledge, 'Landlords and Tenants', p. 13. The 'Mayor's Book' of Norwich, begun in 1526, recorded 57,474 fatalities in 1351: G. Johnson, 'Chronological Memoranda touching the City of Norwich', *Norfolk Archaeology*, i (1847), p. 141.
89. R. Britnell, 'The Black Death in English Towns', *Urban History*, xxi (1994), pp. 199–200. The 'Mayor's Book' of Norwich, begun in 1526, recorded 57,474 fatalities in 1351: G. Johnson, 'Chronological Memoranda touching the City of Norwich', *Norfolk Archaeology*, i (1847), p. 141.
90. P.E. Pobst, ed., *The Register of William Bateman, Bishop of Norwich, 1344–1355, I* (Canterbury and York Society, 1996), pp. xxx–xxxi; C. Harper-Bill, 'The English Church and English Religion after the Black Death', in W.M. Ormrod and P.G. Lindley, eds, *The Black Death in England* (Stamford, 1996), p. 87, and generally, pp. 79–123.
91. Campbell, 'Population Pressure', p. 96.
92. J.C. Russell, *British Medieval Population* (Albuquerque, 1948), p. 142 (the accompanying analysis is less reliable).
93. A. Watkin, ed., *Inventory of Church Goods, temp. Edward III* (2 parts, NRS, xix, 1947–48), i, pp. 9, 26–7.
94. Harper-Bill, 'English Church', p. 97; J. Greatrex, 'Monk Students from Norwich Cathedral Priory at Oxford and Cambridge, *c.* 1300 to 1530', *EHR*, cvi (1991), p. 559; J. Campbell, 'Norwich', in M. Lobel, ed., *Historic Towns, II* (London, 1975), p. 16.
95. Luders, *Statutes of the Realm*, iii, 23 Edward III, cap. v. For background to this legislation, see R. Horrox, ed., *The Black Death* (Manchester, 1994), Parts 6 and 7.
96. *CPR, 1350–1354*, p. 283–4.
97. *CPR, 1359–1361*, p. 76; *1369–1374*, pp. 222, 302.
98. R.B. Dobson, ed., *The Peasants' Revolt of 1381* (second edn, London, 1983), Part 4, passim.
99. Mollat, *Poor in the Middle Ages*, pp. 231–2.
100. Luders, *Statutes of the Realm*, ii, 7 Richard II, cap. v.
101. Hudson and Tingey, *Records of the City of Norwich*, i, p. 302.
102. Harper-Bill, 'English Church', p. 116.
103. NRO, NCR, 24B, no 2; Blomefield, *Norfolk*, iii, pp. 487–92.
104. Blomefield, *Norfolk*, v, pp. 300, 375; vi, pp. 514–15; xi, pp. 146–7, 176; *Curia Regis Rolls, 1225–1226*, no 804; *1237–1242*, no 2230. See also above, pp. 74, 82–3.
105. NRO, NCR, 24B, no 2.
106. Blomefield, *Norfolk*, vi, pp. 514–15. In his will Suffield left £40 to be distributed among the poor living on the dower lands of Maud de Warenne (d. 1248), widowed countess of Surrey, as alms for her soul: NRO, NCR, 24B, no 2.
107. *CPR, 1247–1258*, pp. 469, 477.
108. John le Neve, *Fasti Ecclesiae Anglicanae 1066–1300, II, Monastic Cathedrals*, ed. D. Greenway (London, 1971), pp. 57, 64.
109. *CPL, 1198–1304*, pp. 353, 367. The bishop left money in his will for the repair of Suffield church: NRO, NCR, 24B, no 2.
110. *CPR, 1247–1258*, pp. 139, 457. It was probably to this William that Suffield left 40*s* and a song book: NRO, NCR, 24B, no 2.
111. Blomefield, *Norfolk*, vi, pp. 514–15; xi, 146–7, 176; Arundel Castle Mss, Norfolk, box II, no 110, and Hales Charter, no 104.
112. Tanner, *Decrees*, i, pp. 242–3; *CPR, 1247–1258*, p. 219; *CCR, 1254–1256*, pp. 302, 396. King Henry occasionally gave the bishop gifts of game: *CCR, 1253–1254*, p. 66; *1256–1259*, p. 20.
113. Matthew Paris, *Chronica Majora*, ed. H.R. Luard (7 vols, RS, 1872–84), iv, pp. 640–4.
114. Ibid., iv, p. 261; NRO, NCR, 24B, no 2; Bartholomew Cotton, *Historia Anglicana*, ed. H.R. Luard (RS, 1859), p. 394. J. Greatrex, *Biographical Register of the English Cathedral Priories of the Province of Canterbury* (Oxford, 1997), p. 497, supplies a later death date for Cotton.
115. Matthew Paris, *The Life of St Edmund*, ed. C.H. Lawrence (Stroud, 1996), pp. 9–10.
116. Appendix I, article 13. See also Tanner, *Decrees*, i, p. 240, for Lateran IV (cap. xi), 'On Schoolmasters'.
117. P. Cattermole, 'Schools in Medieval and Early Tudor Norwich', in idem, R. Harries and P. Mackintosh, eds, *A History of Norwich School* (Norwich, 1991), pp. 10–15.
118. Bishop Hobhouse, ed., *Calendar of the Register of John Drokensford* (Somerset Record Society, i, 1887), p. 268. From at least 1267 the hospital of St Nicholas, Pontefract, had distributed forty loaves each week among the local schoolboys, and it seems likely that many other houses offered support of this kind: A.F. Leach, ed., *Early Yorkshire Schools, II* (Yorkshire Archaeological Society, Record Series, xxxiii, 1903), pp. 3–4.

119. N. Orme, *English Schools in the Middle Ages* (London, 1973), pp. 182–3, 261–2, and idem and Webster, *English Hospital*, pp. 66–8, offer a valuable survey. See also J.H. Moran, *The Growth of English Schooling 1340–1548* (Princeton, 1985), pp. 82–3, 93–4.
120. F.C. Hingeston-Randolph, ed., *The Register of John de Grandisson, Bishop of Exeter, 1327–1369* (3 vols, London, 1894–9), ii, pp. 666–9.
121. C.H. Talbot and E.A. Hammond, *The Medical Practitioners in Medieval England* (London, 1965), p. 284; *HMC, Ninth Report, Part I* (London, 1883), p. 49.
122. Appendix I, article 5.
123. R. von Fleishhaker, ed., *Lanfrank's 'Science of Cirurgie'* (EETS, cii, 1894), p. 55; John of Arderne, *Treatises of Fistula in Ano*, ed. D. Power (EETS, cxxxix, 1910), p. 88; Pouchelle, *Body and Surgery*, p. 87.
124. Appendix I, article 32.
125. F.M. Powicke, *Stephen Langton* (Oxford, 1928), pp. 23–74, provides a vivid description of the Paris schools at this time. For the debate on poverty see Bolton, *Innocent III*, Paper xviii, pp. 123–4, 133–5, and Tierney, 'Decretists', pp. 36–73.
126. NRO, NCR, 24B, no 2; J. Jones, ed., *Saint Richard of Chichester* (Sussex Record Society, lxxix, 1993), pp. 201–2. C.H. Lawrence's introduction to Paris', *Life of St Edmund*, pp. 1–27, describes Edmund Rich's background, much of which was shared by Suffield.
127. Paris, *Life of St Edmund*, pp. 4, 18, 136.
128. E.A. Brown, 'Death and the Human Body in the Later Middle Ages: The Legislation of Boniface VIII on the Division of the Corpse', *Viator*, xii (1981), pp. 228–33, records several cases of heart burial, some of which predate Edmund Rich, although he was especially influential in this regard.
129. H.E. Malden, ed., *VCH Surrey, II* (London, 1905), p. 119; R.M. Serjeantson and W.R.D. Adkins, eds, *VCH Northamptonshire, II* (London, 1906), p. 151.
130. *Curia Regis Rolls, 1237–1242*, no 318. The conflict over elections is described in F.M. Powicke, *Henry III and the Lord Edward* (2 vols, Oxford, 1947), i, pp. 270–3.
131. H. Wharton, ed., *Anglia Sacra* (2 vols, London, 1691), i, pp. 174–5; Paris, *Life of St Edmund*, pp. 82–6, 143–8.
132. Tanner, *Decrees*, i, pp. 246–8; Appendix I, article 35.
133. Le Neve, *Fasti*, p. 57, 86; Lambeth Palace Ms 582, p. 62.
134. NRO, NCR, 24B, no 2.
135. Ibid. In his will Suffield also left the monks his great cup and a monstrance in which to display either the Host or relics as they wished, three horses and the contents of his chapel.
136. Paris, *Life of St Edmund*, pp. 7, 119–20.
137. D.H.S. Cranage, 'Eastern Chapels in the Cathedral Church of Norwich', *Antiquaries Journal*, xii (1932), pp. 117–26; E.C. Fernie, 'Two Aspects of Bishop Walter Suffield's Lady Chapel at Norwich Cathedral', in W.M. Ormrod, ed., *England in the Thirteenth Century* (Nottingham, 1985), pp. 52–5; idem, *An Architectural History of Norwich Cathedral* (Oxford, 1993), pp. 162–3.
138. Appendix I, article 1. It was to these three saints that Suffield finally commended his soul: NRO, NCR, 24B, no 2.
139. G. Ryan and H. Ripperger, eds, *The Golden Legend of Jacobus de Voragine* (New York, 1941, reprinted 1969), pp. 516–19.
140. *CPR, 1247–1258*, p. 28; NRO, NCR, 24B, no 2.
141. As, for example, BL, seals, xxxv.238, and D.C.F. xxxix; *Proceedings of the Society of Antiquaries of London*, i (1849), p. 27.
142. John Lydgate, *The Minor Poems*, ed. H.N. MacCracken (EETS, cvii, 1911, reprinted 1961), pp. 171–2.
143. *The Poems of Robert Henryson*, ed. D. Fox (Oxford, 1981), pp. 167–9. See also, Horrox, *Black Death*, pp. 36, 40, 56, 77, 112, 271–3.
144. See, for example, Dyer, *Standards of Living*, p. 241; and J.H.R. Moorman, *Church Life in England in the Thirteenth Century* (Cambridge, 1945), p. 206.
145. NRO, NCR, 24B, no 2.
146. *CPR, 1247–1258*, p. 92; *CCR, 1256–1259*, p. 59.
147. NRO, NCR, 24B, no 2; Bolton, *Innocent III*, Paper xviii, p. 140.
148. Appendix I, articles 14 and 16.
149. Appendix I, article 11; NRO, NCR, 24B, no 2. Straw was, for example, used at St John's hospital, Winchester: D. Keene, *Survey of Medieval Winchester, II* (2 vols, Oxford, 1985), ii, p. 815.
150. Blomefield, *Norfolk*, iv, p. 431.
151. John Stow, *A Survey of London*, ed. C.L. Kingsford (2 vols, Oxford, 1908), i, p. 90; G. Keynes, ed., *The Works of Sir Thomas Browne* (4 vols, London, 1964), iii, p. 132; Paris, *Chronica Majora*, iv, p. 638. See also, Wulfstan of Winchester, *The Life of St Aethelwold*, eds M. Lapidge and M. Winterbottom (Oxford, 1991), pp. 44–7.

152. F.M. Powicke and C.R. Cheney, eds, *Councils and Synods, II, 1205–1313* (2 parts, Oxford, 1964), pp. 451–67.
153. Bolton, *Innocent III*, Paper xviii, pp. 140–1; Jones, *Saint Richard of Chichester*, p. 181. See also, E.F. Jacob, 'St Richard of Chichester', *Journal of Ecclesiastical History*, vii (1956), pp. 174–88.
154. Jones, *Saint Richard of Chichester*, p. 169.
155. Ibid., pp. 165–6.
156. W. Page, ed., *VCH Sussex, II* (London, 1907), p. 109. W.H. Blaauw, 'Will of Richard de la Wych', *Sussex Archaeological Collections*, i (1848), pp. 172–3, confuses Windham with Wymondham in Norfolk.
157. J.M. Reitzel, 'The Medieval Houses of Bons-Enfants', *Viator* xi (1980), p. 37; PRO, C1/131/8.
158. See, for example, K. Wood-Legh, *Perpetual Chantries in Britain* (Cambridge, 1965), p. 224; J.A.F. Thomson, *The Early Tudor Church and Society* (London, 1993), pp. 158–62, 181; N. Orme, 'Sufferings of the Clergy: Illness and Old Age in Exeter Diocese 1300–1540', in M. Pelling and R.M. Smith, eds, *Life, Death and the Elderly* (London, 1991), pp. 62–73.
159. Tanner, *Church in Late Medieval Norwich*, p. 48. The author estimates that seculars and religious together accounted for about 6 per cent of the adult male population (pp. 20–1).
160. N. Orme, 'A Medieval Almshouse for the Clergy: Clyst Gabriel Hospital near Exeter', *Journal of Ecclesiastical History*, xxxix (1988), pp. 1–15; idem and Webster, *English Hospital*, pp. 114–15; E. Rowland-Burdon, 'St Saviour's Hospital, Bury St Edmunds', *PSIA*, xix (1927), p. 264; A.F. Leach, ed., *Early Yorkshire Schools, II* (Yorkshire Archaeological Society, Record Series, xxvii, 1899), p. 37. According to Knowles and Hadcock, *Medieval Religious Houses*, pp. 310–410, a bare minimum of eighteen hospitals made specific provision for 'decayed' clergy, but many others would have accorded them priority.
161. Powicke, *Henry III*, i, p. 269; J.C. Russell, *Dictionary of Writers of Thirteenth Century England* (London, 1936), pp. 81–2.
162. W.D. Peckham, ed., *The Chartulary of the High Church of Chichester* (Sussex Record Society, xlvi, 1942–3), nos 83, 248–52.
163. Blaauw, 'Will of Richard de la Wych', pp. 182–5.
164. C.H. Lawrence, *St Edmund of Abingdon* (Oxford, 1960), pp. 131–2.
165. See, for example, Paris, *Chronica Majora*, iv, pp. 555–6; v, pp. 80, 451–2, 638; vi, pp. 296–7.
166. W.E. Lunt, *The Valuation of Norwich* (Oxford, 1926), pp. 52–68; *CPR, 1247–1258*, pp. 164, 370.
167. *CCR, 1254–1256*, p. 196; *CPR, 1247–1258*, pp. 449, 508–9; NRO, NCR, 24B, no 2.
168. Paris, *Chronica Majora*, v, p. 638; Cotton, *Historia Anglicana*, p. 394.
169. Jacob, 'St Richard of Chichester', p. 183; NRO, NCR, 24B, no 2.
170. For the cost of canonisation see Finucane, *Miracles and Pilgrims*, pp. 36–8.
171. D. Wilkins, ed., *Concilia Magnae Britanniae et Hiberniae* (4 vols, London, 1737), i, pp. 731–6.
172. *CPR, 1247–1258*, p. 28; Paris, *Chronica Majora*, v, pp. 36, 80.
173. Rawcliffe, *Hospitals of Medieval Norwich*, pp. 61–89; C. Harper-Bill, ed., *Charters of the Medieval Hospitals of Bury St Edmunds* (Suffolk Records Society, Suffolk Charters, xiv, 1994), pp. 9–17.
174. W.H. Stevenson, ed., *Records of the Borough of Nottingham, I* (Nottingham, 1882), pp. 29–33; *HMC, Twelfth Report, Appendix IX* (London, 1891), pp. 426–7.
175. J. Raine, ed., *The Register of Walter Gray* (Surtees Society, lvi, 1870), pp. 180–1.
176. Orme and Webster, *English Hospital*, p. 74. The authors list some published statutes on pp. 293–5.
177. For striking similarities see, for example, J. Imbert, *Les Hôpitaux en Droit Canonique* (Paris, 1947), Chapter I, passim, which deals with foundation statutes.
178. Hinnebusch, *Historia Occidentalis*, pp. 147–8.
179. Appendix I, article 19; R.W. Southern, *Western Society and the Church in the Middle Ages* (London, 1972), pp. 241–50.
180. Rubin, *Charity and Community*, pp. 154–6; C.H. Lawrence, *Medieval Monasticism* (London, 1989), pp. 163–9.
181. J. Willis Clark, ed., *The Observances in Use at the Augustinian Priory of St Giles and St Andrew at Barnwell, Cambridgeshire* (Cambridge, 1897), pp. 175, 179.
182. Tanner, *Decrees*, i, pp. 242–4. See also, B.F. Harvey, *Monastic Dress in the Middle Ages: Precept and Practice* (William Urry Memorial Trust, Canterbury, 1988), pp. 8–13, and L. Trichet, *Le Costume du Clergé* (Paris, 1986), pp. 54–7, 60.
183. NRO, DCN 84/14; A.H. Thompson, *The History of the Hospital and the New College of the Annunciation of St Mary in the Newarke, Leicester* (Leicester Archaeological Society, 1937), pp. 30–7; Rubin, *Charity and Community*, p. 153; New College, Oxford, Ms 3691, fos 90r–93r.
184. NRO, NCR, 24B, nos 1 and 4.
185. NRO, DCN 40/7, fos 76r–78v.

186. Doubleday, *VCH Norfolk, II*, p. 442, provides an abstract of the first foundation charter and suggests the date of 1245–6; for the papal letters see *CPL, 1198–1304*, p. 312.
187. NRO, N/MC 15/4.
188. NRO, COL 5/2/1.
189. *CCR, 1251–1253*, p. 510.
190. B. de la Roncière and others, eds, *Les Registres d'Alexandre IV* (3 vols, Paris, 1895–1959), i, no 254; *CPL, 1198–1304*, p. 312; NRO, NCR, 24B, no 3.
191. Appendix I, articles 6 and 8; and Chapter II.
192. NRO, DCN 43/48. This text was used by Blomefield, *Norfolk*, iv, pp. 382–3, when he came to discuss the statutes.
193. NRO, NCR, 17B, Book of Pleas, fos 48r–50r. This volume contains numerous entries concerning the exempt jurisdiction of Holme Street, where the hospital lay. See above, pp. 40–1.

II. THE PRECINCT

1. The siting of hospitals is discussed in Orme and Webster, *English Hospital*, pp. 41–8.
2. R. Gilchrist, 'Christian Bodies and Souls: The Archaeology of Life and Death in Later Medieval Hospitals', in S. Bassett, ed., *Death in Towns: Urban Responses to the Dying and the Dead*, 100–1600 (Leicester, 1992), pp. 113–16.
3. NRO, NCR, 24B, no 1; DCN 43/48.
4. E. Duffy, *The Stripping of the Altars: Traditional Religion in England,* c. *1400–*c. *1580* (New Haven and London, 1992), pp. 367–8; M. Flynn, *Sacred Charity: Confraternities and Social Welfare in Spain 1400–1700* (London, 1989), p. 57.
5. A.C. Harrison, 'Excavations on the Site of St Mary's Hospital, Strood', *Archaeologia Cantiana*, lxxxiv (1969), pp. 139–40; *CIMisc., 1219–1307*, no 1061.
6. Flynn, *Sacred Charity*, pp. 37, 57.
7. Gilchrist, *Contemplation and Action*, pp. 51–3; Brown, *Popular Piety*, pp. 183–4; Doubleday, *VCH Norfolk, II*, p. 451.
8. W. Page, ed., *VCH Nottingham, II* (London, 1910), pp. 168–73. This house was described as the hospital of the Annunciation 'at the Bridge's End': *CPL, 1396–1404*, p. 489.
9. Hudson and Tingey, *Records of the City of Norwich*, ii, pp. xxxii–iii, 217–18.
10. NRO, NCR, 17B, *Liber Albus Civitatis*, fo 14r.
11. P. Brown, *The Body and Society: Men, Women and Sexual Renunciation in Early Christianity* (New York, 1988), p. 304.
12. Moore, *Book of the Foundation*, p. 18.
13. M. Candille, ed., *Livre de la Vie Active de l'Hôtel Dieu de Jehan Henry* (Paris, 1964), p. 29.
14. F.O. Touati, 'Les Léproseries aux XIIème et XIIIème Siècles Lieux de Conversion?', in idem and N. Beriou, *Voluntate Dei Leprosus: Les Lépreux entre Conversion et Exclusion aux XIIème et XIIIème Siècles* (Testi, Studi, Strumenti, iv, 1991), p. 21.
15. A. Suckling, *The History and Antiquities of the County of Suffolk* (2 vols, London, 1846), ii, pp. 21–4.
16. B.G. Durham and others, 'Site Reports from Magdalen College, Oxford', *Medieval Archaeology*, xxxi (1987), pp. 155–6; xxxii (1988), p. 270.
17. J. Imbert, ed., *Histoire des Hôpitaux en France* (Toulouse, 1982), pp. 29–30, 119–20; BL, Cottonian Ms Cleopatra, C V, fos 24v, 33r, 36r–36v; Rawcliffe, 'Hospital Nurses', pp. 51–2. See above, p. 51.
18. D. Gallavotti Cavallero, *Lo Spedale di Santa Maria della Scala in Siena* (Siena, 1985), p. 159; P. Torriti, *Il Pellegrinaio nello Spedale di Santa Maria della Scala a Siena* (Siena, 1987), p. 61.
19. Horrox, *Black Death*, pp. 138, 147–9. See also Brown, *Body and Society*, p. 238.
20. Thomas, Sloane and Phillpotts, *Excavations at St Mary Spital*, p. 43.
21. C. Ross, ed., *Cartulary of St Mark's Hospital, Bristol* (Bristol Record Society, xxi, 1959), pp. 75–6. For a general discussion of the importance of the water supply to medieval religious communities, see C.J. Bond, 'Water Management in the Urban Monastery', in R. Gilchrist and H. Mytum, eds, *Advances in Monastic Archaeology* (BAR, British Series, ccxxvii, 1993), pp. 43–78.
22. B. Geremek, 'Criminalité, Vagabondage, Paupérisme: La Marginalité a l'Aube des Tempes Modernes', *Revue d'Histoire Moderne et Contemporaine*, xxi (1974), p. 371; idem, *Margins of Society*, pp. 172–3.
23. Brown, *Popular Piety*, p. 181.
24. Thomas, Sloane and Phillpotts, *Excavations at St Mary Spital*, pp. 43, 128.
25. PRO, C270/22.

26. NRO, NCR, 24A, GH Norwich accounts, 1415–1460, accounts for 1432–3 to 1441–2; DCN 79/3 (Holme Street court leet, 18 Henry VI).
27. M. Carlin, *Medieval Southwark* (London, 1996), p. 79.
28. Theft from hospitals was by no means uncommon: D. Owen, ed., *The Making of King's Lynn* (Records of Social and Economic History, new series, ix, 1984), p. 430.
29. P.H. Cullum, 'St Leonard's York: The Spatial and Social Analysis of an Augustinian Hospital', in R. Gilchrist and H. Mytum, eds, *Advances in Monastic Archaeology* (BAR, British Series, ccxxii, 1993), p. 16; R. Price and M. Ponsford, *St Bartholomew's Hospital, Bristol: The Excavation of a Medieval Hospital* (Council for British Archaeology, cx, 1998), p. 219.
30. NRO, NCR, 24A, GH Norwich accounts, 1465–1501, account for 1477–8. Almost every building, chamber and gateway at St Giles's could be made fast. The same concern with security is evident in all the larger English hospitals: Cullum, 'St Leonard's York', p. 16; Thomas, Sloane and Phillpotts, *Excavations at St Mary Spital*, p. 109.
31. PRO, C270/22; NRO, NCR, 24A, GH Norwich accounts, 1485–1509, account for 1505–6. Attention was then given, *inter alia*, to the security of 'le quere door', the door leading from the church to the street and 'le cleketgate et le watergate'.
32. Carlin, *Medieval Southwark*, p. 79. Ironically, the hospital had moved shortly after 1212, in order to enjoy the benefits of cleaner air and a better water supply (p. 76).
33. Demaitre, *Doctor Bernard Gordon*, pp. 47, 157.
34. A.R. Myers, ed., *English Historical Documents, IV, 1327–1485* (London, 1969), p. 1055; Atkin, Carter and Evans, *Excavations in Norwich*, p. 3.
35. NRO, NCR, 24A, GH Norwich accounts, 1415–1460, 1465–1501.
36. *CPR, 1446–1452*, p. 533; *LPFD, Addenda*, i (1), nos 384, 1053. For background to these disputes, see C. Jamison, *The History of the Royal Hospital of St Katherine* (Oxford, 1952), pp. 132–3. The alleys around St Katherine's were also a haunt of prostitutes – of both sexes: R.M. Karras and D.L. Boyd, '"Ut cum Muliere"', in L. Fradenburg and C. Freccero, eds, *Premodern Sexualities* (London, 1996), p. 112.
37. Rawcliffe, *Hospitals of Medieval Norwich*, p. 47.
38. Hudson, *Leet Jurisdiction in the City of Norwich*, p. 59.
39. Ibid., pp. 48, 53; Appendix I, article 26. Illicit commerce was specifically forbidden as hindering the sale of goods in 'the public and common market': Hudson and Tingey, *Records of the City of Norwich*, i, pp. 181–3, 187–8.
40. Rawcliffe, *Hospitals of Medieval Norwich*, pp. 61–4; Campbell, 'Norwich', p. 9.
41. Campbell, 'Norwich', pp. 5, 8–9, 12–13.
42. Hudson and Tingey, *Records of the City of Norwich*, i, pp. 117, 326–7; NRO, NCR, 24A, GH Norwich Accounts, 1415–1460, account for 1447–8.
43. A point elaborated in Mary Douglas's classic study, *Purity and Danger: An Analysis of the Concepts of Partition and Taboo* (London and New York, 1994), notably pp. 52–4, 96–7.
44. D.J. Keene, 'Suburban Growth', in R. Holt and G. Rosser, eds, *The Medieval Town: A Reader in English Urban History 1200–1540* (London and New York, 1990), p. 118.
45. Moore, *Book of the Foundation*, pp. 12–13.
46. Rawcliffe, *Medicine and Society*, p. 42.
47. Stirland and Bown, *Criminals and Paupers* (forthcoming).
48. Thomas, Sloane and Phillpotts, *Excavations at St Mary Spital*, pp. 68, 97–8.
49. N. Hidden, 'The Hospital or Priory or Free Chapel of St John the Baptist in Hungerford', *Wiltshire Archaeological and Natural History Magazine*, lxxxiii (1990), p. 97; Keene, *Survey of Medieval Winchester II*, ii, p. 820; G.H. Smith, 'The Excavation of the Hospital of St Mary of Ospringe, Commonly Called Maison Dieu', *Archaeologia Cantiana*, xcv (1979), pp. 92–3; Thomas, Sloane and Phillpotts, *Excavations at St Mary Spital*, p. 90.
50. NRO, NCR, 24A, GH accounts, 1306–1398.
51. Ibid., GH Norwich accounts, 1415–1460, 1465–1501, 1485–1509, 1509–1528, passim. In 1512–13, for example, 8*s* 2*d* was spent on cleansing the hospital's ponds.
52. Archives of St George's Chapel, Windsor, xv 37.21 (10 Henry VII), fo 14v.
53. NRO, NCR, 24A, GH Norwich accounts, 1415–1460. See Bond, 'Water Management', p. 70, for examples of the construction of covered drains with running water to flush privies at St John's hospital, Bridgwater, and St Bartholomew's, London.
54. Campbell, 'Norwich', pp. 4, 9; B. Ayers, *The English Heritage Book of Norwich* (London, 1994), p. 35 and map p. 32; Cattermole, 'Schools in Medieval Norwich', pp. 13–15.
55. Gransden, *Chronicle of Bury St Edmunds*, pp. 22, 54. See also, H. Ellis, ed., *Chronica Johannis de Oxenedes* (RS, 1859), p. 243; and above, pp. 87–8.

56. Cotton, *Historia Anglicana*, p. 172.
57. NRO, NCR, 24A, GH Norwich accounts, 1465–1501, accounts for 1467–8, 1474–5; 1485–1509 account for 1498–9. The great St Leonard's day floods of November 1519 must also have caused damage, but the accounts are silent on this score: Johnson, 'Chronological Memoranda', p. 143.
58. Ibid., GH general accounts, 1485–1508, account of the receiver general, 1499–1500, recording a payment of £20 from Nicholas Goldwell to cover fire damage. See also above, pp. 231–3.
59. Cullum, 'St Leonard's York', p. 14; Thomas, Sloane and Phillpotts, *Excavations at St Mary Spital*, p. 80; Carlin, *Medieval Southwark*, pp. 75–6; D.M. Meade, *Kepier Hospital* (Durham, 1995), pp. 4–5, 17.
60. H.C. Maxwell-Lyte and M.C.B. Dawes, eds, *The Register of Thomas Bekyngton I* (Somerset Record Society, xlix, 1934), pp. 288–300.
61. C. Rawcliffe, 'The Hospitals of Later Medieval London', *Medical History*, xxviii (1984), p. 2.
62. *CPL, 1458–1471*, pp. 356–7.
63. NRO, DCN 79/2 (Holme Street court leet, 19 Henry VI).
64. *CPR, 1446–1452*, pp. 18–19.
65. R. Griffiths, *The Reign of King Henry VI* (London, 1981), pp. 496–7.
66. This development may be traced in unusual topographical and archaeological detail at St Mary's Bishopsgate: Thomas, Sloane and Phillpotts, *Excavations at St Mary Spital*, Chapters I–IV.
67. See above, pp. 110–11.
68. Appendix I, article 15.
69. This should not be underestimated. Erasmus describes how almsmen from the former leper hospital at Harbledown 'ambushed' passers-by with their begging bowls: C.R. Thompson, ed., *Collected Works of Erasmus, XL, Colloquies* (Toronto, 1997), p. 648.
70. F. Woodman, 'Hardley, Norfolk, and the Rebuilding of its Chancel', in D. Buckton and T.A. Heslop, eds, *Studies in Medieval Art and Architecture Presented to Peter Lasko* (Stroud, 1994), p. 208. The hospital of St Giles, Kepier, had moved in order to be nearer its quarries and a better water supply: Meade, *Kepier Hospital*, p. 5.
71. Harvard University, USA, Law School Library, Medieval Deed, no 786. See above, pp. 46, 55–6.
72. NRO, NCR, NPD, box 5, parish of St Helen, nos 1–52.
73. NRO, NCR, 24B, no 3.
74. NRO, NCR, NPD, box 5, parish of St Helen, no 25.
75. Ibid., nos 24, 27 (numbered on dorse only).
76. NRO, NCR, 24B, no 3.
77. Ibid., no 48, *Liber Domus Dei*, fos 16r–16v; NPD, box 5, parish of St Helen, no 41.
78. NRO, NCR, NPD, box 5, parish of St Helen, no 38.
79. Harvard University, USA, Law School Library, Medieval Deed, no 786.
80. Other early gifts, sales and exchanges of more modest holdings in Holme Street are recorded in NRO, NCR, NPD, box 5, parish of St Helen, nos 27 (29 on dorse), 32 (34 on dorse), 37 (26 on dorse), 39 (42 on dorse), 42 (39 on dorse), 43 (40 on dorse), 44 (50 on dorse), 45 (59 on dorse), 46, 47, 48, 51, 52–56, 61 (each numbered dorse only); NCR, 24B, no 27A.
81. NRO, NCR, NPD, box 5, parish of St Helen, nos 33, 34; 24B, no 48, *Liber Domus Dei*, fos 15r–16r. John and Agnes Herman had already disposed of meadowland to the hospital in 1253: PRO, CP25(1) 157/82/1207.
82. NRO, NCR, 24B, nos 27A and 48, *Liber Domus Dei*, fos 2r–2v.
83. NRO, NCR, 24A, GH accounts, 1306–1398, account for 1306; DCN 45/40/16.
84. B.S. Ayers, R. Smith and M. Tillyard, 'The Cow Tower, Norwich: A Detailed Survey and Partial Reinterpretation', *Medieval Archaeology*, xxxii (1988), pp. 184–207. The name 'Cow Tower' was acquired much later, from a neighbouring water meadow known as 'Cowsholme'.
85. *CPR, 1377–1381*, p. 121.
86. Ayers, Smith and Tillyard, 'Cow Tower', pp. 202–6; and above, pp. 122–3.
87. NRO, NCR, NPD, box 5, parish of St Helen, no 101 (numbered on dorse only).
88. Ibid., nos 97, 99, 100 (numbered on dorse); NCR, 20D, GH Lease Book, 1530–1645, fo 31r. The water course is first mentioned in 1294: NPD, box 5, parish of St Helen, no 54. Both creeks are depicted in R. Taylor, *Index Monasticus: The Diocese of Norwich* (London, 1821), map between pp. 75–6.
89. NRO, NCR, 24A, GH general accounts, 1465–1501, account of the steward, 1500–1; Norwich accounts, 1509–1528 (account for 1519–20); Hudson and Tingey, *Records of the City of Norwich*, ii, pp. 391–2. These fish were reserved for special occasions: see C.K. Currie, 'The Role of Fishponds in the Monastic Economy', in R. Gilchrist and H. Mytum, eds, *The Archaeology of Rural Monasteries* (BAR, British Series, cciii, 1989), pp. 147–72.

90. J. Caruth and S. Anderson, *St Saviour's Hospital Bury St Edmunds: A Report on the Archaeological Excavations 1989–1994* (Suffolk County Council Archaeological Service, Report 97/20), pp. 32–7.
91. NRO, NCR, 16A, Norwich Assembly Proceedings, 1434–1491, fos 74r, 75v, 76r.
92. NRO, NCR, 24A, GH accounts, 1306–1398, account for 1375; Norwich accounts, 1465–1501, account for 1467–8.
93. Appendix I, article 42.
94. Thomas, Sloane and Phillpotts, *Excavations at St Mary Spital*, p. 21; Page, *VCH Nottingham, II*, p. 169; NRO, DCN 43/48; NCR, 24B, no 48, *Liber Domus Dei*, fos 16r–16v, 59v.
95. NRO, NCC, reg. Alpe, fos 49v–50r (Richard Hawze); reg. Alblaster, fos 30r–31r (Richard Ponyer); DCN 69/2, fos 68r–68v (William Steele), 73v–74r (Thomas Peerse, a conduct).
96. PRO, C270/22; Thomas, Sloane and Phillpotts, *Excavations at St Mary Spital*, pp. 102, 104, 116–17; NRO, NCR, 24A, GH Norwich accounts, 1415–1460, account for 1436–7; 1465–1501, account for 1468–9.
97. NRO, NCR, 16B, Norwich Assembly Book, 1510–1550, fo 1v. In 1486–7 'divers les popyllez' were cut and prepared by three carpenters to make 'les wateryngledys in le slawterhous': NCR, 24A, GH Norwich accounts, 1485–1509.
98. NRO, NCR, 24A, GH Norwich accounts, 1485–1509. Large quantities of sedge and straw were needed to provide protective cladding while building works were in progress.
99. Ibid., GH Norwich accounts, 1415–1460.
100. Ibid., GH general accounts, 1465–1501, accounts of the steward for 1498–9 and 1499–1500; Bartholomaeus Anglicanus, *Properties of Things*, ii, pp. 720–1.
101. NRO, NCR, 24A, GH Norwich accounts, 1465–1501 (account for 1484–5). Similar arrangements for leasing land in the precinct were made at St Mary's hospital, Bishopsgate, in the fifteenth century: Thomas, Sloane and Phillpotts, *Excavations at St Mary Spital*, pp. 99, 128.
102. NRO, NCR, 24A, GH Norwich accounts, 1485–1509, 1509–1528, passim; DCN 1/2/96–9, 1/6/130–2.
103. NRO, NCR, 24A, GH general accounts, 1485–1508, account for 1502–3.
104. See above, pp. 185–6.
105. C. Noble, 'Norwich Cathedral Priory Gardeners' Accounts, 1329–1530', in eadem, C. Moreton and P. Rutledge, eds, *Farming and Gardening in Late Medieval Norfolk* (NRS, lxi, 1997), pp. 1–27, provides a valuable survey.
106. R. Foreville and G. Keir, eds, *The Book of St Gilbert* (Oxford, 1987), p. 307; BL, Cottonian Ms Cleopatra C V, fos 49r–49v.
107. C. Gittings, *Death, Burial and the Individual in Early Modern England* (London, 1984), pp. 110–14; C. Classen, D. Howes and A. Synott, *The Cultural History of Smell* (London, 1994), pp. 61–6.
108. BL, Cottonian Ms Cleopatra C V, fos 24v, 32v, 36r.
109. Classen, Howes and Synott, *Cultural History of Smell*, p. 61.
110. The pentice was tiled in 1514–15: NRO, NCR, 24A, GH Norwich accounts, 1509–1528. A gutter led from the sisters' garden to the highway, which suggests that it lay on the outskirts of the precinct: ibid., 1465–1501, account for 1484–5.
111. Thomas, Sloane and Phillpotts, *Excavations at St Mary Spital*, p. 72. Access to the kitchen gardens was later denied to the sisters lest they associate with the men: p. 84.
112. NRO, NCR, 24A, GH Norwich accounts, 1415–1460, account for 1444–5 (digging the kitchen garden); 1465–1501, accounts for 1464–5 (garden next to the stable), 1480–1 (garden next to the master's stable); 1485–1509, account for 1486–7 (garden or yard by the church).
113. Ibid., GH Norwich accounts, 1465–1501, 1485–1509, passim. Such arrangements were common in English hospitals: see, for instance, Caruth and Anderson, *St Saviour's Hospital*, p. 97.
114. NRO, Bradfer Lawrence Mss, box V (9): indenture, 24 January 20 Henry VIII.
115. NRO, NCR, 24A, GH accounts, 1306–1398, passim.
116. Caruth and Anderson, *St Saviour's Hospital*, pp. 10, 98; NRO, NCR, 24A, GH Norwich accounts, 1415–1460. And see above, p. 178.
117. W.R. Dawson, ed., *A Leechbook or Collection of Medical Recipes of the Fifteenth Century* (London, 1934), pp. 24, 25, 55, 83, 103, 217, 339–40 (onions), 23–7, 39, 47, 77, 99, 237 (leeks), 55, 57, 75, 77, 191, 223, 261, 275, 295, 323 (garlic).
118. Rawcliffe, *Medicine and Society*, pp. 77, 149. Archaeologists working at the Soutra hospital, in Midlothian, have reported evidence relating to the use of stupefactives and other medicinal plants, but their findings remain controversial: Gilchrist, *Contemplation and Action*, p. 35.
119. NRO, NCR, 24A, GH Norwich accounts, 1415–1460 (account for 1456–7); Noble, 'Norwich Cathedral Priory Gardeners' Accounts', p. 8.

120. Dawson, *Leechbook*, passim.
121. NRO, NCR, 24A, GH Norwich accounts, 1415–1460 and 1465–1501, passim. St Saviour's hospital, Bury St Edmund's, also had a great garden which was liable to flooding: Caruth and Anderson, *St Saviour's Hospital*, p. 101.
122. NRO, NCR, 24A, GH Norwich accounts, 1485–1509, account for 1502–3. In 1440–1 a similar exercise had been attempted in the hospital meadow, when dung, dirt and rubble had been used to 'elevate the land', perhaps through embankment: ibid., Norwich accounts, 1415–1460.
123. L.F. Salzman, *Building in England down to 1540* (Oxford, 1967), pp. 84–6, describes the procedures involved.
124. NRO, NCR, 24A, GH Norwich accounts, 1465–1501, account for 1464–5 (20*s* spent on new walls for the master's garden); 1485–1509, account for 1502–3 (making the buttresses); 1509–1528, account for 1524–5 (making more buttresses); Keene, *Survey of Medieval Winchester II*, p. 820; Price and Ponsford, *St Bartholomew's Hospital*, pp. 85, 117.
125. *CPR, 1388–1392*, p. 484.
126. NRO, NCR, 24B, no 17. Between 1430 and 1435, for example, William Bamburgh leased one chamber with a stable for 10*s* a year: ibid., 24A, GH Norwich accounts, 1415–1460. This was by no means unusual: Caruth and Anderson, *St Saviour's Hospital*, p. 100.
127. NRO, NCR, 24A, GH Norwich accounts, 1415–1460, 1465–1501, 1485–1509, 1509–1528, passim; Thomas, Sloane and Phillpotts, *Excavations at St Mary Spital*, pp. 66–7.
128. NRO, NCR, 24A, GH accounts, 1306–1398, passim.
129. Ibid., GH Norwich accounts, 1415–1460, 1465–1501, 1485–1509, 1509–1528, passim.
130. Smith, 'Excavation of the Hospital of St Mary of Ospringe', plan facing p. 105; Rowland-Burdon, 'St Saviour's Hospital, Bury St Edmunds', p. 267 (where there was a 'duffuszerd' or dove house yard); Caruth and Anderson, *St Saviour's Hospital*, p. 99.
131. NRO, NCR, 24A, GH Norwich accounts, 1465–1501.
132. Ibid., GH Norwich accounts, 1415–1460, account for 1455–6 (when the shed was re-roofed). For the stock accounts, see above, pp. 187–96.
133. Ibid., GH Norwich accounts, 1485–1509, account for 1502–3. For St Mary's in the Newarke, see above, pp. 196–7.
134. NRO, NCR, 24A, GH general accounts, 1485–1508, account for 1502–3.
135. Ibid., GH accounts, 1306–1398, account for 1321–2; general accounts 1465–1501, accounts for 1465–6, 1480–1, 1481–2, 1482–3; 1485–1508, accounts for 1502–3, 1505–6; N.E. Ticehurst, *The Mute Swan in England* (London, 1957), pp. 4–8; T. Southwell, 'The St Helen's Swan-Pit', *Transactions of the Norfolk and Norwich Naturalists*, vi (1897), pp. 387–9.
136. Cullum, 'St Leonard's York', pp. 14–17; Thomas, Sloane and Phillpotts, *Excavations at St Mary Spital*, pp. 86, 101; Jamison, *Hospital of St Katherine*, p. 59; Smith, 'Excavation of the Hospital of St Mary of Ospringe', pp. 81–184, notably plan on p. 85 and reconstruction facing p. 105.
137. NRO, NCR, 24A, GH accounts, 1306–1398, passim. See above, pp. 186–9, for a more detailed discussion of the domestic staff.
138. Ibid., GH general accounts, 1485–1508, account of the receiver general, 1500–1, notes the gallery (see also Salzman, *Building in England*, pp. 575–7). In 1522–3 a lock and key were bought for the brewer's house: general accounts, 1510–1525.
139. A. Jessopp, ed., *Visitations of the Diocese of Norwich, 1492–1532* (Camden Society, new series, xliii, 1888), p. 271; NRO, NCR, 24A, GH Norwich accounts, 1485–1509, account for 1485–6.
140. Smith, 'Excavation of the Hospital of St Mary of Ospringe', reconstruction facing p. 105.
141. NRO, NCR, 24A, GH accounts, 1306–1398, account for 1306.
142. Ibid., GH Norwich accounts, 1415–1460, 1485–1509 and 1509–1528. The watergate is mentioned in 1505–6.
143. Jessopp, *Visitations*, p. 271. In 1476–7, for instance, two thatchers spent five weeks on the bakery at a cost of 16*s* 8*d*, and the two chimneys were repaired; NRO, NCR, 24A, Norwich accounts, 1465–1501.
144. NRO, NCR, 24A, GH general accounts, 1465–1501, account for 1465–6. Work in the brewhouse can have differed little from that described in P. Sambrook, *Country House Brewing in England 1500–1900* (London, 1996), Chapter II.
145. NRO, NCR, 24A, general accounts, 1465–1501, account of the steward for 1500–1 (the new brewer was called Robert Grape); Sambrook, *Country House Brewing*, pp. 133–8; Atkin, Carter and Evans, *Excavations in Norwich*, pp. 83–4, 241. The latter disprove Sambrook's view that domestic beer-brewing was 'exceptional' in 1515.
146. NRO, NCR, 24A, GH general accounts, 1485–1508, account for 1505–6; Norwich accounts, 1485–1509, account for 1505–6. For ale production and consumption, see above, pp. 184–5.
147. NRO, NCR, 24A, GH Norwich accounts, 1415–1460, account for 1415–16. In 1432–3 one Alice Purs was employed to winnow grain as well.

148. Ibid., GH general accounts, 1485–1508, account of the receiver general, 1499–1500.
149. Ibid., GH, general accounts, 1485–1508.
150. Ibid., GH accounts, 1306–1398; general accounts, 1485–1508, 1510–1525, passim.
151. Ibid., GH Norwich accounts, 1485–1509, account for 1502–3.
152. Ibid., GH Norwich accounts, 1415–1460. The account for 1447–8 records an expenditure of 18*s* 10*d* on the labour of a tiler, a clayman and a carpenter, who worked for over forty-six days with their servants on the building.
153. Ibid., GH accounts, 1306–1398, account for 1322–3; general accounts, 1485–1508, account for 1502–3; Norwich accounts, 1485–1509, account for 1502–3.
154. G.R. Owst, *Literature and the Pulpit in Medieval England* (Oxford, 1961), p. 263.
155. *CIMisc., 1377–1388*, no 180.
156. Ibid., *1387–1393*, no 313.
157. Ibid., *1307–1349*, no 1456; *1348–1377*, no 6. The master, Thomas Goldyngton, was, even so, a pluralist with other hospitals in his care: *CPR, 1327–1330*, pp. 256, 461; *1348–1350*, pp. 175–6.
158. J.T. Fowler, ed., *Memorials of the Church of SS Peter and Wilfrid, II* (Surtees Society, lxxviii, 1884), pp. 29–30, 128–32; W. Page, ed., *VCH York, III* (London, 1974), pp. 315–16.
159. NRO, NCR, 24A, GH general accounts, 1485–1508, account for 1502–3.
160. Ibid., GH Norwich accounts, 1415–1460, account for 1447–8.
161. Ibid., accounts for 1436–7 and 1438–9.
162. The various types of remuneration available to servants are discussed in B.F. Harvey, *Living and Dying in England 1100–1540: The Monastic Experience* (Oxford, 1993), Chapter V.
163. NRO, NCR, 24A, GH general accounts, 1465–1501, account for 1478–9.
164. Ibid., GH Norwich accounts, 1415–1460, account for 1443–4.
165. The techniques involved are described in Atkin, 'Medieval Clay-Walled Building in Norwich', pp. 171–85.
166. NRO, NCR, 24A, GH general accounts, 1510–1525, account for 1522–3. See also Woodman, 'Hardley, Norfolk', pp. 208–9.
167. NRO, NCR, 24A, GH accounts, 1306–1398, accounts for 1375 and 1376; Norwich accounts, 1415–1460, 1465–1501.
168. W. Page, ed., *VCH London, I* (London, 1909), pp. 520–4. Elsewhere similar episcopal warnings were taken to heart: Thomas, Sloane and Phillpotts, *Excavations at St Mary Spital*, pp. 79, 84, 87.
169. Cullum, 'St Leonard's York', p. 15; Jamison, *Hospital of St Katherine*, p. 59.
170. NRO, NCR, 24A, GH Norwich accounts, 1465–1501, accounts for 1464–7. Inns were often situated opposite the larger urban hospitals, such as the Bethlehem, in Bishopsgate Street, London. In 1403 the keeper, aptly named Peter the Taverner, had even run a hostelry in the precinct: PRO, C270/22; Andrews and others, *History of Bethlem*, p. 37.
171. NRO, NCR, 24A, GH Norwich accounts, 1465–1501, accounts for 1480–2.
172. Ibid., GH Norwich accounts, 1415–1460, 1485–1509. See above, pp. 152–3.
173. In 1375, for example, the receiver general noted receipts of 74*s* to cover board for the bishop's servants (*famulorum episcopi*): ibid., GH accounts, 1306–1398.
174. Ibid., GH general accounts, 1465–1501, account of the steward for 1500–1.
175. Ibid., GH Norwich accounts, 1415–1460, accounts for 1446–7, 1449–50, 1456–7. The 'inwarde houses' are noted in GH accounts, box 1548–1556, account for June 1551–2.
176. Andrews and others, *History of Bethlem*, pp. 40–3, 70; Smith, 'Excavation of the Hospital of St Mary of Ospringe', p. 103. For corrodians, see above, pp. 84, 171–3.
177. Gilchrist, *Contemplation and Action*, pp. 21–6.
178. Cullum, 'St Leonard's York', pp. 14–15. The hospital of St Mary, Bishopsgate, like many other London houses of Augustinian canons, also sited the cloister to the north of the church because of lack of space: Thomas, Sloane and Phillpotts, *Excavations at St Mary Spital*, p. 100.
179. Appendix I, articles 7 and 18.
180. The 'old' cloisters are mentioned in 1435–6 and 1441–2: NRO, NCR, 24A, GH Norwich accounts, 1415–1460.
181. Thomas, Sloane and Phillpotts, *Excavations at St Mary Spital*, p. 96.
182. NRO, NCR, 24A, GH Norwich accounts, 1415–1460.
183. Ibid., GH Norwich accounts, 1465–1501.
184. Ibid., GH general accounts, 1465–1501, account for 1480–1.
185. See above, pp. 176–7.

186. NRO, NCR, 24A, GH, general accounts, 1485–1508, account for 1500–1; Norwich accounts, 1485–1509, account for 1502–3.
187. Ibid., GH Norwich accounts, 1415–1460, account for 1451–2 (when the parlour was being built); 1465–1501, account for 1477–8 (when rubble was removed from the 'old' hospitality room and a new one was built); and 1485–1509, account for 1502–3. According to depositions taken during a visitation of 1532, the parlour and the roof of the 'great chamber' above it needed repair: Jessopp, *Visitations*, p. 271.
188. NRO, NCR, 24A, GH Norwich accounts, 1415–1460, account for 1448–9.
189. Ibid. A similar system of transport was used later, in 1458–9, when stone was needed to build the chancel of Hardley church: Woodman, 'Hardley, Norfolk', p. 204.
190. NRO, NCR, 24A, GH Norwich accounts, 1415–1460, account for 1456–7; general accounts, 1485–1508, account for 1506–7. A release of 1449 made by Hugh Acton to Bishop Lyhart refers to the chapter house: ibid., 24B, no 52.
191. Appendix I, article 30. At St Leonard's hospital, York, and St Thomas's, Southwark, chapter meetings were to be held daily: Cullum, 'St Leonard's York', p. 14; New College, Oxford, New College Ms 3691, fo 91r.
192. NRO, NCR, NPD, box 9, parish of St Peter Mancroft, nos 369, 373; box 10, parish of SS Simon and Jude, no 20; 20D, GH Lease Book, 1530–1645, fos 1r, 1v, 29r; 24B, no 23; PRO, E322/178; Jessopp, *Visitations*, pp. 12–13.
193. NRO, NCR, 24A, GH accounts, 1306–1398, account for 1375.
194. Ibid., GH Norwich accounts, 1415–1460, passim (mention of a 'new' dormitory being built in 1441 probably refers to the erection of partitions: 24B, no 23); Thomas, Sloane and Phillpotts, *Excavations at St Mary Spital*, p. 80.
195. NRO, NCR, 24A, GH Norwich accounts, 1465–1501, account for 1473–4.
196. Ibid., account for 1466–7; 1485–1509, account for 1502–3; W.W. Skeat, ed., *Pierce the Ploughman's Crede* (EETS, xxx, 1867), p. 7.

III. ESTATES AND FINANCES

1. P.H. Cullum, 'Hospitals and Charitable Provision in Medieval Yorkshire' (University of York, PhD thesis, 1990), pp. 136–7; J. Caley and J. Hunter, eds, *Valor Ecclesiasticus temp. Henrici VIII* (6 vols, London, 1810–34), v, pp. 17–18; Rawcliffe, *Hospitals of Medieval Norwich*, p. 79.
2. W. Farrer and J. Bromhill, eds, *VCH Lancaster, II* (London, 1908), p. 165.
3. See, for example, Knowles and Hadcock, *Medieval Religious Houses*, pp. 41–2; and Rubin, 'Development and Change', pp. 52–53. Horden, '"A Discipline of Relevance"', pp. 365–7, strikes a cautionary note.
4. Harvey, 'Introduction', pp. 1–24.
5. I. Kershaw, 'The Great Famine and Agrarian Crisis in England 1315–22', *Past and Present*, lix (1973), p. 31. See above, p. 14.
6. W. Page, ed., *VCH Gloucester, II* (London, 1907), p. 119.
7. A. Gransden, 'A Fourteenth Century Chronicle from the Grey Friars at Lynn', *EHR*, lxxii (1957), p. 275. See also Bolton, '"The World Turned Upside Down"', pp. 17–78; and Horrox, *Black Death*, pp. 229–47.
8. M. Oliva, *The Convent and Community in Late Medieval England* (Woodbridge, 1998), pp. 90–5.
9. See S. Raban, *Mortmain Legislation and the English Church 1279–1500* (Cambridge, 1982), Chapters I and II.
10. See above, p. 47.
11. NRO, NCR, 24B, nos 59, 60; *CPR, 1408–1413*, p. 187; *1446–1452*, p. 475.
12. For instance, Price and Ponsford, *St Bartholomew's Hospital*, p. 210, speak of 'numerous cases of mismanagement and downright fraud'.
13. Page, *VCH York, III*, p. 339.
14. Price and Ponsford, *St Bartholomew's Hospital*, p. 226.
15. For further background see C.D. Ross and T.B. Pugh, 'Materials for the Study of Baronial Incomes in Fifteenth Century England', *EconHR*, second series, vi (1953), pp. 185–94; R.R. Davies, 'Baronial Accounts, Income and Arrears in the Later Middle Ages', *EconHR*, second series, xxi (1968), pp. 211–29; and E. Stone, 'Profit-and-Loss Accountancy at Norwich Cathedral Priory', *TRHS*, fifth series, xii (1962), pp. 25–47.
16. NRO, NCR, 24A, GH general accounts, 1465–1501: draft paper account for 1478–9.
17. Ibid., GH general accounts, 1510–1525, passim.
18. W. Page, ed., *VCH Kent, II* (London, 1926), p. 209.
19. Tanner, *Decrees*, pp. 374–6; Pobst, *Register of William Bateman*, p. xxvii.
20. Meade, *Kepier Hospital*, p. 29; PRO, C270/22.
21. NRO, NCR, 24B, no 48.

22. NRO, NCR, 24A, GH general accounts, 1509–1528, account for 1509–10; 24D, Cringleford court rolls, 1459–1483, m. 6v.
23. New College, Oxford, Ms 3691, fo 93r.
24. Bodleian Library, Oxford, Ms Rawlinson D, fos 1–31. G. Davis, *Medieval Cartularies of Great Britain* (London, 1958), an incomplete guide so far as English hospitals are concerned, records the existence of forty-five pre-Dissolution cartularies and rolls of evidence from thirty-one different hospitals.
25. See, for example, NRO, NCR, 24I, GH Rental and Cartulary of property in St Stephen's parish, Norwich, temp. Richard II [*recte c.* 1461].
26. Appendix I, article 34; New College, Oxford, Ms 3691, fo 93r.
27. Page, *VCH York, III*, pp. 338, 340.
28. *CPR, 1374–1377*, p. 310; *1388–1392*, p. 374; *CIMisc., 1399–1422*, no 5.
29. Thomas, Sloane and Phillpotts, *Excavations at St Mary Spital*, pp. 80–1.
30. Graham, 'Order of St Antoine de Viennois', p. 364.
31. See above, p. 106.
32. Jones, *Saint Richard of Chichester*, pp. 67, 239.
33. Orme, 'Medieval Almshouse for the Clergy', p. 2.
34. Appendix I, article 41.
35. P. Wade-Martins, ed., *An Historical Atlas of Norfolk* (Norwich, 1994), pp. 76–9; D. Dymond, *The Norfolk Landscape* (Bury St Edmunds, 1990), pp. 147–65.
36. Lunt, *Valuation of Norwich*, pp. 365, 367, 399, 403, 405, 417.
37. See, for example, B.F. Harvey, *Westminster Abbey and its Estates in the Middle Ages* (Oxford, 1977), Chapter V.
38. NRO, NCR, 24C, GH Calthorpe accounts, 1315–1375, accounts for 1315–16 and 1330–1. For price fluctuations see H.P. Brown and S.V. Hopkins, *A Perspective of Wages and Prices* (London, 1981), pp. 28–9.
39. NRO, NCR, 25F, GH Seething accounts, 1400–1416, mm. 6r–7v.
40. NRO, NCR, 24A, GH accounts, 1306–1398.
41. Considerations determining leasing policy by ecclesiastical landowners are discussed in M. Mate, 'The Farming out of Manors: A New Look at the Evidence from Canterbury Cathedral Priory', *Journal of Medieval History*, ix (1983), pp. 331–43.
42. NRO, NCR, 24F, GH Seething accounts, 1461–1482; 24G, GH Repps-cum-Bastwick accounts, 1437–1460, 1461–1482; 24I, GH South Walsham accounts, 1437–1461. The master of St Leonard's, York, was instructed in 1364 to tour the estates each year soon after Easter in order to negotiate the best price for grain sales: Page, *VCH York, III*, p. 340.
43. B.M.S. Campbell, 'The Extent and Layout of Commonfields in Eastern Norfolk', *Norfolk Archaeology*, xxxviii (1983), pp. 5–32.
44. R. Virgoe, 'The Estates of Norwich Cathedral Priory, 1101–1538', in I. Atherton and others, *Norwich Cathedral: Church, City and Diocese, 1096–1996* (London, 1996), pp. 354–6.
45. Rubin, *Charity and Community*, pp. 196–202.
46. NRO, NCR, 24F, GH Seething accounts, 1400–1416, mm. 4r–7r; 24I, GH South Walsham accounts, 1509–1529, mm. 5r–16r; Blomefield, *Norfolk*, xi, p. 143.
47. NRO, NCR, 24D, GH Cringleford accounts, 1461–1482, 1482–1509, 1509–1528, passim; 24G, GH Repps-cum-Bastwick accounts, 1437–1460, passim.
48. NRO, NCR, 24G, GH Repps-cum-Bastwick accounts, 1416–1482, mm. 5–8.
49. NRO, NCR, 24B, no 51; 24E, GH Hardley accounts, 1427–1460, mm. 25r–28r, 1461–1482, mm. 2r–3r; 24G, GH Repps-cum-Bastwick accounts, 1437–1460, mm. 14r–18r. The chancel at Repps cost a further £9 to repair in 1522–3: accounts for 1509–1528, m. 12.
50. NRO, Phi 522. Suffield's friend, Richard Wych, insisted that vicars, 'willing and able to work for the salvation of souls' should be adequately paid so they could assist the poor: Jones, *Saint Richard of Chichester*, p. 63.
51. NRO, NCR, 24D, GH Inquiry into Cringleford churchyard, 1336.
52. NRO, Box 30E1, no 12099.
53. NRO, Phi 521; NCR, 25A, GH Calthorpe deeds, no 186.
54. B.M.S. Campbell, 'Agricultural Progress in Medieval England: Some Evidence from Eastern Norfolk', *EconHR*, second series, xxxvi (1983), pp. 26–46; idem, 'Arable Productivity in Medieval England: Some Evidence from Norfolk', *Journal of Economic History*, xliii (1983), pp. 379–404.
55. PRO, CP25(1) 157/70/907, 71/927; Blomefield, *Norfolk*, v. pp. 300, 375.
56. NRO, Box 30E1, nos 12074–5; Phi 76; NCR, 24B, no 48, *Liber Domus Dei*, fos 50v, 52r. For the conditions imposed by Calthorpe, see above, pp. 163–4.

57. NRO, NCR, 24A, GH accounts, 1306–1398, passim; 24C, GH Calthorpe accounts, 1315–1376, 1377–1399, passim; BL, Add. Roll, 27,456.
58. NRO, NCR, 24C, GH Calthorpe accounts, 1377–1399, m. 13.
59. M. Mate, 'Agrarian Economy after the Black Death: The Manors of Canterbury Cathedral Priory, 1348–1391', *EconHR*, second series, xxxvii (1984), pp. 341–54.
60. NRO, NCR, 24C, GH Calthorpe accounts, 1422–1460, m. 3r.
61. E. Miller, ed., *The Agrarian History of England and Wales, III, 1350–1500* (Cambridge, 1991), pp. 612–14; R.H. Britnell, 'The Pastons and their Norfolk', *Agricultural History Review*, xxxvi (1988), pp. 132–44.
62. NRO, NCR, 24C, GH Calthorpe accounts, 1461–1484, 1484–1502, 1509–1529, passim.
63. Cullum, 'Hospitals and Charitable Provision', pp. 128–9; Page, *VCH York, III*, p. 341. Even more extreme measures were deployed by the monks of Ramsey Abbey, who devastated tracts of woodland after the Black Death to raise money: J.A. Raftis, *The Estates of Ramsey Abbey* (Toronto, 1957), p. 293.
64. NRO, NCR, 24C, GH Calthorpe accounts, 1422–1460.
65. NRO, NCR, 24B, nos 24, 62; 25A, GH Costessey deeds, nos 237–38; Blomefield, *Norfolk*, ii, p. 416.
66. NRO, Box E301, no 12046.
67. NRO, NCR, 24C, GH Costessey accounts, 1338–1374, 1377–1399.
68. Ibid., GH Costessey accounts, 1377–1399: in 1398–9, for instance, carters from Costessey spent two weeks at St Giles's carrying faggots and gorse; four days transporting corn from South Walsham and fuel from Hethel; an unspecified amount of time bringing roofing materials from Cringleford and fish from Cromer to Norwich; and thirty-two days carrying grain to the hospital from various places.
69. Mate, 'Agrarian Economy', p. 348.
70. NRO, NCR, 24C, GH Costessey accounts, 1422–1460, account for 1454–5.
71. NRO, NCR, 24B, no 48, *Liber Domus Dei*, fos 43v–47v; 25A, GH Cringleford deeds, box I, nos 4–6, 8, 15, 23–5, 47–8, 50, 52, 54; box II, nos 1, 3, 7; *HMC, Various Collections, VII*, (London, 1914), p. 165.
72. NRO, NCR, 25A, GH Cringleford deeds, box I, no 44.
73. Ibid., box II, nos 14, 63. For other exchanges, see box III, nos 61 A and B.
74. Ibid., box IV, no 36.
75. NRO, NCR, 24D, GH Cringleford accounts, 1485–1508, mm. 12r–13r; 1509–1528, m. 2r.
76. Ibid., GH Cringleford accounts, 1378–1394, 1412–1414, 1427–1428. See also M. Bailey, *A Marginal Economy? East Anglian Breckland in the Later Middle Ages* (Cambridge, 1989), pp. 289–94.
77. Cullum, 'Hospitals and Charitable Provision', pp. 125–6.
78. Raftis, *Estates of Ramsey Abbey*, pp. 258–9, 293.
79. NRO, NCR, 24A, GH general accounts, 1485–1508, account for 1502–3; 1510–1525, account for 1519–20; 24D, GH Cringleford accounts, 1509–1528, m. 12r.
80. PRO, CP25(1) 157/82/1207; NRO, NCR, 24B, no 48, *Liber Domus Dei*, fos 55v–56v.
81. NRO, NCR, 24A, GH general accounts, 1510–1525, passim.
82. NRO, Box 30E1, no 12056; NCR, 24A, GH general accounts, 1465–1501, 1485–1508, passim.
83. BL, Toph. Cart. 12A; NRO, Phi 378; NCR, 24A, GH general accounts, 1465–1501, passim. In 1465–6, Carrow meadow was planted with alders and reserved for the use of the hospital.
84. NRO, Box 30E1, no 12097; NCR, NPD, box 2, parish of St Augustine, nos 2, 5–11, 23–5; 24B, no 48, *Liber Domus Dei*, fo 58r.
85. NRO, NCR, 24E, GH Journal of John Boys, sergeant of the ploughs, 1428–9. See also, J.C. Tingey, 'The Journals of John Dernell and John Boys, Carters at the Lathes, Norwich', *Norfolk Archaeology*, xv (1904), pp. 114–64.
86. NRO, NCR, NPD, box 2, parish of St Augustine, nos 16, 31; 24E, GH Lathes accounts, 1410–1461.
87. NRO, NCR, 24A, GH Norwich accounts, 1415–1460, account for 1435–6.
88. Rawcliffe, *Hospitals of Medieval Norwich*, pp. 70–1.
89. NRO, Box 30E1, no. 12057; Phi 600; NCR, 25D, GH Hethel and East Carleton deeds, no 1273; BL, Add. Ch. 7,207.
90. NRO, Phi 519; NCR, 24A, GH accounts, 1306–1398, passim.
91. NRO, NCR, 24B, no 19, m. 2v.
92. Ibid., no 3 (*inspeximus* by Bishop Walton and confirmation by the prior of Norwich, 1264); DCN 40/7, fos 75r, 76r; 43/48; Phi, 309, 312; BL, Toph. Cart. 31, 37, 41, 44; Arundel Castle Muniments, Seething Charter, no 280 (I am grateful to Professor Christopher Harper-Bill for a transcript of this document).
93. NRO, NCR, 24A, GH general accounts, 1465–1501, 1485–1508, 1510–1525, passim; DCN, 40/6, fos 44v–46r; Caley and Hunter, *Valor Ecclesiasticus* iii, pp. 291–2.

94. NRO, Phi 311; and see above, pp. 172–3.
95. NRO, NCR, 24F, GH Seething accounts, 1461–1482, 1485–1508, 1509–1528.
96. PRO, CP25(1) 158/84/1263, 98/1604.
97. NRO, Phi 140; Box 30E1, nos 12050, 12053, 12092–4. Two indentures made between the hospital and the incumbent, itemising the 32 acres of demesne and contents of the rectory, are in 24E, GH Hardley indentures, 1374 and 1377.
98. NRO, NCR, 24E, GH Hardley accounts, 1331–1335, 1427–1460, 1461–1482, 1486–1507, 1509–1525, passim.
99. NRO, NCR, 24I, GH South Walsham accounts, 1399–1407, 1411–1412, 1437–1461, 1461–1482, 1484–1509, passim.
100. PRO, CP25(1) 158/88/1369, 159/100/1658; BL, Toph. Cart. 35; Blomefield, *Norfolk*, xi, pp. 142–3. For conflict between the two houses, see above, p. 146.
101. Blomefield, *Norfolk*, xi, pp. 180–3; *Curia Regis Rolls, 1237–1242*, no 356.
102. T. Williamson, *The Norfolk Broads: A Landscape History* (Manchester, 1997), pp. 21–4, 80, 81; C.T. Smith, 'Historical Evidence', in J.M. Lambert and others, *The Making of the Broads* (Royal Geographical Society, Research Series, iii, 1961), pp. 82–3; M. George, *The Land Use, Ecology and Conservation of Broadland* (Chichester, 1992), Chapter IV.
103. PRO, CP25(1) 157/71/936; NRO, DCN 40/7, fo 75v; NCR, 24B, nos 3, 48, *Liber Domus Dei*, fos 52v, 53r.
104. PRO, CP25(1) 158/98/1622; BL, Add. Ch. 14,784; NRO, Box 30E1, nos 12060–1; NCR, 24B, no 48, *Liber Domus Dei*, fos 53r–54v.
105. NRO, NCR, 24A, GH accounts, 1306–1398.
106. Ibid., GH general accounts, 1465–1501, 1485–1508, 1510–1525, passim.
107. Ibid., GH accounts, 1306–1398.
108. See above, pp. 181–2.
109. *CPR, 1317–1321*, p. 236.
110. Ibid., p. 566; NRO, NCR, 24A, GH accounts, 1306–1398, account for 1321–2; Raban, *Mortmain Legislation*, pp. 54, 69, 89.
111. *CPR, 1330–1334*, pp. 148, 518; NRO, NCR, 24A, GH general accounts, 1510–1527, accounts for 1515–16, 1526–7; 24B, nos 15 (10), 54.
112. NRO, NCR, 24A, GH accounts, 1306–1398, account for 1330–1.
113. NRO, Box 30E1, no 12083; NCR, 24A, GH accounts, 1306–1398, account for 1330–1.
114. See, for example, Campbell, 'Population Pressure', pp. 87–134.
115. NRO, NCR, 24A, GH accounts, 1306–1398.
116. Raban, *Mortmain Legislation*, pp. 64–71.
117. Malden, *VCH Surrey, II*, pp. 118–19.
118. J. Strachey and others, eds, *Rotuli Parliamentorum* (6 vols, London, 1767–77), ii, p. 89. See Raban, *Mortmain Legislation*, p. 41, for the significance of Parliament in the process of suing for licences to amortise.
119. *CPR, 1334–1338*, p. 113; NRO, Box 30E1, nos 12085, 12095, 12099; Phi 524–5; NCR, 24A, GH accounts, 1306–1398, account for 1335; 24B, nos 14, 15 (8).
120. NRO, NCR, 24A, GH accounts, 1306–1398, account for 1376. The rectory was farmed out at a mere 5 marks a year in 1390: Box 30E1, no 12107.
121. NRO, Phi 524–5; NCR, 24B, nos 14, 15 (8). The brethren also complained about the heavy fees and pensions they had to pay.
122. *Calendar of Papal Petitions 1342–1419*, pp. 29, 36; *CPL 1342–1362*, pp. 116, 138, 176.
123. Ellis, *Chronica Johannis de Oxenedes*, pp. 270–1. See also, M. Bailey, '*Per Impetum Maris*: Natural Disaster and Economic Decline in Eastern England, 1275–1350', in B.M.S. Campbell, ed., *Before the Black Death: Studies in the Crisis of the Early Fourteenth Century* (Manchester, 1991), pp. 184–208.
124. Hallam, 'Climate of Eastern England', pp. 124–32; Smith, 'Historical Evidence', pp. 81–2, 88–9. Expenditure by the hospital on cutting turves on its estates in Broadland fell from over 35*s* in 1318–19 to 13*s* in 1327–8, and then effectively ceased: NRO, NCR, 24A, GH accounts, 1306–1398. Smith (p. 96) is, however, wrong in assuming that Bartonbury Hall then belonged to St Giles's.
125. NRO, NCR, 24C, GH terrier for Catton, Salhouse and Wroxham, 1385; Smith 'Historical Evidence', pp. 78–81.
126. *CPR, 1334–1338*, p. 21; NRO, NCR, 24B, nos 49, 50; Phi 523; Box 30E1, nos 12087–9; Blomefield, *Norfolk*, viii, p. 60; BL, Add. Ch. 10,648.
127. NRO, NCR, 24A, GH accounts, 1306–1398; Norwich accounts, 1415–1460, valor for 1441–2; 24B, nos 51–2; 24I, GH Thurlton accounts, 1436–1441.

128. *CPR, 1350–1354*, p. 114; PRO, C143/303/15; NRO, NCR, 24B, no 55; Box 30E1, no 12101; Blomefield, *Norfolk*, xi, p. 141.
129. PRO, C270/23/12.
130. *CPR, 1377–1381*, pp. 604–5; *1391–1396*, pp. 134–5; NRO, Box 30E1, no 12106; Phi 144; NCR, 24B, no 57.
131. NRO, NCR, 24A, GH accounts, 1306–1398.
132. *CPR, 1408–1413*, p. 187; PRO, C143/441/18; NRO, NCR, 24B, no 59; Box 30E1, no 12108; Blomefield, *Norfolk*, v, pp. 34–5.
133. NRO, NCR, 25A, GH Cringleford deeds, box IV, nos 14, 15; Blomefield, *Norfolk*, vi, p. 462; Raban, *Mortmain Legislation*, p. 136.
134. NRO, NCR, 24D, GH, Cringleford accounts, 1378–1394, 1412–1414; 25A, GH Cringleford deeds, box IV, no 35. Many hospitals were punctilious in the drafting of leases: see, for instance, N. Kerling, ed., *Cartulary of St Bartholomew's Hospital*, (London, 1973), nos 1243, 1385.
135. NRO, NCC, reg. Surflete, fos 60v–61r.
136. K.B. McFarlane, *England in the Fifteenth Century* (London, 1981), p. 192.
137. Magdalen College, Oxford, Fastolf Additia, no 2, partly reprinted in Blomefield, *Norfolk*, iv, pp. 388–9. I am grateful to Dr Anthony Smith for providing a transcript of this letter.
138. BL, Stowe Ch. 197; see above, pp. 141–3, 149–50.
139. NRO, NCR, 24B, no 60; *CPR, 1446–1452*, p. 475.
140. NRO, NCR, 24A, GH Norwich accounts, 1415–1460: the valor has been mistakenly bound in with these accounts.
141. See above, pp. 147–51.
142. NRO, NCR, 24A, GH general accounts, 1510–1525.
143. NRO, DCN 9/4; NCR, 24A, GH Fobbing accounts, 1521–1528; Blomefield, *Norfolk*, vi, p. 309.
144. NRO, NCR, 24A, GH Fobbing accounts, 1521–1528, passim; 24B, no 26.
145. NRO, NCR, 24B, no 26; 24G, GH Rollesby accounts, 1499–1509 (including the 1413–14 account); Caley and Hunter, *Valor Ecclesiasticus*, iii, pp. 291–2.
146. NRO, NCR, 20D, GH Lease Book, 1530–1645, fo 26v; 24B, no 26.
147. NRO, BR 61/2/19; NCR, 20D, GH Lease Book, 1530–1645, fos 25r–25v; 24B, no 66.
148. NRO, Box 30E1, nos 12112–13; NCR, 24A, GH general accounts, 1485–1508, account for 1507–8; 25B, GH Salhouse deeds, no 701; 25D, GH Fobbing and Trowse deeds, nos 1344–54.
149. NRO, NCR, 20D, GH Lease Book, 1530–1645, fo 1v; Caley and Hunter, *Valor Ecclesiasticus*, iii, pp. 291–2.
150. NRO, DCN 9/4; NCR, 24A, GH Fobbing accounts, 1521–1528.
151. See, for example, Raftis, *Estates of Ramsey Abbey*, p. 293; Bailey, *A Marginal Economy?* pp. 271, 273.
152. NRO, NCR, 24E, GH Hardley accounts, 1506–1507; 24G, GH Repps-cum-Bastwick accounts, 1509–1528, mm. 5–17. Towards the end of this period the farm for tithes was running three years overdue.
153. NRO, NCR, 24B, no 48, *Liber Domus Dei*, fos 1–9r, 11r–13r, 15r–16r, 21v–23v, 26r–29r, 36r–41v.
154. Ibid., fos 6v, 8v.
155. NRO, NCR, 24A, GH Norwich accounts, 1415–1460, passim.
156. Ibid., GH accounts, 1306–1398, account for 1396–7.
157. Ibid., GH general accounts, 1465–1501, steward's account for 1483–84; 24B, nos 24, 62.
158. Ibid., GH general accounts, 1485–1508, 1510–1528; 24G, GH Rollesby accounts, 1499–1509 (containing an account for Skypwyth's for 1502–3).
159. NRO, NCR, NPD, box 10, parish of St Peter Southgate, no 9; box 12, parish of St Vedast, no 51; 20D, GH Lease Book, 1530–1645, fos 28r–28v.
160. J.M. Kaye, ed., *The Cartulary of God's House, Southampton, I* (Southampton Records Society, xix, 1976), pp. lxi–lxxiv, xcviii–ci; Rutledge, 'Landlords and Tenants', pp. 20–1.
161. NRO, NCR, NPD, box 6, parish of SS Simon and Jude, nos 2, 3.
162. NRO, NCR, 24A, GH Norwich accounts, 1415–1460, 1465–1501, passim.
163. A. King, 'The Merchant Class and Borough Finances in Late Medieval Norwich' (University of Oxford, DPhil thesis, 1989), pp. 358, 363–4, 388–9, 393–4.
164. NRO, NCR, 24A, GH Norwich accounts, 1485–1509, account for 1507–8; Rawcliffe, *Hospitals of Medieval Norwich*, p. 84.
165. NRO, DN, reg. VII, book 12, fo 68v.
166. NRO, NCR, 24A, GH general accounts, 1465–1501. The question of corruption or incompetence on Blythe's part can safely be dismissed. He farmed the living at Calthorpe until 1506, when he became vicar there: 24C, GH Calthorpe accounts, 1461–1484, 1484–1502, 1509–1529. The plague of 1479 is noted in Johnson, 'Chronological Memoranda', p. 142.

167. NRO, NCR, 24D, GH Cringleford accounts, 1485–1508, mm. 7r, 8r, 11r, 12r; 1509–1528, m. 4v.
168. Ibid., mm. 7r, 8r, 12r; 1509–1528, mm. 4r, 17r. For comparative information about rabbit farming in Breckland, see Bailey, *A Marginal Economy?* pp. 129–35, 251–6.
169. NRO, NCR, 24D, GH Cringleford court rolls, 1509–1548, mm. 2r, 3v, 4r; M. Bailey, 'The Rabbit and the Medieval East Anglian Economy', *Agricultural History Review*, xxxvi (1988), pp. 6–7, 9, 15–18. For the events of the rebellion, see Chapter VIII.
170. PRO, STAC 2/35/3. See above pp. 146–7.
171. NRO, NCR, 24D, GH Cringleford accounts, 1461–1482, passim.
172. J.K. Allison, 'Flock Management in the Sixteenth and Seventeenth Centuries', *EconHR*, second series, xi (1958), pp. 98–112, especially pp. 103–6.
173. J. Youings, 'The Church', in C. Clay, ed., *Rural Society: Landowners, Peasants and Labourers* (Cambridge, 1990), pp. 76–9; K.J. Allison, 'The Sheep-Corn Husbandry of Norfolk in the Sixteenth and Seventeenth Centuries', *Agricultural History Review*, v (1957), pp. 12–30.
174. NRO, NCR, 24D, GH Cringleford accounts, 1485–1508, 1509–1528.

IV. THE HOSPITAL CHURCH

1. Themes elaborated in Rawcliffe, 'Medicine for the Soul', pp. 316–38.
2. Tanner, *Decrees*, i, pp. 245–6, and above, p. 7.
3. M. Rubin, *Corpus Christi: The Eucharist in Late Medieval Culture* (Cambridge, 1992), pp. 72–82, 236n, 291, 339–42. It was also in 1215 that transubstantiation became an article of faith: G. Macy, 'The Dogma of Transubstantiation in the Middle Ages', *Journal of Ecclesiastical History*, xlv (1994), pp. 11–41.
4. Innocent III, 'De Sacro Altaris Mysterio Liber Sex', in *Patrologia Latina, CCXVII, Innocentius III* (Paris 1890), p. 886; C. Brown, ed., *Religious Lyrics of the Fifteenth Century* (Oxford, 1962), p. 273.
5. N. Davis, ed., *Non-Cycle Plays and Fragments* (EETS, supplementary text, 1, 1970), pp. 74–83. G. McMurray Gibson, *The Theater of Devotion: East Anglian Drama and Society in the Later Middle Ages* (Chicago, 1989), pp. 36–40, wrongly assumes that St Saviour's hospital was 'staffed by an important resident community of physicians'. It offered no professional medical services whatsoever, which makes the contrast between sacred and profane so telling.
6. See A. Hayum, *The Isenheim Altarpiece: God's Medicine and the Painter's Vision* (Princeton, 1989), pp. 37–9; and A. Burkhard, 'The Isenheim Altar', *Speculum*, ix (1934), p. 59, for a discussion of one of the most powerful examples of this topos.
7. R. Arbesmann, 'The Concept of *Christus Medicus* in St Augustine', *Traditio*, x (1954), pp. 13–20. Christ was, indeed, described by some preachers as a visitor to the sick 'in the hospital of this world': J. Ziegler, *Medicine and Religion* c. *1300: The Case of Arnau de Vilanova* (Oxford, 1998), p. 182 and Chapter IV generally.
8. N. Pevsner, *Worcestershire* (London, 1968), p. 327; E. Prescott, *The English Medieval Hospital, 1050–1640* (London, 1992), pp. 16, 21.
9. K. Park and J. Henderson, '"The First Hospital among Christians": The Ospedale di Santa Maria Nuova in Early Sixteenth-Century Florence', *Medical History*, xxxv (1991), p. 183.
10. G. Goldin, *Works of Mercy: A Picture History of Hospitals* (Boston Mills, 1994), p. 31; A. Höppner, *Das Heiligen-Geist-Hospital zu Lübeck* (Lübeck, 1990), p. 27; Rawcliffe, *Medicine and Society*, p. 20.
11. Prescott, *English Medieval Hospital*, p. 21 and plate 31; Orme and Webster, *English Hospital*, p. 120.
12. BL, Seals, lxviii.54, lxix.6, lxviii.17, lxxi.56. See also, xxxvii.51, lx.69, lxiv.74, lxv.53, 54, lxxi.35; Harleian Ch. 44 D. 14; and generally *Catalogue of Seals in the Department of Manuscripts of the British Museum, I* (London, 1887), pp. 422–826, passim.
13. Henry of Lancaster, *Le Livre de Seyntz Medicines*, ed. E.J. Arnould (Oxford, 1940), pp. 180–1, 233.
14. See above, pp. 159–62.
15. Duffy, *Stripping of the Altars*, pp. 310–15.
16. Thompson, *Hospital of the Annunciation of St Mary in the Newarke*, p. 18. Similar regulations obtained at the hospital of St John, Ely: Rubin, 'Development and Change', p. 50.
17. P. Cullum, *Cremetts and Corrodies: Care of the Poor and Sick at St Leonard's Hospital, York, in the Middle Ages* (University of York, Borthwick Paper, lxxix, 1991), p. 8.
18. *CPL, 1502–1513*, no 102.
19. P. Larkin, *High Windows* (London, 1974), pp. 24–6.
20. See, for example, rules of 1267 for the *leprosarium* of St James, Westminster: BL, Cottonian Ms Faustina A III, fos 319v, 321r. Discipline in this hospital was lax, and regulations with regard to confession were not properly enforced: Page, *VCH London, I*, p. 543; A.G. Rosser, *Medieval Westminster 1200–1540* (Oxford, 1989), pp. 300–10.

21. In about 1500, a local priest left money for masses to be sung every week in the hospital of the Holy Cross, Orléans, 'for the sustenance of the *bodies* and souls of the poor'. By then, however, most donors were placing their own spiritual interests first: A. Saunier, *'Le Pauvre Malade' dans le Cadre Hospitalier Médiéval: France du Nord 1300–1500* (Paris, 1993), p. 104, and Chapter III generally.
22. In support of his argument that spiritual gifts were far superior to corporal ones, Thomas Aquinas observed: 'The spirit is more excellent than the body, wherefore, even as a man in looking after himself, ought to look to his soul more than to his body, so ought he in looking after his neighbour, whom he ought to love as himself' (*Summa Theologica*, II, part 2, question 32, article 3).
23. NRO, Phi. 623.
24. See, for example, Dean Spooner, 'The Almshouse Chapel, Hadleigh', *PSIA*, vii (1891), pp. 379–80. Although the founders of late medieval almshouses stressed the inmates' spiritual obligations, concern with the minutiae of their devotions was not new. The statutes of the hospital of St Margaret outside Gloucester, which date from about 1200, made equally heavy demands: *HMC, Twelfth Report, Appendix IX*, pp. 426–7.
25. PRO, PCC, 40 Holgrave (will of Nicholas Goldwell); NRO, NCR, 24A, GH general accounts, 1485–1508 and 1510–1525, passim. The will of Robert Spenser, who died in office as master of St Giles's in 1430, refers to the poor 'each day remaining and praying in the hospital' (NCC, reg. Surflete, fos 60v–61r).
26. Words taken from the statutes of the Ewelme almshouse, compiled in the 1440s by the duke and duchess of Suffolk: *HMC, Ninth Report, Part I*, p. 217. See above, pp. 5–6.
27. A. Kreider, *English Chantries: The Road to Dissolution* (Cambridge, Massachusetts, and London, 1979), p. 41.
28. Orme and Webster, *English Hospital*, pp. 97–8, 206.
29. H.W. Saunders, ed., *The First Register of Norwich Cathedral Priory* (NRS, xi, 1939), p. 67. Archbishop Theobald of Bec offered a further eight days' remission of penance: B. Dodwell, ed., *The Charters of Norwich Cathedral Priory I* (Pipe Roll Society, new series, xl, 1965–6), p. 65. For Suffield's indulgence, see Appendix I, article 43.
30. *CPL, 1362–1404*, p. 393; V.A. O'Mara, *A Study and Edition of Selected Middle English Sermons* (Leeds Texts and Monographs, new series, xiii, 1994), pp. 57–66 and accompanying commentary.
31. As, for instance, at St Anthony's hospital, London: R.N. Swanson, ed., *Catholic England: Faith, Religion and Observance before the Reformation* (Manchester, 1993), pp. 207–10.
32. E.G. O'Donoghue, *The Story of Bethlehem Hospital from its Foundation in 1247* (London, 1914), pp. 100–1; Page, *VCH London I*, pp. 495–6. The fraternity of pouchmakers also met in the hospital to celebrate an annual mass of the Annunciation and arrange funeral services for deceased members, 'for the health of their souls': M.F. Westlake, *The Parish Guilds of Medieval England* (London, 1919), p. 236.
33. A.T. Bannister, ed., *Registrum Johannis Stanbury, Episcopi Herefordensis 1453–1474* (Canterbury and York Society, 1919), p. 101. For the background to this shift in values, see B. Thompson, 'From "Alms" to "Spiritual Services": The Function and Status of Monastic Property in Medieval England', in J. Loades, ed., *Monastic Studies II* (Bangor, 1991), pp. 227–61.
34. Thompson, *Hospital of the Annunciation of St Mary in the Newarke*, pp. 113–14.
35. *CPR, 1446–1452*, p. 475; NRO, NCR, 24B, no 60.
36. PRO, C1/965/58.
37. Aquinas, *Summa Theologica*, III, Supplement, question 71, article 9. The Supplement served to define 'the bonds between the living and the dead and of the way these could be turned to account in suffrages': Le Goff, *Birth of Purgatory*, pp. 274–7, 294.
38. A. Hudson, ed., *Selections from English Wycliffite Writings* (Cambridge, 1978), p. 135.
39. See, for example, Rubin, *Charity and Community*, pp. 184–92; and G.H. Cook, *Medieval Chantries and Chantry Chapels* (London, 1963), pp. 40–3.
40. Tanner, *Church in Late Medieval Norwich*, pp. 162–6.
41. Appendix I, articles 7, 9, 18–20.
42. F.L. Harrison, *Music in Medieval Britain* (London, second edn, 1963), pp. 77–9. As late as 1465–6, a conduct was being paid 6*d* a week for celebrating mass in the chapel of the Blessed Virgin 'according to the old custom': NRO, NCR, 24A, GH general accounts, 1465–1501.
43. See above, pp. 24–5.
44. J. Alexander and P. Binski, *The Age of Chivalry: Art in Plantagenet England 1200–1400* (London, 1987), no 100, p. 232.
45. The use of choirboys at St Giles's may have been influenced by developments nearer home: J. Greatrex, 'The Almonry School of Norwich Cathedral Priory', *Studies in Church History*, xxxi (1994), pp. 169–81.
46. R. Bowers, 'Choral Institutions within the English Church: Their Constitution and Development 1340–1500' (University of East Anglia, PhD thesis, 1975), pp. 2054–6; Jamison, *Hospital of St Katherine*, pp. 13–25; Hobhouse, *Register of John de Drokensford*, p. 268.

47. Ross, *Cartulary of St Mark's Hospital*, no 9.
48. Appendix I, articles 6, 8, 10.
49. NRO, NCR, 24B, no 3 (2); Caley and Hunter, *Valor Ecclesiasticus*, iii, pp. 291–2.
50. Appendix I, article 42; NRO, NCR, 24B, no 48, *Liber Domus Dei*, fo 52v.
51. Cotton, *Historia Anglicana*, p. 394; NRO, NCR, 24A, GH accounts, 1306–1398, passim; 24B, no 2. This source of income clearly declined, for by 1510 (when the altar raised just over 46*s* in oblations) relics are no longer mentioned: NRO, Box 30E2, no 12120.
52. Foreville and Keir, *Book of St Gilbert*, pp. 304–9.
53. Moore, *Book of the Foundation*, passim, is an early fifteenth-century English translation of the Latin original.
54. *CIMisc., 1387–1393*, no 313.
55. See Gilchrist, *Contemplation and Action*, p. 47, for a plan of St Mary's.
56. NRO, NCR, 24B, no 48, *Liber Domus Dei*, fos 2r–2v.
57. Ibid., no 7. The will is printed in Hudson and Tingey, *Records of the City of Norwich*, ii, pp. 360–2.
58. NRO, NCR, 24B, no 48, *Liber Domus Dei*, fo 59v. The site of the first parish church became a garden, and was known by the Norwich monks as 'St Helen's garden' up to the Dissolution: DCN 1/4/24 (I am grateful to Ms Claire Noble for this reference).
59. As was the case at the hospital of St Mary Magdalen, Yarmouth, where the celebration of mass was regulated in 1386 to avoid conflict with St Nicholas's parish church: NRO, Phi 623. Similar tensions are documented in Brown, *Popular Piety*, pp. 190–1; Page, *VCH London, I*, pp. 495–6, and Imbert, *Hôpitaux en Droit Canonique*, pp. 86–7, 142–5.
60. Saunier, '*Le Pauvre Malade*', p. 111, and also pp. 93–4, 110; W. Page, ed., *VCH Nottingham, II* (London, 1910), pp. 168–9.
61. NRO, NCR, 24A, GH Norwich accounts, 1415–1460, account for 1460–1.
62. Orme and Webster, *English Hospital*, pp. 55–6.
63. NRO, NCR, 24B, nos 7 (wills of William Dunwich, Roger de Tybenham and Nicholas de Kirkeby) and 48, *Liber Domus Dei*, fos 6v, 13r–13v, 24r, 38v–39r; NCR, NPD, box 5, parish of St Helen, no 95.
64. NRO, NCR, 24A, GH general accounts, 1485–1508 and 1510–1525, passim (in 1509 the wife of Master Askeley paid 1 mark to be buried there); Box 30E1, no 12083; NCC, reg. Brosyard, fo 288v. For the traditional placement of women to the north side of churches, see M. Aston, 'Segregation in Church', *Studies in Church History*, xxvii (1990), pp. 237–94, notably pp. 275–80.
65. NRO, Box 30E1, no 12105.
66. Ibid., no 12083.
67. See, for example, Thomas, Sloane and Phillpotts, *Excavations at St Mary Spital*, p. 65; and J. Rosenthal, *The Purchase of Paradise* (London, 1972), pp. 54, 57, 69–73, 78, 104–9, 127–8.
68. Wood-Legh, *Perpetual Chantries*, pp. 74–92; Kreider, *English Chantries*, p. 59; Cook, *Medieval Chantries*, pp. 15–16; Thomson, *Early Tudor Church*, pp. 184, 297. Hospital chantries might be funded on a corporate as well as an individual basis: A.G. Rosser, 'The Essence of Medieval Urban Communities: The Vill of Westminster', *TRHS*, fifth series, xxxiv (1984), pp. 91–112.
69. Pobst, *Register of William Bateman*, pp. 7–8; PRO, C143/303/15; *CPR, 1350–1354*, p. 114. See above, p. 89.
70. C. Carpenter, 'The Religion of the Gentry in Fifteenth Century England', in D. Williams, ed., *England in the Fifteenth Century* (Woodbridge, 1987), p. 57.
71. Wood-Legh, *Perpetual Chantries*, Chapters II and III, passim.
72. NRO, NCR, 24A, GH accounts, 1306–1398, account for 1322–3.
73. C. Burgess, 'A Service for the Dead: The Form and Function of the Anniversary in Late Medieval Bristol', *Transactions of the Bristol and Gloucestershire Archaeological Society*, cv (1987), pp. 183–211; B. Haggh, 'The Meeting of Sacred Ritual and Secular Piety: Endowments for Music', in T. Knighton and D. Fallows, eds, *Companion to Medieval and Renaissance Music* (London, 1992), pp. 60–8, notably p. 62.
74. NRO, NCC, reg. Ryxe, fos 448v–50v; Owen, *Making of King's Lynn*, pp. 108–16.
75. NRO, NCR, NPD, box 5, parish of St Helen, no 93.
76. NRO, Box 30E1, no 12095.
77. NRO, NCC, reg. Ryxe, fos 448v–50v.
78. NRO, NCC, reg. Typpes, fos 17v–19v; NCR, 24B, no 26; NPD, box 12, parish of St Vedast, no 51. One of the grievances voiced during Bishop Nykke's visitation of 1532, concerned the master's delay in making these payments: Jessopp, *Visitations*, p. 271.
79. NRO, NCR, 24B, no 28.
80. See above, p. 94.

81. NRO, NCR, 24E, GH grant of land in Hethel and Carleton, 1472.
82. Smith and others, *English Gilds*, pp. 14–44; PRO, C43/47/290–9; C47/44/301, 303. Two guilds were associated with the College of St Mary in the Fields: that of the Annunciation supported two chantry priests and was made up of laymen and women (290), and that of Corpus Christi was for priests (291).
83. NRO, NCR, 24B, no 17.
84. BL, Add. Ms 57,534, fo 135v.
85. NRO, NCR, 24A, GH general accounts, 1465–1501, accounts of the steward for 1483–4, 1488–9 and 1498–9; general accounts, 1485–1508, account of the receiver general for 1499–1500; general accounts, 1510–1525, account for 1524–5.
86. PRO, PCC, 8 Maynwaryng. Soper's reference to the *collegiate church* of the hospital is significant. He asked to be interred before the image of the Virgin in the Lady Chapel.
87. Blomefield, *Norfolk*, iv, p. 386; NRO, Box 30E1, no 12077; NCR, 24A, GH accounts, 1306–1398, passim. In 1375, perhaps because of successive outbreaks of plague, there were only six priests on the staff, at a higher annual stipend of 30*s* each. One more (still at 30*s*) had been added by 1397.
88. NRO, NCC, reg. Harsyk, fos 5r–5v. Bartholomew Peacock (d. 1385), vicar of Surlingham, likewise requested burial in the chancel (ibid., fo 51r). In 1382, Isabel Brook left money for the building of the chancel (ibid., reg. Heydon, fos 196r–96v).
89. NRO, NCR, 24A, GH Norwich accounts, 1415–1460, account for 1455–6, records a payment of 11*s* 8*d* to a mason for thirty-five days' work, including repairs to the great west window. The tracery was replaced in the sixteenth century with four tiers of mullioned openings: A. Oswald, 'The Great Hospital, Norwich I', *Country Life* (12 December, 1947), pp. 1211, 1213.
90. F.W. Bennett-Symons, 'The Hospital of St Giles, Norwich', *Journal of the British Archaeological Association*, xxxi (1925), pp. 55–67. An inspection of the ceiling of the chancel in 1950 revealed a combination of dust, dirt, birds' nests, woodworm and death-watch beetle (S.J. Wearing, 'The Great Hospital, Norwich', *Norfolk Archaeology*, xxxi (1955), pp. 113–15 and plan). At this point, Eagle Ward, as it was known, still housed a number of elderly female residents, the last of whom left two decades later.
91. Rubin, *Charity and Community*, p. 187; Gilchrist, *Contemplation and Action*, pp. 23–9; Thomas, Sloane and Phillpotts, *Excavations at St Mary Spital*, p. 69.
92. M. Aston, '"Caim's Castles": Poverty, Politics and Disendowment', in R.B. Dobson, ed., *The Church, Politics and Patronage in the Fifteenth Century* (Gloucester, 1984), p. 56.
93. Meade, *Kepier Hospital*, pp. 21–5; Orme and Webster, *English Hospital*, p. 120.
94. Harper-Bill, *Medieval Hospitals of Bury St Edmunds*, p. 15; Rowland-Burdon, 'St Saviour's Hospital, Bury St Edmunds', pp. 280–3; *HMC, Fourteenth Report, Appendix VIII* (London, 1895), pp. 129–30; J. Rowe, 'The Medieval Hospitals of Bury St Edmunds', *Medical History*, ii (1958), pp. 260–1.
95. PRO, E135/2/57, fos 2r–3r; Rawcliffe, 'Hospitals of Later Medieval London', p. 16.
96. J. Watney, *Some Account of the Hospital of St Thomas of Acon* (London, 1892), pp. 37–9.
97. Ibid., pp. 105–6.
98. G.H. Martin, ed., *Knighton's Chronicle 1337–1396* (Oxford, 1995), pp. 226–7, 324–5. See also above, pp. 139–40.
99. M. Aston, 'The Impeachment of Bishop Despenser', *Bulletin of the Institute of Historical Research*, xxxviii (1965), pp. 127–48.
100. NRO, NCR, 24A, GH accounts, 1306–1398, accounts for 1396–7 and 1397; 24B, no 17; *CPR, 1408–1413*, p. 187. Derlyngton's career is outlined in Appendix III.
101. NRO, NCR, 24A, GH accounts, 1306–1398, account for 1375 (where Eaton received 40*s* as a hospital chaplain and 12*s* in expenses for supervising the oxen), account of Eaton himself, as overseer of Costessey, for 1385–6, and account for 1396–7; 24B, no 48, *Liber Domus Dei*, fo 42r.
102. J. Harvey, *The Perpendicular Style 1330–1485* (London, 1978), pp. 105–7, 139, 142–5, 168. A line-drawing of the tracery in the east window of the hospital church appears on p. 63, figure 6; idem, *English Medieval Architects* (revised edn, Gloucester, 1984), pp. 342–3.
103. C. Woodforde, *The Norwich School of Glass-Painting* (Oxford, 1950), pp. 10–12.
104. Wearing, 'Great Hospital', p. 115.
105. Thomas Walsingham, *Historia Anglicana*, ed. H.T. Riley (2 vols, RS, 1863–4), ii, pp. 96–7; L.C. Hector and B.F. Harvey, eds, *The Westminster Chronicle 1381–1394* (Oxford, 1982), pp. 42–3; Blomefield, *Norfolk*, iii, p. 112.
106. Myers, *English Historical Documents*, IV, pp. 1156–7; M. Clayton, ed., *Catalogue of Rubbings of Brasses and Incised Slabs* (London, 1968), plate 17; C. Given Wilson, *The Royal Household and the King's Affinity* (New Haven and London, 1986), pp. 201–2. Coins struck in the 1480s still depict the imperial eagle with one head: A. Arnould and J.M. Massing, eds, *Splendours of Flanders* (Cambridge, 1993), pp. 228–9.

107. NRO, NCR, 24B, nos 1 and 2; NCC, reg. Brosyard, fo 288v; McMurray Gibson, *Theater of Devotion*, pp. 82–4.
108. NRO, NCR, 24A, GH general accounts, 1485–1508, account of the receiver general for 1500–1; G. McMurray Gibson, 'Saint Anne and the Religion of Childbed: Some East Anglian Texts and Talismans', in K. Ashley and P. Sheingorn, eds, *Interpreting Cultural Symbols: Saint Anne in Late Medieval Society* (Athens, Georgia, 1990), pp. 85–110; Duffy, *Stripping of the Altars*, pp. 47–8, 181–3.
109. C. Platt, *King Death: The Black Death and its Aftermath in Late-Medieval England* (London, 1996), pp. 149–64, 178–88.
110. *Calendar of Papal Petitions, 1342–1419*, pp. 423–4.
111. Ross, *Cartulary of St Mark's Hospital*, no 176.
112. Carpenter, 'Religion of the Gentry', p. 68.
113. NRO, NCR, 24A, GH accounts, 1306–1398, account for 1396–7; Harper-Bill, *Medieval Hospitals of Bury St Edmunds*, pp. 16, 137–8; *HMC, Fourteenth Report, Appendix VIII*, pp. 129–30..
114. BL, Harleian Ms 328, fos 28r–30r. Cottonian Ch. XIII.10 (transcribed in J.P. Malcolm, ed., *Londinium Redivium* (4 vols, London, 1803–7), i, pp. 28–30).
115. PRO, C270/22; Canterbury Cathedral Chapter Library, Cathedral Priory reg. F, fos 25r–25v.
116. PRO, CP40/1009, rots. 581Av–581Br (I am grateful to Ms Kay Lacey for drawing my attention to this document, overlooked in Meade, *Kepier Hospital*). Inventories made in the 1540s suggest that neither St Giles's nor the Kepier hospital were unusual in their love of ritual. See, for example, C. Cotton, ed., *The Canterbury Chantries and Hospitals* (Kent Records, supplement, 1934), pp. 41–2. Similar developments have likewise been documented in France: Saunier, '*Le Pauvre Malade*', pp. 94–6.
117. J. Raine, ed., *Testamenta Eboracensia, I* (Surtees Society, iv, 1836), pp. 403–4; idem, ed., *Wills and Inventories, I* (Surtees Society, ii, 1835), pp. 66–8. Wycliffe was not the only member of the northern clergy to give books and vestments to a hospital he had served as master. In 1259 the Sherburn *leprosarium* benefited from Martin St Cross's many legacies; and in the 1320s the hospital of St Edmund, Gateshead, was likewise remembered by Master John Denton: idem, *Testamenta Eborascensia, I*, pp. 22–3; *Wills and Inventories, I*, pp. 6–11.
118. BL, Add. Ms 57,534. This volume is briefly described in F. Wormald, 'A Medieval Processional and its Diagrams, in A. Rosenauer and G. Weber, eds, *Kunsthistorische Forschungen fur Otto Pacht zu seinen 70. Geburtstag* (Salzburg, 1972), pp. 129–34.
119. Harrison, *Music in Medieval Britain*, pp. 88–97.
120. BL, Add. Ms 57,534, fo 107v.
121. Ibid., fos 123r–23v. The feast of St Giles was not observed at Norwich cathedral priory: it is not mentioned in J.B.L. Tolhurst, ed., *The Customary of the Cathedral Priory Church of Norwich* (Henry Bradshaw Society, lxxxii, 1948).
122. NRO, NCR, 24A, GH accounts, 1306–1398, account for 1375; general accounts, 1465–1501, account of the steward for 1498–9; general accounts, 1485–1508, account of the steward for 1500–1.
123. Wilkins, *Concilia*, i, p. 733; T. Starkey, *A Dialogue between Cardinal Pole and Thomas Lupset*, ed. J.M. Cowper (EETS, extra series, xxxii, 1878), p. 137.
124. In 1437 one of the hospital chaplains, Edmund Drew, left a processional to the High Altar (NRO, NCC, reg. Doke, fo 36r); and in 1512–13 two were sent for rebinding (NCR, 24A, GH general accounts, 1510–1525).
125. Watkin, *Inventory of Church Goods*, i, pp. xxv, xxxii. The ownership of processionals did, however, became more common: J. Middleton-Stewart, 'The Provision of Books for Church Use in the Deanery of Dunwich, 1370–1547', *PSIAH*, xxxviii (1994), pp. 150–1.
126. BL, Ms Lansdowne 463; Add. Ms, 17,002. The latter (fo 6v) contains a note in a mid-sixteenth-century hand to the effect that 26 August is a feast day in Norwich because of the defeat of Kett's rebels in 1549.
127. BL, Add. Ms 57,534, fo 123v. For the seal, see above p. 24.
128. K.D. Hartzell,'Diagrams for Liturgical Ceremonies', in R.A. Skelton and P.D.A. Harvey, eds, *Local Maps and Plans from Medieval England* (Oxford, 1986), pp. 339–41; C. Wordsworth, ed., *Salisbury Ceremonies and Processions* (Cambridge, 1901), pp. 18, 67, 82, 84, 86–7, 90, 96.
129. BL, Add. Ms 57,534, fos, 54v, 57r, 62v, 63v. For the hospital's connections with the guild see above, pp. 155–6.
130. D.R. Dendy, *The Use of Lights in Christian Worship* (Alcuin Club Collections, xli, 1959), pp. 139–40.
131. R. Hutton, *The Rise and Fall of Merry England: The Ritual Year 1400–1700* (Oxford, 1994), pp. 20–1.
132. Hudson, *English Wycliffite Writings*, p. 26.
133. See above, pp. 190–2.
134. See above, pp. 107, 146–7.
135. W.W. Capes, ed., *Registrum Johannis Trefnant* (Canterbury and York Society, 1916), p. 360; A. Hudson, ed., *Two Wycliffite Texts* (EETS, ccci, 1993), pp. l, 29; *CPL, 1396–1404*, p. 263. Details of Malvern's career may be found in *BRUO*, ii, p. 1211.

136. The pealing of the bells, playing of the organ and singing of a hymn to the Trinity greeted Bishop Goldwell when he made his visitation in 1492: Jessopp, *Visitations*, pp. 12–13.
137. L. Drucker, ed., *Chartulary of the Hospital of St Thomas the Martyr, Southwark, 1213–1525* (London, 1932), no 2; NRO, NCR, 24A, GH Norwich accounts, 1485–1509. A sketch of the medieval oak bell frame may be found in C. Jewson, *History of the Great Hospital Norwich* (Norwich, 1980), p. 10.
138. Aston, '"Caim's Castles"', pp. 66, 80–1; N. Tanner, ed., *Norwich Heresy Trials 1428–31* (Camden Society, fourth series, xx, 1977), pp. 10–11, 19, 22, 49, 54, 58, 61, 67, 81, 190. Bishop Despenser's hatred of lollards is noted by Walsingham, *Historia Anglicana*, ii, p. 189, and his views were almost certainly shared by his close associate, John Derlyngton.
139. E.F. Jacob, ed., *The Register of Henry Chichele, Archbishop of Canterbury* (4 vols, Oxford, 1943–7), ii, pp. 285–7; PRO, PCC, 30 Godyn.
140. NRO, NCR, 24A, GH accounts, 1306–1398, account for 1396–7.
141. The difference between a 'stole' and a choir stall is explained in *OED*, sub stall, 5a. Pewing and paving ('stolying and pathyng') often went together, perhaps spread over decades, as was the case at the church of St Peter and St Paul, Swaffham, in Norfolk: J.F. Williams, 'The Black Book of Swaffham', *Norfolk Archaeology*, xxxiii (1965), pp. 251–2.
142. Aston, 'Segregation in Church', pp. 245, 252–64.
143. NRO, NCR, 16B, Norwich Assembly Book, 1510–1550, fo 255r.
144. NRO, NCR, 24A, GH accounts, box 1548–1556, accounts for June 1548–59, 1550–1; M. Aston, *Lollards and Reformers: Images and Literacy in Late Medieval Religion* (London, 1984), p. 327. The sequences follow the Salisbury Use: see F.H. Dickinson, ed., *Missale ad Usum Insignis et Praeclarae Ecclesiae Sarum* (Oxford, 1861–3), pp. 735, 741–3, 748, 765–76. One of the votive masses was for the health of the people; the Salisbury Missal also offered masses for the sick and for the sick near to death, which would have been especially appropriate in a hospital.
145. NRO, NCR, 24A, GH accounts, 1306–1398, account for 1396–7; Bowers 'Choral Institutions', pp. 5009–11; idem, 'To Chorus from Quartet: The Performing Resource of English Church Polyphony, *c.* 1390–1559', in S. Morehen, ed., *English Choral Practice 1400–1600* (Cambridge, 1995), pp. 1–47; J.H. Moran, *Education and Learning in the City of York 1300–1560* (University of York, Borthwick Paper lv, 1979), pp. 9, 22.
146. F.D. Matthew, ed., *The English Works of Wyclif hitherto Unpublished* (EETS, lxxiv, 1880), pp. 77, 169. Complaints about polyphony in England were not, however, new: P. Matarasso, ed., *The Cistercian World: Monastic Writings of the Twelfth Century* (London, 1993), pp. 191–3.
147. Matthew, *English Works of Wyclif*, p. 91. Bowers, 'Choral Institutions', pp. 4001–9C.
148. See, for example, the wills of William Norwich, 1470 (PRO, PCC, 30 Godyn); John Smith, 1489 (NRO, NCC, reg. Typpes, fos 17v–19v); John Wells, 1496 (PRO, PCC, 27 Vox); Agnes Thorp, 1503 (ibid., 26 Blanyr); Henry Ferman, 1503 (NRO, NCC, reg. Popy, fos 272v–74v); Gregory Clerk, 1517 (PRO, PCC, 28 Holder, fos 216r–18v); William Soper, 1519 (PRO, PCC, 8 Maynwaryng, fos 53r–53v); John Veryes, 1521 (NRO, NCC, reg. Alblaster, fos 107v–8r); William Fualeyn, 1523 (ibid., reg. Herman, fo 5); Thomas Peerse, 1529 (NRO, DCN 69/2, fos 73v–74r); William Stele, 1530 (ibid., fos 68r–68v).
149. NRO, NCR, 24A, GH general accounts, 1465–1501, accounts for 1478–9, 1479–80, 1480–1; and general accounts, 1485–1508, account for 1507–8.
150. Watney, *Hospital of St Thomas Acon*, pp. 88–9; L. Lyell and F.D. Watney, eds, *Acts of Court of the Mercers' Company 1453–1527* (Cambridge, 1936), p. 376.
151. NRO, NCR, 24A, GH general accounts, 1485–1508, account of the receiver general for 1486–7; Jessopp, *Visitations*, pp. 206–7.
152. NRO, NCC, reg. Surflete, fos 60v–61r; Bowers, 'Choral Institutions', pp. A031–35; Cattermole, 'Schools in Medieval Norwich', pp. 8, 39.
153. NRO, NCR, 24A, GH general accounts, 1465–1501, account of the receiver general for 1480–1, records Godfrey's appointment as organist. He himself accounted as receiver in the following year (1481–2), and was thus too busy to continue. In his account for 1485–6 (general accounts, 1485–1508) he paid William Crane a fee as chorister-organist.
154. R.R. Sharpe, ed., *Calendar of Wills Proved and Enrolled in the Court of Husting of London, 1258–1688* (2 vols, London, 1889–90), ii, pp. 524–5; *CPR, 1467–1477*, p. 153.
155. NRO, NCR, 24A, GH general accounts, 1485–1508 and 1510–1525, passim. The style 'gentleman' accorded to him in 1520, when he and the master of St Giles's together acquired a tenement in Colegate, confirms that he never took orders: NPD, box 4, parish of St George, Colegate, no 23.
156. A. Wathey, 'Newly Discovered Fifteenth-Century English Polyphony at Oxford', *Music and Letters*, lxiv (1983), pp. 58, 62. I am grateful to Dr Roger Bowers for drawing this article to my attention.

157. NRO, NCR, 24A, GH general accounts, 1465–1501, account of the steward, 1488–9. For Dynham, see Appendix III.
158. *BRUC*, p. 245; NRO, NCR, 24A, GH Fobbing accounts, 1521–1528, passim.
159. NRO, NCR, 24A, GH general accounts, 1510–1520, receiver general's accounts from 1511 to 1515, passim; Cattermole, 'Schools in Medieval Norwich', p. 19.
160. NRO, NCR, 24A, GH general accounts, 1485–1508, account of the receiver general for 1500–1 (it cost 6*s* 8*d* to transport the organ some 19 miles); Thomson, *Early Tudor Church*, p. 305.
161. T. Easton and S. Bicknell, 'Two Pre-Reformation Organ Soundboards', *PSIAH*, xxxviii (1995), pp. 268–95; NRO, DCN, 69/2, fos 50r–50v.
162. P. Williams, *The Organ in Western Culture 750–1250* (Cambridge, 1993), pp. 93, 298, 332–5; NRO, NCR, 24A, GH general accounts, 1510–1525, account for 1509–10; accounts for Norwich properties, 1510–1528, account for 1515–16. A chantry priest at Much Wenlock, in the mid-sixteenth century, was noted for his 'handy crafte', which encompassed 'the making of organs, of a clocke and chimes': Cook, *Medieval Chantries*, p. 63.
163. PRO, CP40/1009, rot. 581Br. Chiming bells were often extremely complex and the mechanism difficult to maintain, as the will of John Baret of Bury St Edmunds, made in 1463, reveals: S. Tymms, ed., *Wills and Inventories from the Registers of the Commissary of Bury St Edmunds* (Camden Society, xlix, 1850), pp. 20, 28.
164. NRO, DN, reg. VI, book 2, fos 189r–92v.
165. Ordination services attracted a large and influential congregation, drawn from religious houses throughout the diocese: D. Dymond, ed., *The Register of Thetford Priory, I*, 1482–1517 (NRS, lix, 1994), p. 205.
166. R. Swanson, 'Titles to Orders in Medieval Episcopal Registers', in H. Mayr-Harting and R.I. Moore, eds, *Studies in Medieval History Presented to R.H.C. Davis* (London, 1983), pp. 233–45.
167. Orme and Webster, *English Hospital*, pp. 66, 236.
168. NRO, DN, reg. VI, book 2, fos 189r–92v.
169. The figures produced by J.F. Williams, 'Ordination in the Norwich Diocese during the Fifteenth Century', *Norfolk Archaeology*, xxxi (1956, pp. 347–58, are less accurate than those of E.C.K. Underwood, 'Fifteenth Century Clergy in the Diocese of Norwich' (University of Tasmania, PhD thesis, 1993), Table XI, p. 580.
170. Swanson, 'Titles to Orders', pp. 233–45. E.F. Jacob, 'Thomas Brouns, Bishop of Norwich', in H.R. Trevor-Roper, ed., *Essays in British History Presented to Sir Keith Feiling* (London, 1964), pp. 75–6, suggests that 'an impoverished house such as St Giles's would have profited from such sales'.
171. A. Hudson, *The Premature Reformation* (Oxford, 1988), pp. 33, 37, 181–2. Aston, *Lollards and Reformers*, pp. 71–100, provides an important supplement to Tanner, *Norwich Heresy Trials*, which covers only half the cases examined in the city between 1428–31.
172. J.L. Connolly, *John Gerson, Reformer and Mystic* (Louvain, 1928), p. 131; Jean Gerson, *Oeuvres Completes, VII, L'Oeuvre Française*, ed. Mgr. Glorieux (Paris, 1966), p. 407.
173. Kreider, *English Chantries*, p. 31.
174. R.C.E. Hayes, 'William Alnwick, Bishop of Norwich (1426–1437) and Lincoln (1437–1449)' (University of Bristol, PhD thesis, 1989), p. 110. For Acton see below, Appendix III.
175. J. Catto, 'Religious Change under Henry V', in G.L. Harriss, ed., *Henry V: The Practice of Kingship* (Oxford, 1985), pp. 98, 101.
176. NRO, NCR, 24A, GH general accounts, 1485–1501, account of the steward for 1500–1; BL, Add. Ms 57,534, fo 127r.
177. R.W. Pfaff, *New Liturgical Feasts in Later Medieval England* (Oxford, 1970), pp. 3–4, 62–83; Tanner, *Church in Late Medieval Norwich*, pp. 94, 102.
178. N. Davis, ed., *Paston Letters and Papers of the Fifteenth Century* (2 vols, Oxford, 1971–6), i, no 230.
179. NRO, NCC, reg. Alblaster, fos 107v–108r. Richard Hawze, who died in the hospital in 1526, left 20*d* for 'v meassys of the blyssyd v woundes': ibid., reg. Alpe, fos 49v–50r. The devotions at William Pykenham's almshouse were carefully arranged in multiples of five: see above, note 24, and also C. Richmond, 'The English Gentry and Religion *c.* 1500', in C. Harper-Bill, ed., *Religious Belief and Ecclesiastical Careers in Late Medieval England* (Studies in the History of Medieval Religion, iii, 1991), pp. 126–7.
180. M.B. Salu, ed. and trans., *The Ancrene Riwle* (Exeter Medieval English Texts and Studies, 1990), p. 50.
181. NRO, NCC, reg. Brosyard, fo 288v; NCR, 24A, GH Norwich accounts, 1415–1460, passim.
182. BL, Add. Ms 57,534, fos 127v–31r. Richard Holdich of Ranworth was 'the trewe owner . . . withe oute dought' of the processional in 1552 (fo 136v). Joan, daughter of John Fyncham of Outwell, married Robert Holdich of Ranworth, and her obit (1538) is recorded in the Ranworth antiphonal (P. Lasko and N.I. Morgan, eds, *Medieval Art in East Anglia 1300–1520* (Norwich, 1973), pp. 46–7). A John Fyncham was retained as legal counsel by John Selot, master of St Giles's, in 1459, but too much cannot be made of this connection (NRO, NCR, 8A, no 11).

183. NRO, NCR, 24A, GH accounts, 1306–1398, account for 1396–7; Norwich accounts, 1485–1509, account for 1505–6. The latter records expenditure on two reeders and their servants, who spent eleven days thatching the chapel at a cost of 30*s*.
184. Gilchrist, *Contemplation and Action*, p. 30; Kerling, *Cartulary of St Bartholomew's Hospital*, p. 7 and no 1123.
185. Bennett-Symons, 'Hospital of St Giles', p. 66.
186. PRO, PCC 35 Horne; Goldwell's chantry chapel and tomb still survive in Norwich cathedral on the south side of the choir which he revaulted: J. Finch, 'The Monuments', in I. Atherton and others, eds, *Norwich Cathedral: Church City and Diocese 1096–1996* (London, 1996), pp. 472–3.
187. Fernie, *Architectural History of Norwich Cathedral*, pp. 191–3.
188. Harvey, *English Medieval Architects*, pp. 102–3.
189. M.R. James, *The Sculptured Bosses of the Roof of the Bauchun Chapel of Our Lady of Pity in Norwich Cathedral* (Norwich, 1908), pp. ii–iii, 1–7. M. Rose and J. Hedgecoe, *Stories in Stone: The Medieval Roof Carvings of Norwich Cathedral* (London, 1997), pp. 87–95, are mistaken in their assumption that Sekyngton left money for the re-vaulting. He made bequests for his burial in the chapel and for masses to be said there for his soul for two years after his death and in the hospital of St Giles for one: NRO, NCC, reg. Brosyard, fos 226r–27v.
190. For the popularity and significance of this imagery, see N. Morgan, 'The Coronation of the Virgin by the Trinity and other Texts and Images of the Glorification of Mary in the Fifteenth Century', in N. Rogers, ed., *England in the Fifteenth Century* (Stamford, 1994), pp. 223–41.
191. Restoration and repainting of the hospital bosses was begun in 1944 by the artist, John Chaplin, and a team of builders. Chaplin later complained about 'the foolish criticism [such work] aroused and the poor pay', but the exercise was generally deemed successful: Private Correspondence of Mr Michael Youngs, a Trustee of the Great Hospital, 3 and 6 December 1971.
192. Cook, *Mediaeval Chantries*, p. 74. Prescott, *English Medieval Hospital*, plate 18 (plate 17 depicts two of the ornately carved tombs in the chancel of the hospital church). This building was decorated with wall paintings as well as sculpture: M. Gill and H. Hurried, 'Glimpses of Glory: Paintings from St Mark's Hospital, Bristol', in L. Keen, ed., *'Almost the Richest City': Bristol in the Middle Ages* (British Archaeological Association Conference Transactions, xix, 1997), pp. 97–106.
193. NRO, NCC, reg. Typpes, fos 18v–19v; Appendix III.
194. NRO, NCR, 24A, GH general accounts, 1510–1525, account for 1510–11. Ninety-eight pounds of wax were then worked into candles and 3 gallons of oil were bought for altar lamps.
195. PRO, PCC, 15 Horne.
196. Brief biographies of the masters are to be found in Appendix III.
197. Blomefield, *Norfolk*, iv, p. 379.
198. E. Robertson, 'The Corporeality of Female Sanctity in the Life of St Margaret', in R. Blumenfeld-Kosinski and T. Szell, eds, *Images of Sainthood in Medieval Europe* (Ithaca and London, 1991), pp. 268–87, especially p. 285.
199. P.H. Ditchfield, ed., *VCH Buckinghamshire, II* (London, 1907), p. 96.
200. N. Tanner, 'The Reformation and Regionality: Further Reflections on the Church in Late Medieval Norwich', in J.A.F. Thomson, ed., *Towns and Townspeople in the Fifteenth Century* (Gloucester, 1988), pp. 129–47.
201. P. Cattermole, *Notes on Bishop Salmon's Chantry, 1316–1548* (Norwich, privately printed, 1983), pp. 1–16.
202. H.W. Saunders, *A History of the Norwich Grammar School* (Norwich, 1932), pp. 3–48; *CPR, 1416–1422*, pp. 376–7.

V. POLITICS AND PATRONAGE

1. K.B. McFarlane, *The Nobility of Later Medieval England* (Oxford, 1973), p. 114.
2. See, for example, C. Carpenter, 'Political and Constitutional History: Before and After McFarlane', in R.H. Britnell and A.J. Pollard, eds, *The McFarlane Legacy: Studies in Late Medieval Politics and Society* (Stroud, 1995), pp. 175–206.
3. See above, pp. 159–60.
4. Carpenter, 'Political and Constitutional History', p. 195.
5. Davis, *Paston Letters*, ii, p. 232.
6. For biographical details about Smyth and the other medieval masters of St Giles's, see Appendix III.
7. R.N. Swanson, *Church and Society in Late Medieval England* (Oxford, 1993), pp. 54, 68–77.
8. J.H. Lupton, *A Life of John Colet* (London, 1909), pp. 226–7, 296.
9. Tanner, *Decrees*, i, pp. 374–6.
10. See, for example, the case of William Coterell, with his multiple masterships in the 1390s: Price and Ponsford, *St Bartholomew's Hospital*, p. 207.

11. *CPL, 1447–1455*, pp. 128–9, and also pp. 11, 25, 338.
12. Borthwick Institute, York, Diocesan Register, R VII G, fo 125.
13. PRO, CP40/1009, rots 581A–81C. See also Talbot and Hammond, *Medical Practitioners in Medieval England*, pp. 117–19.
14. Doubleday, *VCH Norfolk, II*, pp. 438–9. The masters were John Selot, Thomas Shenkwyn, Robert Honywod and William Soper: see Appendix III.
15. *CCR, 1461–1468*, p. 178.
16. Page, *VCH London, I*, p. 524.
17. Rawcliffe, *Hospitals of Medieval Norwich*, pp. 143–6.
18. PRO, E368/280, rot. 26r.
19. Caley and Hunter, *Valor Ecclesiasticus*, iii, p. 368.
20. *CPL, 1458–1471*, pp. 759–60, and also p. 583; *1484–1492, Part I*, pp. 175–6, 183; *Part II*, no 168.
21. R. Ware, '"Poore Peoples Use": Aspects of Institutional Provision for the Sick Poor of Medieval Ipswich *c.* 1305–1550' (University of East Anglia, MA thesis, 1997), pp. 37–41.
22. PRO, C1/161/35. For Soper's career see Appendix III.
23. See Appendix III.
24. Appendix I, article 35.
25. NRO, NCR, 24B, no 5.
26. Rubin, *Charity and Community*, p. 169.
27. Appendix I, article 37; NRO, DN reg. V, book 9, fos 46v, 88v; book 10, fo 7v; VII, book 12, fos 68v, 138v.
28. NRO, Phi 516–18; Box 30E1 no 12067; NCR, 24B, no 8.
29. See Appendix III.
30. In chronological order, John Derlyngton, William de Sekyngton, John Walpole, John Selot, John Smyth, Oliver Dynham, Thomas Shenkwyn, Nicholas Goldwell, Robert Honywood, William Soper and Thomas Cappe: see Appendix III.
31. John Derlyngton, William de Sekyngton, John Walpole, John Selot, John Smyth, Thomas Shenkwyn, Nicholas Goldwell, Robert Honywood, John Hecker and Thomas Cappe: see Appendix III.
32. John Derlyngton, John de Thornham, William de Sekyngton, Hugh Acton, John Selot, John Smyth, Nicholas Goldwell, Robert Honywood, John Jullys, William Soper, Thomas Cappe and Thomas Simmondes: see Appendix III.
33. See Appendix III.
34. Jamison, *Hospital of St Katherine*, pp. 34–5; Rawcliffe, 'Hospitals of Later Medieval London', pp. 14–17.
35. See above, pp. 117, 120.
36. M.D. Legge, ed., *Anglo Norman Letters and Petitions* (Oxford, 1941), no 75. Morley was married to Despenser's niece, Anne.
37. See Appendix III.
38. NRO, NCR, 24B, no 17. Similar arrangements made in 1348 at St John's hospital, Bristol, for a former master were imposed upon the brethren by the bishop: Price and Ponsford, *St Bartholomew's Hospital*, p. 213.
39. William de Sekyngton, John Walpole, John Selot, John Smyth, Oliver Dynham, Thomas Shenkwyn, Nicholas Goldwell, Robert Honywood, William Soper and Thomas Cappe: see Appendix III.
40. Thomson, *Early Tudor Church*, p. 145.
41. See Appendix III.
42. Griffiths, *King Henry VI*, pp. 271, 285.
43. Thomas Gascoigne, *Loci et Libri Veritatem*, ed. J.E. Thorold Rogers (Oxford, 1881), pp. 42, 151.
44. Briefly but succinctly described in R.L. Storey, *The End of the House of Lancaster* (London, 1966), Appendix III, and at greater length by P.C. Maddern, *Violence and Social Order: East Anglia 1422–1442* (Oxford, 1992), pp. 175–205. B.R. McRee, 'Peacemaking and its Limits in Late Medieval Norwich', *EHR*, cix (1994), pp. 831–66, notably 853–60, and 'Religious Gilds and Civic Order: The Case of Norwich in the Later Middle Ages', *Speculum*, lxvii (1992), pp. 69–97, advances a more consensual interpretation of the evidence, which stresses conciliation rather than conflict.
45. F.J. Furnivall, ed., *Political, Religious and Love Poems* (EETS, original series, xv, 1866), pp. 6–11.
46. Davis, *Paston Letters*, ii, p. 205. The Pastons were not, however, always so critical of Selot. See ibid., i, p. 267, where he emerges in a more compassionate light.
47. R. Virgoe, *East Anglian Society and the Political Community of Late Medieval England*, eds C. Barron, C. Rawcliffe and J. Rosenthal (Norwich, 1997), pp. 122, 123, 127, 128.
48. Davis, *Paston Letters*, ii, p. 528.

49. Ibid., i, pp. 141, 143, 320–2; ii, p. 349.
50. NRO, DCN 2/5/5; NCR, 24A, GH general accounts 1465–1501, account for 1465–6. Bishop Suffield had banned squires as well as 'wanton boys' from the hospital, and had limited the size of the master's retinue: Appendix I, article 31.
51. See Appendix III.
52. Graham, 'Order of St Antoine de Viennois', pp. 363–4, 373–4. The role of John Carpenter, future bishop of Worcester and master of this hospital, as an educationalist is also worth noting: Orme, *English Schools*, p. 200.
53. Blomefield, *Norfolk*, vi, p. 309. During his last years, however, Selot appears to have relaxed his customary vigilance: see above, pp. 98, 100.
54. See Appendix III.
55. See Appendix III.
56. Cullum, *Cremetts and Corrodies*, p. 28.
57. See Appendix III , and above, pp. 129–31.
58. Lambeth Palace Library, reg. Morton, II, fo 83r.
59. See Appendix III.
60. NRO, NCR, 24A, GH general accounts, 1485–1508, 1510–1525, passim.
61. See above, pp. 199–230.
62. Page, *VCH York, III*, p. 315.
63. See, for example, Rubin, *Charity and Community*, pp. 196–200, and above, pp. 49, 110–11, 122.
64. Rawcliffe, *Hospitals of Medieval Norwich*, p. 66; NRO, NCR, 24A, GH accounts, 1306–1398, account for 1397.
65. NRO, DCN 40/6, fos 44v–46r.
66. NRO, NCR, 24D, Cringleford court rolls, 1485–1508, m. 5r.
67. NRO, NCR, 24A, GH general accounts 1510–1525, account for 1526–7, records the payment of damages, which had been awarded in the previous year.
68. NRO, Box 30E1, nos 12098, 12099; NCR, 24B, no 21. The allocation of tithes at Mundham proved a contentious issue throughout the Middle Ages and beyond: in 1435 the hospital was involved in a dispute over boundaries; and in 1507–8 legal fees and settlements in this parish alone cost the hospital 25*s* (24A, GH general accounts, 1485–1508; 24B, no 22).
69. Orme and Webster, *English Hospital*, pp. 103–4; *CPR, 1396–1399*, p. 510. As early as April 1380, the master of St John's hospital, Bridgwater, had been obliged to sue out royal letters of protection because of 'divers dissensions and debates' between his predecessor and the townspeople: *CPR, 1377–1381*, p. 458.
70. William Lambarde, *A Perambulation of Kent* (London, 1826), pp. 329–31.
71. NRO, Box 30E1, nos 12045, 12065, 12068, 12078. In 1342 two men from Thurlton were excommunicated for infringing the hospital's grazing rights: NCR, 24B, no 50D.
72. NRO, Box 30E1, no 12073; BL, Toph. Cart. 52.
73. PRO, STAC 2/35/3.
74. NRO, NCR, 24B, nos 31–2.
75. See above, p. 151.
76. Swanson, *Church and Society*, pp. 179–80.
77. See Appendix III.
78. Appendix I, article 36.
79. Virgoe, *East Anglian Society*, pp. 138, 167, 179, 188, 191. The biographies of John Jenney and his father (also named John) in J.C. Wedgwood, ed., *History of Parliament: Biographies of Members of the Commons House 1439–1509* (London, 1936), pp. 498–9, confuse the two men in many respects. For Wetherby, see W.J. Blake, 'Thomas Wetherby', *Norfolk Archaeology*, xxxii (1961), pp. 60–72.
80. M. Hicks, *False, Fleeting, Perjur'd Clarence: George, Duke of Clarence 1449–78* (Gloucester, 1980), p. 48. For Jenney's strong views on electoral management, see McFarlane, *England in the Fifteenth Century*, pp. 5–6.
81. J. Gairdner, ed., *The Paston Letters* (4 vols, London, 1910), i, pp. 173–4; Davis, *Paston Letters*, ii, p. 48.
82. NRO, NCR, 25A, GH Cringleford deeds, box IV, nos 20, 22, 22A, 27, 29, 38; 25D, GH unnumbered Cringleford miscellanea. Acton had previously leased some of the hospital's demesnes in Cringleford to Jenney: 24D, *Jenney* v *Selot*, 1459.
83. NRO, NCR, 25D, GH unnumbered Cringleford miscellanea.
84. NRO, NCR, 24B, no 20.
85. NRO, NCR, 8A, no 11.
86. NRO, BR 61/2/18.
87. NRO, NCR, 24D, *Jenney* v *Selot*, 1459.

88. NRO, NCR, 24E, GH conveyance of Hethel and Carleton, post 1472; 25A, GH Cringleford deeds, box IV, nos 39, 56; Phi 99.
89. NRO, NCR, 24D, GH Cringleford accounts, 1461–1482, m. 1r; 25A, GH Cringleford deeds, box IV, nos 43–6; PRO, CP25(1) 170/192/3.
90. NRO, Phi 98. In 1461 the prior had agreed to dispose of his interests in Cringleford to the hospital, so this may simply have been a payment of rent: NCR, 25A, GH Cringleford deeds, box IV, nos 41–2.
91. NRO, Phi 621; Box 30E1, no 12111; NCR, 24E, GH conveyance of Hethel and Carleton, post 1472; 25D, GH Hethel and Carleton deeds, no 1249. For the political background, see Griffiths, *King Henry VI*, pp. 741–57.
92. NRO, NCR, 25A, GH East Carleton deeds, no 1297.
93. NRO, NCR, 25D, GH Hethel and Carleton deeds, no 1301. This award was made in 1511, but accounts for 1507–8 record expenses of 15*s* for taking evidence in the dispute to London for examination: 24A, GH general accounts, 1485–1508.
94. NRO, NCR, 25A, GH Cringleford deeds, box IV, nos 54, 56–9; 25B, Mundham deeds, no 544; *CPR, 1467–1477*, p. 516; *1476–1485*, pp. 78, 397; BL, Stowe Ch. 197.
95. *CPL, 1471–1484*, p. 727; *CPR, 1476–1485*, p. 237.
96. It is, perhaps, no coincidence that a payment of £15 made by Selot and Nicholas Ovy to one of the king's yeomen, in 1474, in return for a release of all legal actions, also involved Jenney as one of the latter's associates: *CCR, 1468–1476*, no 1333.
97. NRO, NCR, 24B, nos 24, 62; *CCR, 1468–1476*, no 809.
98. Ross, *Cartulary of St Mark's Hospital*, pp. xx–xxvi, nos 171–5.
99. NRO, Phi 525. Royal letters patent of 1404 similarly describe St John's hospital, Bristol, as 'depressed and loaded with debts by pleas and oppressions': *CPR, 1401–1405*, p. 413.
100. NRO, NCR, 24G, GH Repps-cum-Bastwick accounts, 1509–1528, mm. 16r–17r.
101. NRO, NCR, 24A, GH accounts, 1306–1398. In 1321–2 legal expenses came to 47*s* 10*d*, and in 1322–3 to 53*s* 8*d*: ibid.
102. BL, Toph. Cart. 50.
103. Dugdale, *Monasticon Anglicanum*, vi (part 2), pp. 704–7. The foundation statutes of St Giles's do, however, refer to 'the senior priest' who was to entertain guests in the master's absence: Appendix I, article 18.
104. NRO, NCC, reg. Spyltymber, fos 33r–33v (Braunche was already a hospital chaplain by 1462: ibid., reg. Brosyard, fo 288v); NCR, 24A, GH Norwich accounts, 1465–1501; general accounts 1465–1501; PRO, CP25(1) 170/196/41, 51, 91.
105. NRO, NCR, NPD, box 12, parish of St Vedast, no 51; 24A, GH Norwich accounts, 1465–1501, 1485–1509; general accounts 1465–1501, 1489–1508, passim; 25A, GH Cringleford deeds, box IV, no 53; DN reg. VII, book 12, fo 138v; Jessopp, *Visitations*, pp. 12–13. He is not to be confused with the 'Master Godfray' who joined John Selot in executing the will of John Eastgate, advocate of the consistory court, in 1465: NCC, reg. Jekkys, fo 64r; Davis, *Paston Letters*, i. 315.
106. NRO, NCR, 24A, GH general accounts 1465–1501, account for 1465–6; 24C, GH Costessey accounts, 1422–1460; 24G, GH Repps-cum-Bastwick accounts, 1437–1460; 25A, GH Cringleford deeds, box IV, nos 49, 50, 52; GH Costessey deeds, no 250; 25B, GH Hardley deeds, nos 288–9; 25C, GH Horstead deeds, no 857; 25D, GH East Carleton deeds, no 1259.
107. NRO, NCR, 24A, GH Norwich accounts, 1465–1501, passim; DN, reg. VI, book 11, fo 186r; *BRUC*, p. 327; Davis, *Paston Letters*, ii, pp. 349, 320–1; Jessopp, *Visitations*, p. 10.
108. NRO, NCR, NPD, box 4, parish of St Edward, Conisford, no 16; box 5, parish of St Helen, no 102 (on dorse); 8A, no 11; 24A, GH general accounts, 1485–1509, 1465–1501, passim; 25B, GH Mundham deeds, nos 544, 566; PRO, C1/61/487; CP25(1) 170/192/48, 54, 193/54; Davis, *Paston Letters*, ii, p. 426; *CCR, 1468–1476*, p. 369; Jessopp, *Visitations*, p. 216.
109. NRO, NCR, 24A, GH general accounts, 1465–1501, accounts for 1498–1501; *BRUC*, p. 510.
110. NRO, NCR, 24A, GH general accounts, 1485–1508, account for 1502–3. Between 1514 and 1516, Sir James's ward, Edmund Beaupre, was a boarder, although he had to pay. Was this because Hobart was no longer quite so powerful?: general accounts, 1510–1525.
111. NRO, Box 30E1, nos 12112–13; 24A, GH Fobbing accounts, 1521–1528; 25D, GH Fobbing deeds, nos 1344–54. Hobart's career is described in Wedgwood, *History of Parliament*, pp. 458–9. For his post as recorder, see NRO, NCR, 16A, Norwich Assembly Proceedings, 1491–1553, fo 19v; PRO, KB9/418, rot. 43.
112. See above, p. 66.
113. NRO, NCR, 24B, no 15.
114. Ibid., nos 29, 61; PRO, E368/280, Easter 22 Henry VII, rot. 26.

115. S.J. Gunn, 'The Courtiers of Henry VII', *EHR*, cviii (1993), p. 47; *CPR, 1494–1509*, p. 585; *CCR, 1500–1509*, nos 892, 920. Henry's use of these devices to cow his subjects and fill his coffers is explored in J.R. Lander, *Crown and Nobility, 1450–1509* (London, 1976), pp. 267–300.
116. Davis, *Paston Letters*, i, p. 511; ii, p. 355.
117. PRO, C1/64/31.
118. J.F. Pound, *Tudor and Stuart Norwich* (Chichester, 1988), p. 32.
119. NRO, NCR, 24B, no 7.
120. John de Thornham, Roger Pratt, Robert Spenser, William de Sekyngton, John Selot, John Smyth, Thomas Shenkwyn, John Hecker, Robert Codde: see Appendix III.
121. M. Grace, ed., *Records of the Gild of St George in Norwich 1389–1547* (NRS, ix, 1937), pp. 6–13, 21–4.
122. J.S. Roskell, L. Clark and C. Rawcliffe, eds, *The History of Parliament: The House of Commons 1386–1421* (4 vols, Stroud, 1993), iv, pp. 187–9, 330–1 (*sub* Sedman).
123. PRO, C143/441/18; *CPR, 1408–1413*, p. 187; NRO, NCR, 25A, GH Cringleford deeds, box IV, nos 14, 19.
124. Lambeth Palace Library, reg. Arundel, II, fos 51r–51v.
125. See Appendix III.
126. NRO, NCC reg. Surflete, fos 124v–25r; Tanner, *Church in Late Medieval Norwich*, pp. 135, 243–4.
127. PRO, C1/9/277.
128. Grace, *Gild of St George*, p. 39. As master of St Giles's, Pratt made two contributions of 13*s* 4*d* to the guild's funds, one for repairs to property and the other towards the fabric of the staithe at Fye Bridge: NRO, NCR, 8E-7, guild accounts for 8–9 and 12–13 Henry VI.
129. NRO, NCC, reg. Jekkys, fos 47v–49r; NCR, 1C, rolls 19A, rot. 1, 19B, rot. 2, 19E, rots 2–3; 17B, *Liber Albus Civitatis*, fos 14r, 135r. See above, p. 36.
130. PRO, C1/40/237.
131. NRO, NCR, 24B, no 25; 17B, *Liber Albus Civitatis*, fos 53r–53v.
132. Frost, 'Aldermen of Norwich', p. 215.
133. See, for example, C. Rawcliffe, '"That Kindliness Should be Cherished More, and Discord Driven Out": The Settlement of Commercial Disputes by Arbitration in Later Medieval England', in J. Kermode, ed., *Enterprise and Individuals in Fifteenth-Century England* (Stroud, 1991), pp. 98–117.
134. Legge, *Anglo Norman Letters*, no 75.
135. Davis, *Paston Letters*, ii, pp. 310–11. See above, p. 134.
136. PRO, KB9/84/1; McRee, 'Peacemaking and its Limits', p. 865.
137. NRO, NCR, 1C, roll 19B, rot. 5. In 1401, John Derlyngton was commissioned by the Crown to determine an appeal against a verdict in the Court of Admiralty involving the freighting of a cargo of fish from Winterton, Norfolk: *CPR, 1399–1401*, p. 535.
138. Wood-Legh, *Perpetual Chantries*, p. 203.

VI. PAUPERS AND PROVISIONS

1. A case in point is V.L. Bullough, 'A Note on Medical Care in Medieval English Hospitals', *Bulletin of the History of Medicine*, xxxv (1961), pp. 74–7. See Carlin, 'Medieval English Hospitals', pp. 29–31, for a more realistic assessment.
2. NRO, NCR, 24A, GH Norwich accounts 1415–1460, accounts for 1432–9 (Robert Taylour, leech); 1465–1501, accounts for 1471–3 (Master Geoffrey, leech); GH general accounts, 1485–1508, 1510–1525, passim (payments to barbers). For the Norwich barber-surgeons, see Rawcliffe, *Medicine and Society*, pp. 135–6.
3. D. Jacquart, *Le Milieu Médical en France du XIIe au XIVe Siècle* (Geneva, 1981), pp. 120–1; K. Park, 'Healing the Poor: Hospitals and Medical Assistance in Renaissance Florence', in J. Barry and C. Jones, eds, *Medicine and Charity before the Welfare State* (London, 1991), pp. 26–45; J. Henderson, 'The Hospitals of Late Medieval and Renaissance Florence', in L. Granshaw and R. Porter, eds, *Hospital in History*, pp. 63–92.
4. Imbert, *Histoire des Hôpitaux*, p. 115.
5. Brodman, *Charity and Welfare*, pp. 93–6.
6. The cost and availability of medical and surgical treatment are discussed in Rawcliffe, *Medicine and Society*, Chapters V and VI.
7. Ibid., p. 49; Atherton and others, *Norwich Cathedral*, figures 136, 198.
8. Jessopp, *Visitations*, pp. 4, 22, 24, 28, 54, 62, 111, 139–40, 166–7, 178, 193, 203, 217, 277–8, 281, 286, 289, 290, 313–14; Tolhurst, *Customary of the Cathedral Priory Church of Norwich*, pp. 143–4. Solicitude for the care of sick brethren was likewise a feature of the Augustinian rule: Willis Clark, *Observances*, pp. 199–209.

9. NRO, DCN 1/10/1–38; E.A. Hammond, 'The Westminster Abbey Infirmarers' Rolls as a Source of Medical History', *Bulletin of the History of Medicine*, xxxix (1965), pp. 261–76.
10. For an explanation of this procedure see P. Gil-Sotres, 'Derivation and Revulsion: The Theory and Practice of Medieval Phlebotomy', in L. García-Ballester, *Practical Medicine from Salerno to the Black Death* (Cambridge, 1994), pp. 110–55.
11. NRO, DCN 1/10/6.
12. Wellcome Institute Library, London, Western Ms 408, fos 4r–13r. The author, writing in both Latin and English, was William Bokynham. See Greatrex, *Biographical Register*, p. 485.
13. NRO, DCN 1/6/85, 1/10/14, 15, 17–24, 29; Talbot and Hammond, *Medical Practitioners in Medieval England*, p. 30.
14. Greatrex, *Biographical Register*, pp. 500, 522, 559.
15. Rawcliffe, *Medicine and Society*, pp. 149–52. For the infirmarers' garden see Noble, 'Norwich Cathedral Priory Gardeners' Accounts', pp. 6–9.
16. H.C. Beeching and M.R. James, 'The Library of the Cathedral Church of Norwich', *Norfolk Archaeology*, xix (1917), pp. 109–10; N.R. Ker, 'Medieval Mss from Norwich Cathedral', *Transactions of the Cambridge Bibliographical Society*, i (1949–53), pp. 1–28, qualified by B. Dodwell, 'The Muniments and the Library', in Atherton and others, *Norwich Cathedral*, pp. 332–40.
17. Miller, *Birth of the Hospital*, p. 6.
18. Accounting procedures differed little from those described in K. Mertes, *The English Noble Household 1250–1600* (Oxford, 1988), pp. 75–91.
19. Archives of St George's Chapel, Windsor, Mss xv 37.8, 21, 25, 27, 33.
20. Caley and Hunter, *Valor Ecclesiasticus*, iii, pp. 291–2.
21. NRO, NCR, 24B, no 7. Dunwich also left £30 for his funeral at St Giles's and alms for the sick poor on the day of his burial.
22. Appendix I, article 11.
23. Rawcliffe, 'Hospital Nurses', pp. 50–1.
24. H.E. Salter, ed., *A Cartulary of the Hospital of St John the Baptist, III* (Oxford Historical Society, lxix, 1917), p. 3.
25. NRO, 30E1, no 12075.
26. Cullum, *Cremetts and Corrodies*, pp. 11–12.
27. Maxwell-Lyte and Dawes, *Register of Thomas Bekynton I*, pp. 288–30; Salter, *Cartulary of the Hospital of St John, III*, p. 3; and Rubin, *Charity and Community*, pp. 157–8, where the moral and practical implications of this policy are discussed. For continental examples see Brodman, *Charity and Welfare*, pp. 64–6.
28. Gilchrist, *Contemplation and Action*, pp. 51–2; Orme and Webster, *English Hospital*, pp. 29, 119. In his will Suffield left money to the city's *leprosaria*, and also, significantly, to lepers *attending his funeral*: NRO, NCR, 24B, no 2.
29. See above, pp. 86–8.
30. PRO, E40/11562.
31. NRO, NCR, 24B, no 48, *Liber Domus Dei*, fos 2r–2v. At St Thomas's, Southwark, intercessionary prayers were said 'before the sick every day' at the altar of the Blessed Virgin: Drucker, *Chartulary of the Hospital of St Thomas*, no 937.
32. Appendix I, article 32.
33. R.C. Pickett, *Mental Affliction and Church Law* (Ottawa, 1952), pp. 55–9. But see also Andrews and others, *History of Bethlem*, pp. 98–113.
34. NRO, NCC, reg. Harsyk, fos 5r–5v, and above, pp. 115–17.
35. Thomas, Sloane and Phillpotts, *Excavations at St Mary Spital*, pp. 31–3, 48, 66.
36. Even before the partitioning of infirmaries, bays provided some privacy: M. Thompson, *The Medieval Hall* (Aldershot, 1995), pp. 26–7.
37. NRO, NCR, 24A, GH Norwich accounts, 1415–1460, accounts for 1441–43.
38. Jessopp, *Visitations*, pp. 12–13.
39. NRO, NCR, 24A, GH Norwich accounts, 1465–1501.
40. Ibid., 1485–1509.
41. Ibid., 1510–1528.
42. Prescott, *English Medieval Hospital*, pp. 41–7.
43. Thomas, Sloane and Phillpotts, *Excavations at St Mary Spital*, p. 79; Carlin, *Medieval Southwark*, pp. 81–2.
44. As, for example, Richard Whittington's almshouse in London, where each resident had 'a chamber or small house with a chimney, latrine and other necessities', providing 'leisure to withdraw alone for the contemplation of the divine . . . without the clamour or disturbance of their fellows'. Significantly, no leper, madman or other person suffering from an 'intolerable disease' was to be admitted: Dugdale, *Monasticon Anglicanum*, vi (part 2), pp. 739–44. See also above, pp. 192–3.

45. W. Brown, *The Register of William Wickwane, Lord Archbishop of York, 1279–1285* (Surtees Society, cxiv, 1907), p. 138. For the partitioning of the brothers' dormitory, see above, pp. 63–4.
46. NRO, NCR, 24A, GH general accounts, 1465–1501, 1485–1508, passim.
47. Ibid., 1485–1508, 1510–1525, passim.
48. Caley and Hunter, *Valor Ecclesiasticus*, iii, pp. 291–2.
49. Ibid., pp. 291–2.
50. At the Augustinian priory of Barnwell, for example, strangers could not eat in the refectory without permission: Willis Clark, *Observances*, pp. 159–60. The hierarchy so apparent in lay households probably obtained at St Giles's by this date: F. Heal, *Hospitality in Early Modern England* (Oxford, 1990), pp. 30–6.
51. NRO, NCR, 24B, no 60; *CPR, 1446–1452*, p. 475.
52. *CPR, 1408–1413*, p. 187.
53. BL, Cottonian Ms Cleopatra C V, fo 25r.
54. Kerling, *Cartulary of St Bartholomew's Hospital*, nos 446, 583, 772, 1105–6; Drucker, *Chartulary of the Hospital of St Thomas*, nos 231, 306, 840.
55. NRO, NCR, 24B, no 48, *Liber Domus Dei*, fos 13r–13v, 24r, 50v, 59v.
56. Moore, *Book of the Foundation*, pp. 24–6. On his inspection of St Giles's, Beverley, in 1279, Archbishop Wickwane had assumed that the infirmary could be supported '*de elemosinis patrie*', with limited assistance from the hospital's funds: Brown, *Register of William Wickwane*, p. 138.
57. NRO, NCR, 24A, GH general accounts, 1485–1508.
58. See, for example, J.A.F. Thomson, 'Piety and Charity in Late Medieval England', *Journal of Ecclesiastical History*, xvi (1965), pp. 178–95, and C. Burgess, '"By Quick and by Dead": Wills and Pious Provision in Late Medieval Bristol', *EHR*, cii (1987), pp. 837–58, for a discussion of the limitations of testamentary evidence.
59. NRO, NCC, reg. Brosyard, fos 341v–42r.
60. NRO, NCR, 24A, GH Norwich accounts, 1415–1460.
61. NRO, NCC, reg. Jekkys, fos 84r–85r; PRO, PCC, 7 Blanyr.
62. NRO, NCR, 24A, GH general accounts, 1485–1508, account for 1505–7. See also GH general accounts for 1510–1525, accounts for 1513–14 (three pairs of sheets from Master Aldrich), 1514–15 (a pair from Master Ashby) and 1524–5 (a pair from Ralph Wilkyns, 'for the poor').
63. Jessopp, *Visitations*, pp. 106, 167, 225–6, 249, 295–6.
64. NRO, NCC, reg. Heydon, fos 183r–84r.
65. BL, Cottonian Ms Cleopatra C V, fo 24v. A point overlooked by Slack: *Poverty and Policy*, pp. 120–1.
66. Caley and Hunter, *Valor Ecclesiasticus*, iii, pp. 291–2.
67. For the terminology used to describe nurses, see Pelling, *Common Lot*, pp. 179–202. The unnamed servant first appears in NRO, NCR, 24A, GH Fobbing accounts, 1521–1528, mm. 6–7.
68. NRO, NCC, reg. Alpe, fos 49v–50v.
69. P.H. Cullum, '"And Hir Name Was Charite": Charitable Giving by and for Women in Late Medieval Yorkshire', in P.J.P. Goldberg, ed., *Woman is a Worthy Wight: Women and English Society* c. *1200–1500* (Stroud, 1992), pp. 199–200.
70. Rawcliffe, 'Hospital Nurses', p. 63. Female servants had not always been so welcome. The statutes compiled for St Leonard's hospital, York, in 1364, regarded them as a potential cause of 'sinister suspicion': Page, *VCH York III*, p. 339. Nor were they invariably cooperative. At the hospital of St Nicholas, Pontefract, it was found in 1464 that the two servants (a man and a woman) who received corrodies in return for looking after the other residents had withdrawn their labour: Leach, *Early Yorkshire Schools, II*, p. 7.
71. Rawcliffe, 'Hospital Nurses', pp. 62–3; NRO, NCR, 24A, GH general accounts, 1510–1525, account for 1509–10.
72. J.B. Trapp, ed., *The Complete Works of St Thomas More, IX, The Apologia* (New Haven and London, 1979), p. 105.
73. NRO, NCR, 24A, GH accounts 1306–1398, account for 1396–7. In the following year this allowance came to 50*s* 3*d*.
74. See above, p. 21.
75. For later attitudes to the older female healer, see M. Pelling, 'Thoroughly Resented? Older Women and the Medical Role in Early Modern London', in L. Hunter and S. Hutton, eds, *Women, Science and Medicine* (Stroud, 1997), pp. 62–88.
76. E. Coyecque, *L'Hôtel Dieu de Paris au Moyen Age* (2 vols, Paris, 1889–91), i, pp. 33–4; Appendix I, article 5.
77. Willis Clark, *Observances*, pp. 153–5, 161–3, 187–9, 193–5.
78. Page, *VCH York, III*, p. 339; Rubin, *Charity and Community*, p. 162; Raine, *Register of Walter Gray*, p. 181.
79. Coyecque, *L'Hôtel Dieu*, p. 179. For the Savoy, see above, pp. 217–18.
80. Rawcliffe, 'Hospital Nurses', pp. 54–7.

81. See, for example, N. Roper, W.W. Tierney and A.J. Logan, *The Elements of Nursing* (second edn, Edinburgh, 1985), passim; M. Walsh, *Models in Clinical Nursing* (London, 1991), pp. 53–89. I am grateful to Col. Eric Gruber von Arni, RRC, for providing me with such striking examples of the *regimen sanitatis* in its twentieth-century format.
82. Rawcliffe, 'Hospital Nurses', p. 62; above, pp. 104–5.
83. Saunier, '*Le Pauvre Malade*', p. 37, and Chapter III, passim.
84. Appendix I, articles 5 and 11.
85. Appendix I, articles 10, 32 and 28 respectively.
86. NRO, NCR, 24B, no 2.
87. NRO, Box 30E1, no 12105.
88. NRO, Phi 311.
89. Page, *VCH York, III*, p. 339; Jamison, *Hospital of St Katherine*, p. 29; above, p. 31.
90. *CIMisc., 1307–1349*, no 293.
91. Cullum, *Cremetts and Corrodies*, pp. 22–8; Harper-Bill, *Medieval Hospitals of Bury St Edmunds*, pp. 16–17, 146–51; New College, Oxford, Ms 3691, fos 92r–92v.
92. Heath Barnum, *Dives and Pauper*, i (part 2), p. 195.
93. A point made by Harvey, *Living and Dying*, p. 194, in the context of monastic corrodies, which are discussed pp. 179–209.
94. As at the hospital of St John the Baptist, Winchester, where the distinction between patient and carer remained blurred: Keene, *Survey of Medieval Winchester, II*, p. 816.
95. Harper-Bill, *Medieval Hospitals of Bury St Edmunds*, p. 150.
96. Pelling, 'Old Age, Poverty and Disability', in *Common Lot*, pp. 141–4; eadem, 'Illness among the Poor', pp. 274–5.
97. NRO, NCR, 24D, GH Cringleford accounts, 1461–1482, m. 16.
98. NRO, NCR, 24A, GH accounts, 1306–1398. Another corrody was sold to an anonymous purchaser for about £10 in 1330–1.
99. Rawcliffe, *Hospitals of Medieval Norwich*, pp. 66–7, 72.
100. Caley and Hunter, *Valor Ecclesiasticus*, iii, pp. 291–2, record an annual stipend of 26*s* per sister. The sixteenth-century accounts (to 1527) budgeted 17*s* 4*d* each: NRO, NCR, 24A, GH general accounts, 1485–1508, 1510–1525, passim.
101. *CPR, 1547–1548*, p. 17; E. Phillips, 'God's House, Norwich, 1500–1600' (University of East Anglia, MA thesis, 1997), p. 29.
102. Stevenson, *Records of the Borough of Nottingham I*, p. 33.
103. See above, pp. 31, 38, 59–60.
104. NRO, NCC, reg. Alblaster, fos 107v–8r; NCR, 24A, GH general accounts 1485–1508, account of the receiver general for 1500–1.
105. NRO, DCN 69/2, fos 68r–68v, 73v–74r. The two had arrived at St Giles's together in 1527: NCR, 24A, GH general accounts, 1510–1525, passim.
106. NRO, NCR, 24A, GH general accounts, 1485–1508, 1510–1527.
107. Oliva, *Convent and Community*, pp. 174–83.
108. NRO, NCC, reg. Heydon, fos 196r–96v.
109. Ibid., reg. Harsyk, fo 51.
110. PRO, PCC, 23 Stockton.
111. NRO, NCC, reg. Surflete, fos 124v–25r; reg. Herman, fo 5r.
112. NRO, NCR, 24A, GH Norwich accounts, 1415–1460; 24D, GH Cringleford accounts, 1461–1482, m. 8.
113. NRO, NCR, 24A, GH general accounts, 1485–1508, accounts for 1505–6, 1506–7.
114. NRO, NCC reg. Jekkys, fos 100r–1v, 251r–52v.
115. Davis, *Paston Letters*, i, no 230; NRO, NCC, reg. Popy, fos 272v–74v; PRO, PCC, 26 Blanyr, 9 Jankyn. See also the will of the Norwich grocer, John Reynold (1499), who left each sister 6*d* a year for three years: Lambeth Palace Library, reg. Morton, II, fo 44r.
116. NRO, NCC, reg. Spyltymber, fos 42v–46r. See also the wills of William Ashwell, 1457 (PRO, PCC, 12 Stockton), Agnes Gilbert, 1466 (NRO, NCC, reg. Jekkys, fos 49r–50r), John Wells, 1495 (PRO, PCC, 27 Vox).
117. NRO, NCR, NPD, box 12, parish of St Vedast, no 51.
118. Brown, *Register of William Wickwane*, pp. 137–8.
119. New College, Oxford, Ms 3691, fo 92r; Page, *VCH London, I*, pp. 520–4.
120. Appendix I, article 18.
121. Page, *VCH York, III*, pp. 337–8; PRO, C270/23/12.

122. C. Harper-Bill, 'The Labourer Worthy of His Hire? Complaints about Diet in Late Medieval English Monasteries', in idem and C.M. Barron, eds, *The Church in Pre-Reformation English Society* (Woodbridge, 1985), pp. 95–106.
123. L.B. Larking, ed., *The Knights Hospitallers in England: The Report of Prior Philip de Thame* (Camden Society, lxv, 1857), pp. 61–2; *CIMsc., 1377–1388*, no 180.
124. Cullum and Goldberg, 'Charitable Provision', pp. 24–39.
125. *HMC, Eighth Report, Part I*, p. 628.
126. This is roughly similar to the allowance for scholars at St John's hospital, Exeter, in the 1330s, when 5*d* a week was allocated to each boy for fish, meat and bread, in addition to a daily dish of pottage: Orme and Webster, *English Hospital*, pp. 235–6.
127. Caley and Hunter, *Valor Ecclesiasticus*, iii, pp. 291–2.
128. PRO, PCC 35 Horne.
129. See, for example, NRO, NCR, 24A, GH general accounts, 1465–1501, accounts for 1465–6, 1478–9, 1479–80.
130. Ibid., 1465–1501; and see above, p. 261.
131. Harvey, *Living and Dying*, Chapter II, passim.
132. NRO, NCR, 24C, GH Calthorpe accounts, 1315–1376, m. 3.
133. See above, p. 52.
134. F.J. Furnivall, ed., *Early English Meals and Manners* (EETS, xxxii, 1868), pp. 5–7. See also, Willis Clark, *Observances*, p. 163.
135. Archives of St George's Chapel, Windsor, Mss xv 37.8, 21, 25, 27, 33, passim.
136. J.C. Drummond and A. Wilbraham, *The Englishman's Food: Five Centuries of English Diet* (new edn, London, 1991), pp. 68–9: Thomas, Sloane and Phillpotts, *Excavations at St Mary Spital*, p. 62. It was believed, following Galen, that fresh fruit would raise the body's temperature and thus induce fever.
137. Furnivall, *Early English Meals*, p. 46.
138. Keynes, *Works of Sir Thomas Browne*, i, pp. 424–5.
139. B. Ayers and others, *Waterfront Excavation and Thetford Ware Production, Norwich* (East Anglian Archaeology, xvii, 1983), pp. 33–4.
140. NRO, NCR, 24A, GH general accounts, 1510–1525; above, pp. 48–9.
141. See Dyer, *Standards of Living*, pp. 49–70, for interesting comparisons.
142. Archives of St George's Chapel, Windsor, xv 37.8 (10 Henry VII), fos 3r–4r.
143. Harvey, *Living and Dying*, pp. 62–70.
144. NRO, NCR, 24A, GH general accounts, 1485–1508, account for 1502–3.
145. Harvey, *Living and Dying*, pp. 35–6.
146. See, for example, NRO, NCR, 24A, GH general accounts, 1485–1508, account for 1505–6.
147. Harvey, *Living and Dying*, pp. 46–51; Rawcliffe, *Medicine and Society*, pp. 149–52; Willis Clark, *Observances*, p. 203; Dyer, *Standards of Living*, pp. 62–3.
148. Dyer, *Standards of Living*, pp. 62–3.
149. NRO, NCR, 24A, GH general accounts 1465–1501, account for 1465–6; above, pp. 100–1.
150. Ibid., GH Norwich accounts, 1415–1460, account for 1435–6; above, pp. 148–9.
151. Ibid., GH general accounts, 1510–1525, account for 1513–14.
152. Atkin, Carter and Evans, *Excavations in Norwich*, p. 69; Ayers and others, *Waterfront Excavation*, p. 57.
153. NRO, NCR, 24A, GH general accounts, 1465–1501, account of the steward, 1500–1.
154. Ibid., GH accounts 1306–1398. Annual expenditure is shown in Chapter III, Table A.
155. If expenditure of £39 on land is deducted, the percentage rises from 47.9 to 62.1.
156. If expenditure of £36 on land is deducted the percentage rises from 40.2 to 49.0.
157. Dyer, *Standards of Living*, pp. 55–7; Harvey, *Living and Dying*, p. 34.
158. Brown and Hopkins, *Perspective of Wages and Prices*, p. 29; Hudson and Tingey, *Records of the City of Norwich*, ii, p. xcvii.
159. NRO, NCR, 24A, GH general accounts, 1465–1501, 1485–1508, 1510–1525. Annual expenditure is given in Chapter III, Table B.
160. Jessopp, *Visitations*, pp. 102, 112, 167, 264, 279–80, 287, 289, 291, 203, 250.
161. B.M.S. Campbell and others, *A Medieval Capital and its Grain Supply* (Historical Geography Research Series, xxx, 1993), pp. 191–2.
162. Raine, *Register of Walter Gray*, p. 181. The statutes of 1244 assumed that 200 two-pound loaves could be baked from a quarter of wheat.
163. Jewson, *Great Hospital*, p. 35.
164. Harvey, *Living and Dying*, pp. 58, 64–6; Dyer, *Standards of Living*, pp. 57–8; Campbell, *Medieval Capital*, p. 26.

165. Harvey, *Living and Dying*, p. 58; P. Clark, *The English Alehouse: A Social History 1200–1830* (London, 1983), p. 109.
166. NRO, DCN 79/3–5, Holme Street court leet, 19, 20 and 22 Henry VI; NCR, 24A, GH Norwich accounts, 1415–1460, 1465–1501, passim.
167. NRO, NCR, 24A, GH general accounts, 1465–1501, 1485–1508, 1510–1525.
168. Rawcliffe, *Hospitals of Medieval Norwich*, pp. 83–4.
169. Harvey, *Living and Dying*, p. 50.
170. NRO, NCR, 24A, GH general accounts, 1485–1508, 1510–1525.
171. Brown, *Register of William Wickwane*, p. 137.
172. Orme and Webster, *English Hospital*, p. 52. See also, Lawrence, *Medieval Monasticism*, pp. 178–81.
173. Willis Clark, *Observances*, pp. 223–31.
174. Raine, *Register of Walter Gray*, p. 180.
175. Meade, *Kepier Hospital*, p. 5; Appendix I, articles 4, 21 and 23.
176. NRO, Box 30E1, no 12077. Similar trends are apparent at St Leonard's, York: Cullum, 'Hospitals and Charitable Provision', p. 101.
177. NRO, NCR, 24A, GH accounts 1306–1398, passim.
178. Ferriby was also rent collector in Norwich during Jullys's mastership: Ibid., GH Norwich accounts, 1485–1509, account for 1502–3.
179. Ibid., GH general accounts, 1465–1501, steward's accounts for 1498–9 and 1500–1; general accounts 1485–1508 (Fualeyn was briefly replaced as butler in 1502–3) and 1510–1525, passim; GH Norwich accounts, 1485–1509, 1510–1528, passim.
180. Ibid., GH Norwich accounts, 1510–1528, account for 1515–16; NCC, reg. Popy, fos 272v–74v.
181. NRO, NCC, reg. Surflete, fos 60v–61r; reg. Brosyard, fo 288v. See above, pp. 128–9.
182. Woodman, 'Hardley, Norfolk', p. 204; Harvey, *English Medieval Architects*, pp. 102–3. See above, pp. 48, 58–9.
183. NRO, NCR, 24A, GH Norwich accounts, 1415–1460, passim.
184. Ibid., 1485–1509, 1510–1528, passim.

VII. THE DISSOLUTION

1. See, for example, B. Pullan, 'Catholics and the Poor in Early Modern Europe', *TRHS*, fifth series, xxvi (1976), pp. 15–34; Geremek, 'Criminalité, Vagabondage, Pauperisme', pp. 337–75. N. Zemon Davis, 'Poor Relief, Humanism and Heresy: The Case of Lyon', *Studies in Medieval and Renaissance History*, v (1968), pp. 215–75. And for a revisionist view, a more recent collection of essays edited by O.P. Grell and A. Cunningham, *Health Care and Poor Relief in Protestant Europe 1500–1700* (London, 1997).
2. As an introduction to a large, and growing, body of literature, see Flynn, *Sacred Charity*, passim; R.M. Kingdon, 'Social Welfare in Calvin's Geneva', *American Historical Review*, lxxvi (1971), pp. 50–69; M.K. McIntosh, 'Local Responses to the Poor in Late Medieval and Tudor England', *Continuity and Change*, iii (1988), pp. 209–45; P. Slack, 'Social Policy and the Constraints of Government 1547–58', in J. Loach and R. Tittler, eds, *The Mid Tudor Polity, c. 1540–1560* (London, 1980), pp. 94–115.
3. O.P. Grell, 'The Protestant Imperative of Christian Care and Neighbourly Love', in idem and A, Cunningham, eds, *Health Care and Poor Relief in Protestant Europe 1500–1700* (London, 1997), pp. 50–3.
4. Slack, *Poverty and Policy*, p. 13.
5. Owst, *Literature and the Pulpit*, p. 177. Such complaints were neither new nor confined to England. Writing in the 1220s, Jacques de Vitry made a far more vitriolic attack on corrupt practices in French hospitals: Hinnebusch, *Historia Occidentalis*, pp. 148–9.
6. Hudson, *English Wycliffite Writings*, pp. 135–7; Orme and Webster, *English Hospital*, pp. 134–5.
7. Strachey, *Rotuli Parliamentorum*, iv, pp. 19–20. These concerns were not unique to England: see Imbert, *Histoire des Hôpitaux*, pp. 69–72; and Mollat, *Poor in the Middle Ages*, p. 181.
8. Luders, *Statutes of the Realm*, ii, 2 Hen. V, Stat. I, cap. i; Wilkins, *Concilia*, iii, p. 365; Strachey, *Rotuli Parliamentorum*, iv, pp. 80–1.
9. Orme and Webster, *English Hospital*, pp. 135–6.
10. Carlin, 'Medieval English Hospitals', p. 23, gives the total percentage of almshouse foundations as 67, but this is corrected in Gilchrist, 'Christian Bodies and Souls', p. 102. See also McIntosh, 'Local Responses', pp. 209–45, for an overall survey.
11. P. Cullum, 'For Pore People Harberles': What Was the Function of the Maisondieu?', in D.J. Clayton, R.G. Davies and P. McNiven, eds, *Trade, Devotion and Governance: Papers in Later Medieval History* (Stroud, 1994), pp. 43, 46, 49, 51; Dugdale, *Monasticon Anglicanum*, vi (part 2), pp. 739–43; Page, *VCH Nottingham, II*,

pp. 174–5; J.C. Hodgson, 'The "*Domus Dei*" of Newcastle: Otherwise St Katherine's Hospital of the Sandhill', *Archaeologia Aeliana*, third series, xiv (1917), pp. 191–220. See also, Roskell, Clark and Rawcliffe, *House of Commons 1386–1421*, iii, pp. 401–3 (Holme), iv, pp. 92–3 (Plumtree), 596–8 (Thornton), 846–9 (Whittington).

12. M. Davies, 'The Tailors of London: Corporate Charity in the Late Medieval Town', in R. Archer, ed., *Crown, Government and People in the Fifteenth Century* (Stroud, 1995), pp. 182–9; Cullum, 'Hospitals and Charitable Provision', pp. 368–73 and appendix.
13. Pullan, 'Catholics and the Poor', p. 19, argues that this phenomenon transcended religious barriers – a view amply supported by evidence from pre-Reformation England.
14. Hull, with a population of some 2,300 adults in 1377, had at least fifteen medieval almshouses: Cullum, 'Hospitals and Charitable Provision', Appendix.
15. Cullum and Goldberg, 'Charitable Provision', pp. 31–2.
16. Rawcliffe, *Hospitals of Medieval Norwich*, pp. 146–9.
17. Cullum, '"For Poor People Harberles"', p. 38; eadem, 'Hospitals and Charitable Provision', Appendix; Price and Ponsford, *St Bartholomew's Hospital*, p. 202.
18. R. Gilchrist and M. Oliva, *Religious Women in Medieval East Anglia* (Studies in East Anglian History, i, 1993) pp. 71–3 and Table 3.
19. C.M. Woolgar, ed., *Household Accounts from Medieval England* (Records of Social and Economic History, new series, xvii, 1992), pp. 200–27, (xviii, 1993), pp. 577–9.
20. According to Norman Tanner's analysis of wills made by the laymen and women of Norwich between 1370 and 1532, 95 per cent of testators put their parish church first among their pious bequests: idem, *Church in Late Medieval Norwich*, pp. 136, 223.
21. S.B. Meech, ed., *The Book of Margery Kempe* (EETS, cxxiv, 1904), p. 56. This view had been advanced by St Ambrose (d. 397) and was subsequently given practical expression in the *Forma Subventionus Pauperum*, produced at Ypres in 1525: B. Tierney, 'Decretists', pp. 360–73. See also above, pp. 215–17.
22. Tanner, *Church in Late Medieval Norwich*, pp. 243–4; NRO, NCC, reg. Hyrning, fos 148v–50r.
23. An argument advanced for England as a whole by Rubin, 'Imagining Medieval Hospitals', p. 23.
24. Mollat, *Poor in the Middle Ages*, pp. 267–75.
25. W.K. Jordan, *Philanthropy in England 1480–1660* (London, 1959), pp. 58–9, 114–15. For a discussion of the critical response to Jordan, see, for example, J.H. Hadwin, 'Deflating Philanthropy', *EconHR*, second series, xxi (1978), pp. 105–17.
26. Trapp, *Complete Works of St Thomas More, IX, The Apologia*, p. 104; J.W. Clay, ed., *Yorkshire Monasteries Suppression Papers* (Yorkshire Archaeological Society, xlviii, 1912), p. 48.
27. W.D.R. Jones, *The Tudor Commonwealth 1529–1559* (London, 1970), pp. 118–19.
28. J. Gairdner, ed., *The Historical Collections of a Citizen of London* (Camden Society, new series, xvii, 1876), pp. viii–ix; T. Astle, ed., *The Will of Henry VII* (London, 1785), p. 13.
29. Cited by E.P. de G. Chaney, '"Philanthropy in Italy": English Observations on Italian Hospitals, 1545–1789', in T. Riis, ed., *Aspects of Poverty in Early Modern Europe* (Florence, 1981), p. 189. The number 110 derives from the *Valor Ecclesiasticus*: Kreider, *English Chantries*, pp. 8–9.
30. Jordan, *Philanthropy in England*, pp. 114–15, 258–9. These views are replicated, for example, in B.G. Gale, 'The Dissolution and the Revolution in London Hospital Facilities', *Medical History*, xi (1967), pp. 91–100.
31. Jessopp, *Visitations*, pp. 264–8. The finances of the priory are discussed in Virgoe, 'Estates of Norwich Cathedral Priory', pp. 339–59.
32. Rawcliffe, *Hospitals of Medieval Norwich*, pp. 83–5; Caley and Hunter, *Valor Ecclesiasticus*, ii, pp. 489–94; NRO, DCN 1/1/22; Oliva, *Convent and Community*, pp. 143–5.
33. W.T. Mellows and P.I. King, eds, *The Book of William Morton, Almoner of Peterborough Monastery 1448–1467* (Northamptonshire Record Society, xvi, 1951), pp. xxv–xxviii.
34. Pound, *Tudor and Stuart Norwich*, p. 141. According to the infirmarer, by 1532 the chief beneficiaries of monastic largesse were canine rather than human: Jessopp, *Visitations*, p. 264. This complaint is not noted by Heal, *Hospitality in Early Modern England*, p. 244, who takes a more sanguine view of the provision of relief in Norwich diocese.
35. See above, p. 173; and Rawcliffe, *Hospitals of Medieval Norwich*, pp. 69–82.
36. Caley and Hunter, *Valor Ecclesiasticus*, iii, p. 368. And see above, p. 136.
37. Rawcliffe, *Hospitals of Medieval Norwich*, pp. 143–6.
38. Jessopp, *Visitations*, pp. 206–7; Carlin, *Medieval Southwark*, p. 84.
39. Jessopp, *Visitations*, pp. 271–2.
40. Ibid., pp. 285–9.
41. Thompson, *Hospital of the Annunciation of St Mary in the Newarke*, pp. 183–93.

42. Thomas Cappe, the master, and the six brethren of St Giles's took the oath on 30 August 1534: PRO, E25/94/3.
43. Luders, *Statutes of the Realm*, iii, 26 Hen. VIII, cap. iii.
44. Caley and Hunter, *Valor Ecclesiasticus*, iii, pp. 291–2.
45. William Allen, *A Defense and Declaration of the Catholike Churchies Doctrine Touching Purgatory* (John Latius, Antwerp, 1565), fos 132r–32v.
46. See, for example, Burgess, '"By Quick and by Dead"', p. 857.
47. *BRUC*, p. 123. His career is described in Appendix III.
48. D. MacCulloch, *Suffolk and the Tudors: Politics and Religion in an English County 1500–1600* (Oxford, 1986), Chapter IV, passim.
49. E.D. Stone and B. Cozens-Hardy, eds, *Norwich Consistory Court Depositions, 1499–1512 and 1518–1530* (NRS, x, 1938), nos. 324, 339, 344, 366.
50. NRO, NCC, reg. Puntyng, fos 169r–71r.
51. Blomefield, *Norfolk*, iv, pp. 173, 399.
52. *LPFD*, xii (1), no. 795 (33). The regnal year of this grant is mistakenly given here as 28 Henry VIII (April 1536–7), but the see was vacant in March 1536, and Codde was in office as master by June: NRO, NCR, NPD, box 6, parish of St Martin at Palace, unnumbered indenture 10 June 1536. Codde evidently obtained the mastership through the auspices of the conservative, Robert Sherburne, as the award is endorsed 'the bishop of Chichester, for an hospital in Norwich for the prior of Pentney that was lately'.
53. Jessopp, *Visitations*, pp. xxviii–ix, 154, 251, 312; *LPFD*, x, nos 364 (p. 143), 563.
54. *LPFD*, xii (1), no. 512; F. Wormald, 'The Rood of Bromholm', *Journal of the Warburg Institute*, i (1937–8), pp. 31–45.
55. NRO, NCC, reg. Hyll, fos 280r–82v.
56. Grace, *Gild of St George*, pp. 141, 143, 145, 148–9; T. Hawes, ed., *An Index to Norwich City Officers, 1453–1835* (NRS, lii, 1986), p. 40.
57. Grace, *Gild of St George*, p. 151.
58. Kreider, *English Chantries*, p. 147.
59. S.E. Lehmberg, *The Reformation of Cathedrals: Cathedrals in English Society 1485–1603* (Princeton, 1988), pp. 81–2.
60. R.A. Houlbrooke, 'Refoundation and Reformation, 1538–1628', in Atherton and others, *Norwich Cathedral*, pp. 507–10.
61. NRO, NCR, 16A, Norwich Assembly Proceedings, 1491–1553, fos 165v–66r, 171v, 177v, 179v. The Dominicans had been subject to intimidation. They complained about 'light persons breaking their glass windows': Cattermole, 'Schools in Medieval Norwich', p. 25.
62. S.T. Bindoff, ed., *The History of Parliament: The House of Commons 1509–1558* (3 vols, London, 1982), iii, pp. 383–5.
63. *LPFD*, xv, no 832 (72); Blomefield, *Norfolk*, iv, p. 339.
64. NRO, NCR, 18A, Chamberlains' Account Book, 1541–1550, fos 122v–23v; Blomefield, *Norfolk*, iv, pp. 339–42; H. Sutermeister, *The Norwich Blackfriars: A Historical Guide to the Friary and its Buildings up to the Present Day* (Norwich, 1977), pp. 8–9.
65. Cattermole, 'Schools in Medieval Norwich, pp. 25–6.
66. See above, pp. 20–1, 124–6, 177.
67. Catternole, 'Schools in Medieval Norwich', pp. 19–22, 39. Augustine Steward, MP for Norwich in 1539, and one of Cromwell's leading local supporters, exploited the political situation to improve the terms of an award made earlier, in 1524, by Cardinal Wolsey. This had already placed some of the exempt liberties (including Holme Street) under the jurisdiction of the city: N. Tanner, 'The Cathedral and the City', in Atherton and others, *Norwich Cathedral*, p. 267; Houlbrooke, 'Refoundation and Reformation', pp. 524–5; M.C. McClendon, *The Quiet Reformation: Magistrates and the Emergence of Protestantism in Tudor Norwich* (Stanford, 1999), p. 59
68. NRO, NCR, NPD, box 6, parish of St Martin at Palace, unnumbered indenture of 10 June 1536.
69. PRO, SP1/159, fo 47. The surrender was dispatched, quite literally, by return. Kreider, *English Chantries*, Appendix I, citing *LPFD*, xv, no 506, dates this letter 1540, but only the day and month [12 April] appear in the original.
70. Orme and Webster, *English Hospital*, p. 157.
71. As at St Thomas's, Southwark: Carlin, *Medieval Southwark*, p. 84.
72. *Memoranda, References and Documents Relating to the Royal Hospitals of the City of London* (London, 1863), Appendix, no 1.
73. Carlin, *Medieval Southwark*, p. 84; S. Brigden, *London and the Reformation* (Oxford, 1989), p. 473. According to Thomas Cranmer, Henry VIII initially took great exception to the proposal, advanced by the more evangelically minded of his bishops, that some monastic property confiscated in 1536 should go to 'the building of hospitals, where poor and impotent people should have been sufficiently provided for with physicians and surgeons, which should have ministered physic and surgery freely, not only to them but also to all other poor folk within the realm': J.E. Cox, ed., *Miscellaneous Writings and Letters of Thomas Cranmer* (Parker Society, 1846), p. 16.

74. Orme and Webster, *English Hospital*, pp. 156–8; Kreider, *English Chantries*, p. 65.
75. Luders, *Statutes of the Realm*, iii, 31 Hen. VIII, cap. ix; J.J. Scarisbrick, *The Reformation and the English People* (London, 1984), p. 78, describes these words as a 'lure'.
76. Orme and Webster, *English Hospital*, pp. 158–9.
77. Houlbrooke, 'Refoundation and Reformation', p. 509. These were later to be 'men oppressed by poverty and afflicted with want, broken and mutilated in war, stricken with old age or otherwise enfeebled and reduced to helplessness'. Yet since their duties included bell-ringing and sweeping and cleaning the church, they must have been reasonably active: J.F. Williams and B. Cozens-Hardy, eds, *Extracts from the Two Earliest Minutes Books of the Dean and Chapter of Norwich Cathedral 1566–1649* (NRS, xxiv, 1953), p. 11.
78. NRO, DCN 48/26A/1.
79. W.K. Jordan, *The Charities of Rural England 1480–1660* (London, 1961), pp. 119–20 lists individual bequests made to the hospital between 1480–1540 and 1550–71.
80. Rawcliffe, *Hospitals of Medieval Norwich*, p. 78.
81. Ibid., pp. 47–55; NRO, 16A, Norwich Assembly Proceedings, 1434–1491, fo 95v.
82. For the general impact of the pox on hospital provision, see J. Arrizabalaga, J. Henderson and R. French, *The Great Pox: The French Disease in Renaissance Europe* (New Haven and London, 1997), pp. 155–232.
83. See, for example, PRO, PCC, 28 Holder (will of Gregory Clerk, 1517), for a reference to each 'lasar man, woman and child' in the five hospitals at the gates. NRO, NCC, reg. Jekkys, fos 47v–49r (will of John Gilbert, 1466), 49r–50r (will of Ann Gilbert, 1466), 100r–1v (will of John Northalis, 1468), refer likewise to 'sick men, women and children', and 84r–85r (will of Richard Hosst, 1465) to 'euery seke howse with lascers'.
84. NRO, MSC 1/5.
85. Hudson and Tingey, *Records of the City of Norwich*, ii, pp. 169–70.
86. Here the master was 'an heile and clene man with dieurs [various] servaunts' (ibid.), a remark which suggests that at this date (but not for much longer) the keeper himself was supposed to be a leper or otherwise disabled.
87. In 1568, for example, the bishop of Norwich and the mayor together expelled John Bradley from the keepership of the leper house of SS Mary and Clement: Blomefield, *Norfolk*, iv, p. 461.
88. M. Pelling, 'Healing the Sick Poor: Social Policy and Disability in Norwich 1550–1640', *Medical History*, xxix (1985), pp. 126–7. Pelling notes that in London five of the ten old leper houses were officially attached to St Bartholomew's after its refoundation, whereas in Norwich the links were less formal. See above, pp. 222–3.
89. Cullum, 'Hospitals and Charitable Provision', pp. 393–4. D. Palliser, *Tudor York* (Oxford, 1979), p. 222, notes that thirteen of the city's twenty-two hospitals closed between 1530 and 1560.
90. As, for example, NRO, NCR, NPD, box 3, parish of St Crouch, no 3; box 9, parish of St Peter Mancroft, no 381; box 10, parish of SS Simon and Jude, no 20; box 12, parish of St Vedast, no 52; 20D, GH Lease Book, 1530–1645, fos 28v–31r, 32r.
91. NRO, NCR, NPD, box 2, parish of St Augustine, no 31.
92. Each of these men was a lessee of hospital estates at the time of the city's take-over in 1547: *CPR, 1547–1548*, pp. 13–17.
93. Kreider, *English Chantries*, p. 156. This was no new phenomenon. In 1325 it was reported that successive masters of the same hospital had 'despoiled the goods of the aforesaid house, and wasted the buildings and reduced the alms to nothing, and converted the outgoings of the house to their own profit': Stevenson, *Records of the Borough of Nottingham*, I, pp. 92–3.
94. PRO, C1/965/58–59. The petitions are undated, but the two chaplains, John Fysher (d. 1567/8) and Robert Dowe (d. 1552), were later retained by the city to serve in the new poor house. Dowe had witnessed Codde's letter of surrender to the Crown (PRO, SP1/159, fo 47), along with Edward Osborne and John Blomeville, who then resigned or retired. Fysher was new to the staff in 1532 (Jessopp, *Visitations*, p. 271), but, unlike Dowe, is not named in the *Valor Ecclesiasticus* (iii, pp. 291–2) of 1535 or in the deed of surrender.
95. Luders, *Statutes of the Realm*, iii, 37 Hen. VIII, cap. iv.
96. Edward Hall, *Chronicle Containing the History of England* (London, 1809), pp. 864–6.
97. Scarisbrick, *Reformation and the English People*, pp. 113–19.
98. P. Slack, The *Impact of Plague in Tudor and Stuart England* (London, 1985), pp. 27, 127–8; NRO, NCR, 16A, Norwich Assembly Proceedings, 1491–1553, fo 188r; 18A, Chamberlains' Account Book, 1541–1550, fos 122v–23v.
99. NRO, NCR, 16A, Mayor's Court Book, 1540–1549, p. 265.
100. See, for example, Zemon Davis, 'Poor Relief, Humanism and Heresy', p. 236.
101. NRO, NCR, 16A, Mayor's Court Book, 1540–1549, p. 309.
102. Bindoff, *House of Commons 1509–1588*, iii, p. 209; PRO, PCC, 12 Tashe. Jordan, *Charities of Rural England*, pp. 102–3, describes in some detail the charitable bequests made by him and his wife, Katherine. See also above, pp. 236–7.

103. NRO, NCR, 16A, Mayor's Court Book, 1540–1549, p. 313. At exactly the same time, the Assembly decided to pass an order to prevent the owners of tenements in Norwich letting them 'unto persons pore resortyng to this citie to lyue here only by beggyng': ibid., Norwich Assembly Proceedings, 1491–1553, fo 193r.
104. NRO, NCR, 18A, Chamberlains' Account Book, 1537–1547, fos 231r–31v.
105. Bindoff, *House of Commons 1509–1588*, i, pp. 593–4. The importance of parliamentary lobbying for the acquisition of hospitals was clearly understood. See, for example, A. Raine, ed., *York Civic Records*, V (Yorkshire Archaeological Society, cx, 1946), p. 93.
106. Bindoff, *House of Commons 1509–1588*, i, pp. 698–9.
107. Ibid., ii, pp. 575–6.
108. NRO, NCR, 16A, Mayor's Court Book, 1540–1549, p. 319.
109. MacCulloch, *Suffolk and the Tudors*, pp. 76–7.
110. *CPR, 1547–1548*, p. 15; Bindoff, *House of Commons 1509–1588*, ii, pp. 221–2.
111. Bindoff, *House of Commons 1509–1588*, ii, pp. 296–7.
112. Ibid., iii, pp. 354–6; Blomefield, *Norfolk*, iii, p. 279; Jordan, *Charities of Rural England*, p. 117.
113. Bindoff, *House of Commons 1509–1558*, iii, pp. 653–65; T.H. Swales, 'The Redistribution of Monastic Lands in Norfolk at the Dissolution', *Norfolk Archaeology*, xxxiv (1969), pp. 28–9.
114. NRO, NCR, 16A, Mayor's Court Book, 1540–1549, pp. 321–2.
115. Raine, *York Civic Records, V*, pp. 75–6; R.H. Skaife, ed., *The Register of the Guild of Corpus Christi* (Surtees Society, lvii, 1872), pp. xii–xiii.
116. NRO, NCR, 16A, Mayor's Court Book, 1540–1549, p. 338.
117. NRO, NCC, reg. Hyll, fos 280r–82v.
118. Ibid., reg. Colman, fos 431r–37r; McClendon, *Quiet Reformation*, p. 140; Blomefield, *Norfolk*, iv, pp. 97–8. The will was proved on 20 June 1559.
119. *LPFD*, xxi (2), no 134. Within five days the royal council in London had despatched to the councillors then with the King 'a note of the hospital at Norwich for which Mr Shaxton sues': ibid., no 155.
120. J. Venn, *Caius College* (London, 1901), p. 34; BL, Cottonian Ms Cleopatra E V, fo 389v. See also, C. Brooke, *A History of Gonville and Caius College* (Woodbridge, 1985), pp. 16, 49.
121. NRO, NCR, 1C, rolls 19A, rot. 6, 19B, rot. 4.
122. Details of Shaxton's academic career, which culminated in 1531 in the award of a doctorate in divinity, may be found in J. Venn and J.A. Venn, *Alumni Cantabrigiensis, I, from the Earliest Times to 1751* (4 vols, Cambridge, 1922–7), p. 54; J. Venn, *Biographical History of Gonville and Caius College 1349–1713* (Cambridge, 1897), p. 19. Buttes's influence and circle are discussed by M. Dowling, *Humanism in the Age of Henry VIII* (London, 1986), pp. 66–7; and eadem, 'The Gospel and the Court: Reformation under Henry VIII', in eadem and P. Lake, eds, *Protestantism and the National Church in Sixteenth Century England* (London, 1987), pp. 48–53.
123. *LPFD*, iv (3), no 6247. In June 1534 Shaxton wrote to Thomas Cromwell expressing his delight at being called upon to preach on the royal supremacy, and urging him to 'go on stil from one thing to another . . . til the usurped power of that man of Rome be clean abolished and put out of the hearts of the King's subjects': J. Strype, ed., *Ecclesiastical Memorials* (3 vols, Oxford, 1822), i (part 2), p. 204.
124. *LPFD*, v, no 297.
125. M. Dowling, 'Anne Boleyn and Reform', *Journal of Ecclesiastical History*, xxxv (1984), pp. 37–8; R.A. Houlbrooke, 'Persecution of Heresy and Protestantism in the Diocese of Norwich under Henry VIII', *Norfolk Archaeology*, xxxv (1970–2), pp. 313–14; McClendon, *Quiet Reformation*, pp. 62–3, 66–7.
126. Simon Fish, *A Supplicacyon for the Beggers*, ed. F.J. Furnivall (EETS, extra series, xiii, 1871), pp. 13–14. See also, Dowling, 'Anne Boleyn and Reform', p. 36, and E.W. Ives, *Anne Boleyn* (Oxford, 1986), pp. 327–8.
127. Ives, *Anne Boleyn*, pp. 327–8. See above, p. 217.
128. M. Dowling, ed., 'William Latymer's Chronickille of Anne Bulleyne', *Camden Miscellany XXX* (Camden Society, fourth series, xxxix, 1990), p. 51.
129. *LPFD*, vii, nos 30, 89.
130. Dowling, 'William Latymer's Chronickille', pp. 53–4.
131. D. MacCulloch, *Thomas Cranmer: A Life* (Yale, 1996), p. 83; Dowling, 'Anne Boleyn and Reform', pp. 30–46; Cox, *Miscellaneous Writings of Thomas Cranmer*, p. 309.
132. *LPFD*, vi (2), no 1195 (18); vii (1), nos 30, 89, 589 (8); viii, nos 481 (26), 632 (1), 766. Shaxton and Latimer each received loans of £200 from the Queen to pay the first fruits due to the King: ibid., x, no 912; xi, no 117.
133. His letter to Cromwell on this occasion is well known (*LPFD*, x, no 942); G.R. Elton, *Reform and Reformation* (London, 1977), pp. 250–6.
134. R.B. Merriman, ed., *The Life and Letters of Thomas Cromwell* (2 vols, Oxford, 1902), ii, no 248.

135. G.R. Dickens, *The English Reformation* (London, 1989), p. 194.
136. Wordsworth, *Ceremonies and Processions*, pp. 40–1. See also, Duffy, *Stripping of the Altars*, pp. 414–15.
137. *LPFD*, xii (1), nos 746, 756; xii (2), nos 52, 1114; xiii (1), nos 64, 147, 264, 571–2; xiii (2), nos 214, 283; xiv (1), nos 611, 777–8.
138. Strype, *Ecclesiastical Memorials*, i, part 2, pp. 222–8.
139. *LPFD*, xiv (1), no 1040.
140. Ibid., nos 1157, 1217, 1220, 1260; Charles Wriothesley, *A Chronicle of England* (2 vols, Camden Society, new series, xi, 1875, and xx, 1877), i, p. 103.
141. *LPFD*, xiv (2), nos 236, 400, 423. 'If myn offence be suche that ye maye not speke for me, hang me evyn vp now', wrote Shaxton with ominous foresight. 'And if it be a pardonable fawt and may stond with your honour to speke for me to the gentle prince . . . mi sute in two wordes is to be at libertie and that by your mediacion the kynge's highnes woll gyff me a pencion to lyve by': BL, Cottonian Ms Cleopatra E IV, fo 65r.
142. *LPFD*, xvi, no 578.
143. MacCulloch, *Thomas Cranmer*, p. 353; idem, *Suffolk and the Tudors*, p. 163.
144. Dowling, 'Gospel and the Court', pp. 69–70; Houlbrooke, 'Persecution of Heresy', pp. 317–19.
145. *Acts of the Privy Council, I, 1542–1547* (London, 1890), pp. 417, 492.
146. John Foxe, *The Acts and Monuments of John Foxe* (8 vols, New York, 1965), v, Appendix 17.
147. Wriothesley, *Chronicle of England*, pp. 169–70.
148. 'Thou saidest at thy departing from us, when thou were sent for to London, that either thou wouldest burne, or els forsake God's truth . . . thou stomblest at the stone wher other wyth a stronge fayth went ouer . . . thou hast betrayed the innocent bloud': Robert Crowley, *The Confutation of xiij Articles, wherunto Nicolas Shaxton, Late Byshop of Salisburye Subscribed* (London, John Day, 1548), fos 5v–8v.
149. Ibid., fos 3r–8v. For Cranmer's difficulties as a married priest, see MacCulloch, *Thomas Cranmer*, pp. 72, 77, 75, 98, 249–50, 361. At the time of his death, Shaxton's library contained a number of books on, or relevant to, the subject of clerical marriage: E.S. Leedham-Green, *Books in Cambridge Inventories, I, The Inventories* (Cambridge, 1986), pp. 156–9.
150. J.S. Craig, 'The Marginalia of Dr Rowland Taylor', *Historical Research*, lxiv (1991), pp. 414–15.
151. The antiquary, Thomas Tanner, notes in his list of masters of St Giles's that Shaxton 'and Mrs Watson his wife' lived in the hospital in 1549, but no reference is given: NRO, DN reg. XXX, p. 51.
152. Cambridge University Library, Vice-Chancellor's Court, Probate Wills 1501–58, fo 100. Shaxton tersely commended his soul to God, but left no other indications of personal piety. I am grateful to Dr E.S. Leedham-Green, Assistant Keeper of the University Archives, for providing me with a copy of this document and the accompanying inventory.

VIII. GODDES HOWSE

1. K. Thomas, 'Cleanliness and Godliness in Early Modern England', in A. Fletcher and P. Roberts, eds, *Religion, Culture and Society in Early Modern Britain* (Cambridge, 1994), pp. 77–9.
2. Paris, *Life of St Edmund*, pp. 123, 129; Classen, Howes and Synott, *Cultural History of Smell*, pp. 53–4.
3. A.G. Carmichael, *Plague and the Poor in Renaissance Florence* (Cambridge, 1986), pp. 103–4, 123–6; Geremek, 'Criminalité, Vagabondage, Paupérisme', pp. 369–70; B. Pullan, 'Plague and Perceptions of the Poor in Early Modern Italy', in T. Ranger and P. Slack, eds, *Epidemics and Ideas: Essays on the Historical Perception of Pestilence* (Cambridge, 1992), pp. 101–23, notably pp. 106–7; Raine, *York Civic Records, V*, pp. 56–7; Slack, *Impact of Plague*, p. 204; idem, *Poverty and Policy*, pp. 115–16.
4. M. Healy, 'Discourses of the Plague in Early Modern London', in J.A.I Champion, ed., *Epidemic Diseases in London* (Centre for Metropolitan History, Working Paper, series 1, 1993), pp. 19–34; Geremek, 'Criminalité, Vagabondage, Paupérism', p. 371.
5. J. Sawday, *The Body Emblazoned: Dissection and the Human Body in Renaissance Culture* (London, 1995), p. 190; Jones, *Tudor Commonwealth*, pp. 16–17.
6. Raphael Holinshed, *Chronicles of England, Scotland and Ireland* (6 vols, New York, 1965), iii, pp. 1003–5.
7. J.F. Pound, *Poverty and Vagrancy in Tudor England* (London, 1971), pp. 109–10; idem, *Tudor and Stuart Norwich*, pp. 110–11, 140–4.
8. Pound, *Norwich Census of the Poor*, pp. 7–9; Blomefield, *Norfolk*, iii, p. 295.
9. R.H. Tawney and E. Power, eds, *Tudor Economic Documents* (3 vols, 1924), ii, pp. 316–17.
10. Stone and Cozens-Hardy, *Norwich Consistory Court Depositions*, nos 112, 122, 126, 266, 271, 318, 396.
11. B. Pullan, *Rich and Poor in Renaissance Venice* (Oxford, 1971), pp. 219–23.
12. F.R. Salter, ed., *Some Early Tracts on Poor Relief* (London, 1926), p. 41. See above, pp. 21–5.

13. Salter, *Some Early Tracts*, p. 69; Arrizabalaga and others, *Great Pox*, pp. 155–76, although these influential ordinances are not noted by the authors.
14. G.R. Elton, 'An Early Tudor Poor Law', *EconHR*, second series, vi (1953–4), p. 59; Luders, *Statutes of the Realm*, iii, 27 Hen. VIII, cap. xxv; Slack, *Poverty and Policy*, pp. 118–19.
15. E. Surtz and J.H. Hexter, eds, *The Complete Works of St Thomas More, IV, Utopia* (New Haven and London, 1965), p. 141.
16. Slack, *Impact of Plague*, p. 201. For More see above, p. 239.
17. Chaney, '"Philanthropy in Italy"', pp. 183–217, notably p. 192.
18. Park and Henderson, '"First Hospital Among Christians"', pp. 164–87, passim.
19. BL, Cottonian Ms Cleopatra C V, fo 33r.
20. C. Webster, 'Thomas Linacre and the Foundation of the College of Physicians', in F. Maddison, M. Pelling and C. Webster, eds, *Essays on the Life and Work of Thomas Linacre c. 1460–1524* (Oxford, 1977), pp. 198–222; P. Slack, 'Some Comparative Problems in the English Case', in T. Riis, ed., *Aspects of Poverty in Early Modern Europe* (Florence, 1981), pp. 281–5; idem, *Poverty and Policy*, pp. 8–14, 116–17.
21. Pound, *Tudor and Stuart Norwich*, pp. 54, 140–1. See also, for example, Zemon Davis, 'Poor Relief, Humanism and Heresy', pp. 222–6.
22. Hudson and Tingey, *Records of the City of Norwich*, ii, p. xcviii. In 1571, the mayor scathingly attacked beggars who 'wente dayely abroade from dore to dore counterfeattinge a kinde of worke', and reproved the householders who offered them help: Tawney and Power, *Tudor Economic Documents*, ii, p. 316.
23. Pound, *Poverty and Vagrancy*, pp. 40–1; Slack, *Poverty and Policy*, pp. 27–32.
24. Rawcliffe, *Hospitals of Medieval Norwich*, p. 149, and above, pp. 8–9.
25. PRO, E315/506 (Inventories of church goods, Norwich, October 1547).
26. Salter, *Some Early Tracts*, pp. 10, 17–20. This rationale lay, for example, behind the refoundation of London's three major new hospitals in 1553 and is expressed in Edward VI's charter: *A History of the Royal Foundation of Christ's Hospital* (London, 1834), Appendix, pp. xliii–lxii.
27. NRO, NCR, 16B, Norwich Assembly Book, 1510–1550, fo 231r.
28. NRO, NCR, 17B, *Liber Albus Civitatis*, fos 20r–21r.
29. Kreider, *English Chantries*, p. 177.
30. NRO, NCR, 17B, *Liber Ruber Civitatis*, fos 80v–84v, a seventeenth-century copy of the indenture tripartite between Edward VI, the executors of Henry VIII and the city of Norwich, 8 March 1547. This is reproduced by Blomefield, *Norfolk*, iv, pp. 390–4, and abstracted in *CPR, 1547–1548*, pp. 16–17. A shorter, slightly different version, as sealed by the mayor and commonalty on 8 April following, is preserved in the hospital archive: NRO, NCR, 24B, no 34.
31. There were, however, some delays, perhaps of a legal nature, with regard to their appointment. On 21 September 1547 it was agreed that the Assembly should 'take of advysement touching th'ensealyng of ij ritinges made to Sir John Fissher and to Sir Robert Dowe of the hospitall un till the next assemble': NRO, NCR, 16B, Norwich Assembly Book, 1510–1550, fo 238v.
32. NRO, NCR, 24B, no 34.
33. P. Griffiths, *Youth and Authority: Formative Experiences in England 1560–1640* (Oxford, 1996), p. 82.
34. *LPFD*, xxi (2), no 260; Sir Thomas Elyot, *The Boke Named the Gouernor*, ed. H.H.S. Croft (2 vols, London, 1883), i, pp. 163–9.
35. Pullan, *Rich and Poor*, pp. 225–6. The inventory of Shaxton's books shows him to have been a thoroughly Erasmian humanist: Leedham-Green, *Books in Cambridge Inventories, I*, pp. 156–9.
36. H. Manship, *The History of Great Yarmouth*, ed. C.J. Palmer (Great Yarmouth, 1854), p. 232. The first master, Walter Hawe, had been master of the boys at Norwich: Saunders, *History of Norwich Grammar School*, p. 252; NRO, NCR, 24A, GH accounts, box 1548–1556, accounts for June 1548–9, 1549–50, 1550–1.
37. NRO, Y/C/19/1, p. 15. I am grateful to Ms Elaine Phillips for this reference.
38. J. Simon, *Education and Society in Tudor England* (Cambridge, 1966), pp. 187, 194.
39. Saunders, *History of Norwich Grammar School*, p. 261. This telling example of 'moral rigorism' supports an argument advanced by Richmond, 'English Gentry and Religion', p. 145.
40. Pullan, *Rich and Poor*, pp. 402–3.
41. NRO, NCR, 17B, *Liber Ruber Civitatis*, fo 83r.
42. Contrary, however, to Michel Foucault's belief that the insane were admitted to suburban leper houses during this period, the Norwich evidence suggests otherwise: Rawcliffe, *Hospitals of Medieval Norwich*, pp. 54–5.
43. NRO, NCR, 16A, Mayor's Court Book, 1540–1549, p. 530 (17 November 1548).
44. R.A. Houlbrooke, *The Letter Book of John Parkhurst, Bishop of Norwich* (NRS, xliii, 1975), p. 187. It is interesting to compare these arrangements with developments at the former leper house of St Mary Magdalen, Beccles.

Here licences to beg were issued by the Crown, and the terminally sick from a wide catchment area were admitted: W. Page, ed., *VCH Suffolk, I* (London, 1907), p. 133.

45. Pelling, 'Appearance and Reality', pp. 95–102.
46. NRO, NCR, 24A, GH accounts, box 1556–1566, account for June 1560–1; box 1566–1575, account for June 1572–3. Between 1560 and 1592 thirteen paupers in all were transferred to civic leper houses from the hospital: Phillips, 'God's House', p. 23. The removal of patients under such circumstances was, of course, no new development: see above, pp. 11–12, 163–4.
47. BL, Cottonian Ms Cleopatra C V, fos 20v–21v; PRO, E135/8/48, fo 2v. NRO, NCR, 24A, GH accounts, box 1583–1592, account for June 1585–6, still refers to 'Mr Shaxton's hous at the hospitall'.
48. NRO, NCR, 17B, *Liber Ruber Civitatis*, fo 84r.
49. Kingdon, 'Social Welfare', pp. 56–7.
50. NRO, NCC, reg. Wymer, fos 46v–48v. Whetacre's legacy of £20 was recorded in the hospital accounts for 1552–3: NCR, 24A, GH accounts, box 1548–1556.
51. Bindoff, *House of Commons 1509–1558*, iii, pp. 354–6.
52. NRO, NCR, 24B, no 27B; PRO, E322/178 (also recording instructions of 13 February 1547 to the King's commissioners, Miles Spencer and Andrew Manfield, to take possession of St Giles's). The final agreement was entered in the civic records: NRO, NCR, 17B, *Liber Albus Civitatis*, fos 20r–21r.
53. NRO, NCR, 16A, Norwich Assembly Proceedings, 1491–1553, fo 198v.
54. *CPR, 1547–1548*, pp. 13–17; NRO, NCR, 17B, *Liber Ruber Civitatis*, fos 81r–81v; 16B, Norwich Assembly Book, 1510–1550, fo 236r.
55. *CPR, 1547–1548*, p. 16 (which gives a yearly valuation of £143, after payment of £9 rent to the Crown); Caley and Hunter, *Valor Ecclesiasticus*, iii, pp. 291–2.
56. Receipts came, on paper, to £203 in 1548–9, but just over £4 had to be written off in dead rents: NRO, NCR, 24A, GH accounts, box 1548–1556.
57. NRO, NCR, 24B, no 34.
58. In his account for 1547–8, for example, the chamberlain recorded expenses sustained in riding to Bury St Edmunds for discussions with the King's auditors. Besides paying certain small rents to the Crown, he then dealt with 'other thynges concerning the cite and the hospytall', noting that all his business was discharged 'for the profyght of the comminalte': NRO, NCR, 18A, Chamberlains' Account Book, 1541–1550, fo 279r.
59. NRO, NCR, 16A, Mayor's Court Book, 1540–1549, p. 265.
60. NRO, NCR, 16B, Norwich Assembly Book, 1510–1550, fo 238v. In 1548, however, Rogers resigned as an alderman, 'declaryng therby that he entended to kepe in the country ffor his helthe': ibid., fo 243v. In 1550 the Assembly decreed that the four surveyors should be appointed on an annual basis: 16A, Norwich Assembly Proceedings, 1491–1553, fo 227v.
61. NRO, NCR, 16B, Norwich Assembly Book, 1510–1550, fo 239r. These grants appear to have been fairly modest, producing about 25*s* a year in 1548–9: 24A, GH accounts, box 1548–1556.
62. A memorandum drafted at the beginning of James I's reign for attention at Westminster accused the aldermen of overt corruption in the management of God's House. 'The manors and revenues, *et cetera*, are graunted privily among them selves. All [entry] fines of the land come to theyr owne purses with out regard of the poore or the King's fondation', noted the author, Thomas Phillips: PRO, SP14/5, fo 130.
63. NRO, NCR, 16B, Norwich Assembly Book, 1510–1550, fos 239v–240r, 243v, 245r, 248r.
64. Ibid., fo 245r; 24A, GH accounts, box 1548–1556, account for June 1548–9.
65. NRO, NCR, 24A, GH accounts, box 1548–1556, passim.
66. J.M. Cowper, ed., *Henry Brinklow's Complaint* (EETS, extra series, xxii, 1874), p. 52.
67. As was the case at St Bartholomew's hospital in London by 1552: F.J. Furnivall and P. Furnivall, eds, *The Anatomie of the Bodie of Man* (EETS, extra series, liii, 1888), p. 312.
68. E.S. Welch, *Art and Authority in Renaissance Milan* (New Haven and London, 1995), p. 117. At the protestant hospital of Haina, in Hesse, which had previously been a Cistercian monastery, light work was advocated 'so as not through idleness to give the devil room': H.C.E. Midelfort, 'Protestant Monastery? A Reformation Hospital in Hesse', in P.N. Brooks, ed., *Reformation Principle and Practice* (London, 1980), p. 79.
69. See above, pp. 172–3. The idea that almsmen and women should labour was by no means new: K.J. Evans, 'The Maison Dieu, Arundel', *Sussex Archaeological Collections*, cvii (1969), pp. 65–6.
70. Both practices were forbidden at St Bartholomew's: Furnivall and Furnivall, *Anatomie of the Bodie of Man*, p. 312. For information about Norwich barber-surgeons, see M. Pelling, 'Occupational Diversity: Barbersurgeons and the Trades of Norwich 1550–1640', *Bulletin of the History of Medicine*, lvi (1982), pp. 484–511.
71. NRO, NCR, 16A, Mayor's Court Book, 1534–1549, fo 62v; 1540–1549, pp. 279, 324, 539. Porter may have continued to visit the poor in the hospital on an *ad hoc* basis, as he clearly attended patients in the area. In the aftermath of Kett's Rebellion, in the summer of 1549, he was paid 33*s* 4*d* 'for helyng of certen of Capteyn

Drury's men, whiche ware hurte at Byshopps gate the same nyght that my lord of Warwyke entryd the cyte': 18A, Chamberlains' Account Book, 1541–1550, fo 313.

72. NRO, NCR, 24A, GH accounts, box 1548–1556. In 1553–4, Reynolds was assisted by Philip Attlee, surgeon. He may already have been quite elderly, as he died in 1558: DCN, 69/2, fos 174v–75v.
73. Raine, *York Civic Records, V*, p. 64.
74. NRO, NCR, 16B, Norwich Assembly Book, 1510–1550, fo 250v.
75. Ibid., fo 253v.
76. Ibid., fos 254r–54v. The surveyors were Thomas Marsham and Alexander Mather, the appraisers Thomas Necton, John Aldryche, Thomas Sotherton and Ralph Marsham. Sotherton appears to have done most of the work, as he was credited with raising £20 through these sales: see above, p. 226.
77. NRO, NCR, 16A, Norwich Assembly Proceedings, 1491–1553, fo 211r; 16B, Norwich Assembly Book, 1510–1550, fo 255r.
78. Discussed in detail by D. MacCulloch, 'Kett's Rebellion in Context', *Past and Present*, lxxxiv (1979), pp. 36–59; idem, 'Kett's Rebellion in Context: A Rejoinder', ibid., xciii (1981), pp. 165–73; and idem, *Suffolk under the Tudors*, pp. 75–8, 300–10. The best general account of the uprising in Norwich remains S.T. Bindoff, *Ket's Rebellion 1549* (Historical Association, reprinted 1968).
79. C. Davies, '"Poor Persecuted Little Flock" or "Commonwealth of Christians": Edwardian Protestant Concepts of the Church', in M. Dowling and P. Lake, *Protestantism and the National Church in Sixteenth Century* (London, 1987), pp. 86–7.
80. J.M. Cowper, ed., *The Select Works of Robert Crowley* (EETS, extra series, xv, 1872), pp. 11–12; Jones, *Tudor Commonwealth*, pp. 21–3, 32–42, 78–9, 95, 110–14.
81. M.C. McClendon, '"Against God's Word": Government, Religion and the Crisis of Authority in Early Reformation Norwich', *Sixteenth Century Journal*, xxv (1994), pp. 353–69, especially pp. 357–62.
82. Kreider, *English Chantries*, pp. 186–93; Brigden, *London and the Reformation*, pp. 472–4.
83. Furnivall and Furnivall, *Anatomie of the Bodie of Man*, pp. 291–5.
84. Pound, *Poverty and Vagrancy*, pp. 107–8.
85. PRO, E301/45, fo 8v.
86. *CPR, 1548–1549*, pp. 18–19. He and Sir Robert Southwell paid £276 for the hospital and a free chapel in Rainham, Essex, which had been seized by the Crown under the terms of the second Chantry Act. The price was high, as the hospital had been assessed at only £10 a year in 1535, but it included the right to hold the annual Magdalen fair: Caley and Hunter, *Valor Ecclesiasticus*, iii, p. 315; Blomefield, *Norfolk*, iv, pp. 440–1.
87. Holinshed, *Chronicles*, iii, p. 965.
88. BL, Harleian Ms 1576, fo 254r. The account has been edited by B. L. Beier, 'The Commoyson in Norfolk, 1549: A Narrative of Popular Rebellion in Sixteenth Century England', *Journal of Medieval and Renaissance Studies*, vi (1976). One of the city's guns was left behind at the hospital, where it still remains: W. Rye, 'An Old Cannon at the Great Hospital, Norwich', *Norfolk Archaeology*, xvi (1907), pp. 85–90.
89. NRO, NCR, 24A, GH accounts, box 1548–1556, account for June 1549–50.
90. Holinshed, *Chronicles*, iii, p. 974.
91. BL, Harleian Ms 1576, fo 256r.
92. Ibid., fo 256v.
93. NRO, NCR, 24A, GH accounts, box 1548–1556, account for June 1549–50.
94. BL, Harleian Ms 1576, fo 258r.
95. NRO, NCR, 24A, GH accounts, box 1548–1556, account for June 1549–50. For King and Necton see Hawes, *Index to Norwich City Officers*, pp. 92, 111.
96. This arrangement was regularised retrospectively, in July 1550, by the corporation, which was still anxious to avoid charges of collusion. Codde and his associates were to enjoy a forty-year lease of the property at £3 a year, but would forfeit both the lease and a bond of 40*s* if they failed to rebuild within a decade. These terms were extremely attractive, but we should remember that Codde was then owed substantial sums by the hospital: NRO, NCR, 16B, Norwich Assembly Book, 1510–1550, fo 265r.
97. Bennett Symmons, 'Hospital of St Giles', pp. 65–6, gives a rather exaggerated impression of the extent of rebuilding in 1585–6, not supported by the outlay on re-roofing the west end of the south aisle of the church: NRO, NCR, 24A, GH accounts, box 1583–1592.
98. I am grateful to Mr Michael Youngs for showing me this item of private correspondence, dated 6 December 1971.
99. PRO, PCC, 19 Populwell; Jordan, *Charities of Rural England*, p. 116.
100. Hudson and Tingey, *Records of the City of Norwich*, ii, pp. xcix-c, 126, 174; Pound, *Tudor and Stuart Norwich*, p. 141.
101. NRO, NCR, 18A, Chamberlains' Account Book, 1541–1550, fos 297r–97v; 16A, Norwich Assembly Proceedings, 1491–1553, fo 213r.

102. NRO, NCR, 24A, GH accounts, box 1548–1556, account for June 1549–50.
103. Attacks on church property caused some problems at this time: B. Cozens-Hardy and E.A. Kent, *The Mayors of Norwich 1403 to 1835* (Norwich, 1938), p. 51.
104. Blomefield, *Norfolk*, iv, pp. 77–8.
105. Ibid., pp. 299–300, 439; NRO, NCR, 24A, GH accounts, box 1548–1556, account for June 1549–50; 24B, no 35.
106. NRO, NCR, 24A, GH accounts, box 1548–1556, account for June 1550–1. Another 'gift and benevolence' of £67 was raised for the hospital in 1551–2, this time by the civic authorities alone: ibid., June 1551–2.
107. Pound, *Poverty and Vagrancy*, pp. 59–60, 107–8.
108. Furnivall and Furnivall, *Anatomie of the Bodie of Man*, p. 293.
109. NRO, NCR, 24A, GH accounts, box 1548–1556, account for June 1551–2; 16A, Norwich Assembly Proceedings, 1491–1553, fo 228v. It is thus not surprising that on the same day as he recovered the money, Necton warned the Assembly 'to prouyde a nother ffermour to the late hospitall against mydsomer next' as he intended to resign: fo 228r.
110. NRO, NCR, 16B, Norwich Assembly Book, 1510–1550, fo 263r; 18A, Chamberlains' Account Book, 1541–1550, fos 332v–33r, 334r–37v.
111. Blomefield, *Norfolk*, iv, pp. 55–61; NRO, NCR, 24A, GH accounts, box 1548–1556, account for June 1550–1; 25D, grant of the Charnel House [Carnary Chapel] to Catlyn and Sir Edward Warner.
112. Saunders, *History of Norwich Grammar School*, pp. 17–34; R. Harries, 'Regulations, Rhetoric, Ruins and Remuneration 1547–1859', in P. Cattermole and others, *A History of Norwich School* (Norwich, 1991), pp. 43–6.
113. Brooke, *History of Gonville and Caius College*, pp. 53–4; *Dictionary of National Biography*, xvii, p. 1392; NRO, NCR, 24A, GH accounts, box 1548–1556, account for June 1550–1.
114. Hudson and Tingey, *Records of the City of Norwich*, ii, pp. xcix, 387–9.
115. NRO, NCC, reg. Folklin, fos 325r–26r. The rules of the Haina hospital, Hesse, of *c.* 1534, specified that a sermon should be preached *daily*. The underlying concerns evident in these statutes were identical to those of God's House: Midelfort, 'Protestant Monastery?', pp. 78–82.
116. NRO, NCR, 20C, Mayor's Book of the Poor, 1571–1579, fo 5r. For the importance of sermons in training the young, see Griffiths, *Youth and Authority*, pp. 40–5.
117. Appendix I, articles 10 and 26.
118. Slack, 'Social Policy and the Constraints of Government', pp. 97, 108. For a wider discussion of this theme, see Clark, *English Alehouse*, Chapter VII, passim.
119. See J.A. Sharpe, *Crime in Early Modern England 1550–1750* (London, 1984), Chapter VII, passim, for a wider application of these ideas.
120. Hudson and Tingey, *Records of the City of Norwich*, ii, pp. 387–9.
121. PRO, PCC, 12 Tashe (will dated 10 March 1553).
122. NRO, NCR, 24A, GH accounts, box 1548–1556, accounts for June 1548–9, 1549–50, 1552–3; 16A, Mayor's Court Book, 1534–1549, fo 66r. On the importance of clean linen, see Pelling, 'Healing the Sick Poor', p. 118, and eadem, 'Appearance and Reality', p. 93. It is worth noting that the 1533 statutes of the hospital of the Holy Spirit, Stockholm, prohibited drunkenness, expected all but the truly incapacitated to work and required the inmates to bathe regularly: E.I. Kouri, 'Health Care and Poor Relief in Sweden and Finland', in O.P. Grell and A. Cunningham, eds, *Health Care and Poor Relief in Protestant Europe 1500–1700* (London, 1997), p. 171.
123. NRO, NCR, 17B, Book of St George's Guild, 1452–1602, fos 79r–79v, 94r.
124. PRO, PCC 12 Tashe and 18 Ketchyn (Katherine Rogers' will is dated 12 April 1557).
125. NRO, NCR, 24A, GH accounts, box 1548–1556, accounts for June 1550–1, 1552–3.
126. NRO, NCR, 24B, no 36 (1).
127. Phillips, 'God's House', pp. 13–14.
128. PRO, PCC, 43 Holney. The hospital had the power to remove women who were 'not of good behaviour', and replace them with more suitable candidates.
129. NRO, NCC, reg. Lyncolne, fos 233v–34r.
130. These developments are discussed at greater length in Phillips, 'God's House', Chapter III, passim.
131. Pound, *Poverty and Vagrancy*, p. 67.
132. Slack, 'Social Policy and the Constraints of Government', pp. 112–13; idem, *Poverty and Policy*, pp. 70–1, 121.
133. Pound, *Norwich Census of the Poor*, p. 13. A further 400 or so found accommodation in the private sector, often in lodgings owned by members of the ruling elite. Some aldermen tried to make more money by cramming as many people as possible into overcrowded houses, in blatant disregard of public health. Cases of up to twenty-five and even thirty-four adults in a single building come to light: idem, *Tudor and Stuart Norwich*, pp. 82, 130–1.
134. C. Wilson, *England's Apprenticeship 1603–1763* (London, 1965), p. 77.
135. Surtz and Hexter, *Complete Works of St Thomas More, IV, Utopia*, pp. 121, 127, 139, 147.

BIBLIOGRAPHY

I MANUSCRIPT SOURCES

ARUNDEL CASTLE MUNIMENTS

Hales Charter, no 104
Norfolk Mss, box II, no 110
Seething Charter, no 280

BODLEIAN LIBRARY, OXFORD

Ms Ashmole, 191
Ms Rawlinson D

BORTHWICK INSTITUTE, YORK

Diocesan Register, R VII G

BRITISH LIBRARY, DEPARTMENT OF MANUSCRIPTS

Add. Chs 7,207, 10,648, 14,784
Add. Mss 17,002, 57,534
Add. Roll 27,456
Cottonian Ch. XIII.10
Cottonian Mss Cleopatra C V, E IV–V; Faustina A III
Harleian Ch. 44 D. 14
Harleian Mss 328, 1576
Lansdowne Ms 463
Seals, xxxv.238 lxviii.54, lxix.6, lxviii.17, lxxi.56, xxxvii.51, lx.69, lxiv.74, lxv.53, 54, lxxi.35; D.C.F. xxxix
Stowe Ch. 197
Toph. Cart. 12A, 31, 32, 35, 37, 41, 44, 50, 52, 56

CAMBRIDGE UNIVERSITY LIBRARY

Vice-Chancellor's Court, Probate Wills 1501–1558

CANTERBURY CATHEDRAL CHAPTER LIBRARY

Cathedral Priory, reg. F

HARVARD UNIVERSITY, USA, LAW SCHOOL LIBRARY

Medieval Deeds, nos 180, 786

LAMBETH PALACE LIBRARY

Ms 528
Reg. Arundel, II
Reg. Morton, II

MAGDALEN COLLEGE, OXFORD

Fastolf Additia, no 2

NEW COLLEGE, OXFORD

New College Ms 3691

NORFOLK RECORD OFFICE

Box 30E1 (Micellaneous Deeds), nos 12045–6, 12050, 12053, 12056–7, 12059–62, 12064–8, 12070–1, 12073–5, 12077–8, 12083, 12085, 12087–9, 12092–9, 12100–1, 12104–8, 12111–13
Box 30E2 no 12120
BR 61/2/18, 19
Bradfer Lawrence Mss, box V (9)
COL 5/2/1
DCN (Dean and Chapter of Norwich) 1/1/22, 1/2/96–9, 1/4/24, 1/6/85, 130–2, 1/10/1–38; DCN 2/5/5; DCN 9/4; DCN 40/6, 7; DCN 43/48, 45/40/16; DCN 48/26A/1; DCN 69/2; DCN 79/2–7; DCN 84/14
DN (episcopal registers) III, book 6; IV, book 7; V, books 9, 10; VI, books 2, 11; VII, books 7, 12; VIII, book 13; IX, book 14; XXX
N/MC 15/4
NCC (Norwich Consistory Court): registers Alblaster, Alpe, Brosyard, Colman, Doke, Folklin, Harsyk, Herman, Heydon, Hyll, Hyrning, Jekkys, Lyncolne, Popy, Puntyng, Ryxe, Spyltymber, Surflete, Typpes, Wymer
MSC 1/5
NCR (Norwich City Records) 1C, rolls 19A, 19B, 19E
NCR, 3–4, Norwich Private Deeds (NPD)
NCR, 8A, no 11
NCR, 8E-7, Accounts of the Guild of St George
NCR, 16A, Mayor's Court Books, 1510–1532, 1534–1549, 1540–1549; Norwich Assembly Proceedings, 1434–1491, 1491–1553
NCR, 16B, Norwich Assembly Book, 1510–1550
NCR, 17B, *Liber Albus Civitatis; Liber Ruber Civitatis*; Book of Pleas; Book of St George's Guild, 1452–1602
NCR, 18A, Chamberlains' Account Books, 1384–1448, 1537–1547, 1541–1550
NCR, 20D, Great Hospital Lease Book, 1530–1645
NCR, 21F, Papers of the antiquary, John Kirkpatrick (d. 1728)
NCR, 20C, Mayor's Book of the Poor, 1571–1579
NCR, 24–25, Archive of the Great Hospital
Phillipps (Phi) Mss 76, 98, 99, 140, 144, 292–93, 309, 311–12, 378, 516–19, 521–25, 600, 621, 623
Y/C/19/1

PUBLIC RECORD OFFICE, LONDON

C1/9/277, 12/165, 19/65, 28/394, 40/237, 45/233, 61/487, 64/31, 131/8, 161/35–6, 163/54, 242/72, 583/52–3, 965/58–9
C43/47/290–9
C47/44/301, 303
C143/303/15, 441/17–18, 442/18
C270/22, 23/12
CP25(1) 157/70/907, 71/927, 936, 81/1185, 82/1207; 158/84/1263, 88/1369, 98/1604, 1622; 159/100/1658; 169/184/120, 128, 185/37, 44; 170/192/3, 48, 54, 193/53–4, 196/41–2, 51, 91
CP40/1009
E25/94/3
E40/11562
E117/11/58, 12/29
E135/2/57, 8/48
E301/45
E315/506
E322/178

E368/280
KB9/84/1, 418
PCC (Probate Court of Canterbury), 26 Blanyr, 2 Bodfelde, 30 Godyn, 28 Holder, 40 Holgrave, 43 Holney, 15, 30, 35 Horne, 9 Jankyn, 18 Ketchyn, 8 Maynwaryng, 9 Moone, 19 Populwell, 12, 23 Stockton, 12 Tashe, 27 Vox
SP1/159
SP14/5
STAC 2/18/118, 35/3

ST GEORGE'S CHAPEL, WINDSOR

Records of St Anthony's Hospital, London, xv 37.8, 21, 25, 27, 33

WELLCOME INSTITUTE LIBRARY, LONDON

Western Ms 408

II PRIMARY PRINTED SOURCES

Acts of the Privy Council, I, 1542–1547 (London, 1890)
Allen, William, *A Defense and Declaration of the Catholike Churchies Doctrine Touching Purgatory* (John Latius, Antwerp, 1565)
Aquinas, Thomas, *Summa Theologica*, eds The Fathers of the English Dominican Province (22 vols, London, 1922)
Arnould, A., and Massing, J.M., eds, *Splendours of Flanders* (Cambridge, 1993)
Astle, T., ed., *The Will of King Henry VII* (London, 1785)
Bannister, A.T., ed., *Registrum Johannis Stanbury, Episcopi Herefordensis 1453–1474* (Canterbury and York Society, 1919)
Bartholomaeus Anglicanus, *On the Properties of Things: John Trevisa's Translation of Bartholomaeus Anglicus' De Proprietatis Rerum*, ed. M.C. Seymour (3 vols, Oxford, 1975–88)
Black, W.H., ed., *Catalogue of the Manuscripts Bequeathed unto the University of Oxford by Elias Ashmole* (Oxford, 1845)
Boüquet, M., ed., *Rerum Gallicarum et Francicarum Scriptores*, XX (Paris, 1840)
Brown, C., ed., *Religious Lyrics of the Fifteenth Century* (Oxford, 1962)
Brown, W., ed., *The Register of William Wickwane, Lord Archbishop of York, 1279–1285* (Surtees Society, cxiv, 1907)
Calendar of Close Rolls (London, HMSO, 1892 onwards)
Calendar of Inquisitions Miscellaneous (London, HMSO, 1916 onwards)
Calendar of Letters and Papers, Foreign and Domestic, Henry VIII (London, HMSO, 1864 onwards)
Calendar of Nottinghamshire Coroners' Inquests 1485–1558 (Thoroton Society, xxv, 1969)
Calendar of Papal Letters (London, HMSO, 1894 onwards)
Calendar of Papal Petitions, 1342–1419 (London, HMSO, 1897)
Calendar of Patent Rolls (London, HMSO, 1891 onwards)
Caley, J., and Hunter, J., eds, *Valor Ecclesiasticus, temp Henrici VIII* (6 vols, London, 1810–34)
Candille, M., ed., *Livre de la Vie Active de l'Hôtel Dieu de Jehan Henry* (Paris, 1964)
Capes, W.W., ed., *Registrum Johannis Trefnant* (Canterbury and York Society, 1916)
Catalogue of Seals in the Department of Manuscripts of the British Museum I (London, 1887)
Clay, J.W., ed., *Yorkshire Monasteries Suppression Papers* (Yorkshire Archaeological Society, xlviii, 1912)
Clayton, M., ed., *Catalogue of Rubbings of Brasses and Incised Slabs* (London, 1968)
Cotton, Bartholomew, *Historia Anglicana*, ed. H.R. Luard (RS, 1859)
Cotton, C., ed., *The Canterbury Chantries and Hospitals* (Kent Records, supplement, 1934)
Cowper, J.M., ed., *The Select Works of Robert Crowley* (EETS, extra series, xv, 1872)
——, ed., *Henry Brinklow's Complaint* (EETS, extra series, xxii, 1874)
Cox, J.E., ed., *Miscellaneous Writings and Letters of Thomas Cranmer* (Parker Society, 1846)
Crowley, Robert, *The Confutation of xiij Articles, wherunto Nicolas Shaxton, Late Byshop of Salisburye Subscribed* (London, John Day, 1548)
Curia Regis Rolls (London, HMSO, 1923 onwards)
Davis, N., ed., *Non-Cycle Plays and Fragments* (EETS, supplementary text, 1, 1970)
——, ed., *Paston Letters and Papers of the Fifteenth Century* (2 vols, Oxford, 1971–6)
Dawson, W.R., ed., *A Leechbook or Collection of Medical Recipes of the Fifteenth Century* (London, 1934)
Dickinson, F.H., ed., *Missale ad Usum Insignis et Praeclarae Ecclesiae Sarum* (Oxford, 1861–3)
Dobson, R.B., ed., *The Peasants' Revolt of 1381* (second edn, London, 1983)

Dodwell, B., ed., *The Charters of Norwich Cathedral Priory I* (Pipe Roll Society, new series, xl, 1965–6)

Dowling, M., ed., 'William Latymer's Chronickille of Anne Bulleyne', *Camden Miscellany XXX* (Camden Society, fourth series, xxxix, 1990)

Drucker, L., ed., *Chartulary of the Hospital of St Thomas the Martyr, Southwark, 1213–1525* (London, 1932)

Dugdale, William, *Monasticon Anglicanum*, eds J. Caley and others (6 vols, London, 1817–30)

Dymond, D., ed., *The Register of Thetford Priory, I, 1482–1517* (NRS, lix, 1994)

Ellis, H., ed., *Chronica Johannis de Oxenedes* (RS, 1859)

Elyot, Sir Thomas, *The Boke Named the Gouernor*, ed. H.H.S. Croft (2 vols, London, 1883)

Fish, Simon, *A Supplicacyon for the Beggers*, ed. F.J. Furnivall (EETS, extra series, xiii, 1871)

Fleishhaker, R. von, ed., *Lanfrank's 'Science of Cirurgie'* (EETS, cii, 1894)

Foreville, R., and Keir, G., eds, *The Book of St Gilbert* (Oxford, 1987)

Fowler, J.T., ed., *Memorials of the Church of SS Peter and Wilfrid, II* (Surtees Society, lxxviii, 1884)

Foxe, John, *The Acts and Monuments of John Foxe* (8 vols, New York, 1965)

Furnivall, F.J., ed., *Political, Religious and Love Poems* (EETS, original series, xv, 1866)

——, ed., *Early English Meals and Manners* (EETS, xxxii, 1868)

——, and Furnivall, P., eds, *The Anatomie of the Bodie of Man* (EETS, extra series, liii, 1888)

Gairdner, J., ed., *The Historical Collections of a Citizen of London* (Camden Society, new series, xvii, 1876)

——, ed., *The Paston Letters* (4 vols, London, 1910)

Gascoigne, Thomas, *Loci et Libri Veritatem*, ed. J.E. Thorold Rogers (Oxford, 1881)

Gerson, Jean, *Oeuvres Completes, VII, L'Oeuvre Française*, ed. Mgr. Glorieux (Paris, 1966)

Goulburn, E.M., and Symonds, H., eds, *The Life, Letters and Sermons of Bishop Herbert de Losinga* (2 vols, Oxford, 1878)

Grace, M., ed., *Records of the Gild of St George in Norwich 1389–1547* (NRS, ix, 1937)

Gransden, A., ed., *The Chronicle of Bury St Edmunds 1212–1301* (London, 1964)

Hall, Edward, *Chronicle Containing the History of England* (London, 1809)

Harper-Bill, C., ed., *Charters of the Medieval Hospitals of Bury St Edmunds* (Suffolk Records Society, Suffolk Charters, xiv, 1994)

Heath Barnum, P., ed., *Dives and Pauper* (EETS, cclxxv, 1976, and cclxxx, 1980)

Hector, L.C., and Harvey, B.F., eds, *The Westminster Chronicle 1381–1394* (Oxford, 1982)

Henry of Lancaster, *Le Livre de Seyntz Medicines*, ed. E.J. Arnould (Oxford, 1940)

Henryson, Robert, *The Poems of Robert Henryson*, ed. D. Fox (Oxford, 1981)

Hingeston-Randolph, F.C., ed., *The Register of John de Grandisson, Bishop of Exeter, 1327–1369* (3 vols, London, 1894–9)

Hinnebusch, J.F., ed., *The Historia Occidentalis of Jacques de Vitry* (Fribourg, 1972)

HMC, *Eighth Report, Part I* (London, 1881)

HMC, *Ninth Report, Part I* (London, 1883)

HMC, *Twelfth Report, Appendix IX* (London, 1891)

HMC, *Fourteenth Report, Appendix VIII* (London, 1895)

HMC, *Various Collections, VII* (London, 1914)

Hobhouse, Bishop, ed., *Calendar of the Register of John de Drokensford* (Somerset Record Society, i, 1887)

Holinshed, Raphael, *Chronicles of England, Scotland and Ireland* (6 vols, New York, 1965)

Horrox, R., ed., *The Black Death* (Manchester, 1994)

Houlbrooke, R.A., *The Letter Book of John Parkhurst, Bishop of Norwich* (NRS, xliii, 1975)

Hudson, A., ed., *Selections from English Wycliffite Writings* (Cambridge, 1978)

——, *Two Wycliffite Texts* (EETS, ccci, 1993)

Hudson, W., ed., *Leet Jurisdiction in the City of Norwich during the Thirteenth and Fourteenth Centuries* (Selden Society, v, 1892)

——, and Tingey, J.C., eds, *The Records of the City of Norwich* (2 vols, Norwich, 1906–10)

Innocent III, 'De Sacro Altaris Mysterio Liber Sex', *Patrologia Latina, CCXVII, Innocentius III* (Paris, 1890)

Jacob, E.F., ed., *The Register of Henry Chichele, Archbishop of Canterbury* (4 vols, Oxford, 1943–7)

Jessopp, A., ed., *Visitations of the Diocese of Norwich, 1492–1532* (Camden Society, new series, xliii, 1888)

John of Arderne, *Treatises of Fistula in Ano*, ed. D. Power (EETS, cxxxix, 1910)

Jones, J., ed., *Saint Richard of Chichester* (Sussex Record Society, lxxix, 1993)

Kaye, J.M., ed., *The Cartulary of God's House Southampton, I* (Southampton Records Series, xix, 1976)

Kerling, N., ed., *Cartulary of St Bartholomew's Hospital* (London, 1973)

Keynes, J., ed., *The Works of Sir Thomas Browne* (4 vols, London, 1964)

Kirby, T.F., ed., *Annals of Winchester College* (London, 1892)

Kirkpatrick, John, *History of the Religious Orders and Communities, and of the Hospitals and Castle, of Norwich, Written about the Year 1725*, ed. D. Turner (Yarmouth, 1845)

Lambarde, William, *A Perambulation of Kent* (London, 1826)
Larkin, Philip, *High Windows* (London, 1974)
Larking, L.B., ed., *The Knights Hospitallers in England: The Report of Prior Philip de Thame* (Camden Society, lxv, 1857)
Leach, A.F., ed., *Early Yorkshire Schools, I* (Yorkshire Archaeological Society, Record Series, xxvii, 1899)
——, ed., *Early Yorkshire Schools, II* (Yorkshire Archaeological Society, Record Series, xxxiii, 1903)
Legge, M.D., ed., *Anglo Norman Letters and Petitions* (Oxford, 1941)
Le Neve, John, *Fasti Ecclesiae Anglicanae 1066–1300, II, Monastic Cathedrals*, ed. D. Greenway (London, 1971)
Luders, A., and others, eds, *Statutes of the Realm* (11 vols, London, 1810–28)
Lydgate, John, *The Minor Poems*, ed. H.N. MacCracken (EETS, cvii, 1911, reprinted 1961)
Lyell, L., and Watney, F.D., eds, *Acts of Court of the Mercers' Company 1453–1527* (Cambridge, 1936)
Malcolm, J.P., ed., *Londinium Redivivum* (4 vols, London, 1803–7)
Martin, G.H., ed., *Knighton's Chronicle 1337–1396* (Oxford, 1995)
Matarasso, P., ed., *The Cistercian World: Monastic Writings of the Twelfth Century* (London, 1993)
Matthew, F.D., ed., *The English Works of Wyclif hitherto Unpublished* (EETS, lxxiv, 1880)
Maxwell-Lyte, H.C., and Dawes, M.C.B., eds, *The Register of Thomas Bekyngton I* (Somerset Record Society, xlix, 1934)
Meech, S.B., ed., *The Book of Margery Kempe* (EETS, cxxiv, 1904)
Mellows, W.T., and King, P.I., eds, *The Book of William Morton, Almoner of Peterborough Monastery 1448–1467* (Northamptonshire Record Society, xvi, 1951)
Memoranda, References and Documents Relating to the Royal Hospitals of the City of London (London, 1863)
Merriman, R.B., ed., *The Life and Letters of Thomas Cromwell* (2 vols, Oxford, 1902)
Moore, N., ed., *The Book of the Foundation of St Bartholomew's Church in London* (EETS, clxiii, 1923)
Myers, A.R., ed., *English Historical Documents, IV, 1327–1485* (London, 1969)
Noble, C., 'Norwich Cathedral Priory Gardeners' Accounts, 1329–1530', in eadem, C. Moreton and P. Rutledge, eds, *Farming and Gardening in Late Medieval Norfolk* (NRS, lxi, 1997)
O'Mara, V.A., ed., *A Study and Edition of Selected Middle English Sermons* (Leeds Texts and Monographs, new series, xiii, 1994)
Owen, D., ed., *The Making of King's Lynn* (Records of Social and Economic History, new series, ix, 1984)
Paris, Matthew, *Chronica Majora*, ed. H.R. Luard (7 vols, RS, 1872–84)
——, *The Life of St Edmund*, ed. C.H. Lawrence (Stroud, 1996)
Pearsall, D., ed., *Piers Plowman by William Langland: An Edition of the C-Text* (York Medieval Texts, second series, 1978)
Peckham, W.D., ed., *The Chartulary of the High Church of Chichester* (Sussex Record Society, xlvi, 1942–3)
Pobst, P.E., ed., *The Register of William Bateman, Bishop of Norwich, 1344–1355, I* (Canterbury and York Society, 1996)
Pound, J.F., ed., *The Norwich Census of the Poor, 1570* (NRS, xl, 1971)
Powicke, F.M., and Cheney, C.R., eds, *Councils and Synods, II, 1205–1313* (2 parts, Oxford, 1964)
Raine, A., ed., *York Civic Records, V* (Yorkshire Archaeological Society, cx, 1946)
Raine, J., ed., *Wills and Inventories, I* (Surtees Society, ii, 1835)
——, ed., *Testamenta Eboracensia, I* (Surtees Society, iv, 1836)
——, ed., *The Register of Walter Gray* (Surtees Society, lvi, 1870)
Roncière, B. de la, and others, eds, *Les Registres d'Alexandre IV* (3 vols, Paris, 1895–1959)
Ross, C., ed., *The Cartulary of St Mark's Hospital, Bristol* (Bristol Record Society, xxi, 1959)
Ryan, G., and Ripperger, H., eds, *The Golden Legend of Jacobus de Voragine* (New York, 1941, reprinted 1969)
Salter, F.R., ed., *Some Early Tracts on Poor Relief* (London, 1926)
Salter, H.E., ed., *A Cartulary of the Hospital of St John the Baptist, III* (Oxford Historical Society, lxix, 1917)
Salu, M.B., ed. and trans., *The Ancrene Riwle* (Exeter Medieval English Texts and Studies, 1990)
Saunders, H.W., ed., *The First Register of Norwich Cathedral Priory* (NRS, xi, 1939)
Sharpe, R.R., ed., *Calendar of Wills Proved and Enrolled in the Court of Husting of London, 1258–1688* (2 vols, London, 1889–90)
Skaife, R.H., ed., *The Register of the Guild of Corpus Christi* (Surtees Society, lvii, 1872)
Skeat, W.W., *Pierce the Ploughman's Crede* (EETS, xxx, 1867)
Smith, T., Smith, L.T., and Brentano, L., eds, *English Gilds* (EETS, xl, 1890)
Starkey, Thomas, *A Dialogue between Cardinal Pole and Thomas Lupset*, ed. J.M. Cowper (EETS, extra series, xxxii, 1878)
Stevenson, W.H., ed., *Records of the Borough of Nottingham, I* (Nottingham, 1882)
Stone, E.D., and Cozens-Hardy, B., *Norwich Consistory Court Depositions, 1499–1512 and 1518–1530* (NRS, x, 1938)
Stow, John, *A Survey of London*, ed. C.L. Kingsford (2 vols, Oxford, 1908)
Strachey, J., and others, eds, *Rotuli Parliamentorum* (6 vols, London, 1767–77)
Strype, J., ed., *Ecclesiastical Memorials* (3 vols, Oxford, 1822)
Surtz, E., and Hexter, J.H., eds, *The Complete Works of St Thomas More, IV, Utopia* (New Haven and London, 1965)

Swanson, R.N., ed., *Catholic England: Faith, Religion and Observance before the Reformation* (Manchester, 1993)
Tanner, N., ed., *Norwich Heresy Trials 1428–31* (Camden Society, fourth series, xx, 1977)
——, ed., *Decrees of the Ecumenical Councils* (2 vols, Georgetown, 1990)
Tawney, R.H., and Power, E., eds, *Tudor Economic Documents* (3 vols, 1924)
Thomas of Monmouth, *The Life and Miracles of St William of Norwich*, eds A. Jessopp and M.R. James (Cambridge, 1896)
Thompson, C.R., ed., *Collected Works of Erasmus, XL, Colloquies* (Toronto, 1997)
Thomson, T., and Ines, C., eds, *The Acts of the Parliament of Scotland* (12 vols, Edinburgh, 1844–75)
Tolhurst, J.B.L., ed., *The Customary of the Cathedral Priory Church of Norwich* (Henry Bradshaw Society, lxxxii, 1948)
Trapp, J.B., ed., *The Complete Works of St Thomas More, IX, The Apologia* (New Haven and London, 1979)
Tymms, S., ed., *Wills and Inventories from the Registers of the Commissary of Bury St Edmunds* (Camden Society, xlix, 1850)
Villon, François, *Oeuvres*, ed. L. Thuasne (3 vols, Geneva, 1967)
Wade-Martins, P., ed., *An Historical Atlas of Norfolk* (Norwich, 1994)
Walsingham, Thomas, *Historia Anglicana*, ed. H.T. Riley (2 vols, RS, 1863–4)
Watkin, A., ed., *Inventory of Church Goods temp. Edward III* (2 parts, NRS, xix, 1947–8)
Wenzel, S., ed., *Fasciculus Morum: A Fourteenth-Century Preacher's Handbook* (Pennsylvania, 1989)
Wharton, H., ed., *Anglia Sacra* (2 vols, London, 1691)
Wilkins, D., ed., *Concilia Magnae Britanniae et Hiberniae* (4 vols, London, 1737)
William de Malmesbury, *Gesta Rerum Anglorum*, ed. W. Stubbs (2 vols, RS, 1887–9)
Williams, J.F., and Cozens-Hardy, B., eds, *Extracts from the Two Earliest Minute Books of the Dean and Chapter of Norwich Cathedral 1566–1649* (NRS, xxiv, 1953)
Willis Clark, J., ed., *The Observances in Use at the Augustinian Priory of St Giles and St Andrew at Barnwell, Cambridgeshire* (Cambridge, 1897)
Woolgar, C.M., ed., *Household Accounts from Medieval England* (Records of Social and Economic History, new series, xvii, 1992; xviii, 1993)
Wordsworth, C., ed., *Salisbury Ceremonies and Processions* (Cambridge, 1901)
Wright, T., ed., *The Historical Works of Giraldus Cambrensis* (London, reprint, 1968)
Wriothesley, Charles, *A Chronicle of England* (2 vols, Camden Society, new series, xi, 1875, and xx, 1877)
Wulfstan of Winchester, *The Life of St Aethelwold*, eds M. Lapidge and M. Winterbottom (Oxford, 1991)

III SECONDARY PRINTED SOURCES

Alexander, J., and Binski, P., eds, *The Age of Chivalry: Art in Plantagenet England 1200–1400* (London, 1987)
Alexander, J.W., 'Herbert of Norwich, 1091–1119', *Studies in Medieval and Renaissance History*, vi (1969)
Allison, J.K., 'The Sheep-Corn Husbandry of Norfolk in the Sixteenth and Seventeenth Centuries', *Agricultural History Review*, v (1957)
——, 'Flock Management in the Sixteenth and Seventeenth Centuries', *EconHR*, second series, xi (1958)
Amundsen, D.W., *Medicine, Society and Faith in the Ancient and Medieval Worlds* (Baltimore, 1996)
Andrews, J., and others, *The History of Bethlem* (London, 1997)
Arbesmann, R., 'The Concept of *Christus Medicus* in St Augustine', *Traditio*, x (1954)
Arrizabalaga, J., Henderson, J., and French, R., *The Great Pox: The French Disease in Renaissance Europe* (New Haven and London, 1997)
Aston, M., 'The Impeachment of Bishop Despenser', *Bulletin of the Institute of Historical Research*, xxxviii (1965)
——, '"Caim's Castles": Poverty, Politics and Disendowment', in R.B. Dobson, ed., *The Church, Politics and Patronage in the Fifteenth Century* (Gloucester, 1984)
——, *Lollards and Reformers: Images and Literacy in Late Medieval Religion* (London, 1984)
——, 'Segregation in Church', *Studies in Church History*, xxvii (1990)
Atherton, I., and others, eds, *Norwich Cathedral: Church, City and Diocese 1096–1996* (London, 1996)
Atkin, M., 'Medieval Clay-Walled Building in Norwich', *Norfolk Archaeology*, xli (1991)
——, Carter, A., and Evans, D.H., *Excavations in Norwich 1971–78, II* (East Anglian Archaeology, xxvi, 1985)
Ayers, B.S., and others, *Waterfront Excavation and Thetford Ware Production, Norwich* (East Anglian Archaeology, xvii, 1983)
——, *Digging Deeper: Recent Archaeology in Norwich* (Norfolk Museums Service, 1987)
——, *The English Heritage Book of Norwich* (London, 1994)
——, Smith, R., and Tillyard, M., 'The Cow Tower, Norwich: A Detailed Survey and Partial Reinterpretation', *Medieval Archaeology*, xxxii (1988)
Bailey, M., 'The Rabbit and the Medieval East Anglian Economy', *Agricultural History Review*, xxxvi (1988)

——, *A Marginal Economy? East Anglian Breckland in the Later Middle Ages* (Cambridge, 1989)

——, '*Per Impetum Maris*: Natural Disaster and Economic Decline in Eastern England, 1275–1350', in B.M.S. Campbell, ed., *Before the Black Death: Studies in the 'Crisis' of the Early Fourteenth Century* (Manchester, 1991)

Beeching, H.C., and James, M.R., 'The Library of the Cathedral Church of Norwich', *Norfolk Archaeology*, xix (1917)

Beier, B.L., 'The Commoyson in Norfolk, 1549: A Narrative of Popular Rebellion in Sixteenth Century England', *Journal of Medieval and Renaissance Studies*, vi (1976)

Bennett-Symons, F.W., 'The Hospital of St Giles, Norwich', *Journal of the British Archaeological Association*, xxxi (1925)

Bindoff, S.T., *Ket's Rebellion 1549* (Historical Association, reprinted 1968)

——, ed., *The History of Parliament: The House of Commons 1509–1558* (3 vols, London, 1982)

Blaauw, W.H., 'Will of Richard de la Wych', *Sussex Archaeological Collections*, i (1848)

Blake, W.J., 'Thomas Wetherby', *Norfolk Archaeology*, xxxii (1961)

Blomefield, F., *An Essay towards a Topographical History of the County of Norfolk* (11 vols, London, 1805–10)

Bloomfield, M.W., *The Seven Deadly Sins* (Michigan, 1952)

Bolton, B., *Innocent III: Studies in Papal Authority and Pastoral Care* (Aldershot, 1995)

Bolton, J.M., '"The World Turned Upside Down": Plague as an Agent of Economic and Social Change', in W.M. Ormrod and P.G. Lindley, eds, *The Black Death in England* (Stamford, 1996)

Bond, C.J., 'Water Management in the Urban Monastery', in R. Gilchrist and H. Mytum, eds, *Advances in Monastic Archaeology* (BAR, British Series, ccxxvii, 1993)

Bowers, R., 'To Chorus from Quartet: The Performing Resource of English Church Polyphony, *c.* 1390–1559', in S. Morehen, ed., *English Choral Practice 1400–1600* (Cambridge, 1995)

Brigden, S., *London and the Reformation* (Oxford, 1989)

Britnell, R.H., 'The Pastons and their Norfolk', *Agricultural History Review*, xxxvi (1988)

——, 'The Black Death in English Towns', *Urban History*, xxi (1994)

Brodman, J.W., *Charity and Welfare: Hospitals and the Poor in Medieval Catalonia* (Philadelphia, 1998)

Brooke, C., *A History of Gonville and Caius College* (Woodbridge, 1985)

Brown, A.D., *Popular Piety in Late Medieval England: The Diocese of Salisbury 1250–1550* (Oxford, 1995)

Brown, E.A., 'Death and the Human Body in the Later Middle Ages: The Legislation of Boniface VIII on the Division of the Corpse', *Viator*, xii (1981)

Brown, H.P., and Hopkins, S.V., *A Perspective of Wages and Prices* (London, 1981)

Brown, P., *The Body and Society: Men, Women and Sexual Renunciation in Early Christianity* (New York, 1988)

Bullough, V.L., 'A Note on Medical Care in Medieval English Hospitals', *Bulletin of the History of Medicine*, xxxv (1961)

Burgess, C., 'A Service for the Dead: The Form and Function of the Anniversary in Late Medieval Bristol', *Transactions of the Bristol and Gloucestershire Archaeological Society*, cv (1987)

——, '"By Quick and by Dead": Wills and Pious Provision in Late Medieval Bristol', *EHR*, cii (1987)

Burkhard, A., 'The Isenheim Altar', *Speculum*, ix (1934)

Campbell, B.M.S., 'The Extent and Layout of Commonfields in Eastern Norfolk', *Norfolk Archaeology*, xxxviii (1983)

——, 'Agricultural Progress in Medieval England: Some Evidence from Eastern Norfolk', *EconHR*, second series, xxxvi (1983)

——, 'Arable Productivity in Medieval England: Some Evidence from Norfolk', *Journal of Economic History*, xliii (1983)

——, 'Population Pressure, Inheritance and the Land Market in a Fourteenth-Century Peasant Community', in R.M. Smith, ed., *Land, Kinship and Life-Cycle* (Cambridge, 1984)

——, and others, *A Medieval Capital and its Grain Supply* (Historical Geography Research Series, xxx, 1993)

Campbell, J., 'Norwich', in M. Lobel, ed., *Historic Towns, II* (London, 1975)

Carlin, M., 'Medieval English Hospitals', in L. Granshaw and R. Porter, eds, *The Hospital in History* (London, 1989)

——, *Medieval Southwark* (London, 1996)

Carmichael, A.G., *Plague and the Poor in Renaissance Florence* (Cambridge, 1986)

Carpenter, C., 'The Religion of the Gentry in Fifteenth Century England', in D. Williams, ed., *England in the Fifteenth Century* (Woodbridge, 1987)

——, 'Political and Constitutional History: Before and After McFarlane', in R.H. Britnell and A.J. Pollard, eds, *The McFarlane Legacy: Studies in Late Medieval Politics and Society* (Stroud, 1995)

Caruth, J., and Anderson, S., *St Saviour's Hospital Bury St Edmunds: A Report on the Archaeological Excavations 1989–1994* (Suffolk County Council Archaeological Service, Report 97/20)

Cattermole, P., *Notes on Bishop Salmon's Chantry, 1316–1548* (Norwich, privately printed, 1983)

——, 'Schools in Medieval and Early Tudor Norwich', in idem, R. Harries and P. Mackintosh, eds, *A History of Norwich School* (Norwich, 1991)

Catto, J., 'Religious Change under Henry V', in G.L. Harriss, ed., *Henry V: The Practice of Kingship* (Oxford, 1985)

Chaney, E.P. de G., '"Philanthropy in Italy": English Observations on Italian Hospitals, 1545–1789', in T. Riis, ed., *Aspects of Poverty in Early Modern Europe* (Florence, 1981)

Clark, E., 'Mothers at Risk of Poverty in the Medieval English Countryside', in J. Henderson and R. Wall, eds, *Poor Women and Children in the European Past* (London, 1994)

Clark, P., *The English Alehouse: A Social History 1200–1830* (London, 1983)

Classen, C., Howes, D., and Synott, A., *The Cultural History of Smell* (London, 1994)

Cockayne, G.E., and others, eds, *The Complete Peerage* (12 vols, 1910–59)

Connolly, J.L., *John Gerson, Reformer and Mystic* (Louvain, 1928)

Cook, G.H., *Medieval Chantries and Chantry Chapels* (London, 1963)

Coyecque, E., *L'Hôtel Dieu de Paris au Moyen Age* (2 vols, Paris, 1889–91)

Cozens-Hardy, B., and Kent, E.A., *The Mayors of Norwich 1403 to 1835* (Norwich, 1938)

Craig, J.S., 'The Marginalia of Dr Rowland Taylor', *Historical Research*, lxiv (1991)

Cranage, D.H.S., 'Eastern Chapels in the Cathedral Church of Norwich', *Antiquaries Journal*, xii (1932)

Cullum, P.H., *Cremetts and Corrodies: Care of the Poor and Sick at St Leonard's Hospital, York, in the Middle Ages* (University of York, Borthwick Paper, lxxix, 1991)

——, '"And Hir Name Was Charite": Charitable Giving by and for Women in Late Medieval Yorkshire', in P.J.P. Goldberg, ed., *Woman is a Worthy Wight: Women and English Society c. 1200–1500* (Stroud, 1992)

——, 'St Leonard's York: The Spatial and Social Analysis of an Augustinian Hospital', in R. Gilchrist and H. Mytum, eds, *Advances in Monastic Archaeology* (BAR, British Series, ccxxvii, 1993)

——, 'Poverty and Charity in Early Fourteenth-Century England', in N. Rogers, ed., *England in the Fourteenth Century* (Stamford, 1993)

——, and Goldberg, P.J.P., 'Charitable Provision in Late Medieval York: "To the Praise of God and the Use of the Poor"', *Northern History*, xxix (1993)

——, '"For Pore People Harberles": What Was the Function of the Maisondieu?', in D.J. Clayton, R.G. Davies and P. McNiven, eds, *Trade, Devotion and Governance: Papers in Later Medieval History* (Stroud, 1994)

Currie, C.K., 'The Role of Fishponds in the Monastic Economy', in R. Gilchrist and H. Mytum, eds, *The Archaeology of Rural Monasteries* (BAR, British Series, cciii, 1989)

Darby, H.C., *The Domesday Geography of Eastern England* (Cambridge, 1971)

Davies, C., '"Poor Persecuted Little Flock" or "Commonwealth of Christians": Edwardian Protestant Concepts of the Church', in M. Dowling and P. Lake, eds, *Protestantism and the National Church in Sixteenth Century England* (London, 1987)

Davies, M., 'The Tailors of London: Corporate Charity in the Late Medieval Town', in R. Archer, ed., *Crown, Government and People in the Fifteenth Century* (Stroud, 1995)

Davies, R.R., 'Baronial Accounts, Income and Arrears in the Later Middle Ages', *EconHR*, second series, xxi (1968)

Davis, G., *Medieval Cartularies of Great Britain* (London, 1958)

Dawes, J.D., and Magilton, J.R., *The Cemetery of St Helen-on-the-Walls, Aldwark* (York Archaeological Trust, 1980)

Demaitre, L., *Doctor Bernard Gordon, Professor and Practitioner* (Toronto, 1980)

Dendy, D.R., *The Use of Lights in Christian Worship* (Alcuin Club Collections, xli, 1959)

Dickens, G.R., *The English Reformation* (London, 1989)

Ditchfield, P.H., ed., *VCH Buckinghamshire, II* (London, 1907)

Dodwell, B., 'The Muniments and the Library', in I. Atherton and others, *Norwich Cathedral: Church, City and Diocese 1096–1996* (London, 1996)

Doubleday, H.A., ed., *VCH Norfolk, II* (London, 1901)

Douglas, M., *Purity and Danger: An Analysis of the Concepts of Partition and Taboo* (London and New York, 1994)

Dowling, M., 'Anne Boleyn and Reform', *Journal of Ecclesiastical History*, xxxv (1984)

——, *Humanism in the Age of Henry VIII* (London, 1986)

——, 'The Gospel and the Court: Reformation under Henry VIII', in eadem and P. Lake, eds, *Protestantism and the National Church in Sixteenth Century England* (London, 1987)

Drummond, J.C., and Wilbraham, A., *The Englishman's Food: Five Centuries of English Diet* (new edn, London, 1991)

Duffy, E., *The Stripping of the Altars: Traditional Religion in England* c. *1400–*c. *1580* (New Haven and London, 1992)

Durham, B.G., and others, 'Site Reports from Magdalen College, Oxford', *Medieval Archaeology*, xxxi (1987), xxxii (1988)

Dyer, C., *Standards of Living in the Later Middle Ages* (Cambridge, 1989)

Dymond, D., *The Norfolk Landscape* (Bury St Edmunds, 1990)

Easton, T., and Bicknell, S., 'Two Pre-Reformation Organ Soundboards', *PSIAH*, xxxviii (1995)

Elton, G.R., 'An Early Tudor Poor Law', *EconHR*, second series, vi (1953–4)

——, *Reform and Reformation* (London, 1977)

Emden, A.B., *A Biographical Register of the University of Oxford to 1500* (3 vols, Oxford, 1957–9)
——, *A Biographical Register of the University of Cambridge* (Cambridge, 1963)
Evans, J.K., 'The Maison Dieu, Arundel', *Sussex Archaeological Collections*, cvii (1969)
Farrer, W., and Bromhill, J., eds, *VCH Lancaster, II* (London, 1908)
Fein, D.A., *A Reading of Villon's Testament* (Alabama, 1984)
Fernie, E.C., 'Two Aspects of Bishop Walter Suffield's Lady Chapel at Norwich Cathedral', in W.M. Ormrod, ed., *England in the Thirteenth Century* (Nottingham, 1985)
——, *An Architectural History of Norwich Cathedral* (Oxford, 1993)
Finch, J., 'The Monuments', in I. Atherton and others, eds, *Norwich Cathedral: Church, City and Diocese 1096–1996* (London, 1996)
Finucane, R.C., *Miracles and Pilgrims: Popular Beliefs in Medieval England* (New York, 1995)
Flynn, M., *Sacred Charity: Confraternities and Social Welfare in Spain 1400–1700* (London, 1989)
Gale, B.G., 'The Dissolution and the Revolution in London Hospital Facilities', *Medical History*, xi (1967)
Gallavotti Cavallero, D., *Lo Spedale di Santa Maria della Scala in Siena* (Siena, 1985)
George, M., *The Land Use, Ecology and Conservation of Broadland* (Chichester, 1992)
Geremek, B., 'Criminalité, Vagabondage, Puaperisme: La Marginalité a l'Aube des Temps Modernes', *Revue d'Histoire Moderne et Contemporaine*, xxi (1974)
——, *The Margins of Society in Late Medieval Paris* (Cambridge, 1987)
Gilchrist, R., 'Christian Bodies and Souls: The Archaeology of Life and Death in Later Medieval Hospitals', in S. Bassett, ed., *Death in Towns: Urban Responses to the Dying and the Dead, 100–1600* (Leicester, 1992)
——, *Contemplation and Action: The Other Monasticism* (Leicester, 1995)
——, and Oliva, M., *Religious Women in Medieval East Anglia* (Studies in East Anglian History, i, 1993)
Gill, M., and Hurried, H., 'Glimpses of Glory: Paintings from St Mark's Hospital, Bristol', in L. Keen, ed., '*Almost the Richest City: Bristol in the Middle Ages* (British Archaeological Association Conference Transactions, xix, 1997)
Gil-Sotres, P., 'Derivation and Revulsion: The Theory and Practice of Medieval Phlebotomy', in L. García-Ballester, *Practical Medicine from Salerno to the Black Death* (Cambridge, 1994)
Gittings, C., *Death, Burial and the Individual in Early Modern England* (London, 1984)
Given Wilson, C., *The Royal Household and the King's Affinity* (New Haven and London, 1986)
Goldin, G., *Works of Mercy: A Picture History of Hospitals* (Boston Mills, 1994)
Graham, R., 'The Order of St Antoine de Viennois', *Archaeological Journal*, lxxxiv (1927)
Gransden, A., 'A Fourteenth-Century Chronicle from the Grey Friars at Lynn', *EHR*, lxxii (1957)
——, ed., *The Chronicle of Bury St Edmunds, 1212–1301* (London, 1964)
Greatrex, J., 'Monk Students from Norwich Cathedral Priory at Oxford and Cambridge *c.* 1300 to 1530', *EHR*, cvi (1991)
——, 'The Almonry School of Norwich Cathedral Priory', *Studies in Church History*, xxxi (1994)
——, *Biographical Register of the English Cathedral Priories of the Province of Canterbury* (Oxford, 1997)
Grell, O.P., 'The Protestant Imperative of Christian Care and Neighbourly Love', in idem and A. Cunningham, eds, *Health Care and Poor Relief in Protestant Europe 1500–1700* (London, 1997)
Griffiths, P., *Youth and Authority: Formative Experiences in England 1560–1640* (Oxford, 1996)
Griffiths, R., *The Reign of King Henry VI* (London, 1981)
Gunn, S.J., 'The Courtiers of Henry VII', *EHR*, cviii (1993)
Gutman Rosencrantz, R., 'The Trouble with Bovine Tuberculosis', *Bulletin of the History of Medicine*, lix (1985)
Guy, J.R., 'Of the Writing of Hospital Histories there is No End', *Bulletin of the History of Medicine*, lix (1985)
Hadwin, J.H., 'Deflating Philanthropy', *EconHR*, second series, xxi (1978)
Haggh, B., 'The Meeting of Sacred Ritual and Secular Piety: Endowments for Music', in T. Knighton and D. Fallows, eds, *Companion to Medieval and Renaissance Music* (London, 1992)
Hallam, H.E., 'The Climate of Eastern England, 1250–1350', *Agricultural History Review*, xxxi (1983)
Hammond, E.A., 'The Westminster Abbey Infirmarers' Rolls as a Source of Medical History', *Bulletin of the History of Medicine*, xxxix (1965)
Harper-Bill, C., 'The Labourer Worthy of His Hire? Complaints about Diet in Late Medieval English Monasteries', in idem and C.M. Barron, eds, *The Church in Pre-Reformation English Society* (Woodbridge, 1985)
——, 'The English Church and English Religion after the Black Death', in W.M. Ormrod and P.G. Lindley, eds, *The Black Death in England* (Stamford, 1996)
Harries, R., 'Regulations, Rhetoric, Ruins and Remuneration, 1547–1859', in idem, P. Cattermole and P. Mackintosh, eds, *A History of Norwich School* (Norwich, 1991)
Harrison, A.C., 'Excavations on the Site of St Mary's Hospital, Strood', *Archaeologia Cantiana*, lxxxiv (1969)

Harrison, F.L., *Music in Medieval Britain* (London, second edn, 1963)
Hartzell, K.D.,'Diagrams for Liturgical Ceremonies', in R.A. Skelton and P.D.A. Harvey, eds, *Local Maps and Plans from Medieval England* (Oxford, 1986)
Harvey, B.F., *Westminster Abbey and its Estates in the Middle Ages* (Oxford, 1977)
——, *Monastic Dress in the Middle Ages: Precept and Practice* (William Urry Memorial Trust, Canterbury, 1988)
——, 'Introduction', in B.M.S. Campbell, ed., *Before the Black Death: Studies in the 'Crisis' of the Early Fourteenth Century* (Manchester, 1991)
——, *Living and Dying in England 1100–1540: The Monastic Experience* (Oxford, 1993)
Harvey, J., *The Perpendicular Style 1330–1485* (London, 1978)
——, *English Medieval Architects* (revised edn, Gloucester, 1984)
Hawes, T., ed., *An Index to Norwich City Officers, 1453–1835* (NRS, lii, 1986)
Hayum, A., *The Isenheim Altarpiece: God's Medicine and the Painter's Vision* (Princeton, 1989)
Heal, F., *Hospitality in Early Modern England* (Oxford, 1990)
Healy, M., 'Discourses of the Plague in Early Modern London', in J.A.I Champion, ed., *Epidemic Diseases in London* (Centre for Metropolitan History, Working Paper, series 1, 1993)
Henderson, J., 'The Hospitals of Late Medieval and Renaissance Florence', in L. Granshaw and R. Porter, eds, *The Hospital in History* (London, 1989)
Hicks, M., *False, Fleeting, Perjur'd Clarence: George, Duke of Clarence 1449–78* (Gloucester, 1980)
Hidden, N., 'The Hospital or Priory or Free Chapel of St John the Baptist in Hungerford', *Wiltshire Archaeological and Natural History Magazine*, lxxxiii (1990)
Hilton, R.H., 'Small Town Society in England before the Black Death', *Past and Present*, cv (1984)
Hodgson, J.C., 'The "Domus Dei" of Newcastle: Otherwise St Katherine's Hospital of the Sandhill', *Archaeologia Aeliana*, third series, xiv (1917)
Höppner, A., *Das Heiligen-Geist-Hospital zu Lübeck* (Lübeck, 1990)
Horden, P., '"A Discipline of Relevance": The Historiography of the Later Medieval Hospital', *Social History of Medicine*, i (1988)
Houlbrooke, R.A., 'Persecution of Heresy and Protestantism in the Diocese of Norwich under Henry VIII', *Norfolk Archaeology*, xxxv (1970–2)
——, 'Refoundation and Reformation, 1538–1628', in I. Atherton and others, eds, *Norwich Cathedral: Church, City and Diocese 1096–1996* (London, 1996)
Hudson, A., *The Premature Reformation* (Oxford, 1988)
Hudson, W., and Tingey, J.C., *The Revised Catalogue of the Records of the City of Norwich* (Norwich, 1898)
Hutton, R., *The Rise and Fall of Merry England: The Ritual Year 1400–1700* (Oxford, 1994)
Imbert, J., *Les Hôpitaux en Droit Canonique* (Paris, 1947)
——, ed., *Histoire des Hôpitaux en France* (Toulouse, 1982)
Ives, E.W., *Anne Boleyn* (Oxford, 1986)
Jacob, E.F., 'St Richard of Chichester', *Journal of Ecclesiastical History*, vii (1956)
——, 'Thomas Brouns, Bishop of Norwich', in H.R. Trevor-Roper, ed., *Essays in British History Presented to Sir Keith Feiling* (London, 1964)
Jacquart, D., *Le Milieu Médical en France du XIIe au XIVe Siècle* (Geneva, 1981)
James, M.R., *The Sculptured Bosses of the Roof of the Bauchun Chapel of Our Lady of Pity in Norwich Cathedral* (Norwich, 1908)
Jamison, C., *The History of the Royal Hospital of St Katherine* (Oxford, 1952)
Jewson, C., *History of the Great Hospital Norwich* (Norwich, 1980)
Johnson, G., 'Chronological Memoranda touching the City of Norwich', *Norfolk Archaeology*, i (1847)
Johnstone, H., 'Poor Relief in the Royal Households of Thirteenth-Century England', *Speculum*, iv (1929)
Jones, W.D.R., *The Tudor Commonwealth 1529–1559* (London, 1970)
Jordan, W.K., *Philanthropy in England 1480–1660* (London, 1959)
——, *The Charities of Rural England 1480–1660* (London, 1961)
Karras, R.M., and Boyd, D.L., '"Ut cum Muliere"', in L. Fradenburg and C. Freccero, *Premodern Sexualities* (London, 1996)
Kealey, E.J., *Medieval Medicus* (Baltimore, 1981)
Keene, D., *Survey of Medieval Winchester II* (2 vols, Oxford, 1985)
——, 'Suburban Growth', in R. Holt and G. Rosser, eds, *The Medieval Town: A Reader in English Urban History 1200–1540* (London and New York, 1990)
Ker, N.R., 'Medieval Mss from Norwich Cathedral', *Transactions of the Cambridge Bibliographical Society*, i (1949–53)
Kershaw, I., 'The Great Famine and Agrarian Crisis in England 1315–22', *Past and Present*, lix (1973)

Kingdon, R.M., 'Social Welfare in Calvin's Geneva', *American Historical Review*, lxxvi (1971)
Kirby, T.F., *Winchester Scholars* (London, 1888)
——, 'On some Fifteenth-Century Drawings in Winchester College', *Archaeologia*, liii (part 1, 1892)
Knowles, D., and Hadcock, R.N., *Medieval Religious Houses, England and Wales* (London, second edn, 1971)
Kouri, E.I., 'Health care and Poor Relief in Sweden and Finland', in O.P. Grell and A. Cunningham, eds, *Health Care and Poor Relief in Protestant Europe 1500–1700* (London, 1997)
Kreider, A., *English Chantries: The Road to Dissolution* (Cambridge, Massachusetts, and London, 1979)
Lacroix, M.T., *L'Hôpital Saint Nicolas du Bruille a Tournai de sa Fondacion a sa Mutation en Cloître* (2 vols, Louvain, 1977)
Lander, J.R., *Crown and Nobility, 1450–1509* (London, 1976)
Lasko, P., and Morgan, N.I., eds, *Medieval Art in East Anglia 1300–1520* (Norwich, 1973)
Lawrence, C.H., *St Edmund of Abingdon* (Oxford, 1960)
——, *Medieval Monasticism* (London, 1989)
Leedham-Green, E.S., *Books in Cambridge Inventories, I, The Inventories* (Cambridge, 1986)
Le Goff, J., *The Birth of Purgatory* (London, 1984)
——, *Saint Louis* (Paris, 1996)
Lehmberg, S.E., *The Reformation of Cathedrals: Cathedrals in English Society 1485–1603* (Princeton, 1988)
Ludmerer, K.M., 'Writing the History of Hospitals', *Bulletin of the History of Medicine*, lvi (1982)
Lunt, W.E., *The Valuation of Norwich* (Oxford, 1926)
Lupton, J.H., *A Life of John Colet* (London, 1909)
MacCulloch, D., 'Kett's Rebellion in Context', *Past and Present*, lxxxiv (1979)
——, 'Kett's Rebellion in Context: A Rejoinder', *Past and Present*, xciii (1981)
——, *Suffolk and the Tudors: Politics and Religion in an English County 1500–1600* (0xford, 1986)
——, *Thomas Cranmer: A Life* (Yale, 1996)
Macy, G., 'The Dogma of Transubstantiation in the Middle Ages', *Journal of Ecclesiastical History*, xlv (1994)
Maddern, P.C., *Violence and Social Order: East Anglia 1422–1442* (Oxford, 1992)
Maddicott, J.R., *The English Peasantry and the Demands of the Crown, 1294–1341* (Past and Present Supplement, i, 1975)
Malden, H.E., ed., *VCH Surrey, II* (London, 1905)
Manchester, K., 'Tuberculosis and Leprosy in Antiquity: An Interpretation', *Medical History*, xxviii (1984)
Manship, H., *The History of Great Yarmouth*, ed. C.J. Palmer (Great Yarmouth, 1854)
Mate, M., 'The Farming Out of Manors: A New Look at the Evidence from Canterbury Cathedral Priory', *Journal of Medieval History*, ix (1983)
——, 'Agrarian Economy after the Black Death: The Manors of Canterbury Cathedral Priory, 1348–1391', *EconHR*, second series, xxxvii (1984)
McClendon, M.C., '"Against God's Word": Government, Religion and the Crisis of Authority in Early Reformation Norwich', *Sixteenth Century Journal*, xxv (1994)
——, *The Quiet Reformation: Magistrates and the Emergence of Protestantism in Tudor Norwich* (Stanford, 1999)
McFarlane, K.B., *The Nobility of Later Medieval England* (Oxford, 1973)
——, *England in the Fifteenth Century* (London, 1981)
McIntosh, M.K., 'Local Responses to the Poor in Late Medieval and Tudor England', *Continuity and Change*, iii (1988)
——, 'Finding Language for Misconduct: Jurors in Fifteenth-Century Local Courts', in B.A. Hanawalt and D. Wallace, eds, *Bodies and Disciplines: Intersections of Literature and History in Fifteenth Century England* (Minneapolis, 1996)
McMurray Gibson, G., *The Theater of Devotion: East Anglian Drama and Society in the Later Middle Ages* (Chicago, 1989)
——, 'Saint Anne and the Religion of Childbed: Some East Anglian Texts and Talismans', in K. Ashley and P. Sheingorn, eds, *Interpreting Cultural Symbols: Saint Anne in Late Medieval Society* (Athens, Georgia, 1990)
McRee, B.R., 'Religious Gilds and Civic Order: The Case of Norwich in the Later Middle Ages', *Speculum*, lxvii (1992)
——, 'Charity and Gild Solidarity in Late Medieval England', *Journal of British Studies*, xxxii (1993)
——, 'Peacemaking and its Limits in Late Medieval Norwich', *EHR*, cix (1994)
Meade, D.M., *Kepier Hospital* (Durham, 1995)
Meeres, F., *Guide to the Records of Norwich Cathedral* (Norwich, 1998)
——, *A History of Norwich* (Chichester, 1998)
Mertes, K., *The English Noble Household 1250–1600* (Oxford, 1988)
Middleton-Stewart, J., 'The Provision of Books for Church Use in the Deanery of Dunwich, 1370–1547', *PSIAH*, xxxviii (1994)
Midelfort, H.C.E., 'Protestant Monastery? A Reformation Hospital in Hesse', in P.N. Brooks, ed., *Reformation Principle and Practice* (London, 1980)

Miller, E., ed., *The Agrarian History of England and Wales, III, 1350–1500* (Cambridge, 1991)
Miller, T.S., *The Birth of the Hospital in the Byzantine Empire* (Baltimore, 1985)
Mollat, M., *The Poor in the Middle Ages* (New Haven, 1986)
Moore, R.I., 'Heresy as a Disease', in W. Lourdaux and V. Verhelst, eds, *The Concept of Heresy in the Middle Ages* (Louvain, 1976)
——, *The Formation of a Persecuting Society* (Oxford, 1987)
Moorman, J.H.R., *Church Life in England in the Thirteenth Century* (Cambridge, 1945)
Moran, J.H., *Education and Learning iin the City of York 1300–1560* (University of York, Borthwick Paper, lv, 1979)
——, *The Growth of English Schooling 1340–1548* (Princeton, 1985)
Morgan, N. , 'The Coronation of the Virgin by the Trinity and other Texts and Images of the Glorification of Mary in the Fifteenth Century', in N. Rogers, ed., *England in the Fifteenth Century* (Stamford, 1994)
O'Donoghue, E.G., *The Story of Bethlehem Hospital from its Foundation in 1247* (London, 1914)
Oliva, M., *The Convent and the Community in Late Medieval England* (Woodbridge, 1998)
Orme, N., *English Schools in the Middle Ages* (London, 1973)
——, 'A Medieval Almshouse for the Clergy: Clyst Gabriel Hospital near Exeter', *Journal of Ecclesiastical History*, xxxix (1988)
——, 'Sufferings of the Clergy: Illness and Old Age in Exeter Diocese 1300–1540', in M. Pelling and R.M. Smith, eds, *Life, Death and the Elderly* (London, 1991)
——, and Webster, M., *The English Hospital 1070–1570* (New Haven and London, 1995)
Oswald, A., 'The Great Hospital, Norwich I', *Country Life* (12 December, 1947)
Owst, G.R., *Literature and the Pulpit in Medieval England* (Oxford, 1961)
Page, W., ed., *VCH Suffolk, I* (London, 1907)
——, ed., *VCH Gloucester, II* (London, 1907)
——, ed., *VCH Sussex, II* (London, 1907)
——, ed., *VCH London, I* (London, 1909)
——, ed., *VCH Nottingham, II* (London, 1910)
——, ed., *VCH Kent II* (London, 1926)
——, ed., *VCH York, III* (London, reprint 1974)
Palliser, D., *Tudor York* (Oxford, 1979)
Palmer, R., 'The Church, Leprosy and Plague in Medieval and Early Modern Europe', *Studies in Church History*, xix (1982)
Park, K., 'Healing the Poor: Hospitals and Medical Assistance in Renaissance Florence', in J. Barry and C. Jones, eds, *Medicine and Charity before the Welfare State* (London, 1991)
——, and Henderson, J., '"The First Hospital among Christians": The Ospedale di Santa Maria Nuova in Early Sixteenth Century Florence', *Medical History*, xxxv (1991)
Pelling, M., 'Occupational Diversity: Barbersurgeons and the Trades of Norwich 1550–1640', *Bulletin of the History of Medicine*, lvi (1982)
——, 'Healing the Sick Poor: Social Policy and Disability in Norwich 1550–1640', *Medical History*, xxix (1985)
——, 'Appearance and Reality: Barber-Surgeons, the Body and Disease', in A.L. Beier and R. Finlay, eds, *London 1500–1700: The Making of the Metropolis* (London, 1986)
——, 'Illness among the Poor in an Early Modern English Town: The Norwich Census of 1570', *Continuity and Change*, iii (1988)
——, 'Old Age, Poverty and Disability in Early Modern Norwich', in eadem and R.M. Smith, *Life Death and the Elderly: Historical Perspectives* (London, 1991)
——, 'Apprenticeship, Health and Social Cohesion in Early Modern London', *History Workshop*, xxxvii (1994)
——, 'Thoroughly Resented? Older Women and the Medical Role in Early Modern London', in L. Hunter and S. Hutton, eds, *Women, Science and Medicine* (Stroud, 1997)
——, *The Common Lot: Sickness, Medical Occupations and the Urban Poor in Early Modern England* (London, 1998)
Pevsner, N., *Worcestershire* (London, 1968)
Pfaff, R.W., *New Liturgical Feasts in Later Medieval England* (Oxford, 1970)
Pickett, R.C., *Mental Affliction and Church Law* (Ottawa, 1952)
Platt, C., *King Death: The Black Death and its Aftermath in Late-Medieval England* (London, 1996)
Pouchelle, M., *The Body and Surgery in the Middle Ages* (Oxford, 1990)
Pound, J.F., *Poverty and Vagrancy in Tudor England* (London, 1971)
——, *Tudor and Stuart Norwich* (Chichester, 1988)
Powicke, F.M., *Stephen Langton* (Oxford, 1928)
——, *Henry III and the Lord Edward* (2 vols, Oxford, 1947)
Prescott, E., *The English Medieval Hospital, 1050–1640* (London, 1992)

Price, R., and Ponsford, M., *St Bartholomew's Hospital, Bristol: The Excavation of a Medieval Hospital* (Council for British Archaeology, cx, 1998)

Pugh, T.B., 'The Magnates, Knights and Gentry', in S.B. Chrimes and others, eds, *Fifteenth-Century England* (Manchester, 1972)

Pullan, B., *Rich and Poor in Renaissance Venice* (Oxford, 1971)

——, 'Catholics and the Poor in Early Modern Europe', *TRHS*, fifth series, xxvi (1976)

——, 'Plague and Perceptions of the Poor in Early Modern Italy', in T. Ranger and P. Slack, eds, *Epidemics and Ideas: Essays on the Historical Perception of Pestilence* (Cambridge, 1992)

Quarré, P., *Les Primitifs Flamands, XIII, L'Hôtel Dieu de Beaune* (Brussels, 1973)

Raban, S., *Mortmain Legislation and the English Church 1279–1500* (Cambridge, 1982)

Raftis, R.A., *The Estates of Ramsey Abbey* (Toronto, 1957)

Rawcliffe, C., 'The Hospitals of Later Medieval London', *Medical History*, xxviii (1984)

——, '"That Kindliness Should be Cherished More, and Discord Driven Out": The Settlement of Commercial Disputes by Arbitration in Later Medieval England', in J. Kermode, ed., *Enterprise and Individuals in Fifteenth-Century England* (Stroud, 1991)

——, *Medicine and Society in Later Medieval England* (Stroud, 1995)

——, The Hospitals of Medieval Norwich (Studies in East Anglian History, ii, 1995)

——, 'Hospital Nurses and their Work', in R. Britnell, ed., *Daily Life in the Late Middle Ages* (Stroud, 1998)

——, 'Medicine for the Soul: The Medieval English Hospital and the Quest for Spiritual Health', in R. Porter and J. Hinnells, eds, *Religion, Health and Suffering* (London, 1999)

Reitzel, J.M., 'The Medical Houses of Bons-Enfants', *Viator*, xi (1980)

Richmond, C., 'The English Gentry and Religion *c.* 1500', in C. Harper-Bill, ed., *Religious Belief and Ecclesiastical Careers in Late Medieval England* (Studies in the History of Medieval Religion, iii, 1991)

——, 'Landlord and Tenant: The Paston Evidence', in J. Kermode, ed., *Enterprise and Individuals in Fifteenth Century England* (Stroud, 1991)

Robertson, E., 'The Corporeality of Female Sanctity in the Life of St Margaret', in R. Blumenfeld-Kosinski and T. Szell, eds, *Images of Sainthood in Medieval Europe* (Ithaca and London, 1991)

Roper, N., Tierney, W.W., and Logan, A.J., *The Elements of Nursing* (second edn, Edinburgh, 1985)

Rose, M., and Hedgecoe, J., *Stories in Stone: The Medieval Roof Carvings of Norwich Cathedral* (London, 1997)

Rosenthal, J., *The Purchase of Paradise* (London, 1972)

Roskell, J.S., Clark, L., and Rawcliffe, C., eds, *The History of Parliament: The House of Commons 1386–1421* (4 vols, Stroud, 1993)

Ross, C.D., and Pugh, T.B., 'Materials for the Study of Baronial Incomes in Fifteenth Century England', *EconHR*, second series, vi (1953)

Rosser, A.G., 'The Essence of Medieval Urban Communities: The Vill of Westminster', *TRHS*, fifth series, xxxiv (1984)

——, *Medieval Westminster 1200–1540* (Oxford, 1989)

Rowe, J., 'The Medieval Hospitals of Bury St Edmunds', *Medical History*, ii (1958)

Rowland-Burdon, E., 'St Saviour's Hospital, Bury St Edmund's', *PSIA*, xix (1927)

Rubin, M., *Charity and Community in Medieval Cambridge* (Cambridge, 1987)

——, 'Development and Change in English Hospitals, 1100–1500', in L. Granshaw and R. Porter, *The Hospital in History* (London, 1989)

——, 'Imagining Medieval Hospitals', in J. Barry and C. Jones, eds, *Medicine and Charity before the Welfare State* (London, 1991)

——, *Corpus Christi: The Eucharist in Late Medieval Culture* (Cambridge, 1992)

Russell, J.C., *Dictionary of Writers of Thirteenth Century England* (London, 1936)

——, *British Medieval Population* (Albuquerque, 1948)

Rutledge, E., 'Immigration and Population Growth in Early Fourteenth-Century Norwich: Evidence from the Tithing Roll', *Urban History Yearbook* (1988)

——, 'Landlords and Tenants: Housing and the Rented Property Market in Early Fourteenth-Century Norwich', *Urban History*, xxii (1995)

Rye, W., 'An Old Cannon at the Great Hospital, Norwich', *Norfolk Archaeology*, xvi (1907)

Salzman, L.F., *Building in England down to 1540* (Oxford, 1967)

Sambrook, P., *Country House Brewing in England 1500–1900* (London, 1996)

Saunders, H.W., *A History of the Norwich Grammar School* (Norwich, 1932)

Saunier, A., *'Le Pauvre Malade' dans le Cadre Hospitalier Médiéval: France du Nord 1300–1500* (Paris, 1993)

Sawday, J., *The Body Emblazoned: Dissection and the Human Body in Renaissance Culture* (London, 1995)

Scarisbrick, J.J., *The Reformation and the English People* (London, 1984)

Serjeantson, R.M., and Adkins, W.R.D., eds, *VCH Northamptonshire, II* (London, 1906)

Sharpe, J.A., *Crime in Early Modern England 1550–1750* (London, 1984)

Simon, J., *Education and Society in Tudor England* (Cambridge, 1966)

Slack, P., 'Social Policy and the Constraints of Government 1547–58', in J. Loach and R. Tittler, eds, *The Mid Tudor Polity, c. 1540–1560* (London, 1980)

——, 'Some Comparative Problems in the English Case', in T. Riis, ed., *Aspects of Poverty in Early Modern Europe* (Florence, 1981)

——, *The Impact of Plague in Tudor and Stuart England* (London, 1985)

——, *Poverty and Policy in Tudor and Stuart England* (London, 1988)

Smith, C.T., 'Historical Evidence', in J.M. Lambert and others, *The Making of the Broads* (Royal Geographical Society Research Series, iii, 1961)

Smith, G.H., 'The Excavation of the Hospital of St Mary of Ospringe, Commonly Called Maison Dieu', *Archaeologia Cantiana*, xcv (1979)

Smith, R.M., 'Some Issues Concerning Families and their Property in Rural England 1250–1800', in idem, ed., *Land, Kinship and Life-Cycle* (Cambridge, 1984)

Southern, R.W., *Western Society and the Church in the Middle Ages* (London, 1972)

Southwell, T., 'The St Helen's Swan Pit', *Transactions of the Norfolk and Norwich Naturalists*, vi (1897)

Spooner, Dean, 'The Almshouse Chapel, Hadleigh', *PSIA*, vii (1891)

Stell, P.M., *Medical Practice in Medieval York* (University of York, Borthwick Paper, xc, 1996)

Stirland, A., 'The Human Bones', in B. Ayers, ed., *Excavations within the North-East Bailey of Norwich Castle, 1979* (East Anglian Archaeology, xxviii, 1985)

——, 'Care in the Community', *International Journal of Osteology*, vii (1997)

——, and Bown, J., *Criminals and Paupers: Excavations at the Site and Churchyard of St Margaret Fyebridgegate* (East Anglian Archaeology, forthcoming)

Stone, E., 'Profit-and-Loss Accountancy at Norwich Cathedral Priory', *TRHS*, fifth series, xii (1962)

Storey, R.L., *The End of the House of Lancaster* (London, 1966)

Suckling, A., *The History and Antiquities of the County of Suffolk* (2 vols, London, 1846)

Sutermeister, H., *The Norwich Blackfriars: A Historical Guide to the Friary and its Buildings up to the Present Day* (Norwich, 1977)

Swales, T.H., 'The Redistribution of Monastic Lands in Norfolk at the Dissolution', *Norfolk Archaeology*, xxxiv (1969)

Swanson, R.N., 'Titles to Orders in Medieval Episcopal Registers', in H. Mayr-Harting and R.I. Moore, eds, *Studies in Medieval History Presented to R.H.C. Davis* (London, 1983)

——, *Church and Society in Late Medieval England* (Oxford, 1993)

Talbot, C.H., and Hammond, E.A., *The Medical Practitioners in Medieval England* (London, 1965)

Tanner, N., *The Church in Late Medieval Norwich* (Toronto, 1984)

——, 'The Reformation and Regionality: Further Reflections on the Church in Late Medieval Norwich', in J.A.F. Thomson, ed., *Towns and Townspeople in the Fifteenth Century* (Gloucester, 1988)

——, 'The Cathedral and the City', in I. Atherton and others, eds, *Norwich Cathedral: Church, City and Diocese 1096–1996* (London, 1996)

Taylor, R., *Index Monasticus: The Diocese of Norwich* (London, 1821)

Thomas, C., Sloane, B., and Phillpotts, C., *Excavations at the Priory and Hospital of St Mary Spital, London* (Museum of London Archaeology Service, Monograph 1, 1997)

Thomas, K., 'Cleanliness and Godliness in Early Modern England', in A. Fletcher and P. Roberts, eds, *Religion, Culture and Society in Early Modern Britain* (Cambridge, 1994)

Thompson, A.H., *The History of the Hospital and the New College of the Annunciation of St Mary in the Newarke, Leicester* (Leicestershire Archaeological Society, 1937)

Thompson, B., 'From "Alms" to "Spiritual Services": The Function and Status of Monastic Property in Medieval England', in J. Loades, ed., *Monastic Studies II* (Bangor, 1991)

Thompson, M., *The Medieval Hall* (Aldershot, 1995)

Thomson, J.A.F., 'Piety and Charity in Late Medieval London', *Journal of Ecclesiastical History*, xvi (1965)

——, *The Early Tudor Church and Society* (London, 1993)

Ticehurst, N.E., *The Mute Swan in England* (London, 1957)

Tierney, B., 'The Decretists and the "Deserving Poor"', *Comparative Studies in Society and History*, i (1958–9)

Tingey, J.C., 'The Journals of John Dernell and John Boys, Carters at the Lathes, Norwich', *Norfolk Archaeology*, xv (1904)

Torriti, P., *Il Pellegrinaio nello Spedale di Santa Maria della Scala a Siena* (Siena, 1987)

Touati, F.O., 'Les Léproseries aux XIIème et XIIIème Siècles Lieux de Conversion?', in idem and N. Beriou, *Voluntate Dei Leprosus: Les Lépreux entre Conversion et Exclusion aux XIIème et XIIIème Siècles* (Testi, Studi, Strumenti, iv, 1991)
——, *Maladie et Société au Moyen Age* (Paris, 1998)
Trichet, L., *Le Costume du Clergé* (Paris, 1986)
Trollope, W., *A History of the Royal Foundation of Christ's Hospital* (London, 1834)
Venn, J., *Biographical History of Gonville and Caius College 1349–1713* (Cambridge, 1897)
——, *Caius College* (London, 1901)
——, and Venn, J.A., *Alumni Cantabrigiensis, I, from the Earliest Times to 1751* (4 vols, Cambridge, 1922–7)
Virgoe, R., 'The Estates of Norwich Cathedral Priory, 1101–1538', in I. Atherton and others, eds, *Norwich Cathedral: Church, City and Diocese 1096–1996* (London, 1996)
——, *East Anglian Society and the Political Community of Late Medieval England*, eds C.M. Barron, C. Rawcliffe and J.T. Rosenthal (Norwich, 1997)
Vos, D. de, *Hans Memling* (Bruges, 1994)
Walsh, M., *Models in Clinical Nursing* (London, 1991)
Wathey, A., 'Newly Discovered Fifteenth-Century English Polyphony at Oxford', *Music and Letters*, lxiv (1983)
Watney, J., *Some Account of the Hospital of St Thomas of Acon* (London, 1892)
Wearing, S.J., 'The Great Hospital, Norwich', *Norfolk Archaeology*, xxxi (1955)
Webster, C., 'Thomas Linacre and the Foundation of the College of Physicians', in F. Maddison, M. Pelling and C. Webster, eds, *Essays on the Life and Work of Thomas Linacre c. 1460–1524* (Oxford, 1977)
Wedgwood, J.C., ed., *History of Parliament: Biographies of Members of the Commons House 1439–1509* (London, 1936)
Welch, E.S., *Art and Authority in Renaissance Milan* (New Haven and London, 1995)
Westlake, M.F., *The Parish Guilds of Medieval England* (London, 1919)
Williams, J.F., 'Ordination in the Norwich Diocese during the Fifteenth Century', *Norfolk Archaeology*, xxxi (1956)
——, 'The Black Book of Swaffham', *Norfolk Archaeology*, xxxiii (1965)
Williams, P., *The Organ in Western Culture 750–1250* (Cambridge, 1993)
Williamson, T., *The Norfolk Broads: A Landscape History* (Manchester, 1997)
Wilson, C., *England's Apprenticeship, 1603–1763* (London, 1965)
Wood-Legh, K., *Perpetual Chantries in Britain* (Cambridge, 1965)
Woodforde, C., *The Norwich School of Glass-Painting* (Oxford, 1950)
Woodman, F., 'Hardley, Norfolk, and the Rebuilding of its Chancel', in D. Buckton and T.A. Heslop, eds, *Studies in Medieval Art and Architecture Presented to Peter Lasko* (Stroud, 1994)
Wormald, F., 'The Rood of Bromholm', *Journal of the Warburg Institute*, i (1937–8)
——, 'A Medieval Processional and its Diagrams', in A. Rosenauer and G. Weber, eds, *Kunsthistorische Forschungen fur Otto Pacht zu seinen 70. Geburtstag* (Salzburg, 1972)
Youings, J., 'The Church', in C. Clay, ed., *Rural Society: Landowners, Peasants and Labourers* (Cambridge, 1990)
Zemon Davis, N., 'Poor Relief, Humanism and Heresy: The Case of Lyon', *Studies in Medieval and Renaissance History*, v (1968)
Ziegler, J., *Medicine and Religion c. 1300: The Case of Arnau de Vilanova* (Oxford, 1998)

UNPUBLISHED PHD AND MA DISSERTATIONS

Bowers, R., 'Choral Institutions within the English Church: Their Constitution and Development 1340–1500' (University of East Anglia, PhD thesis, 1975)
Cullum, P.H., 'Hospitals and Charitable Provision in Medieval Yorkshire' (University of York, PhD thesis, 1990)
Frost, R.H., 'The Aldermen of Norwich, 1461–1509: A Study of a Civic Elite' (University of Cambridge, PhD thesis, 1996)
Hayes, R.C.E., 'William Alnwick, Bishop of Norwich (1426–1437) and Lincoln (1437–1449)' (University of Bristol, PhD thesis, 1989)
King, A., 'The Merchant Class and Borough Finances in Late Medieval Norwich', (University of Oxford, DPhil thesis, 1989)
Metzler, I., 'Disability in the Middle Ages', (University of Reading, MA thesis, 1995)
Phillips, E., 'God's House, Norwich, 1550–1600' (University of East Anglia, MA thesis, 1997)
Underwood, E.C.K., 'Fifteenth Century Clergy in the Diocese of Norwich' (University of Tasmania, PhD thesis, 1993)
Ware, R., '"Poore Peoples Use": Aspects of Institutional Provision for the Sick Poor of Medieval Ipswich *c.* 1305–1550' (University of East Anglia, MA thesis, 1997)

INDEX

Masters of St Giles's hospital have been identified by the abbreviation (m); references to all hospitals other than St Giles's have been indexed here under the subject heading 'hospitals' and not by place.

bp	bishop
n.	endnote
Pl.	Plate
w.	wife